Principles of Arithmetic and Geometry for Elementary School Teachers

PRINCIPLES OF

+ − × ÷

Arithmetic and Geometry
FOR
Elementary School Teachers

CARL B. ALLENDOERFER
Professor of Mathematics/University of Washington

THE MACMILLAN COMPANY
New York

Collier-Macmillan Limited *London*

PRINTING   456789   YEAR   456789

Library of Congress catalog card number : 71-112280

THE MACMILLAN COMPANY
866 THIRD AVENUE, NEW YORK, NEW YORK 10022
COLLIER-MACMILLAN CANADA, LTD., Toronto, Ontario

PRINTED IN THE UNITED STATES OF AMERICA

Preface

Who Should Read This Book?

This book is intended as a textbook for a course in mathematics given to students who are preparing to be elementary school teachers. It is assumed that readers have studied algebra and geometry in high school for a period of one year each, but students with less preparation can handle the book if enough time is taken to fill the gaps in their preparation. An essential prerequisite, however, is that the students feel comfortable with the use of letters to represent unspecified numbers.

Parts I through IV of the book present a treatment of the structure of the number system. As such they cover the material suggested by CUPM in its "Level I" course on number systems. Although this book was written independently of the CUPM suggested outline, its organization agrees remarkably well with the 1968 version of the syllabus proposed by CUPM.

Part V is concerned with informal geometry, which is an essential topic for elementary teachers. The five chapters devoted to geometry cover the topics suggested for instruction in the elementary school by the K-13 Geometry Committee of the Ontario Curriculum Institute. These chapters differ from the suggestions of CUPM on geometry in that the coverage is less rigorous and more informal and that geometric transformations have been included.

How Long Is Required to Teach This Book?

This book is intended for a year course meeting three hours per week. Experimental teaching of it has shown that the number system can be taught in less than the full year recommended by CUPM, and that there is ample time to include the material on geometry in such a course. As a matter of fact, we have covered almost the entire book at the University of Washington in two quarters with well-prepared students.

Detailed suggestions for the pacing of the course and the time required for each chapter are included in the *Instructor's Manual* which is published separately.

What Is the General Approach of This Book?

Since most of the students entering such a course should be reasonably competent in the mechanics of arithmetic, we have reviewed these mechanics but have not drilled heavily on them. The major object of the book is to present the *ideas* behind these mechanics so that the students will understand the *why* as well as the *how*.

All new concepts are presented initially in an intuitive fashion before their formal treatment. This approach is intended to be similar to the method by which the material should be taught in the elementary school, although this book is written at a higher level of sophistication than that of an elementary school book.

How Is This Book Constructed?

Each section of the book begins with conventional text material with numerous illustrative examples. The text is followed by a series of programmed exercises of varying levels of difficulty. Each chapter is preceded by a Readiness Test intended to review those concepts and skills needed in the chapter. At the end of each chapter there is a Post Test which reviews the chief ideas of the chapter and which the students can use to measure their comprehension of them. There is a Summary Test at the end of each part that should help the students review for midterm examinations which will normally be scheduled after each part of the book.

What Supplementary Films Are Available?

This book was written as one portion of a "multimedia" presentation of the contents of a Level I course. In addition to this text, this multimedia package includes 13 films which are closely coordinated with the text itself. These were produced partly by the Mathematical Association of America with funds from the National Science Foundation, and partly as a private enterprise. All the films are distributed by Modern Learning Aids, P.O. Box 302, Rochester, N.Y. 14603. The titles of the films and the chapters to which they relate are as follows:

Film Title	*Chapter*
What Is a Set? Parts 1 and 2	3. Sets
One-to-One Correspondence	4. One-to-One Correspondence
Counting	5. Whole Numbers and Counting
Sets: Union and Intersection	6. Union, Intersection, and Complement of Sets
Ordered Pairs and Cartesian Products	7. Cartesian Products
Binary Operations and the Commutative Property	8. Binary Operations
Associative Property	8. Binary Operations
Addition and Subtraction	9. Addition
	10. Subtraction
Multiplication and Division	11. Multiplication and Division
Distributive Property	12. The Distributive Law
Geometric Concepts	28. Geometric Concepts
Area and Pi	29. Measurement
Rigid Motions	30. Geometric Transformations in the Plane

The films are all animated and in color with music and sound effects. Their lengths run from six minutes to fourteen minutes, but mostly are about eight to ten minutes.

It is intended that the film for each chapter be shown at the beginning of the period in which that chapter is begun. The purpose of the films is to motivate the ideas of the respective chapters and to remove anxieties which are frequently encountered with students in this course. The films do not give a complete coverage of the chapter, so there is still plenty for the instructor to do after they have been shown. It should be emphasized, however, that the book is complete in itself and does not depend upon the films. The films are very helpful, but not essential.

Preface

How Was This Book Written?

This book had its origin in the work of the Level I and Programmed Learning Panels of the Committee on Educational Media of the Mathematical Association of America. With support from the National Science Foundation these panels undertook to prepare a multimedia presentation of the materials for this Level I course. During the summer of 1964 experimental films were produced and a preliminary programmed text was written, titled "Programmed Lessons on the Structure of the Number System".

Later revisions of this material appeared under the auspices of the MAA as preliminary publications titled "The Whole Numbers" and "Lessons on the Rational Numbers", and seven of the films listed above were produced by the MAA.

These preliminary versions could not be released for general use until they had been class-tested and revised. The testing (described below) was carried on at the University of Washington during 1966–69, and the present text is a very substantial revision of these earlier works, except that the geometry is entirely new.

Through the kindness of the NSF and the MAA, the author has received permission to issue this revision in its present form. It should be clearly understood that he is solely responsible for the present form of the book, and that the book does not carry any endorsement from the NSF, the MAA, or CEM.

So many people have been involved in this project since its inception that all their names cannot be included here (partly because the author does not have a complete list of them). The following people, however, deserve special mention for their work in the later stages of the project: William B. Allendoerfer, Boyd L. Earl, Brewster H. Gere, Frank T. Kocher, Jr., Charles W. Seekins, and William B. Woolf.

How Was This Book Tested?

The preliminary versions were taught during 1966 and 1967 at the University of Washington by instructors not connected with the project. They reported considerable success with the materials, and so a more detailed evaluation was considered worthwhile. The design for the evaluation was prepared by Arthur A. Lumsdaine, Professor of Psychology at the University of Washington in collaboration with Robert R. Pagano, Assistant Professor of Psychology at the University of Washington. Assistance was provided by Mrs. Lee Wood, a graduate student in psychology, and funds were obtained from a grant to the University of Washington by the Ford Foundation.

The most detailed testing was done on Chapters 2 to 17 of "The Whole Numbers". Behavioral objectives for each section of these chapters were written together with questions intended to show whether the objective was attained. These questions were then class-tested in the autumn of 1968. It appeared that Chapters 2 and 5 needed the most revision, so these were revised and all chapters were tested again when the course was taught in the winter of 1969.

"Lessons on the Rational Numbers" was revised without initial testing. Then the revised version plus the new material on geometry was tested in the same way in the spring of 1969.

A full account of the testing procedures together with the behavioral objectives, test scores, and commentary is available from the author in the pamphlet "An Experiment in Evaluation and Revision of Text Materials". The behavioral objectives and test questions are included in the *Instructor's Manual* which accompanies this book and which is available from The Macmillan Company.

The author intends to continue this testing procedure on the present book as soon as it is issued. It would be helpful if others who teach the book at other institutions would be willing to cooperate in such a program. Those who are interested in doing so should communicate with the author.

Can the Students Learn from This Book?

Since this book is more detailed and more mathematically complete than many other books with similar objectives, it is a fair question to ask: "Can the students handle it?" The answer is an unqualified "yes". Narrative accounts from instructors who taught preliminary versions of it are enthusiastic. A considerable number of students who studied it have gone out of their way to make complimentary remarks, and the book has been very successful in correspondence courses.

To convince the skeptic who may say that all this praise is just from people who are buttering up a senior colleague, here is some hard evidence. The overall average scores which the students obtained in the testing program of the preliminary edition are:

Part I	84.7%
Part II	83.5
Part III	83.2
Part IV	88.4
Part V	73.2

These are raw data and deserve careful and detailed analysis, but they are solid evidence that the book does its job. The lower geometry score may be alibied on two grounds: (1) the geometry was in first draft when it was taught whereas the other parts were in at least third draft. (2) The instruction in geometry was overly rushed because of bad pacing of the earlier part of the course. The revised version, which is incorporated in this edition, should be as successful as the rest of the book if adequate time is allowed for it.

Finally the author wishes to reiterate his thanks to all those mathematicians who participated in this project throughout its life, to the NSF, the MAA, the Ford Foundation, and the University of Washington and to Orliss Wildemuth without whose help this book would never have been written.

CARL B. ALLENDOERFER

To the Student

What This Book Is About

The purpose of this book is to prepare you to teach arithmetic and informal geometry in the elementary school. Although you may know *how* to do problems in arithmetic, you will also need to know *why* the usual procedures are correct if you are to be able to explain them to your pupils. Our purpose in this book is to review the *how* and to explain the *why*.

All instruction in mathematics should begin at the intuitive level. When you grasp the ideas and can relate them to the world around you, you are ready for a more formal treatment. We have followed this procedure in this book, and you should do the same thing in your own teaching. We should emphasize, however, that this book is written for mature college students, and that your own teaching must be at a much less sophisticated level.

In Part I we introduce the fundamental ideas of logic, sets, and whole numbers which are needed for the development of the arithmetic to follow. In Part II we discuss the usual operations of the arithmetic of the whole numbers on the basis of the properties of sets. These two parts lay the theoretical foundations for ordinary arithmetic.

Part III is devoted to the usual procedures for doing arithmetic. These are justified in terms of the theoretical presentation in Parts I and II. You will note that we introduce several algorithms for each arithmetic operation; there is not just *one* way to do arithmetic. The algorithms have varied through the centuries, and still vary from country to country, and even from school to school.

Part IV extends the whole numbers to other number systems such as the integers and rational numbers. You will notice that here the approach is quite different. We do not base these upon set theory, but consider the new types of number systems to be extensions of the whole numbers which have certain desirable properties.

In Part V we introduce you to informal geometry which should be taught in the elementary school as a preparation for the deductive geometry to be taught in high school.

How to Study This Book

If there is a film for a chapter (Chapters 3 to 12 and 28 to 30), you should view it before beginning the chapter. Next you should work the Readiness Test to be sure that you understand the ideas in previous chapters that you will need. Then you should begin the text material in the chapter. You may read it rapidly once, and then come back to the parts that are unfamiliar to you. The proofs are important, and you should study them in detail.

When you have finished a portion of text material, you are ready to work the following programmed exercises. To do this most effectively, you should follow these instructions:

1. Have pencil and paper at hand and use them to write your answers.
2. Keep the answer blocks covered until you have written your answers for *all* questions which precede the answer block.

3. Compare your answer with the one given. If your answer is the same as, or equivalent to, the one given, continue the program. If your answer is incorrect, reread until you discover what you have done wrong, and then write the correct answer. In some answer blocks, alternative responses or explanations are given in parentheses, and these are not expected to be a part of your answer.

When you have finished a chapter, review the essential concepts and skills contained in it. Then check your comprehension by working the corresponding Post Test. Complete the Post Test before checking your answers against those given below. If you missed any questions, review the chapter to determine why you were wrong, and then write the correct answer.

At the end of each part there is a Summary Test which you should use as directed by your instructor. These Summary Tests and the chapter Post Tests should be helpful to you in reviewing for midterm and final examinations.

Contents

Contents

Contents

Contents

Contents

PART 1
Logic, Sets, and Whole Numbers

Chapters 1 through 7

1

Introduction

If you have not read "To the Student", please do so now. Then read Sections 1.1 through 1.4 of the text. When you finish Section 1.4, work the program that follows. Refer back to the text whenever you wish while working any of the programs in the book.

1.1 Purpose of the Course

You are now beginning your study of a course in arithmetic intended for college students who are planning to be teachers in an elementary school. All of you studied arithmetic when you were in school, and some of you may have taken high school or college courses in algebra, geometry, and even calculus. Whatever your background, much of what we have to say here will be new to you. Our objective is to discuss arithmetic from an advanced standpoint and to explain to you the reasoning that lies behind the ordinary arithmetic computations. As we go along, we shall review arithmetic itself and justify many of the computational procedures which you doubtless perform every day without even thinking about them.

It is our intention to cover all the details of arithmetic that you will need as an elementary teacher, but we also will go considerably beyond anything that you are likely to encounter in your teaching. In this way you will be able to understand what is behind the arithmetic of your classroom, to cope with new methods and materials that are being introduced into contemporary arithmetic textbooks, and to relate your teaching to the mathematics your students will meet in high school and college.

Although this statement of our purposes should suffice, we wish to be doubly clear by issuing a warning. *We do not intend that you teach arithmetic in the same way that we are teaching it to you*! You are adults and thus our methods of communicating with you are necessarily different from those you will use with your pupils. This course will touch only briefly on the methods you will use in your teaching; you must learn about these from another course, by watching an experienced teacher, by reading on your own, and by experimenting when you begin your teaching.

1.2 Numbers

Since this course is about arithmetic, it is not surprising that the main emphasis will be on numbers. Since the numbers of arithmetic are of several kinds, our first task is to make sure that you can make these distinctions and use the appropriate terminology.

The simplest numbers are those used in ordinary counting. These are the numbers we call

one, two, three, four, ...

NATURAL NUMBERS Such numbers are called *counting numbers*, *natural numbers*, or (later) *positive integers*. As their name implies, these numbers arise most naturally from the process of counting. In order to count, we must have before us a

3

collection of objects that are to be counted and with which we can experiment to discover the properties of our counting numbers. The name given by mathematicians for such a collection is "set". Since the idea of a set is fundamental to the counting numbers, we shall devote several chapters to a discussion of sets and their properties.

Since the use of sets in the teaching of arithmetic has been a public issue in recent years, we should digress at this point to explain our point of view on this question. The word "set" itself is the simplest English word that denotes a collection of objects. In common use it has many synonyms, such as "collection", "group", and "aggregate". In specialized uses other words have the same meaning, such as "*pair* of shoes", "*pack* of dogs", or "*herd* of cattle". Since collections of many kinds of things will appear in our discussions, it is clearer to use a single, simple word—*set*—than to vary the name for this idea from example to example and thus run the risk of confusion.

In the early grades instruction in arithmetic is developed by exposing the children to a variety of collections of concrete objects such as blocks, stones, fingers, leaves, and milk cartons. These are all *sets*, but the teacher does not need to use the word explicitly. The important thing is that the teacher have a firm grasp of the idea involved so that the children's intuition can be guided in the proper direction. So we say *set* to you, but you are not expected to use it in your class until the children are ready to shift into a formal vocabulary.

When we come to investigate the notions of addition and multiplication, we cannot help observing that these ideas are based upon the construction of new sets from old ones. Thus it is necessary for us to discuss certain set operations such as union, intersection, complement, and Cartesian product. The teacher must understand these thoroughly, but the children will proceed at the intuitive level under the teacher's guidance. We introduce these operations as an *aid* to understanding of arithmetic and not for their *own sake*.

In summary, sets are not a formal topic for instruction in arithmetic. Nevertheless, the ideas associated with them are essential for the understanding of the notion of counting numbers and of arithmetic processes. The teacher, therefore, must be well informed about sets and their operations, will use this knowledge to guide the students' intuition, and much later (when they are ready) will be able to show the students the set-theoretic way of looking at what they have been doing.

1.3 Other Types of Numbers

It soon becomes evident that the counting numbers are not adequate for the applications of arithmetic to our daily lives. New kinds of numbers must be invented and joined to these if we are to have a workable number system.

The first of these that we consider is the number *zero*. Zero may well be thought to be a special kind of counting number, which we use to say that there are no objects in the collection which we are counting. When we join *zero* to the other counting numbers, we obtain the *whole numbers*.

1.3 Other Types of Numbers

WHOLE NUMBERS

DEFINITION. The set of *whole numbers* is the collection of numbers whose names are

zero, one, two, three, four, ...

NUMBER LINE

The whole numbers can be used in another way as *measuring numbers.* If we write them at even intervals along a line (Figure 1.1) they represent the number of steps of equal length needed to move a certain distance to

FIGURE 1.1. *One-way number line.*

the right of the point marked with zero. It is very natural to introduce new numbers to represent distances measured to the left. These have the symbols −1, −2, −3, ... and are located as in Figure 1.2.

FIGURE 1.2. *Two-way number line.*

INTEGERS

DEFINITION. The entire collection consisting of the counting numbers, zero, and the numbers written −1, −2, −3, ... is called the set of *integers.*

As special cases, the counting numbers, 1, 2, 3, ... are called *positive integers* and the new numbers −1, −2, −3, ... are called *negative integers.*

In a later chapter we shall give you many more details about the integers, which we have merely introduced here in an intuitive fashion.

The next step in the construction of our number system is the introduction of the familiar fractions such as $\frac{1}{2}, \frac{3}{4}, \frac{9}{5}$. Fractions may also be negative such as $-\frac{6}{7}, -\frac{12}{5}, -\frac{8}{3}$. When we join all of these to the integers, we obtain the system of *rational numbers.* Since a precise definition of these has several points of delicacy, let us settle for a preliminary definition of them.

RATIONAL NUMBERS

DEFINITION. (preliminary). The system of *rational numbers* consists of the integers together with the numbers represented by positive and negative fractions.

We can easily find places for the rational numbers on our number line (Figure 1.3) and may suspect that every point on the line can be represented by such a rational number. Later we will show you that there are

FIGURE 1.3. *Rational numbers on the number line.*

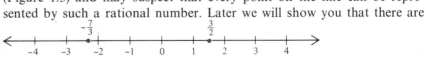

points (such as that $\sqrt{2}$ units to the right of zero) that do not correspond to rational numbers. These points are of geometric importance and the corresponding numbers also appear in arithmetic. As a consequence we must again enlarge our number system by joining *irrational* numbers such as $\sqrt{2}$ and π to the system of rational numbers. In this way we can obtain a number corresponding to each point of the line. Irrational numbers may be negative as well as positive. We must postpone the details of this process to a later chapter and again settle for a preliminary definition.

REAL NUMBERS **DEFINITION.** (preliminary). The system of *real numbers* consists of the system of rational numbers together with the collection of all the irrational numbers.

Although elementary arithmetic is generally confined to the system of rational numbers, occasional examples of irrational numbers do appear quite naturally. The teacher must, therefore, be prepared to deal intelligently with these when they arise.

1.4 Numbers and Numerals

In a strictly logical sense we have been careless thus far in referring to our numbers. A number is an abstract concept that cannot be visualized or written on paper; the best that we can do is to say or write a name or symbol that will represent the number. Since numbers can be represented by a variety of names or symbols, there is a possibility of confusion here.

For example, the number that is commonly called *two* has the following symbols (among others):

$$2, \text{II}, \tfrac{6}{3}, 8 - 6, \sqrt{4}$$

These are called *numerals*.

NUMERALS **DEFINITION.** A *numeral* is a symbol that is a name for a number.

Because two different numerals may represent the same number it is convenient to have a simple way to indicate such a fact. This is precisely the function of the equality sign. For example, the equation

$$8 - 6 = \tfrac{6}{3}$$

is a mathematical sentence which expresses the fact that the number represented by $8 - 6$ *is the same as* the number represented by $\tfrac{6}{3}$. We read this sentence "Eight minus six equals six divided by three".

The general rule for using the equality sign, $=$, is this: An equation consisting of the symbol $=$ placed between two numerals is a sentence indicating that *the number represented by the numeral on the left is the same as the number represented by the numeral on the right*.

To indicate that two numerals represent *different* numbers we use the symbol $\neq$. For example,

$$2 + 3 \neq 4 - 1$$

indicates that the number represented by $2 + 3$ is different from the number represented by $4 - 1$.

Strictly speaking, we should distinguish between numbers and numerals when we speak or write. Precise adherence to such a requirement, however, sometimes leads to long and confusing sentences and to intolerable pedantry in the classroom. We recommend, therefore, that you be sure that you understand this distinction so that you are clear about it in the rare cases where it must be made explicit, but that in the classroom you make no special effort to preserve the distinction in your speaking or writing. We ourselves shall behave in this way in this book.

---

1. The numbers 1, 2, 3, 4, ... are *natural* numbers or *counting* numbers. The dots are read "and so forth". The next natural number after 4 is __5__.

> 5

2. The numbers 1, 2, 3, ... are called __natural__ numbers.

> natural (or counting)

3. The sets of numbers designated by 1, 2, 3, ... and 1, 2, 3, 4, ... are __the same__.
(the same, different)

> the same

4. Which of the following are natural numbers? 0, 7, $2\frac{1}{2}$, 3674. __7, 3674__

> 7, 3674.

5. The set of natural numbers is the collection of numbers whose names are __1, 2, 3, ...__.

> 1, 2, 3, ...

6. The number 0 is not a __natural__ number. However, it is a
(natural, whole)
__whole__ number.
(natural, whole)

> natural   whole

7. The whole numbers are the numbers __0, 1, 2, 3, ...__

> 0, 1, 2, 3, ...

8. True or false: Every natural number is a whole number? __True__

> True.

---

9. Not every whole number is a natural number because __0__ is a whole number but not a natural number.

> 0

10. The number -2 __is not__ a whole number. This number is
(is, is not)
called a __negative integer__

> is not   negative integer

11. Another phrase for positive integer is __natural number__.

> natural number (or counting number)

12. An integer that is neither positive or negative is the integer __0__.

> 0

13. The integers consist of the whole numbers $0, 1, 2, \ldots$ and the numbers __$-1, -2, -3, \ldots$__.

> $-1, -2, -3, \ldots$

14. True or false: (a) Every integer is a whole number. __False__
(b) Every natural number is an integer. __True__

> (a) False.   (b) True.

15. Classify the following as positive integer, negative integer, or neither: (a) -257. __negative__ (b) $-4\frac{1}{2}$. __neither__
(c) $1,658,371$. __positive__ (d) $\frac{5}{12}$. __neither__
(e) -10. __negative__

> (a) negative integer   (b) neither   (c) positive integer
> (d) neither   (e) negative integer

16. Numbers such as $\frac{5}{12}$ and $\frac{9}{2}$ are fractions. The integers together with the positive and negative fractions form the set of __rational__ numbers.

> rational

17. Although $\frac{5}{12}$ is not an integer, it is a <u>rational</u> number.

rational (or real)

18. To which of the following sets does the number 34 not belong? (a) natural numbers, (b) whole numbers, (c) integers, (d) negative integers, (e) rational numbers. <u>d</u>

Only (d).

19. True or false:
(a) Every rational number is an integer. <u>False</u>
(b) Every whole number is a rational number. <u>True</u>
(c) Every natural number is an integer. <u>True</u>
(d) Zero is a rational number. <u>True</u>

(a) False.   (b) True.   (c) True.   (d) True.

20. Which of the following are *not* rational numbers? $-\frac{1}{2}$, $4\frac{1}{3}$, $\sqrt{2}$, -37, 0, π. <u>$\sqrt{2}$, π</u>

$\sqrt{2}$, π.

21. A real number such as $\sqrt{2}$ which is not rational is called <u>irrational</u>

irrational

22. An irrational number is a <u>real</u> number.

real

23. The rational numbers together with the irrational numbers form the set of <u>real</u> numbers.

real

24. To which of the following sets does the number $-\frac{3}{2}$ not belong? (a) real numbers, (b) rational numbers, (c) integers, (d) irrational numbers. <u>c, d</u>

(c) and (d).

25. The rational and irrational numbers have no number in common. Which pair(s) of the following sets have no number in common? Real numbers, rational numbers, negative integers, whole numbers, natural numbers. *negative integers, natural numbers*
negative integers, whole numbers

> negative integers, natural numbers   negative integers, whole numbers

26. Every natural number, whole number, integer, rational number and irrational number is a *real* _____ number.

> real

27. A numeral is a symbol for a *number*.

> number

28. The symbol that represents a number is called a *numeral*.

> numeral

29. The symbol that represents the number of letters in our alphabet is *26*.

> 26

30. The numbers represented by $3 + 4$ and $5 + 2$ are *the same*.
(the same, different)

> the same

31. The equation $3 + 4 = 5 + 2$ indicates that the *numerals*
(numbers, numerals)
$3 + 4$ and $5 + 2$ represent the same *number*.

> numerals   number

32. The statement $2 + 5 \neq 1 + 3$ indicates that the numerals $2 + 5$ and $1 + 3$ represent *different* numbers.
(the same, different)

> different

You have now completed Chapter 1 and may proceed to Chapter 2.

2

Logic

Before beginning this chapter you should have completed Chapter 1 and should know the definitions of the several systems of numbers presented there. In addition, you will need to know the meanings of several symbols and terms that you have probably encountered in your earlier experience. A review of these is given in the following Readiness Test.

R E A D I N E S S   T E S T

1. A whole number is even if it is divisible by __2__ .

> 2

2. An even number a can be written in the form $a = 2n$, where n is some other whole number.

> $2n$

3. The first five even whole numbers are __0, 2, 4, 6, 8__ .

> 0, 2, 4, 6, 8

4. A whole number is odd if it is not __even__ .

> even

5. An odd number a can be written in the form $a = 2n + 1$, where n is some other whole number.

> $2n + 1$

6. The first five odd whole numbers are __1, 3, 5, 7, 9__ .

> 1, 3, 5, 7, 9

7. A natural number, n, which is not equal to 1, is a prime if its only divisors are __1__ and __n__ .

> 1 n

8. The first five prime natural numbers are __2, 3, 5, 7, 11__ .

> 2, 3, 5, 7, 11

9. The symbol $<$ means __less than__ .

> less than

---

10. The symbol > means __more than__.

> greater than

11. Write the correct symbol in each of the following situations:
(a) 3 __<__ 6, (b) 4 __>__ 1, (c) 72 __>__ 7.2.
    (<, >)   (<, >)   (<, >)

> (a) <   (b) >   (c) >

12. The whole numbers x that satisfy $x < 4$ are __0, 1, 2, 3__.

> 0, 1, 2, 3

13. The whole numbers x that satisfy $x > 10$ and $x < 16$ are
__11, 12, 13, 14, 15__.

> 11, 12, 13, 14, 15

14. True or false: (a) All primes are odd. __F__ (b) All odd numbers
are prime. __F__

> (a) F.   (b) F.

Read Sections 2.1 through 2.3. When you finish Section 2.3, complete the program that follows the text. Refer back to the text, whenever you wish, while you are working the program.

2.1 Introduction

The process of mathematical inference must necessarily follow some collection of prescribed rules, which we commonly call the *laws of logic*. These are nothing more than a formal compilation of common methods of reasoning, but we need to write them down explicitly so that all of us know precisely what is generally agreed upon. This chapter is an introduction to those principles of logic which we shall use in this course; it is only a small portion of the whole subject of logic, which is developed in detail in more advanced books.

2.2 Propositions and Open Sentences

In everyday speech and in much of mathematics we encounter straight-forward statements such as:

> New York is the largest city in the United States.
> Bob Hope is a physicist.
> 3 is a natural number.
> $10 + 2 = 17$

Some of these are true and some are false. The essential quality of such a statement is that it is either true or false. Perhaps we do not know which it is, as in the case

> There is life on Mars.

but in every case the statement is definitely true or false (not both). Such statements are called propositions.

PROPOSITION **DEFINITION.** A *proposition* is an ordinary statement to which one and only one of the words "true" or "false" can be meaningfully applied.

In mathematics we run across statements of a quite different kind, such as

$$3x + 2 = 8$$

$$y + 1 > 4$$

$$x^2 - 5x + 6 = 0$$

$$(-x) + (-y) = -(x + y)$$

VARIABLE As they stand, it is not meaningful to call these true or false, for we are not given the values of the *variables* x and y. Nevertheless, if we agree (for example) that x and y can be replaced by any whole numbers, we find that

> $3x + 2 = 8$ becomes true when x is replaced by 2, and is false when x is replaced by any whole number different from 2.

> $y + 1 > 4$ becomes true when y is replaced by $4, 5, 6, \ldots$ and is false when y is replaced by 0, 1, 2, and 3.

> $x^2 - 5x + 6 = 0$ becomes true when x is replaced by 2 or 3 and is false when x is replaced by any other whole numbers.

> $(-x) + (-y) = -(x + y)$ becomes true when x and y are replaced by any whole numbers whatever.

Thus the truth or falsehood of statements like these is not meaningful until whole numbers are substituted for x and y. Such statements are called open sentences.

Of course, our requirement that x and y be whole numbers could be altered. We could ask that they be natural numbers, rational numbers, real numbers, or something else. The only important point is that we decide in advance what kind of numbers may be substituted for these variables.

DEFINITION. An *open sentence* is a statement involving one or more variables, which becomes true or false each time that specific values are given to the variables. These values must be chosen from a set of numbers that is specified in advance.

Our notation for an open sentence will be a symbol such as p_x, q_y, or $r_{x,y}$, in which the variable (or variables) involved is written as a subscript.

2.3 Conversion of Open Sentences into Propositions

We have just observed that the open sentence $3x + 2 = 8$ becomes the true proposition $(3 \cdot 2) + 2 = 8$ when x is replaced by 2, and that it becomes the false proposition $(3 \cdot 3) + 2 = 8$ when x is replaced by 3. Thus the *replacement* of a variable in an open sentence by a number converts the open sentence into a proposition. We may describe this procedure more generally as follows.

(1) FIRST METHOD OF CONVERSION

An open sentence p_x is converted into a proposition when the variable x is replaced by any number that is chosen from a given set of numbers. Similarly, $p_{x,y}$ is converted into a proposition when the variables x and y are replaced by numbers. The resulting proposition will be either true or false.

There is a second method of converting an open sentence into a proposition which will be of great importance to us in this course. Let us consider some examples.

The open sentence

$$x^2 - 9 = (x + 3)(x - 3)$$

becomes a true proposition when *any* number is substituted for x.

Similarly, the open sentence

$$x + y = y + x$$

becomes a true proposition when *any* numbers are substituted for x and y.

These examples lead us to consider the related propositions, which are true:

For all $x: x^2 - 9 = (x + 3)(x - 3)$.
For all x and $y: x + y = y + x$.

On the other hand, the proposition

For all $x: x^2 + 9 = (x + 3)(x + 3)$

is false. For, when 1 is substituted for x, we obtain

$$1 + 9 = (1 + 3)(1 + 3)$$

14

or

$$10 = 16$$

which is false.

More generally we can describe this procedure as follows.

(2) SECOND METHOD OF CONVERSION

If we are given an open sentence p_x with variable x, we can convert it into a proposition by inserting "For all x" in front of p_x and writing

$$\text{For all } x : p_x.$$

The resulting proposition is either true or false.

Similarly, for an open sentence $p_{x,y}$ with variables x and y,

$$\text{For all } x \text{ and } y : p_{x,y}$$

is a proposition that is either true or false.

The great majority of propositions to be considered in this course are of this type, and our task will be to decide whether they are true or false. Of course, we are chiefly interested in true propositions and shall give you proofs of them wherever they arise. But you (or your pupils) may wonder why certain propositions of this type are false, and we can now explain how to demonstrate the falsehood of such a proposition.

For example, how did we prove that the proposition

$$\text{For all } x : x^2 + 9 = (x + 3)(x + 3)$$

is false? We found a number 1 whose substitution for x gave the false relation $10 = 16$. Hence $x^2 + 9 = (x + 3)(x + 3)$ is not true for *all* x. Such a value for x is called a *counterexample*. More generally, we have the following procedure.

(3) METHOD FOR PROVING FALSEHOOD OF
  "*For all $x : p_x$*"

COUNTEREXAMPLE

To show that the proposition "For all $x : p_x$" is false (when it is indeed false), find a particular number c such that when x is replaced by c in p_x, the result is a false proposition. Such a number c is called a counterexample.

Similarly, to show that the proposition "For all x and $y : p_{x,y}$" is false, find particular numbers c and d such that when x is replaced by c and y by d in $p_{x,y}$ the result is a false proposition. Again the pair of numbers (c, d) is called a counterexample.

In the ordinary day-to-day practice of mathematics, we often abbreviate the statements of propositions like

$$\text{For all } x \text{ and } y : x + y = y + x$$

and merely write

$$x + y = y + x$$

where the "For all x and y" is to be understood. In doing so we run the risk of confusion by not saying exactly what we mean.

15

In this book we shall be careful to insert "For all" when it is needed and you should do this in your exercise material. We caution you, however, that this is not the universal practice in mathematical books and that you should be prepared to supply the "For all" where it is implied by the context.

1. A proposition in mathematics is a statement that is either _true_ or _false_ but not both.

> true   false

2. The statement "$3x + 2 = 8$" is true for one value of x and false for other values. This statement _is not_ a proposition.
(is, is not)

> is not

3. A statement that is either true or false but not both is called a _proposition_.

> proposition

4. In the statement "$3x + 2 = 8$", x is called a _variable_.

> variable

5. A statement involving variables which becomes true or false when specific values are given to the variables is called an _open sentence_.

> open sentence

6. The statement "$3x + 2 = 8$" is an _open sentence_.

> open sentence

7. An open sentence always involves at least one _variable_.

> variable

8. Classify these statements as propositions or open sentences:
(a) $2x + 5 = 3x$. _open_   (b) $4 + 5 = 6$. _proposition_
(c) $x + y = y + x$. _open_   (d) 0 is a whole number. _proposition_

> (a) Open sentence.   (b) Proposition.   (c) Open sentence.
> (d) Proposition.

9. In the open sentence $3x + 2y = 16$, the variables are _x, y_ .

> x and y

10. In the open sentence $x + y = 4$, let x be replaced by 3 and y by 1. The resulting proposition is _T_ . If x is replaced by 2 and y by 2, the
(T, F)
resulting proposition is _T_ . If x is replaced by 3 and y by 3, the
(T, F)
resulting proposition is _F_ .
(T, F)

> T   T   F

11. Although the letters x and y are used frequently as variables, other letters or symbols may also be used. For example, a and b are variables in the open sentence $2a - 3b = 6$. When a is replaced by 3 and b by 0 in this open sentence, the resulting proposition is _T_ . When a is
(T, F)
replaced by 5 and b by 1, the resulting proposition is _F_ .
(T, F)

> T   F

12. In other examples letters with subscripts may be used as variables. The statement "$2a_1 + a_2 = 7$" is an _open sentence_ . The number of variables is _2_ .

> open sentence   2

13. The symbol p_x is used in the text to denote an _open sentence_ involving the variable _x_ .

> open sentence x

14. An open sentence involving the variables x and y may be denoted by the symbol _$p_{x, y}$_ .

> $p_{x,y}$

15. The symbol r_{a_1, a_2} could denote _an open sentences using variable a_1 and a_2_ .

> an open sentence involving the variables a_1 and a_2

16. The proposition "For all $x: x + 5 = 7$" is ___F___.
(T, F)

> F

17. The open sentence $x + 4 = 4$ becomes a proposition if it is preceded by the phrase FOR All X .

> "For all x"

18. The open sentence $x + 4 = 4$ becomes a proposition if Any number is substituted for x.

> any number

19. If we are given an open sentence, p_x, we obtain a proposition when we (1) substitute Any number for x; (2) write the phrase "FOR ALL X" before p_x.

> any number   "For all x"

20. The statement "For all $x: x + 0 = x$" is 2 proposition .
(a proposition, an open sentence)

> a proposition

21. In the statement "For all a_1 and $a_2: a_1 + a_2 = a_2 + a_1$", "$a_1 + a_2 = a_2 + a_1$" is an _____ and the entire statement is a _____.

> open sentence   proposition

22. Are the following propositions about *integers* true or false?
(a) For all $x: x + (-x) = 0$. T
(b) For all $x: 2x + 1 = 7$ F
(c) For all $x: x^2 - 4 = (x + 2)(x - 2)$. T
(d) For all $x: x + 0 = x$. T
(e) For all $x: x^2 - 2x + 1 = 0$. F

> (a) T.   (b) F.   (c) T.   (d) T.   (e) F.

23. The proposition "For all integers $x: 2x + 1 = 7$" is false. A *counterexample* is $x =$ 4 .

> Any integer except 3 will do.

24. The proposition "For all integers x and y: $x + y = y$" is false. A counterexample is $x =$ ___Any___, $y =$ ___Any___.

> Any value of x except 0, and any value of y will do.

25. If we can find a value of x for which p_x is false, then "For all x: p_x" is ___False___. Such a value of x is called a ___Counterexple___

> false   counterexample

26. A general method for proving that "For all x: p_x" is false (when it is indeed false) is to find a ___Counterexample___. On the other hand, can we show that "For all x: p_x" is true (when it is indeed true) by finding a single number c such that when c is substituted for x, p_x becomes a true proposition? ___No___

> counterexample   No.

You should now read Sections 2.4 and 2.5. These sections are concerned with certain open sentences that are formed from other given open sentences. Truth tables, which are of assistance in the analysis of open sentences, are introduced in these sections. When you finish reading the text, continue with the program.

2.4 Compound Open Sentences

When we have at our disposal several open sentences, we can combine pairs of these in different ways to form new open sentences.

Suppose that we are given the following two open sentences, for whose variables whole numbers may be substituted:

$$x > 3$$

$$x \text{ is even}$$

CONJUNCTION   We can connect these with an *and* to form a new open sentence, called the *conjunction* of the two given open sentences:

$$(x > 3) \text{ and } (x \text{ is even})$$

When we substitute a value for x in this new open sentence, we need a rule that will tell us whether the resulting proposition is true or false. In accordance with common usage we state this rule as follows:

RULE FOR CONJUNCTIONS. When x is given a specific value in a conjunction (p_x and q_x), the resulting proposition is *true* if for this value of

19

x *both* p_x and q_x are true. If either or both of the open sentences p_x and q_x is false for this value of x, the conjunction is false for this value of x.

The rule can be stated in another form through the use of a truth table. In Table 1 the columns represent the three open sentences p_x, q_x, and

TRUTH TABLE

TABLE 1. **Truth Table for Conjunction (Preliminary)**

p_x	q_x	$(p_x$ and $q_x)$
T	T	
T	F	
F	T	
F	T	

$(p_x$ and $q_x)$. As x takes on various values, p_x may be true (T) or false (F) and similarly for q_x. The complete set of these possibilities is presented by writing T or F in the four rows under p_x and under q_x. Now the rule is applied to fill in the column headed $(p_x$ and $q_x)$, Table 2.

TABLE 2. **Truth Table for Conjunction (Completed)**

p_x	q_x	$(p_x$ and $q_x)$
T	T	T
T	F	F
F	T	F
F	F	F

When we apply this rule to the conjunction

$$(x > 3) \text{ and } (x \text{ is even})$$

and consider $x = 0, 1, \ldots, 6$ we obtain Table 3:

TABLE 3. **Table for "$(x > 3)$ and $(x$ is even)",** **where $x = 0, 1, \ldots, 6$**

x	$x > 3$	x is even	Conjunction
0	F	T	F
1	F	F	F
2	F	T	F
3	F	F	F
4	T	T	T
5	T	F	F
6	T	T	T

DISJUNCTION

A second way of combining two open sentences is to connect them with an "or". The open sentence thus formed is the *disjunction* of the two original ones. For example, the disjunction of

$$x > 3$$

$$x \text{ is even}$$

is

$$(x > 3) \text{ or } (x \text{ is even})$$

As in the case of conjunctions we must give a rule that will determine the truth or falsehood of a disjunction when x is given any specific value.

RULE FOR DISJUNCTION. When x is given a specific value in a disjunction (p_x or q_x), the resulting proposition is *true* if for this value of x at least one of the open sentences p_x and q_x has the value T. If both p_x and q_x have the value F, then so does (p_x or q_x).

The corresponding truth table is shown as Table 4.

TABLE 4. Truth Table for Disjunction

p_x	q_x	(p_x or q_x)
T	T	T
T	F	T
F	T	T
F	F	F

When we apply this rule to the disjunction

$$(x > 3) \text{ or } (x \text{ is even})$$

and consider $x = 0, 1, \ldots, 6$, we obtain Table 5.

TABLE 5. Table for ($x > 3$) or (x is even), where $x = 0, 1, \ldots, 6$

x	$x > 3$	x is even	Disjunction
0	F	T	T
1	F	F	F
2	F	T	T
3	F	F	F
4	T	T	T
5	T	F	T
6	T	T	T

You should pay close attention to the differences between the tables for conjunction and disjunction.

There is a source of ambiguity in the use of the word "or" in everyday language. You will observe that we have used it in the *inclusive* sense in which

21

OR it means *either or both*. It thus carries the meaning sometimes expressed in English by the expression *and/or*. Sometimes, however, "or" is used in everyday speech in the *exclusive* sense in which it means *either but not both*; hence there is a possibility of confusion. In this book, and in mathematics in general, "or" is always used in the *inclusive* sense unless an explicit statement is made to the contrary.

2.5 Negation of an Open Sentence

From any open sentence we can form a new open sentence, called its *negation*.

NEGATION **DEFINITION.** The *negation* of the open sentence p_x is the open sentence "It is false that p_x". We write the negation of p_x in short form as "not p_x".

From this definition it is clear that "not p_x" is false for those values of x which make p_x true. Similarly, "not p_x" is true for those values of x for which p_x is false. These facts are conveniently stated in a truth table, Table 6.

TABLE 6. Truth Table for Negation

p_x	not p_x
T	F
F	T

The expression "It is false that p_x" is clumsy in ordinary speech, and so we frequently replace this by other expressions that have the same meaning. We shall continue to call these negations of p_x.

In simple cases it is easy to write such negations in various equivalent forms. For example, we have the following negations:

Open Sentence	Negation
$3x + 6 = 15$	It is false that "$3x + 6 = 15$" Not "$3x + 6 = 15$" $3x + 6 \neq 15$
x is even	It is false that "x is even" Not "x is even" x is not even x is odd
$x > 3$	It is false that "$x > 3$" Not "$x > 3$" x is not greater than 3 x is less than or equal to 3

In compound sentences we must be more subtle, and we shall discuss this question in some detail in the next section.

---

1. What is the conjunction of the two open sentences (where x is a natural number) (1) x is even; (2) x is a prime. _____

(x is even) and (x is a prime).

2. When 3 is substituted for x, is the conjunction of "$2x + 4 = 11$" and "$x^2 = 16$" true or false? _____

F.

3. When 4 is substituted for y, is the conjunction of "y is a whole number" and "y is a rational number" true or false? _____

T.

4. Complete the table for $x = 7, 8, 9, 10$ (see Table 3) by inserting T or F, as appropriate.

x	$x > 3$	x is even	Conjunction
7			
8			
9			
10			

x	$x > 3$	x is even	Conjunction
7	T	F	F
8	T	T	T
9	T	F	F
10	T	T	T

5. What is the disjunction of the two open sentences (where x is a whole number) (1) $x^2 = 4$; (2) $x < 6$? _____

($x^2 = 4$) or ($x < 6$).

6. What is the disjunction of the two open sentences (1) triangle T is isosceles; (2) triangle T is equilateral? _____

(triangle T is isosceles) or (triangle T is equilateral).

7. When 3 is substituted for x, is the disjunction of (1) $2x + 4 = 10$; (2) $x^2 = 16$ true or false? _____

T.

8. When 4 is substituted for y, is the disjunction of (1) y is a whole number; (2) y is odd true or false? _____

T.

9. When 5 is substituted for x is the disjunction of (1) $x + 5 = 11$; (2) $x^2 = 36$ true or false? _____

F.

10. Complete the table for $x = 7, 8, 9, 10$ (see Table 5) by inserting T or F, as appropriate.

x	$x > 3$	x is even	Disjunction
7			
8			
9			
10			

x	$x > 3$	x is even	Disjunction
7	T	F	T
8	T	T	T
9	T	F	T
10	T	T	T

11. The negation of the open sentence "p_x" can be written in either of the forms (1) It is _____ that p_x; (2) _____ p_x.

false   not

12. The negation of the open sentence "$2x = 5$" can be written in any of the forms (1) It is ——————— "$2x = 5$"; (2) ——————— "$2x = 5$"; (3) $2x$ ——————— 5.

(1) false that   (2) Not   (3) $\neq$

13. The negation of the open sentence "x is odd" can be written in any of the forms (1) ——————— "x is odd"; (2) ——————— "x is odd"; (3) x is ——————— odd ; (4) x is ———————.

(1) It is false that   (2) Not   (3) Not   (4) even

14. When 3 is substituted for x in $3x + 2 = 11$, the result is a ———————
(T, F)
proposition. Hence when 3 is substituted for x in the negation of $3x + 2 = 11$, the result is a ——————— proposition.
(T, F)

T   F

15. When 4 is substituted for x in "x is odd", the result is a ———————
(T, F)
proposition. Hence when 4 is substituted for x in the negation of "x is odd", the result is a ——————— proposition.
(T, F)

F   T

16. True or false: When the same number is substituted for x in "p_x" and in "not p_x", the two resulting propositions can both be true. ———————

F.

2.6 Logical Equivalence of Open Sentences

Two open sentences may have quite different statements and still convey the same meaning. For example, consider

$$(x^2 = 4) \quad \text{and} \quad (x \text{ is positive})$$

$$x = 2$$

Each of these becomes a true proposition when 2 is substituted for x and becomes a false proposition when any other number is substituted for x. In such a situation we say that these two open sentences are logically equivalent. The general definition is as follows.

LOGICAL EQUIVALENCE   **DEFINITION.** Two open sentences are said to be *logically equivalent* if for each x the truth value of the first is equal to the truth value of the second.

To show that two open sentences are logically equivalent we proceed as in the following example by completing their truth tables and comparing the results.

EXAMPLE. Show that the open sentences

$$\text{not } (p_x \text{ and } q_x)$$

$$(\text{not } p_x) \text{ or } (\text{not } q_x)$$

are logically equivalent.

Solution. First we complete the truth table for "not $(p_x$ and $q_x)$" as follows:

p_x	q_x	p_x and q_x	not $(p_x$ and $q_x)$
T	T	T	F
T	F	F	T
F	T	F	T
F	F	F	T

Second, we complete the truth table for "(not p_x) or (not q_x)".

p_x	q_x	not p_x	not q_x	(not p_x) or (not q_x)
T	T	F	F	F
T	F	F	T	T
F	T	T	F	T
F	F	T	T	T

Since the right-hand columns in these truth tables are identical, we conclude that the two given open sentences are logically equivalent. Frequently it is more convenient to combine these two tables into a single one:

p_x	q_x	p_x and q_x	not $(p_x$ and $q_x)$	not p_x	not q_x	(not p_x) or (not q_x)
T	T	T	F	F	F	F
T	F	F	T	F	T	T
F	T	F	T	T	F	T
F	F	F	T	T	T	T

We can use the result of this example to find alternative expressions for the negations of conjunctions:

2.6 Logical Equivalence of Open Sentences

NEGATION OF CONJUNCTION

Open Sentence (Conjunction)	Alternative Forms for the Negation
$(x > 4)$ *and* (x is even)	It is false that "$(x > 4)$ *and* (x is even)" Not "$(x > 4)$ *and* (x is even)" (Not "$x > 4$") *or* (Not "x is even") (x is not greater than 4) *or* (x is not even) ($x \leq 4$) *or* (x is odd)
$(x^2 = 4)$ *and* (x is positive)	It is false that "$(x^2 = 4)$ *and* (x is positive)" Not "$(x^2 = 4)$ *and* (x is positive)" (Not "$x^2 = 4$") *or* (not "x is positive") ($x^2 \neq 4$) *or* (x is not positive)

1. What disjunction has been shown to be logically equivalent to the negation of $(p_x$ and $q_x)$? _____

(not p_x) or (not q_x).

2. Write a disjunction that is logically equivalent to the negation of "$(2x + 5 = 13)$ and $(x - 4 = 0)$". _____

_____

$(2x + 5 \neq 13)$ or $(x - 4 \neq 0)$.

3. Write a disjunction that is logically equivalent to the negation of "$(x + 3 = 5)$ and $(x + 4 = 7)$". _____

_____

$(x + 3 \neq 5)$ or $(x + 4 \neq 7)$.

4. Notice that "not $(p_x$ and $q_x)$" is different from "(not p_x) and q_x". Complete the table and compare its last column with the last column of the truth table for "not $(p_x$ and $q_x)$".

p_x	q_x	not p_x	(not p_x) and q_x
T	T		
T	F		
F	T		
F	F		

p_x	q_x	not p_x	(not p_x) and q_x
T	T	F	F
T	F	F	F
F	T	T	T
F	F	T	F

5. Are the open sentences "not $(p_x$ and $q_x)$" and "(not $p_x)$ and q_x" logically equivalent? _____

No.

6. Write a truth table for "not $(p_x$ or $q_x)$".

p_x	q_x	p_x or q_x	not $(p_x$ or $q_x)$
T	T	T	F
T	F	T	F
F	T	T	F
F	F	F	T

7. Write a truth table for "(not $p_x)$ and (not $q_x)$".

p_x	q_x	not p_x	not q_x	(not $p_x)$ and (not $q_x)$
T	T	F	F	F
T	F	F	T	F
F	T	T	F	F
F	F	T	T	T

NEGATION OF DISJUNCTION

8. Draw a conclusion by comparing frames 6 and 7: Not $(p_x$ or $q_x)$ is _____ to (not $p_x)$ and (not $q_x)$.

logically equivalent

9. Write a conjunction logically equivalent to the negation of "$(x^2 + 5 = 9)$ or $(x = 3)$". _____

$(x^2 + 5 \neq 9)$ and $(x \neq 3)$.

10. Write a conjunction that is logically equivalent to the negation of "$(x = 3)$ or $(x$ is even)"._____

$(x \neq 3)$ and $(x$ is odd).

11. Is "not $(p_x$ or $q_x)$" logically equivalent to "(not $p_x)$ or q_x"? (Determine your answer by writing the appropriate truth tables on a separate piece of paper.) _____
  (yes, no)

No.

12. Is "not (p_x or q_x)" logically equivalent to "(not p_x) or (not q_x)"? (Determine your answer by writing the appropriate truth tables on a separate piece of paper.)_____
(yes, no)

No.

2.7 Conditional Sentences

CONDITIONAL   The great majority of theorems in mathematics have the form

$$\text{If } p_x, \text{ then } q_x$$

where p_x and q_x are open sentences. Statements of this form are called *conditionals*. We call p_x the *hypothesis* and q_x the *conclusion* of the conditional. Algebraic examples of conditionals are

If $2x + 4 = 6$, then $2x = 2$.
If $x^2 - 4x + 3 = 0$, then $(x - 3)(x - 1) = 0$.
If $x = 2$, then $x^2 = 4$.

Most geometric theorems are of the same type, although they are expressed differently. For example, consider the familiar theorem:

If a triangle is isosceles, then its base angles are equal.

Let our variable x now stand for a triangle; that is, wherever x appears in our statement we may substitute any specific triangle we please. Then the above theorem can be written in the form "If p_x, then q_x" as follows:

If x is isosceles, then the base angles of x are equal.

You should observe that conditionals such as these are *open sentences* and thus are not true or false. Usually, however, they are given a different interpretation when they appear as theorems in mathematical books: We are supposed to understand that the expression "For all x" is written in front of them. Thus the statements above should have been written

For all x: if $2x + 4 = 6$, then $2x = 2$.
For all x: if $x^2 - 4x + 3 = 0$, then $(x - 3)(x - 1) = 0$.
For all x: if $x = 2$, then $x^2 = 4$.
For all x: if x is isosceles, then the base angles of x are equal.

These statements are *propositions* and not *open sentences*. Although in other books, you are likely to find the "For all x" omitted, we shall include it here so that there is no possibility of your forgetting about it. When you go to other books, you must supply it for yourself.

The problem before us now is to discuss the properties of the conditional "if p_x, then q_x". When we substitute a value for x in this open sentence, we need a rule that will tell us whether the resulting proposition is true or false. This is best given by a truth table. The choice of T or F in the right-hand column of Table 7 is an arbitrary one that has been accepted by most logicians

TABLE 7. **Truth Table for Conditional**

p_x	q_x	if p_x, then q_x
T	T	T
T	F	F
F	T	T
F	F	T

and mathematicians. It may be motivated as follows. In the first line of Table 7 we say that if we reason from a true hypothesis to a true conclusion, then we are reasoning correctly and the conditional must be true. In the second line we observe that we must be reasoning incorrectly if we derive a false conclusion from a true hypothesis; hence in this case the conditional must be false. The third and fourth lines tell us that starting from a false hypothesis we may derive either a true or a false conclusion by correct reasoning. For example, if we start from the false statement

$$1 = 2$$

we may derive a true conclusion by the following steps:

$$1 = 2$$
$$\underline{2 = 1}$$
$$3 = 3$$

But by correct reasoning we may equally well derive a false conclusion in the following fashion:

$$1 = 2$$
$$\underline{3 = 3}$$
$$4 = 5$$

If we apply this table to the conditional

"if x is even, then x is divisible by 4"

and consider $x = 1, 2, \ldots, 8$, we obtain Table 8.

TABLE 8. **Table for "if x is even, then x is divisible by 4", where $x = 1, \ldots, 8$**

x	x is even	x is divisible by 4	Conditional
1	F	F	T
2	T	F	F
3	F	F	T
4	T	T	T
5	F	F	T
6	T	F	F
7	F	F	T
8	T	T	T

Now that we have the truth table for the conditional, we can develop a procedure for establishing the truth or falsehood of

$$\text{For all } x: \text{if } p_x, \text{ then } q_x.$$

This will be true if for every x (belonging to the preassigned set of numbers) there is a T in the right-hand column of the truth table for the conditional. This means that there is to be no x for which p_x is true and q_x is false. Hence we have the following rule of inference:

TRUTH OF CONDITIONAL

RULE FOR TRUTH OF "FOR ALL x: IF p_x, THEN q_x."
(1) Examine every x for which p_x is true. If q_x is true for every such x, then from the first line of the truth table, "For all x: if p_x, then q_x" is true.
(2) There may be no x for which p_x is true. In this case p_x is false for every x. Then from the third and fourth lines of the truth table, "For all x: if p_x, then q_x" is true. In this case we say that the proposition "For all x: if p_x, then q_x" *holds vacuously.*

EXAMPLE. Find the truth value of the proposition

$$\text{For all } x: \text{If } x - 5 = 0, \text{ then } x^2 = 25$$

where x is an integer.

Solution. The only integer for which the hypothesis is true is $x = 5$. Since $5^2 = 25$, the conclusion is also true for $x = 5$. Hence the proposition is true.

EXAMPLE. Find the truth value of the proposition

$$\text{For all } x: \text{If } (x + 4)(x - 3) = 0, \text{ then } x^2 = 9 \text{ where } x \text{ is an integer.}$$

Solution. The only values of x for which the hypothesis is true are $x = -4$ and $x = 3$. When $x = -4$, the conclusion is false. Hence the proposition is false. A counterexample is $x = -4$.

EXAMPLE. Find the truth value of the proposition

$$\text{For all } x: \text{If } 3x + 5 = 0, \text{ then } 2x + 7 = 0$$

where x is an integer.

Solution. There are no integral values of x for which the hypothesis is true. Hence the proposition is (vacuously) true.

This rule is basic to most proofs in algebra and geometry that you will encounter. The best way to learn how to construct proofs is through experience gained by studying a large number of them in various contexts. We hope that you will be able to make your own proofs as you gain this experience in this course.

On the other hand, there is a simple and direct way of proving that "For all x: if p_x, then q_x" is false (when it is, indeed, false). Suppose that we can find a value of x for which p_x is true and q_x is false. Then "For all x: if p_x, then q_x" cannot be true, for its truth requires that q_x be true for *every* x for which p_x is true. Hence our statement is false if we can find a value of x for which p_x is true and q_x is false. Such a value of x is called a *counterexample*. For instance, in Table 8 $x = 2$ and $x = 6$ are counterexamples which show that

"For all x: if x is even, then x is divisible by 4" is false.

---

1. When 2 is substituted for x in the conditional "if $x^2 = 4$, then $x = 2$", the result is a _____ proposition. When -2 is substituted for x
    (T, F)
in the same conditional, the result is a _____ proposition.
    (T, F)

T	F

2. Complete the truth table for the conditional "if $x^2 = 4$, then $x = 2$" for $x = 1, 2, \ldots, 6$.

x	$x^2 = 4$	$x = 2$	if $x^2 = 4$, then $x = 2$
1			
2			
3			
4			
5			
6			

x	$x^2 = 4$	$x = 2$	if $x^2 = 4$, then $x = 2$
1	F	F	T
2	T	T	T
3	F	F	T
4	F	F	T
5	F	F	T
6	F	F	T

3. In frame 2 every entry in the right-hand column is T. Does this prove that "For all integers x: if $x^2 = 4$, then $x = 2$" is true? _____
    (yes, no)

No; consider negative values of x.

4. When 3 is substituted for x in the conditional "if x is even, then $x^2 = 9$", the result is a _____ proposition. If 4 is substituted for x in the same
$$(T, F)$$
conditional, the result is a _____ proposition.
$$(T, F)$$

T F

5. Complete the truth table for the conditional "if $(x - 1)(x - 2) = 0$, then $(x - 1)(x - 3) = 0$" for $x = 1, 2, 3, 4$.

x	$(x - 1)(x - 2) = 0$	$(x - 1)(x - 3) = 0$	Conditional
1			
2			
3			
4			

x	$(x - 1)(x - 2) = 0$	$(x - 1)(x - 3) = 0$	Conditional
1	T	T	T
2	T	F	F
3	F	T	T
4	F	F	T

6. Give the correct truth value (T or F) for each of the following propositions, where x is an integer. When your answer is F give a counter-example.
   (a) For all x: if $x - 3 = 0$, then $x^2 = 9$._____
   (b) For all x: if $(x + 1)(x - 2) = 0$, then $(x + 1)(x - 3) = 0$._____
   (c) For all x: if $2x + 3 = 0$, then $5x + 9 = 0$. _____
   (d) For all x: if $2x + 3 = 0$, then $x = 5$. _____
   (e) For all x: if $x^2 = 16$, then $x = 4$. _____

(a) T.
(b) F; $x = 2$ is a counterexample.
(c) T; both parts are false for every integer.
(d) T; no integer satisfies $2x + 3 = 0$.
(e) F; $x = -4$ is a counterexample.

7. In the conditional "if p_x, then q_x", p_x and q_x can be any open sentences. They can, for example, be conjunctions or disjunctions of other open sentences. Truth tables for these more complicated cases can be constructed by adding more columns. The final column is completed by writing T for those entries for which either the conclusion is true or the

hypothesis is false, and F for the others. Complete the truth table.

p_x	q_x	p_x or q_x	If p_x or q_x, then q_x
T	T		
T	F		
F	T		
F	F		

p_x	q_x	p_x or q_x	If p_x or q_x, then q_x
T	T	T	T
T	F	T	F
F	T	T	T
F	F	F	T

8. Show that the proposition "For all x: if p_x and q_x, then p_x" is true, where p_x and q_x are any open sentences whatever. Make a truth table on a separate sheet of paper.

p_x	q_x	p_x and q_x	if p_x and q_x, then p_x
T	T	T	T
T	F	F	T
F	T	F	T
F	F	F	T

9. Complete the truth table to investigate the conditional "if (not q_x), then (not p_x)".

p_x	q_x	not q_x	not p_x	if (not q_x), then (not p_x)
T	T			
T	F			
F	T			
F	F			

p_x	q_x	not q_x	not p_x	if (not q_x), then (not p_x)
T	T	F	F	T
T	F	T	F	F
F	T	F	T	T
F	F	T	T	T

10. Draw a conclusion by comparing the truth table for "if p_x, then q_x" with the result of frame 9: "If p_x, then q_x" is _____ to "if (not q_x), then (not p_x)".

logically equivalent

11. By writing the appropriate truth tables on a separate piece of paper, show that "if p_x, then q_x" is logically equivalent to "not [p_x and (not q_x)]."

p_x	q_x	not q_x	p_x and (not q_x)	not [p_x and (not q_x)]
T	T	F	F	T
T	F	T	T	F
F	T	F	F	T
F	F	T	F	T

Now compare the right-hand column with the right-hand column of Table 7.

12. Give the correct truth value (T or F) for each of the following propositions, where x is an integer.
   (a) For all x: if $x^2 - 9 = 0$ and $x \neq 3$, then $x = -3$. _____
   (b) For all x: if $x - 1 = 0$ or $x - 2 = 0$, then $(x - 1)(x - 2) = 0$. ____
   (c) For all x: if $x^2 = 16$, then $x = 4$ or $x = -4$. _____
   (d) For all x: if $x^2 + 16 = 0$, then $x = 4$ or $x = -4$. _____
   (e) For all x: if $x^2 = 25$, then $x = 5$ and $x = -5$. _____

(a) T.   (b) T.   (c) T.
(d) T; there are no integers for which $x^2 + 16 = 0$.
(e) F; the conclusion is false for every value of x.

Now read Section 2.8, in which the discussion of conditionals is continued to include the converse and the contrapositive. When you finish reading the section, work the program that follows.

2.8 Derived Conditionals

(1) CONVERSE

If we begin with a conditional "if p_x, then q_x", we may reverse the clauses and consider the conditional "if q_x, then p_x". This is called the *converse* of the given conditional.

CONVERSE   **DEFINITION.**   The *converse* of the conditional "if p_x, then q_x" is the conditional "if q_x, then p_x".

The important question before us is: Is a conditional logically equivalent to its converse? This can be answered quickly by examining the appropriate truth table. Table 9 shows us immediately that in general a *conditional is*

TABLE 9. Conditional and its Converse

p_x	q_x	if p_x, then q_x	if q_x, then p_x
T	T	T	T
T	F	F	T
F	T	T	F
F	F	T	T

not logically equivalent to its converse. For if they were to be logically equivalent, the last two columns would have to be identical. The table shows, however, that there may be values of x for which "if p_x, then q_x" is true and "if q_x, then p_x" is false, and vice versa.

As an illustration let

$$p_x \text{ be } x = 2 \qquad q_x \text{ be } x^2 = 4$$

Then we have Table 10.

TABLE 10. Truth Table for "if $x = 2$, then $x^2 = 4$" and its converse

x	$x = 2$	$x^2 = 4$	if $x = 2$, then $x^2 = 4$	if $x^2 = 4$, then $x = 2$
2	T	T	T	T
-2	F	T	T	F
Any number other than 2 or -2	F	F	T	T

For some conditionals, however, there are no values of x for which p_x is true and q_x is false, or vice versa. Such conditionals *are* logically equivalent to their converses, for the second and third lines of Table 9 do not appear.

As an example, let p_x be "$x^2 = 16$" and q_x be "$x = 4$ or $x = -4$". Then we have Table 11. Since the entries in the last two columns are equal, the

TABLE 11. Table for "if $x^2 = 16$, then $x = 4$ or $x = -4$" and its converse

x	$x^2 = 16$	$x = 4$ or $x = -4$	if $x^2 = 16$, then $x = 4$ or $x = -4$	if $x = 4$ or $x = -4$, then $x^2 = 16$
4	T	T	T	T
-4	T	T	T	T
Any number except 4 or -4	F	F	T	T

conditional "if $x^2 = 16$, then $x = 4$ or $x = -4$" is logically equivalent to its converse.

(2) IF AND ONLY IF

In order to consider a conditional and its converse simultaneously, it is helpful to write their conjunction:

$$(\text{if } p_x, \text{then } q_x) \text{ and } (\text{if } q_x, \text{then } p_x)$$

BICONDITIONAL This is a new open sentence called the *biconditional* of p_x and q_x. As an abbreviation for the full statement of the biconditional we often write

$$p_x \text{ if and only if } q_x$$

or

$$q_x \text{ if and only if } p_x$$

DEFINITION. The *biconditional* "p_x if and only if q_x" is defined to be the conjunction of "if p_x, then q_x" and its converse.

Now let us examine the circumstances under which the proposition

$$\text{For all } x: p_x \text{ if and only if } q_x$$

is true. Since a conjunction is involved, this requires that both of the propositions

$$\text{For all } x: \text{if } p_x, \text{then } q_x$$
$$\text{For all } x: \text{if } q_x, \text{then } p_x$$

be true. Therefore, to prove the truth of the proposition

$$\text{For all } x: p_x \text{ if and only if } q_x$$

two steps are required:

(1) Prove the truth of "For all x: if p_x, then q_x".
(2) Prove the truth of "For all x: if q_x, then p_x".

As an illustration let us consider the proposition "For all positive integers $x: x$ is even if and only if x^2 is even". To prove this true we must prove the truth of the two propositions

(1) "For all positive integers x: if x is even, then x^2 is even".
(2) "For all positive integers x: if x^2 is even, then x is even".

The proofs that these propositions are true are given in the frames that follow this section.

EXAMPLE. Find the truth value of the biconditional "For all x: $x^2 = 4$ if and only if $x = 2$", where x is an integer.

Solution. We must examine the two conditionals

(1) If $x^2 = 4$, then $x = 2$.
(2) If $x = 2$, then $x^2 = 4$.

We see that $x = -2$ is a counterexample for (1), so (1) is false. Even though (2) is true, this is enough to prove that the biconditional is false.

CONTRAPOSITIVE

(3) CONTRAPOSITIVE

Associated with a conditional "if p_x, then q_x" is another conditional called its contrapositive:

Contrapositive: "if not q_x, then not p_x".

The important fact about contrapositives is that a conditional and its contrapositive *are* logically equivalent. We proved this in frame 10 of the last section but did not introduce the name "contrapositive" at that time.

The reason for introducing the contrapositive to you is that the propositions

(1) For all x: if p_x, then q_x
(2) For all x: if not q_x, then not p_x

are both true or both false. Suppose that we wish to prove that (1) is true, but cannot make any progress toward such a proof. It is then wise to try to prove that (2) is true. If we succeed in doing so, we can also conclude that (1) is true, and we have achieved our objective.

A common illustration of this use of the contrapositive in geometry is the following.

Prove: For all pairs of distinct lines in the plane, if two lines are cut by a transversal so that the alternate interior angles are equal, then the lines are parallel (i.e., do not intersect).

CONTRAPOSITIVE. For all pairs of distinct lines in the plane, if the lines are not parallel (i.e., do intersect), then the alternate interior angles in which they are cut by a transversal are not equal (Figure 2.1).

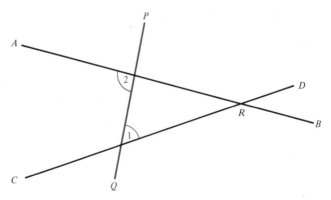

FIGURE 2.1. *Two nonparallel lines cut by the transversal PQ.*

Proof of Contrapositive. Let the lines AB and CD meet at R, and let them be cut by the transversal PQ. Let $\angle 1$ and $\angle 2$ be the alternate interior angles. We are asked to show that $\angle 1 \neq \angle 2$. But $\angle 2$ is an exterior angle of the triangle PQR and $\angle 1$ is an interior angle of this triangle, remote from $\angle 2$. Hence $\angle 1 \neq \angle 2$, for an exterior angle of a triangle is greater than either of the remote interior angles (i.e., those at the other vertices).

Since this argument holds for all pairs of intersecting lines, AB and CD, we have proved the contrapositive to be a true proposition. Therefore, the given statement is also a true proposition.

1. The converse of the proposition, "if p_x, then q_x" is the proposition _____.

"if q_x, then p_x"

2. For all integers x: if $x = 0$, then $x^2 = 0$. This proposition is _____.
(T, F)

The converse of the proposition is, "For all integers x: _____".
The converse is _____.
(T, F)

T   if $x^2 = 0$, then $x = 0$ T

3. For all polygons x, if x is a rectangle, then x is a quadrilateral. This proposition is _____. The converse of this proposition is _____.
(T, F)   (T, F)

T   F

4. If the conditional "if p_x, then q_x" is true for a particular value of x, then its converse _____ be true for that value
(must, may, cannot)
of x.

may

5. The open sentence "p_x if and only if q_x" means "if p_x, then _____" and "if _____, then _____".

q_x q_x p_x

6. If $x + 2 = 5$, then $x = 3$; and if $x = 3$, then $x + 2 = 5$. We can express the same thing more concisely by saying $x + 2 = 5$ _____
$x = 3$.

if and only if

7. Construct a truth table for the biconditional "p_x if and only if q_x" by filling in the blanks in the table.

p_x	q_x	if p_x, then q_x	if q_x, then p_x	p_x if and only if q_x
T	T			
T	F			
F	T			
F	F			

p_x	q_x	if p_x, then q_x	if q_x, then p_x	p_x if and only if q_x
T	T	T	T	T
T	F	F	T	F
F	T	T	F	F
F	F	T	T	T

8. If x is given a value such that p_x is false and q_x is true, then "p_x if and only if q_x" is _____.
(T, F)

F

9. The proposition "For all integers x: $x = 2$ if and only if $x^2 = 4$" is _____.
(T, F)

F

10. Complete the table.

x	$x^2 = 3x$	$x = 3$	$x^2 = 3x$ if and only if $x = 3$
2	F	F	T
1			
3			
0			

x	$x^2 = 3x$	$x = 3$	$x^2 = 3x$ if and only if $x = 3$
2	F	F	T
1	F	F	T
3	T	T	T
0	T	F	F

11. The proposition "For all integers x: if $x = 3$, then $x^2 = 3x$" is _____. The converse of this proposition is the proposition "For all
(T, F)

integers x: _____". The converse is _____.
(T, F)

> T   if $x^2 = 3x$, then $x = 3$ F

12. The conditional "if $x^2 \neq 3x$, then $x \neq 3$" is called the _____ of the conditional "if $x = 3$, then $x^2 = 3x$".

> contrapositive

13. The contrapositive of the proposition "For all integers x: if $x + 2 = 6$, then $x = 4$" is "For all integers x: _____".

> if $x \neq 4$, then $x + 2 \neq 6$

14. The contrapositive of "For all x: if q_x, then p_x" is "For all x: _____".

> if not p_x, then not q_x

15. Complete the table.

x	$x^2 = 3x$	$x = 3$	if $x^2 = 3x$, then $x = 3$	$x \neq 3$	$x^2 \neq 3x$	if $x \neq 3$, then $x^2 \neq 3x$
2	F	F	T	T	T	T
3						
0						
1						

x	$x^2 = 3x$	$x = 3$	if $x^2 = 3x$, then $x = 3$	$x \neq 3$	$x^2 \neq 3x$	if $x \neq 3$, then $x^2 \neq 3x$
2	F	F	T	T	T	T
3	T	T	T	F	F	T
0	T	F	F	T	F	F
1	F	F	T	T	T	T

16. If x has a value for which the conditional "if p_x, then q_x" is false, then for this value of x the contrapositive "_____" is _____.

(T, F)

"if not q_x, then not p_x"   F

17. Write the contrapositive of "For all triangles: if two angles are equal, then the sides opposite those angles are equal".

For all triangles: if the sides opposite two angles are not equal, then the two angles are not equal.

18. The proposition "For all x: (if p_x, then q_x) if and only if (if not q_x, then not p_x)" is _____.
(T, F)

T

19. If a conditional is true for a particular value of x, then its converse _____ be true for this value of x. If a conditional is true for
(must, may, cannot)
a particular value of x, then its contrapositive _____ be
(must, may, cannot)
true for this value of x.

may   must

20. *Prove:* "For all positive integers x: if x is even, then x^2 is even" by means of the following steps:
   (a) If x is even, then x can be written $x = 2n$, where n is an integer.
   (b) Since $x = 2n$, $x^2 = $ _____ $= 2($_____$)$.
   (c) Therefore, x^2 is a multiple of 2 and hence is _____.

(b) $4n^2$, $2n^2$ (c) even

21. *Prove:* "For all positive integers x: if x^2 is even, then x is even" by means of the following steps:
   (a) The contrapositive of the given proposition is: "For all positive integers x: if x is odd, then x^2 is _____".
   (b) If x is odd, x can be written $x = 2n + 1$, where n is an integer.
   (c) Since $x = 2n + 1$, $x^2 = $ _____ $= 2($_____$) + 1$.
   (d) Therefore, x^2 is _____.

(a) odd   (c) $4n^2 + 4n + 1$, $2n^2 + 2n$ (d) odd

22. Frames 20 and 21 give a complete proof of the proposition "For all integers x: _____ if and only if _____.

> x is even x^2 is even

In Chapter 2 we have discussed some elements of logic. The vocabulary for this discussion has included the following terms and phrases:

proposition	conjunction	converse
variable	disjunction	biconditional
open sentence	negation	contrapositive
counterexample	conditional	

Whereas a proposition is true or false but not both, an open sentence becomes true or false only when values are given to the variables in it.

Truth tables were constructed for the compound open sentences "p_x and q_x"; "p_x or q_x"; "not p_x"; "if p_x, then q_x"; and "p_x if and only if q_x".

The open sentence "p_x if and only if q_x" means the same as the sentence "if p_x, then q_x; and if q_x, then p_x". A conditional and its contrapositive are logically equivalent, but a conditional need not be logically equivalent to its converse.

To test your understanding of the material of this chapter, work the Post Test that follows. Do not *refer back to the text while working the test. Work the entire test before checking your answers.*

POST TEST

1. A statement involving one or more variables which becomes true or false when specific numbers are substituted for the variables is called a (an) _____.

2. State which of the given statements are propositions and which are open sentences.
   (a) 5 is an integer. _____
   (b) $x^2 - 9 = (x - 3)(x + 3)$. _____
   (c) $x + 1 = 1 + x$. _____
   (d) For all x: $x + 3 = 3 + x$. _____

3. In the open sentence $4x - 5y = 3$, what do we call x and y? _____

4. Using the two methods discussed in the text, convert the following open sentence into two distinct propositions: $2x - 4$ is even.
   (a) _____
   (b) _____

5. State whether each of the following propositions about integers (x and y) is true or false. Justify your reasoning when false.

(a) For all $x: x + 5 = 5 + x.$ _____
(T, F)

(b) For all x and $y: x + y = x.$ _____
(T, F)

Justification if your answer is F : _____

_____

6. Find the truth value of the following conjunction when -3 is substituted for $x: (x^2 = 9)$ and $(x + 4 = 6).$ _____
(T, F)

7. Complete the truth table for the conjunction "p_x and q_x".

p_x	q_x	p_x and q_x
T	T	

8. Write the disjunction of the pair of open sentences : x is even; x is a prime. _____

9. In a disjunction which meaning of the word "or" is understood? (a) Either but not both? (b) either or both? _____

10. Complete the truth table for the disjunction "p_x or q_x".

p_x	q_x	p_x or q_x
T	T	

11. Write the negation of the following open sentence in three equivalent forms: $2x - 7 = 6.$ _____

_____

12. Find the truth value of the negation of $x^2 = 4$, where 1 is substituted for x. _____
(T, F)

13. Complete the truth table for the negation "not p_x".

p_x	not p_x

14. In order to show that two open sentences are logically equivalent write their truth tables and show that the two resulting right-hand columns are _____.

15. Are the open sentences "not (p_x and q_x)" and "p_x and (not q_x)" logically equivalent? Justify your answer. _____
(yes, no)

Justification:

p_x	q_x	p_x and q_x	not (p_x and q_x)	not q_x	p_x and (not q_x)

Discussion: _____

16. Write a disjunction that is logically equivalent to the negation of "(x^2 is odd) and (x is even)". _____

17. Write a conjunction that is logically equivalent to the negation of "(x is odd) or (x is a multiple of 4)". _____

18. Find the truth value that is obtained when
(a) 2 is substituted for x in: If $x^2 = 4$, then $x = 3$. _____
(b) 3 is substituted for x in: If $x^2 = 6$, then $x = 3$. _____
(c) 4 is substituted for x in: If $x^2 = 9$, then $x = 3$. _____

19. Find the truth values of each of the following propositions, where x is an integer. In case your answer is F, give a counterexample.
(a) For all x: If $(x - 4)(x - 3) = 0$, then $x^2 = 9$. _____;
(T, F)

_____
(counterexample, if required)
(b) For all x: If $x - 2 = 0$ then $x^2 = 4$. _____; _____
(T, F) (counterexample,

_____
if required)

20. Write the converses of the following true conditionals. Which of these converses are true? The variable x can be replaced by any integer.
(a) For all x: If x is even, then x^2 is even. _____
(converse)

_____; _____
(converse T or F)
(b) For all x: If $x = 2$, then $x^2 = 4$. _____
(converse)

_____; _____
(converse T or F)

45

21. If a conditional "For all x: If p_x, then q_x" is false, then its converse _____ be false.

    (must, may, cannot)

22. A biconditional is the _____ of a conditional and its _____.

23. Find the truth value of the following biconditional: "For all x: x is a whole number if and only if x is a positive integer". _____

                                                  (T, F)

24. Write the contrapositive of the following true conditional: Is this contrapositive true? For all x: If $x^5 = 32$, then $x = 2$. _____

                                                  (contrapositive)

_____ ; _____

              (T, F)

25. If a conditional "For all x: If p_x, then q_x" is true, then its contrapositive _____ be true.

            (must, may, cannot)

---

1. open sentence.

2. (a) Proposition. (b) Open sentence. (c) Open sentence. (d) Proposition.

3. Variables.

4. (a) Possible answer: $2(1) - 4$ is even. Other answers obtained by other substitutions for x. (b) For all x: $2x - 4$ is even.

5. (a) T. (b) F; one counterexample is $x = 1$, $y = 1$.

6. F.

7. See the text—Table 2.

8. (x is even) or (x is a prime).

9. Either or both.

10. See the text—Table 4.

11. It is false that $2x - 7 = 6$; Not $(2x - 7 = 6)$; $2x - 7 \neq 6$.

12. T.

13. See the text—Table 6.

14. Identical (equal).

15. No.

p_x	q_x	p_x and q_x	not $(p_x$ and $q_x)$	not q_x	p_x and (not q_x)
T	T	T	F	F	F
T	F	F	T	T	T
F	T	F	T	F	F
F	F	F	T	T	F

Since the fourth and sixth columns are not identical, the two open sentences are not logically equivalent.

16. (x^2 is even) or (x is odd).

17. (x is even) and (x is not a multiple of 4).

18. (a) F. (b) T. (c) T.

19. (a) F; counterexample $x = 4$. (b) T.
20. (a) If x^2 is even, then x is even; T. (b) If $x^2 = 4$, then $x = 2$; F; counterexample $x = -2$.
21. may
22. conjunction; converse
23. F.
24. If $x \neq 2$, then $x^5 \neq 32$; T.
25. must.

If you missed any of the questions in this test, review the sections of the text indicated.

Question	Section of Text
1 to 5	2.2 and 2.3
6 to 13	2.4 and 2.5
14 to 17	2.6
18 to 19	2.7
20 to 25	2.8

After you are convinced that you have mastered Chapter 2, proceed to Chapter 3.

3

Sets

You should have read Chapter 2 and completed the Post Test before proceeding. In Chapter 3 we define the concept of set, define the relations of inclusion and equality of sets, and introduce mathematical notation for sets. Before reading Chapter 3, you should know

    the meaning of the terms "whole number" and "natural number"
    the distinction between numbers and numerals
    the proper usage of the connectives "and", "or", "if and only if", and their truth tables
    the use of variables, including those with subscripts
    The following Readiness Test is designed to check your understanding of these topics.

R E A D I N E S S   T E S T

1. The smallest whole number is ___0___. The smallest natural number is ___1___.

> 0   1

2. The Roman numeral for the number five is ___V___. The Arabic numeral for five is ___5___. A numeral is a name for a _number_.

> V   5   number

3. If p_x and q_x are open sentences and x is given a value for which p_x is *true* and q_x is *false*, then for that value of x,
   (a) "p_x and q_x" is ___F___.   (b) "p_x or q_x" is ___T___.
          (T, F)   (T, F)
   (c) "if p_x, then q_x" is ___F___.   (d) "p_x if and only if q_x" is ___F___.
            (T, F)   (T, F)

> (a) F   (b) T   (c) F   (d) F

In the next question and in other multiple-choice questions that follow, more than one answer may be correct. Find all correct answers.

4. Another way of saying "For all $x: 2x = 6$ if and only if $x = 3$" is which of the following?
   (a) For all x: if $2x = 6$, then $x = 3$.
   (b) For all x: if $x = 3$, then $2x = 6$.
   (c) For all x: (if $2x = 6$, then $x = 3$) and (if $x = 3$, then $2x = 6$).
   ___C___

> (c)

5. If p_x and q_x are open sentences and we assert "For all $x : p_x$ if and only if q_x" is a true statement, then p_x and q_x are (a) identical, (b) both true, (c) both false, (d) both true or both false. ___d___

(d)

6. When we speak of the natural numbers a_1 and a_2, we imply that (a) $a_1 = 1$ and $a_2 = 2$. (b) $a_1 = a_2$. (c) $a_1 \neq a_2$. (d) a_1 and a_2 may or may not be equal. ___d___

(d)

7. True or false:
(a) All natural numbers are whole numbers. ___T___
(b) All whole numbers are natural numbers. ___F___
(c) Some whole numbers are not natural numbers. ___T___
(d) Some natural numbers are whole numbers. ___T___

(a) T.　　(b) F.　　(c) T.　　(d) T.

If you missed frame 1, you should reread Sections 1.1 and 1.3. If you missed frame 2, reread Section 1.4. If you missed any of frames 3 through 5, reread Sections 2.4 through 2.7.

Next, read Sections 3.1 through 3.5.

3.1 Introduction

In the previous chapters we gave you a bird's-eye view of the course and mentioned some of the ideas which need to be discussed in more detail. Here we get down to business. Since the main theme of the course is arithmetic, which deals with numbers, it is essential that we begin by discussing the properties of numbers. Indeed, our aim here is a restricted one—we shall limit ourselves to a discussion of the *whole numbers*, which are commonly written 0, 1, 2, 3, 4, ...

We have seen that the symbols 0, 1, 2, 3, 4, . . . are not numbers but are names for numbers just as I, II, III, IV, . . . (Roman numerals) are names for numbers. So familiarity with these symbols does not tell us what a whole number is. In our usual language we do have an idea of the meaning of a number such as *three* when we speak of "three girls", "three houses", "three dollars", and so on. But here *three* is an adjective that states a numerical property of certain collections of girls, houses, dollars, and so on. What, then, is *three* when used by itself as a noun? Clearly it is not an object in the real world which we can physically touch or look at; it seems to exist only in our minds. Thus it is an *abstraction*. There is no reason to shudder at the thought of something abstract, but for many people abstractions do require a change in their way of thinking. Numbers are abstract things and there is no getting around it. So now we must approach them gently so that you will understand their true meaning.

3.2 Sets

Our intuition tells us that numbers have something to do with counting and that the act of counting implies a collection of objects to be counted. Hence it is reasonable to begin our story with a look at such collections. In common speech we use many different words to express this notion of a collection. Some examples are

> *school* of fish
> a football *team*
> a *flock* of birds
> a *crowd* of shoppers
> a *crop* of wheat
> a *train* of cars
> a *bed* of roses

In other cases we naturally use the word *set* to represent such a collection:

> a *set* of golf clubs
> a *set* of tools
> a croquet *set*
> a *set* of rules

In mathematics it is inconvenient to have all these different names for collections, and so we use the word *set* for all of them.

SET   **INTUITIVE IDEA.** A *set* is any collection, assemblage, or aggregate of objects, people, ideas, or the like.

Since a set is a collection of things, we need a technical name for the things that make up the collection. They are called *members* or *elements* of the set.

MEMBER OR ELEMENT   **INTUITIVE IDEA.** The objects, people, or whatever that are considered together as forming a set are called its *members* or its *elements*.

Thus
George Washington is a member of the set of men who have been President of the United States.
Chicago is a member of the set of all American cities.
"Thou shall not steal" is an element of the set of precepts called the "Ten Commandments".

There is nothing difficult about this notion of a set from the point of view of intuition. The essential idea is that a set is a collection of objects. In order to deal with a set the elements must be so clearly described that we can say for certain that any particular object is or is not a member of the given set. In giving a description of a set we must be careful in our use of English or symbols so that there can be no mistake as to which objects are to be members of the set. There are two kinds of ambiguity which we must avoid:

(1) *All terms in our description must have clear meanings.* For example, the set description

"The set of grade-A universities in the United States"

is ambiguous, for it is not clear without elaboration what we mean by "grade-A universities".

There are similar problems concerning what set is meant by the following descriptions:

"The set of beautiful airline stewardesses"
"The set of rich Texans"
"The set of interesting TV programs"

(2) *The general context must be clear.* For example, "the set of girls whose names are Mary, Susan, or Lois" might mean all the girls in the world at all times with these names, or possibly only those girls now living in your class or your community. In any particular case the context should make this clear, but if it does not you must be more specific.

As another example of this kind consider the following:

The set of cities whose names are "London", "Paris", or "Rome".

Most people would interpret this to mean the set of capitals of England, France, and Italy. But there are other cities in the world with these names. If there is any doubt as to your meaning, you should write

The set consisting of London (England), Paris (France), and Rome (Italy).

A related problem is of the following kind. Consider the set whose members are John, James, and Joe. Ordinarily this means the set of boys with these names, but you might interpret it to be the set of names themselves. The context should make this clear, but if it is not, you must say what you mean. In this case there are two alternatives:

(1) The set of boys whose names are John, James, or Joe
(2) The set of boys' names whose members are "John", "James", and "Joe"

Similarly, the set whose elements are 1, 2, 3, and 4 is usually interpreted to be the set of numbers whose names are these numerals. If you wish to refer to the corresponding set of numerals, you can write

The set of numerals whose members are "1", "2", "3", and "4"

We do not wish to be pedantic about these matters. Clarity is essential, but it can be obtained in various ways. Simplicity is also highly desirable, for a lack of simplicity can often interfere with clarity. There are no general rules for clarity or simplicity—you will just have to use good judgment.

3.3 Sets Described by Lists of Members

So far we have described sets in simple language, and now we must introduce some more formal notation. The simplest way to describe a set is to list its members. Thus, as mentioned above, we can speak of the set of boys whose names are John, James, and Joe. As a shorthand for this we write

$$\{John, James, Joe\}$$

CURLY-BRACKET NOTATION where the curly brackets (or braces) tell us that we are considering the set whose members are the objects named within them. Similarly, we can write the sets

$$\{London, Paris, Rome\}$$
$$\{mathematics, history, French, economics\}$$

In the film that supplements this chapter, we have placed pictures of objects between braces to indicate the sets of objects of which these are the pictures. No sensible person would interpret the sets so illustrated to be sets of pictures of objects. As you can see, it is very difficult to be universally precise about such matters; common sense is your best guide. Use it!

Sets described by English sentences can easily be translated into this notation. For example,

The set of integers between 4 and 8 (inclusive) is $\{4, 5, 6, 7, 8\}$.
The set of letters in the alphabet is $\{a, b, c, \ldots, x, y, z\}$.
The set of natural numbers is $\{1, 2, 3, 4, \ldots\}$.
The set of even natural numbers is $\{2, 4, 6, 8, \ldots\}$.

REMARKS

1. When we list the members of a set in this way we are not interested in the order in which they are written. The set $\{a, b, c, d\}$ is the same set as the set $\{d, c, a, b\}$. These are just two different ways of describing it.

2. In listing the members of a set, we include each member once and only once. Thus we never write $\{a, a, b, c, d\}$ to indicate the set whose members are a, b, c, d. Hence the set of letters occurring in the word "bookkeeper" is $\{b, o, k, e, p, r\}$. The fact that some of these letters are repeated in "bookkeeper" is irrelevant to the definition of this set.

In later chapters we shall consider sets such as $\{a_1, a_2, a_3, a_4, a_5\}$, where a_1, a_2, a_3, a_4, and a_5 are names for certain unspecified objects. This notation then implies that these five objects are distinct, no two of them being identical. Sometimes it is convenient to write sets in the form

$$\{\square, \square, \square, \bigcirc, \bigcirc, \bigcirc, \bigcirc\}$$

which appears to be a set consisting of three squares and four circles. This is not the best practice, for it appears to violate the requirement just stated.

It must be understood that in this set the squares have slight differences so that they can be distinguished, and similarly for the circles. Since these differences may not be evident to the naked eye, it would be better to suggest them by a notation such as

$$\{ \boxed{a}, \boxed{b}, \boxed{c}, \textcircled{a}, \textcircled{b}, \textcircled{c}, \textcircled{d} \}$$

To do this, however, soon becomes tedious and pedantic. When there is no chance of misunderstanding, therefore, we shall write sets such as

$$\{x\ x\ x\ x\ x\ x\ x\}$$
$$\{.\ .\ .\ .\ .\ .\ .\}$$

or

$$\{\triangle\ \triangle\ \triangle\ \triangle\ \triangle\}$$

3. We have already seen that if we are given an informal description of a set in ordinary English, we can often describe the set by using the notation discussed in this section. We can also proceed in the opposite direction:

{a, b, c} is the set of the first three letters of the alphabet.
{January, June, July} is the set of months whose names begin with the letter "J".

3.4 Members or Elements of a Set

We have previously said that the objects, ideas, or whatever that compose a set are called its *members* or its *elements*. To indicate membership we use the symbol ε (sometimes ∈) as in the examples below:

$$a\ \varepsilon\ \{a, b, c, d\}$$

This is to be read

"*a* is an element of the set {a, b, c, d}".

Other examples are

Rome ε {London, Paris, Rome}
tiger ε {cat, lion, tiger, puma, lynx}
△ ε {□, △, ○, ☆}

When we wish to say that a certain object is *not* an element of a given set we use the symbol ∉, read "not an element of" as in the example

$$h \notin \{a, b, c, d\}$$

This is to be read

"*h* is not an element of the set {a, b, c, d}".

Other examples are

New York ∉ {London, Paris, Rome}
robin ∉ {cat, lion, tiger, puma, lynx}
○ ∉ {□, △, ○, ☆}

Although it may seem strange at first, there are sets which have only one element. Such sets are called *singletons*. For example, we may wish to consider the set of all cities in Illinois with a population of over 2 million. This is the set

$$\{\text{Chicago}\}$$

It has only one element, Chicago, so we can write

$$\text{Chicago } \varepsilon \{\text{Chicago}\}$$

Observe closely the difference between the *element* on the left, the city of *Chicago*, and the *set* on the right, {Chicago}.

We can even consider sets with *no* elements. For example, consider the set of cities in Illinois whose population is over 20 million. Since there are no such cities, this set has no elements. We call this the *empty set* and denote it by the symbol $\emptyset$, which is a modified "oh" in the alphabets of Scandinavian languages. It should not be confused with the somewhat similarly shaped Greek letter "phi". You may read $\emptyset$ as "canceled oh".

EMPTY SET $\emptyset$

The elements of a set may themselves be sets. Thus we can consider the set

$$\{\{x\}, \{y\}, \{z\}\}$$

whose elements are the sets $\{x\}$, $\{y\}$, $\{z\}$. It is very important to distinguish this set from the set

$$\{x, y, z\}$$

whose elements are x, y, and z. We can illustrate this distinction as follows:

$$\{x\} \varepsilon \{\{x\}, \{y\}, \{z\}\}$$
$$x \varepsilon \{x, y, z\}$$

But

$$x \notin \{\{x\}, \{y\}, \{z\}\}$$
$$\{x\} \notin \{x, y, z\}$$

Similarly, we must distinguish between the empty set $\emptyset$ which has no elements and the singleton set $\{\emptyset\}$ whose only element is the set $\emptyset$.

As an additional matter of notation we shall frequently represent sets by capital letters $A, B, \ldots, X, Y, Z$ and their elements by lowercase letters $a, b, \ldots, x, y, z$. Thus we understand the formula

$$x \varepsilon A$$

to mean that "*object x is an element of set A*". Similarly,

$$b \notin Y$$

means that "object b is not an element of set Y". In particular, the statement

$$\text{For all } x : x \notin \emptyset$$

is a true proposition. Alternatively, we can say that the open sentence "$x \varepsilon \emptyset$" is false for every object x.

55

We can now translate certain statements in ordinary English into statements concerning membership in sets. For example,

$$5 \text{ is an odd number}$$

can be rewritten

$$5 \text{ is an element of the set of odd numbers}$$

or as

$$5 \, \varepsilon \, \{1, 3, 5, 7, 9, \ldots\}$$

Similarly, we can rewrite the statement "4 is not an integer between 6 and 10 (inclusive)" as

$$4 \notin \{6, 7, 8, 9, 10\}$$

3.5 Sets Described by Properties

The method of describing a set by listing its members is useful only when there are relatively few members of the set; otherwise, the list becomes cumbersome. Of course, if the set has infinitely many members, we cannot list them all no matter how long we try.

Another way to describe a particular set is to say that it consists of all objects that have a particular property in common. In order not to be ambiguous, we first must say from what totality of objects we are going to draw those with the particular property. This collection of objects is called the *universal set*, U. Thus the universal set defines the domain of discourse (i.e., what we are talking about) and tells us whether we are focusing our attention on numbers, or on people, or on automobiles, or on geometrical figures, or whatever. Usually the universal set is clear from the context of a discussion, but if there is the slightest doubt, it must be precisely specified in advance.

UNIVERSAL SET

Suppose, for purposes of illustration, that we take the universal set to be the set of all students in your university. Although various useful things can be said about this set, we may wish to examine smaller groups of students which have one or more characteristics in common. For instance, suppose that our interest centers upon the sophomore class. Then we shall write

$$\{x \,|\, x \text{ is a sophomore}\}$$

This notation is to be read "The set of all x, such that x is a sophomore", the vertical bar standing for "such that". The symbol x is a variable that may be replaced by any element of the universal set.

SET-BUILDER NOTATION

DEFINITION. The notation $\{x \,|\, x \text{ has a given property}\}$ is called the *set-builder notation* for sets.

This notation can be translated into ordinary English as in the example

$$\{x \,|\, x \text{ is a sophomore}\}$$

can be read

> "The set of all students at your university who are sophomores"

or

> "The set of all sophomores at your university"

Other sets in which you might be interested are (the universal set is still the set of all students at your university)

$$\{x | x \text{ is a coed}\}$$
$$\{x | x \text{ is unmarried}\}$$
$$\{x | x \text{ is a varsity athlete}\}$$

When the universal set is not unmistakably clear, we can indicate it by using the notation

$$\{x \text{ (universities)} | x \text{ has more than 10,000 students}\}$$

This is then the set of universities which have more than 10,000 students. The universal set here is the set of all universities.

This notation may be used to describe sets which are given in terms of ordinary English. For example,

> The set of even numbers

can be rewritten as

$$\{x \text{ (numbers)} | x \text{ is even}\}$$

Using this procedure, we can rewrite the statement

> 4 is an even number

as

> 4 is an element of the set of even numbers

or

$$4 \, \varepsilon \, \{2, 4, 6, 8, \ldots\}$$

or

$$4 \, \varepsilon \, \{x \text{ (numbers)} | x \text{ is even}\}$$

This approach to the definition of a set can be rephrased in terms of the ideas already presented in Chapter 2. Let us suppose that the universal set is the set of all books in the library of your university. Then

> x is an algebra book

is an open sentence with variable x. When we substitute any particular book for x, we obtain a proposition that is true or false. It is true when x is an algebra book and false when x is any other type of book. The set

$$\{x | x \text{ is an algebra book}\}$$

is then the set of those books in the library for which

> x is an algebra book

becomes a true proposition. It may, therefore, be called the *truth set* of this open sentence.

As a further example, let U be the set of whole numbers. Then

$$\{x|(x - 4)(x - 5) = 0\}$$

is the set of whole numbers each of which makes the open sentence

$$(x - 4)(x - 5) = 0$$

true. Thus this is the set $\{4, 5\}$.

In summary, if we are given a universal set U and an open sentence p_x (for whose variable x we can substitute any element of U), the set

$$\{x|p_x\}$$

is the set of those elements of U whose substitution for x in p_x results in a true proposition.

We can complicate this discussion by asking that the members of a set have two properties in common. Again taking U to be the set of all students in your university, we can consider examples like

$\{x|x$ is a girl *and* x is unmarried$\}$
$\{x|x$ is a senior *and* x is a varsity athlete$\}$
$\{x|x$ is a girl *and* x is a varsity football quarterback$\}$

In this last example we can get a much shorter name for the set. Presumably no girls play football, so there are no students who meet both requirements specified in our description of this set. Hence this set has no elements; it is the *empty set*, $\varnothing$.

You will observe that we have just used the idea of the conjunction of two open sentences that we introduced in Chapter 2. Using the notation of that chapter, we see that

$$\{x|p_x \text{ and } q_x\}$$

is the set of those x in the universal set for which *both* p_x and q_x are true.

As another variation, we can look at sets whose elements have either or both of two properties. For example,

$\{x|x$ is a freshman, *or* x is a sophomore$\}$
$\{x|x$ has blonde hair, *or* x has blue eyes$\}$

You will recognize this as a use of the disjunction of two open sentences. In the notation of Chapter 2,

$$\{x|p_x \text{ or } q_x\}$$

is the set of those x in the universal set for which either p_x is true, or q_x is true, or both are true.

58

The following exercises are designed to test and to supplement the knowledge you have gained from your reading of the preceding text.

1. The set of natural numbers does not contain 0. However, 0 is a member or element of the ___set___ of whole numbers.

> set

2. The members or ___elements___ of a set of dishes are ___the dishes___.

> elements   the dishes

3. An hour is a set of exactly __60__ minutes. A minute is a __set__ of exactly __60__ seconds.

> 60   set   60

4. The United Nations is a ___set___ of nations. The United States is a __member__ of the set called the "United Nations".

> set   member (or element)

5. Which of the following descriptions of sets are ambiguous or unclear?
   - (a) The natural numbers.
   - (b) The great books.
   - (c) The Cleveland Indians.
   - (d) The inhabitants of Mars.
   - (e) The Republican Party.
   - (f) The major political parties in the United States.

   ___All except A.___

> You should probably have answered "all except (a)". (c) might refer to a baseball team or to descendants of the original Americans who live in Cleveland. (d) is unclear because of doubt as to the meaning of "inhabitant". In (e) the criterion for membership is in doubt. Each of (c), (e), and (f) needs to have a date specified.

6. By supplying a context for each of the ambiguously described sets in the preceding question, remove the ambiguity. (*Note*: There are many possible answers.) Do this on a separate piece of paper.

> (Different readers will supply different answers. Some hints may be found in the preceding answer. If you had trouble with the last two questions, reread Section 3.2.)

7. Translate the following mathematical expressions into ordinary English:

(a) $\{a, b, c\}$. *The set whose members are a, b & c.*
(b) $\{c_1, c_2\}$. *The set " " " "c_1 & c_2"*
(c) $\{y \mid y$ is a natural number$\}$. *The set of all y such that y is a natural no.*
(d) $\emptyset$. *empty set*
(e) $\{n$ (numbers)$\mid n \neq 1\}$. *set of all numbers n such that n≠1*

> (a) The set whose members are a, b, and c.
> (b) The set whose members are c-one and c-two.
> (c) The set of all y such that y is a natural number (or the set of all natural numbers).
> (d) The empty set.
> (e) The set of all numbers n such that n is not equal to one (or the set of all numbers except one).

8. Use the curly-bracket notation or the symbol $\emptyset$ (as appropriate) to write symbols for these sets:

(a) The set of the first six letters of our alphabet. *{a, b, c, d, e, f}*
(b) The set whose elements are m and n. *{m, n}*
(c) The empty set. *{∅}*
(d) The set of all whole numbers that are not natural numbers. *{0}*
(e) The set of all natural numbers that are not whole numbers. *∅*

> (a) $\{a, b, c, d, e, f\}$.   (b) $\{m, n\}$.   (c) $\emptyset$.   (d) $\{0\}$.   (e) $\emptyset$.

9. Since no restriction has been placed on the members of sets other than that they be clearly specified, a set may have sets as members. For example, if $A = \{\{a, b\}, \{a, c, e\}\}$, the set A has as members *{a, b}* and *{a, c, e}* If $C = \{\emptyset, \{a\}\}$, then C has as members *∅* and *{A}*.

> $\{a, b\}$ $\{a, c, e\}$ $\emptyset$ $\{a\}$

If you had difficulty with the last three questions, you should reread Sections 3.3 and 3.4. Then continue with frame 10. Remember that you may refer back to the text whenever you wish.

10. The set that defines the domain of discourse is called the *universal* _____ set. The symbol used for this set is *U*.

> universal U

11. In a discussion about baseball teams that have won the World Series, the universal set would probably be ~~the set of major league teams~~

> the set of major league teams

12. Let $S = \{y \text{ (cities)} | y \text{ is the capital of the United States}\}$. For the set S, the universal set is ~~the set of cities~~. A simpler symbol for S is $\{Washington, D.C.\}$

> the set of cities   {Washington, D.C.}

13. If U is the set of letters in the word "Mississippi", then $\{x | x$ is a vowel$\}$ = ___. If U is the set of letters in "tsk", then $\{x | x$ is a vowel$\}$ = $\emptyset$.

> $\{i\}$ $\emptyset$

14. Assume the universal set to be the set of letters of our alphabet. True or false: (a) $u \, \varepsilon \, \{x | x$ is a vowel$\}$. ___ (b) $t \, \varepsilon \, \{x | x$ is a consonant$\}$. ___ (c) $i \notin \{x | x$ is a vowel$\}$. ___

> (a) T.   (b) T.   (c) F.

15. The set of all elements in the domain of discourse which are *not* in the universal set is ~~the empty set~~

> the empty set

16. Translate the given set descriptions into ordinary English:
(a) $\{x \text{ (numbers)} | x \text{ is a whole number}\}$. The set of whole no.
(b) $\{x \text{ (buildings)} | x \text{ is a hotel}\}$. the set of hotels
(c) $\{x \text{ (candies)} | x \text{ is striped}\}$. the set of striped candies
(d) $\{x \text{ (natural numbers)} | x \text{ is even and } x \text{ is less than 3}\}$. the set whose element is
(e) $\{x \text{ (integers)} | x \text{ is a natural number or } x \text{ is zero}\}$. the set of whole no.

> (a) The set of whole numbers.
> (b) The set of hotels.
> (c) The set of striped candies.
> (d) The set of even natural numbers less than 3, *or* the set whose only element is 2.
> (e) The set of whole numbers.

17. Translate into set-builder notation:
(a) The set of multiples of 3. $\{x | x$ is a multiple of 3$\}$
(b) The set of numbers that are squares of natural numbers. $\{x | x$ is the sq. of natural no.$\}$
(c) The set of odd numbers. $\{x | x$ is an odd no.$\}$

(d) 7 is an odd number. $7 \varepsilon \{x | x \text{ is odd}\}$
(e) 11 is a prime. $11 \varepsilon \{x | x \text{ is prime}\}$
(f) 12 is not a prime. $12 \notin \{x | x \text{ is prime}\}$

(a) $\{x | x \text{ is a multiple of 3}\}$.
(b) $\{x | x \text{ is the square of a natural number}\}$.
(c) $\{x | x \text{ is odd}\}$.
(d) $7 \varepsilon \{x | x \text{ is odd}\}$.
(e) $11 \varepsilon \{x | x \text{ is prime}\}$.
(f) $12 \notin \{x | x \text{ is prime}\}$.

If you had difficulty with frames 10 through 17, you should reread Section 3.5.

Now read Sections 3.6 through 3.8 on equality of sets, subsets, and set notation. When you finish, work the exercises that follow Section 3.8. Refer back to the text whenever you wish while working the exercises.

3.6 Equality of Sets

As in the case of numbers, we shall say that sets A and B are equal and write $A = B$ if and only if they are identical.

EQUAL SETS   **DEFINITION.** Two sets are *equal* if and only if they contain precisely the same elements.

Thus we write

$\{a, b, c, d\} = \{b, c, a, d\}$
$\{a, b, c, d\}$ = the set whose members are the first four letters of the alphabet
$\{$London (England), Paris (France), Rome (Italy) $=$
    $\{x \text{ (cities)} | x \text{ is the capital of England or France or Italy}\}$

Observe that we use the equality sign to mean that the two *sets* involved are identical. We do not mean that the two names for the sets are identical.

3.7 Subsets

If we look at the two sets

$$X = \{a, b, c\} \qquad \text{and} \qquad Y = \{a, b, c, d\}$$

we see that there is a simple relationship between them: Every element of X is also an element of Y. Therefore, it seems reasonable to call X a "subset" of Y. In general, we may define a subset as follows:

3.7 Subsets

SUBSETS

DEFINITION. A set X is a *subset* of a set Y if and only if every element of X is also an element of Y.

Another formulation of this definition is the following: X is a subset of Y if and only if the following is a true proposition:

For all x: if $x \, \varepsilon \, X$, then $x \, \varepsilon \, Y$.

Note that according to this definition X is a subset of Y in the particular case that $X = Y$. For example, if $X = \{a, b, c\}$ and $Y = \{b, c, a\}$, then X is a subset of Y, for every element of X is an element of Y.

When X is a subset of Y, we sometimes say that X is *included* in Y. The notations expressing this idea are

$$X \subseteq Y \qquad \text{or} \qquad Y \supseteq X$$

which are read "X is a subset of Y", or "X is included in Y".

Quite often, however, we want a stronger notion of subset and wish to exclude the possibility that X and Y are equal. In other words, we want not only that every element of X is an element of Y, but also that there are elements of Y which are not in X. When these conditions are fulfilled, we say that X is a *proper subset* of Y.

PROPER SUBSETS

DEFINITION. A set X is a *proper subset* of a set Y if and only if every element of X is an element of Y and $X \neq Y$. To express this idea we use the notations $X \subset Y$, or $Y \supset X$, which are read "X is a proper subset of Y".

ILLUSTRATION

(1) If $X = \{a, b, c\}$ and $Y = \{a, b, c, d\}$, then $X \subset Y$.

(2) Let U be the universal set of all natural numbers and X be the set

$$\{x | x \text{ is divisible by } 2\}$$

Then $X \subset U$.

The following theorem is often useful in proving that two sets are identical.

THEOREM 1. If $A \subseteq B$ and $B \subseteq A$, then $A = B$.

For, since $A \subseteq B$, every element of A is an element of B. Also, since $B \subseteq A$, every element of B is an element of A. Therefore, A and B have exactly the same elements, and hence A and B are identical, or $A = B$.

As a consequence of these definitions we can prove Theorem 2, which states an important property of the empty set:

THEOREM 2. The empty set $\emptyset$ is a subset of every set and is a proper subset of every set except itself. A proper subset cannot equal itself

To prove this, suppose that A is an arbitrary set (which may be $\emptyset$ itself). To prove that $\emptyset \subseteq A$ we must show that the proposition

For all x: if $x \, \varepsilon \, \emptyset$, then $x \, \varepsilon \, A$

63

is true. Since $\emptyset$ has no elements, $x \, \varepsilon \, \emptyset$ is false for every x. According to our Rule for Truth in Section 2.7, it follows that the stated proposition is true.

Finally, when $\emptyset \neq A$, we have by the definition of a proper subset that $\emptyset \subset A$.

REMARK

You should be careful not to confuse the meanings of

$$x \, \varepsilon \, A \qquad \text{and} \qquad X \subseteq A$$

The first says that x is an element of A and the second that X is a subset of A. Although these ideas are clearly distinct, there is a possibility of confusion when X is a singleton subset. Consider the example

$$A = \{\text{Paris, Rome, London}\}$$
$$x = \text{Paris}$$
$$X = \{\text{Paris}\}$$

Then

$$x \, \varepsilon \, A$$

says that Paris is an element of the set $\{\text{Paris, Rome, London}\}$. On the other hand,

$$X \subseteq A$$

says that the singleton set $\{\text{Paris}\}$ is a subset of the set $\{\text{Paris, Rome, London}\}$. Be sure that this distinction is clear to you!

3.8 Summary of Set Notation

SUMMARY OF NOTATION   For convenience of reference, we summarize the various notations for sets which we shall use hereafter in this book.

Capital letters, $A, B, \ldots, X, Y, Z$ will refer to sets.

Lowercase letters, $a, b, \ldots, x, y, z$ will refer to elements of sets.

The symbol ε means "is an element of" and is used in statements such as

$$x \, \varepsilon \, A$$

which means that object x is an element of set A.

The symbol $\notin$ means "is not an element of".

U is the universal set for a given discussion or problem.

$\emptyset$ is the empty set.

Curly brackets or braces, $\{\ \}$, refer to sets.

$\{x | x \text{ has a given property}\}$ is the set of those elements x of the universal set which share this property.

$X \subseteq Y$ (or $Y \supseteq X$) means that X is a subset of Y.

$X \subset Y$ (or $Y \supset X$) means that X is a proper subset of Y.

$X \nsubseteq Y$ (or $Y \nsupseteq X$) means that X is not a subset of Y.

$X \not\subset Y$ (or $Y \not\supset X$) means that X is not a proper subset of Y.

1. order does not matter.
2. include each element only once.

3.8 Summary of Set Notation

As you can see, mathematicians like to use special symbols. This has two advantages. One is brevity. The second advantage is ease of translation. The symbols belong to a universal language that conveys the same idea to persons whose native language is English, French, Russian, or Hindi. Ordinarily, a special symbol is introduced only if the phrase it represents is used over and over. Frames 1 and 2 are intended for practice in using some of these symbols.

1. Translate these mathematical expressions into English:
(a) $A = \{a, b, c\}$. _____
(b) $B = \varnothing$. _____
(c) $M \subseteq N$. _____
(d) $P \subset Q$. _____
(e) $a \, \varepsilon \, \{a, b, c\}$. _____
(f) $\varnothing \subseteq A$. _____
(g) $3 \, \varepsilon \, \{x | x$ is a natural number$\}$. _____
(h) $c \, \varepsilon \, \{c\}$. _____

(a) A is (or equals) the set whose members are a, b, and c.
(b) B is the empty set.
(c) M is a subset of N.
(d) P is a proper subset of Q.
(e) a is a member of the set whose members are a, b, and c.
(f) The empty set is a subset of A.
(g) Three is a member of the set of all x such that x is a natural number, *or* three is a member of the set of natural numbers.
(h) c is a member of the set whose only member is c.

2. Use mathematical symbols wherever possible to write these sentences.
(a) Y is a subset of the universal set. _____
(b) R is a proper subset of S. _____
(c) a is a member of the set N. _____
(d) 2 is an element of the set of all y such that y is a natural number and y is even. _____
(e) The set of all x such that x is a vowel is a proper subset of A. _____

(a) $Y \subseteq U$.
(b) $R \subset S$.
(c) $a \, \varepsilon \, N$.
(d) $2 \, \varepsilon \, \{y | y$ is a natural number and y is even$\}$.
(e) $\{x | x$ is a vowel$\} \subset A$.

3. Let U be the set of letters of our alphabet. True or false: (a) $d \notin \{x|x$ is a vowel$\}$. _____ (b) $k \notin \{x|x$ is a consonant$\}$. _____ (c) $m \notin \emptyset$. _____ (d) $\emptyset \notin U$. _____

(a) T.   (b) F.   (c) T.   (d) T.

4. If $U = \{\emptyset, \{a, b\}, \{a, c, e\}\}$, then the sentence "$\emptyset \notin U$" is _____.
(T, F)

F.

5. True or false: (a) For all sets A, $\emptyset \varepsilon A$. _____ (b) For all sets A, $\emptyset \subseteq A$.

(a) F.   (b) T.

6. The notation $X \nsubseteq Y$ means that X is not a subset of Y. True or false: (a) If $A = \{a, b\}$ and $B = \{a, b, c\}$, then $B \nsubseteq A$. _____ (b) For all sets P and Q, if $Q \nsubseteq P$, then $P \nsubseteq Q$. _____

(a) T.   (b) F.

7. The sentence "$a \notin \{b, c\}$" is true because the *members* of $\{b, c\}$ are _____ and _____ but not _____.

b c a

8. The sentence "$\{a\} \nsubseteq \{b, c\}$" is true because the *subsets* of $\{b, c\}$ are _____, _____, _____, _____, but not _____.

$\emptyset$ $\{b\}$ $\{c\}$ $\{b, c\}$ (in any order) $\{a\}$

9. True or false: (a) $r \notin \{r, s\}$. _____ (b) $\{r\} \nsubseteq \{r, s\}$. _____ (c) $\{r, s\} \not\subset \{r, s\}$. _____

(a) F.   (b) F.   (c) T.

10. Use mathematical symbols to write these sentences:
(a) k is not a member of the set A. _____
(b) The universal set is not a proper subset of the empty set. _____
(c) P is not a subset of Q. _____

(a) $k \notin A$.   (b) $U \not\subset \emptyset$.   (c) $P \nsubseteq Q$.

11. If A is a set and x is an element, then either $x \varepsilon A$ or $x \notin A$ but not both. Let $A = \{\{r\}, \{r, s, t\}, \{s, t\}\}$. Insert the symbol ε or $\notin$ which makes each sentence true: (a) $\{r\}$ _____ A. (b) $\{r, s\}$ _____ A. (c) $\{t\}$ _____ A. (d) $\emptyset$ _____ A.

(a) ε (b) $\notin$ (c) $\notin$ (d) $\notin$

66

12. Similarly, if A and B are sets, then $A \subseteq B$ or $A \nsubseteq B$ but not both. Insert the proper symbol, $\subseteq$ or $\nsubseteq$: (a) $\{r, s\}$ _____ $\{r, t, w\}$. (b) $\{r\}$ _____ $\{r, t, w\}$. (c) $\varnothing$ _____ $\{r, t, w\}$. (d) $\{r, t, w\}$ _____ $\{r, t\}$.

> (a) $\nsubseteq$ (b) $\subseteq$ (c) $\subseteq$ (d) $\nsubseteq$

13. Likewise, for sets A and B, $A \subset B$ or $A \not\subset B$ but not both. Insert the proper symbol, $\subset$ or $\not\subset$:
   (a) $\{r\}$ _____ $\{r, t, w\}$
   (b) $\{t, w, r\}$ _____ $\{r, t, w\}$
   (c) $\{w, t\}$ _____ $\{r, t, w\}$
   (d) $\varnothing$ _____ $\{r, t, w\}$
   (e) $\varnothing$ _____ $\varnothing$

> (a) $\subset$ (b) $\not\subset$ (c) $\subset$ (d) $\subset$ (e) $\not\subset$

14. Supply the symbol or symbols ε, $=$, $\subseteq$, or $\subset$ which make each sentence true : (a) $\{t, w, r\}$ _____ $\{r, t, w\}$. (b) r _____ $\{r\}$. (c) $\varnothing$ _____ $\{r\}$.
   (d) $\varnothing$ _____ $\varnothing$.

> (a) $=$ (or $\subseteq$)   (b) ε (c) $\subset$ (or $\subseteq$)   (d) $=$ (or $\subseteq$)

15. In order to show that for all sets A, $A \subseteq A$, we must show that every element of A is _____. Since this is certainly the case, any set A is a subset of _____.

> an element (or member) of A itself (or A)

16. The empty set is a _____ of any set A. May we conclude from this and the previous frame that all sets have at least two subsets? (Be careful!) _____. Give a reason. _____
       (yes, no)

> subset   No   The empty set has only one subset.

17. List all the subsets of $\{r, t, w\}$. _____

> $\varnothing$, $\{r\}$, $\{t\}$, $\{w\}$, $\{r, t\}$, $\{r, w\}$, $\{t, w\}$, $\{r, t, w\}$

18. How many of these subsets of $\{r, t, w\}$ are *not* proper subsets?

> only one, $\{r, t, w\}$.

19. True or false:
(a) Every set is a subset of itself. _____
(b) No set is a proper subset of itself. _____
(c) The empty set is a proper subset of every set. _____
(d) For all sets, A and B, if A and B are equal, then $A \subseteq B$ and $B \subseteq A$. _____

(a) T.   (b) T.   (c) F.   (d) T.

20. True or False:
(a) For all sets, A, B, and C, if $A \subseteq B$ and $B \subseteq C$, then $A \subseteq C$. _____
(b) For all sets, A, B, and C, if $A \subset B$ and $B \subset C$, then $A \subset C$. _____
(c) For all sets A and B, $A \subseteq B$ or $B \subseteq A$. _____
(d) For all sets A and B, $A \subset B$ or $B \subset A$. _____
(e) For all sets A and B, $A = B$ or $A \subseteq B$ or $B \subseteq A$. _____

(a) T.   (b) T.   (c) F.   (d) F.   (e) F.

21. (*Discovery Exercise*) Count the numbers of subsets of each of the sets

$$\{a\}, \{a, b\}, \{a, b, c\}, \{a, b, c, d\}$$

Using these results, guess a formula for the number of subsets of a set which has n elements. This is a "discovery exercise", so no answer is given. If you are able to do so, prove that your guess is correct.

In Chapter 3 we have discussed these terms:

    set
    member (or element) of a set
    universal set
    empty set
    equal sets
    subset
    proper subset

We have introduced symbols for describing sets and their properties. These symbols are summarized in Section 3.8. We have shown for all sets A, $A \subseteq U$ and $A \subseteq A$ and $\varnothing \subseteq A$. We have proved for all sets A, if $A \subseteq B$ and $B \subseteq A$, then $A = B$.

To test your understanding of the material of this chapter, we have prepared a test, which follows immediately. If you feel unsure of the work that has just been presented, you may review the chapter. Do not refer back to the text while working the test. Work the whole test before checking your answers.

POST TEST

1. Revise the following set description to make it unambiguous: "The set of long books". _____
_____

2. Use $\varnothing$ or braces with a listing to describe each of the following sets:
(a) The set of vowels. $\{a, e, i, o, u\}$
(b) The set of letters that are elements of $\{a, b\}$ and also are elements of $\{b, c, d\}$. $\{b\}$
(c) The set of even numbers that are odd. $\{\varnothing\}$
(d) The set of vowels in the first half of the alphabet. $\{a, e, i\}$
3. Insert the symbols $=$, $\subset$, or ε to make true sentences
(a) r ___ε___ $\{r, t, w\}$
(b) $\{r\}$ ___$\subset$___ $\{r, t, w\}$
(c) $\{t, w, r\}$ ___$=$___ $\{r, t, w\}$
(d) $\varnothing$ ___$\subset$___ $\{r, t, w\}$
(e) $\{r, w\}$ ___$\subset$___ $\{r, t, w\}$
4. Write a description of each of the following sets in set-builder notation:
(a) The set of even integers. _____
(b) The set of hotels in a town. _____
5. What might be the universal set implied in the set description: $\{x | x$ is odd$\}$? _____
6. Write a description of each of the following sets in set-builder notation
(a) The set of letters which are either vowels or consonants. _____
_____

(b) The set of letters which are vowels and which come after m in the alphabet. _____
_____

7. Answer true or false:
(a) $\varnothing = \{\varnothing\}$. __F__
(b) If $A \subseteq B$, then $A \subset B$, for all sets A and B. __F__
(c) If $A \subset B$, then $A \subseteq B$, for all sets A and B. _____
(d) If $A = B$, then $A \subseteq B$, for all sets A and B. _____
(e) If $A \subseteq B$, then $A = B$, for all sets A and B. _____
(f) If $A \neq \varnothing$ and if $A \subseteq B$, then $B \neq \varnothing$, for all sets A and B. _____
(g) If $A \subseteq B$ and if $B = \varnothing$, then A is a proper subset of B, for all sets A and B. _____
(h) If $A = B$, then $B \subseteq A$, for all sets A and B. _____
8. Let A and B be any two sets. For each verbal statement select the relation $A = B$, $A \subseteq B$, or $A \subset B$ which expresses precisely the same meaning.
(a) Every element of A is an element of B. _____
(b) Both A and B contain exactly the same elements. _____
(c) Every member of A is a member of B, and every member of B is a member of A. _____
(d) The sets A and B are not equal, but A is a subset of B. _____

9. Write each of the following sentences in symbolic form:
(a) r is not an element of $\{a, b, c\}$. _____
(b) $\{r, s\}$ is not a proper subset of $\{r, t, w\}$. _____
(c) A is not a subset of B. _____
(d) $\varnothing$ is not a member of $\{a, b, c\}$. _____
10. Answer true or false:
(a) $w \varepsilon \{w, x, y, z\}$. _____
(b) $\{w\} \varepsilon \{w, x, y, z\}$. _____
(c) $\{w\} \notin \{w, x, y, z\}$. _____
(d) $w \notin \{\{w\}, \{x\}, \{y\}, \{z\}\}$. _____

---

1. The set of books having more than (say) 500 pages.
2. (a) $\{a, e, i, o, u, y\}$. (b) $\{b\}$. (c) $\varnothing$. (d) $\{a, e, i\}$.
3. (a) ε. (b) $\subset$. (c) $=$. (d) $\subset$. (e) $\subset$.
4. (a) $\{x \text{ (integers)}|x \text{ is even}\}$. (b) $\{x \text{ (buildings)}|x \text{ is a hotel}\}$.
5. Integers, natural numbers, or whole numbers.
6. (a) $\{x \text{ (letters)}|x \text{ is a vowel or } x \text{ is a consonant}\}$. (b) $\{x \text{ (letters)}|x$ is a vowel and x comes after m in the alphabet$\}$.
7. (a) F. (b) F. (c) T. (d) T. (e) F. (f) T. (g) F. (h) T.
8. (a) $A \subseteq B$. (b) $A = B$. (c) $A = B$. (d) $A \subset B$.
9. (a) $r \notin \{a, b, c\}$. (b) $\{r, s\} \not\subset \{r, t, w\}$. (c) $A \nsubseteq B$. (d) $\varnothing \notin \{a, b, c\}$.
10. (a) T. (b) F. (c) T. (d) T.

If you made mistakes on the Post Test, read the relevant parts of Chapter 3 until you are sure of the correct answers. Then proceed to the Readiness Test for Chapter 4.

4
One-to-One Correspondence

You should have read Chapter 3 and completed the Post Test before proceeding. In Chapter 4 we define the concept of a one-to-one correspondence and discuss the properties of such correspondences.

Before reading Chapter 4 you should know the meanings of the terms "set", "element of a set", "subset", "proper subset", "equal sets", and "empty set".

The following Readiness Test is designed to check your understanding of these topics.

R E A D I N E S S   T E S T

Which of the following statements is (are) true?

(a) $\{a, b, c, d\} = \{a, c, d, b\}$.   (b) $\{a, b, c, d\} \subset \{a, b, c\}$.

(c) $\{a\} \,\varepsilon\, \{a, b, c, d\}$.   (d) $\{a\} \subset \{a, b, c, d\}$.

(e) $a \,\varepsilon\, \{a, b, c, d\}$.   (f) $\{\{a\}\} \subset \{a, b, c, d\}$.

(g) $\varnothing \subset \{a, b, c, d\}$.   (h) $\{\{a, b, c\}\}$ is a singleton set.

(i) $\{x|x$ is a natural number$\} = \{1, 2, 3, \ldots\}$.

(j) $\varnothing \,\varepsilon\, \{a, b, c, d\}$.   (k) $\varnothing \,\varepsilon\, \{\varnothing, a, b, c\}$.

(l) $\varnothing \subseteq \{\varnothing, a, b, c\}$.   (m) $\varnothing \subset \{\varnothing, a, b, c\}$.

(a), (d), (e), (g), (h), (i), (k), (l), (m).

If you gave these answers and only these, you are ready for Chapter 4. If you either omitted some of them or had some additional ones marked true, make sure you understand the notations and meanings before proceeding.

4.1 Introduction

As our first application of sets, we turn to the use of set theory as a tool for the understanding of the notions of number and counting. We begin by examining the process of counting.

When a child uses his fingers to count blocks on the table before him, he identifies each block with a separate finger and holds up the appropriate set of fingers to indicate how many blocks there are. Thus he is matching a set of his fingers with the set of blocks. It is this fundamental process of matching that we shall discuss in this chapter.

4.2 One-to-One Correspondence

The crucial idea in the matching process we have described is that of *pairing*. The child has paired each block on the table with a finger on his hand

(Figure 4.1). This gives us the idea for the formal definition of what we shall call a *one-to-one correspondence*.

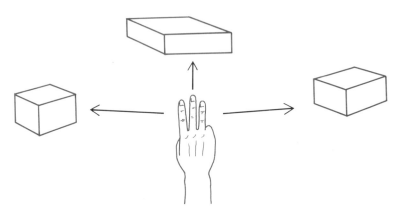

FIGURE 4.1. *One-to-one correspondence*.

ONE-TO-ONE CORRESPONDENCE

DEFINITION. A *one-to-one correspondence* between two sets, A and B, is a pairing of the elements of A with the elements of B such that each element of A is paired with precisely one element of B and each element of B is paired with precisely one element of A.

The simplest way of indicating a one-to-one correspondence is by a diagram such as the following: Let $A = \{a, b, c\}$ and $B = \{x, y, z\}$. Then a one-to-one correspondence between A and B is given by

$$\{a \quad b \quad c\}$$
$$\updownarrow \; \updownarrow \; \updownarrow$$
$$\{x \quad y \quad z\}$$

There is nothing unique about such a pairing, for another one-to-one correspondence between A and B is given by

$$\{a \quad b \quad c\}$$
$$\{x \quad y \quad z\}$$

Undoubtedly you can find others, for example

$$\{a \quad b \quad c\}$$
$$\{x \quad y \quad z\}$$

For a one-to-one correspondence to be defined, the arrows must actually appear. If they are absent, as in the diagram

NO CORRESPONDENCE INDICATED

$$\{1, 2, 3, 4\}$$
$$\{a, b, c, d\}$$

72

no correspondence is defined, even though many one-to-one correspondences can be found.

Another way of describing a one-to-one correspondence is to state a rule for the pairing. Let A be the set of states in the United States and B be the set of state capitals. Then we have a one-to-one correspondence between A and B by pairing each state with its capital. This is a natural one-to-one correspondence between these sets, but it is not the only one. For we can scramble the capitals and have a one-to-one correspondence such as

$$\{\text{Alabama} \quad \text{Alaska} \quad \text{Arkansas} \quad \cdots\}$$
$$\updownarrow \qquad\quad \updownarrow \qquad\quad \updownarrow$$
$$\{\text{ Albany} \quad \text{Trenton} \quad \text{Boston} \quad \cdots\}$$

In the examples just given the two sets involved have no elements in common, but there is no need for such an assumption. For example, we might have the two committees

$$\text{nominating committee} = \{\text{Ray, Harry, Phil, Al}\}$$

$$\text{program committee} = \{\text{Henry, Peter, Lloyd, Phil}\}$$

where Phil is a member of both of them. Nevertheless, we can establish various one-to-one correspondences between them, such as

$$\{ \text{ Ray} \quad \text{Harry} \quad \text{Phil} \quad \text{Al} \}$$
$$\updownarrow \qquad \updownarrow \qquad \updownarrow \qquad \updownarrow$$
$$\{\text{Henry} \quad \text{Peter} \quad \text{Lloyd} \quad \text{Phil}\}$$

$$\{ \text{ Ray} \quad \text{Harry} \quad \text{Phil} \quad \text{Al} \}$$
$$\times \qquad\qquad\quad \times$$
$$\{\text{Henry} \quad \text{Peter} \quad \text{Lloyd} \quad \text{Phil}\}$$

In a similar fashion we can describe a one-to-one correspondence between the set of odd numbers and the set of even numbers. We recall that any even number has the form $2n$ and any odd number the form $2n - 1$, where n is a natural number. The correspondence is given by the pairing

$$\{1 \quad 3 \quad 5 \quad 7 \quad 9 \quad \cdots \quad 2n - 1 \quad \cdots\}$$
$$\updownarrow \ \ \updownarrow \ \ \updownarrow \ \ \updownarrow \ \ \updownarrow \qquad\qquad \updownarrow$$
$$\{2 \quad 4 \quad 6 \quad 8 \quad 10 \quad \cdots \quad 2n \quad \cdots\}$$

where the odd number $2n - 1$ is paired with the even number $2n$. We write this $2n - 1 \leftrightarrow 2n$.

It is surprising to observe that there is a one-to-one correspondence between the natural numbers and the even numbers given by

$$\{1 \quad 2 \quad 3 \quad 4 \quad 5 \quad 6 \quad \cdots\}$$
$$\updownarrow \ \ \updownarrow \ \ \updownarrow \ \ \updownarrow \ \ \updownarrow \ \ \updownarrow$$
$$\{2 \quad 4 \quad 6 \quad 8 \quad 10 \quad 12 \quad \cdots\}$$

or $n \leftrightarrow 2n$, where n is a natural number. The remarkable fact about this correspondence is that it is between a set and one of its proper subsets.

Finally, we note that there is a trivial one-to-one correspondence between a nonempty set and itself. Let

$$A = \{a, b, c, d, \ldots\}$$
$$B = \{a, b, c, d, \ldots\}$$

so that $A = B$. Then we have the one-to-one correspondence between A and B,

$$
\begin{array}{ccccc}
\{a & b & c & d & \cdots\} \\
\updownarrow & \updownarrow & \updownarrow & \updownarrow & \\
\{a & b & c & d & \cdots\}
\end{array}
$$

4.3 Other Correspondences

So that the special properties of one-to-one correspondences will be clear, let us consider some correspondences that are not one-to-one.

As a simple example consider

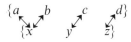

in which the two elements, a and b, are paired with the single element x.

Also we can write the correspondence

which is certainly not one-to-one even though a one-to-one correspondence does exist between these two sets.

Other examples of correspondences which are not one-to-one are

> The set of all football players ↔ the set of all football coaches in which each player is paired with his coach
> The set of all living persons ↔ the set of all mothers of living people in which each person is paired with his mother
> The set of all calendar dates ↔ the set of days of the week in which each date is paired with the proper day of the week

Although correspondences like these are worthy of study, we shall restrict ourselves in this book to those which are one-to-one.

---

1. Set up a one-to-one correspondence between the sets $S = \{a, b\}$ and $T = \{x, y\}$.

$$
\begin{array}{cc}
\{a & b\} \\
\updownarrow & \updownarrow \\
\{x & y\}
\end{array}
$$

Two are possible: $\{x \quad y\}$ and $\{y \quad x\}$.

2. How many one-to-one correspondences can be set up between the sets $S = \{a, b, c\}$ and $T = \{x, y, z\}$? _____*12*_____

Six.

3. How many one-to-one correspondences can be set up between the sets $S = \{a\}$ and $T = \{x\}$? _____*a to x*_____

Only one, $a \leftrightarrow x$.

4. In general, if any one-to-one correspondence is possible, more than one is. The only exception is the one-to-one correspondence between *singleton* sets.

singleton

5. Two sets S and T, having one element, x, in common, are in one-to-one correspondence, but x in S is not paired with x in T. Describe another one-to-one correspondence in which x is paired with itself. *x is paired w/ itself while the other elements are paired off.*

One way: If a (in S) $\leftrightarrow x$ (in T) and x (in S) $\leftrightarrow z$ (in T) make $a \leftrightarrow z$ and $x \leftrightarrow x$. Keep all other pairings unchanged.

6. Consider the sets S and T and the correspondence shown.

$$S = \{a \quad b \quad c \quad d \quad e \quad f\}$$
$$\updownarrow \ \updownarrow \ \updownarrow \ \updownarrow \ \updownarrow \ \updownarrow$$
$$T = \{d \quad f \quad x \quad y \quad z \quad e\}$$

Using the process described in the answer to frame 5, set up another one-to-one correspondence in which each common element is paired with itself.

$$\{a \quad b \quad c \quad d \quad e \quad f\}$$
$$\updownarrow \ \updownarrow \ \updownarrow \ \updownarrow \ \updownarrow \ \updownarrow$$
$$\{ \ *x \ y \ z \ d \ e \ f* \}$$

$\{y \quad z \quad x \quad d \quad e \quad f\}$

7. Set up a one-to-one correspondence between the set of natural numbers $\{1, 2, 3, \ldots\}$ and their squares $\{1, 4, 9, \ldots\}$. _____*4 ↔ 16*_____

$n \leftrightarrow n^2$ is one.

8. The correspondence in frame 7 is one-to-one between a set and one of its <u>proper subset</u>

> proper subsets (or subsets)

9. Which of the following are one-to-one correspondences?

(a) $\{a \quad b \quad c\}$
$\updownarrow \quad \times$
$\{x \quad y \quad z\}$

(b) $\{a \quad b \quad c \quad d\}$
$\updownarrow \quad \updownarrow \quad \updownarrow$
$\{x \quad y \quad z\}$

(c) $\{a \quad b \quad c\}$

$\{x \quad y \quad z\}$ <u>only (a)</u>

(d) $\{a \quad b \quad c\}$

$\{w \quad x \quad y \quad z\}$

> (a) only

10. Textbooks at an elementary school are to be issued one per student. The storeroom clerk prepares a proper-sized pile of books for each teacher in the school. Let us refer to the set of books to be issued as B, the set of piles of books as P, the set of teachers as T, and the set of students as S.

Can a one-to-one correspondence be set up between B and P? <u>No</u>
(yes, no)

> No.

11. Can a one-to-one correspondence be set up between P and T?
<u>yes</u>
(yes, no)

> Yes.

12. Between B and T? <u>No</u>
(yes, no)

> No.

13. Between T and S? <u>No</u>
(yes, no)

> No.

14. Between P and S? <u>No</u>
(yes, no)

No.

15. Between *B* and *S*? __yes__
    (yes, no)

Yes.

16. If two teachers inadvertently exchange different-sized piles of books, will they have a one-to-one correspondence between their supply of books and their students? __No__
    (yes, no)

No.

17. Would this mixup cause you to change your answer to frame 15? __No__
(yes, no)

It shouldn't. The fact that a correct pairing hasn't been found doesn't mean that such a pairing doesn't exist.

Now read Sections 4.4 through 4.7 and work the program that follows Section 4.7.

4.4 Equivalent Sets

The child counting blocks with his fingers is establishing a one-to-one correspondence between the set of blocks and a certain set of fingers. The particular pairing (one-to-one correspondence) that he uses is not so important to him as the fact that there is at least one such correspondence. We want terminology that indicates the existence of a one-to-one correspondence between two sets, without reference to the particular pairing. So we make the following definition of the *equivalence* of two sets:

EQUIVALENT SETS   **DEFINITION.** Two nonempty sets *A* and *B* are said to be *equivalent*, written $A \sim B$, if there exists a one-to-one correspondence between *A* and *B*. In addition, the empty set $\emptyset$ is said to be equivalent to itself.

4.5 Properties of *A ~ B*

Since the concept of equivalent sets that we have just defined is the basis for our discussion of the idea of a whole number, we should take some time to develop an understanding of its properties.

Consider the sets of blocks, fingers, and coins shown in Figure 4.2. Several very obvious remarks can be made about these examples. It will be seen as we go on that these remarks are very useful, so we will formalize them as theorems.

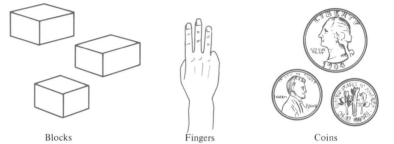

FIGURE **4.2.** *Equivalent sets.*

Blocks   Fingers   Coins

The first, and most trivial, is that any set A (for example, the blocks) is equivalent to itself.

The set of blocks $\sim$ the set of blocks.

REFLEXIVE

This property of equivalence is called the *reflexive* property, and the formal statement is:

THEOREM 1.   For any set A, we have $A \sim A$.

Proof.   We have already proved this, for in Section 4.2 we showed that there is a one-to-one correspondence between any set and itself.

SYMMETRIC

A second simple property we observe is called *symmetry*:

THEOREM 2.   If the sets A and B satisfy $A \sim B$, then also $B \sim A$.

Proof.   This requires us to show that if there is a one-to-one correspondence between A and B, then we can construct one between B and A.

This, however, is immediately evident, for the pairings used to establish $A \sim B$ equally well show that $B \sim A$.

Finally, we see that the set of blocks is equivalent to the set of fingers, and that the set of fingers is equivalent to the set of coins. It does not surprise us that the set of blocks is equivalent to the set of coins.

This simple property of equivalence is called *transitivity* and is formalized as follows:

TRANSITIVE

THEOREM 3.   *Transitive Law for Set Equivalence.* For any three sets, if $A \sim B$ and $B \sim C$, then $A \sim C$.

Proof.   In this theorem, the hypotheses state that there exist two one-to-one correspondences, S and T, the first between A and B, and the second between B and C. Our task is to provide a third one-to-one correspondence, say V, between A and C. But each $a \varepsilon A$ is associated (in S) with a unique $b \varepsilon B$, and such a b is paired (in T) with a unique $c \varepsilon C$. We then associate the given $a \varepsilon A$ with the $c \varepsilon C$ which is found in this way.

The process also goes in the opposite direction: If we pick $c \varepsilon C$, T gives us a unique $b \varepsilon B$ and S yields a unique $a \varepsilon A$. Thus the desired V which associates the a's and the c's in this way is a one-to-one correspondence.

It is helpful to look at this argument in an example. Suppose

$$A = \{a, b, c, d, e\}$$

$$B = \{m, n, o, p, q\}$$

$$C = \{u, v, w, x, y\}$$

Then we can establish one-to-one correspondences between A and B, and between B and C, for example:

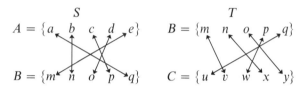

From these we can construct a one-to-one correspondence V as follows:

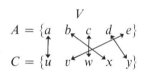

This transitive property is of great importance in practice. Suppose that we wish to establish the equivalence of a set of persons hoping to board an airplane and the set of empty seats on the plane. Quite often the airline posts a diagram of the seats in the plane on which is hung a small tab for each empty seat. The travelers pick up these tabs as they report at the counter in the terminal. When the tabs are all gone, there is a one-to-one correspondence between passengers and empty seats. The equivalences involved are

$$\{\text{empty seats}\} \sim \{\text{tabs}\}$$

$$\{\text{passengers}\} \sim \{\text{tabs}\}$$

Therefore, we have the desired equivalence,

$$\{\text{passengers}\} \sim \{\text{empty seats}\}$$

Sets like that of the set of tabs in this example are often referred to as "intermediate sets".

REMARKS

1. It is important that we keep in mind the distinction between the concepts of equality and equivalence of sets. The statement $A = B$ means simply that A and B are the same set. On the other hand, the statement $A \sim B$ states

EQUALITY VERSUS EQUIVALENCE

that there is a one-to-one correspondence between A and B. We know from Theorem 1 that if $A = B$, then $A \sim B$; but from the knowledge that $A \sim B$ it is not possible to conclude that $A = B$.

2. You have probably observed that equivalent sets have the same numbers of elements, and you may have concluded that the easiest way to establish equivalence is to count the elements. Such a conception (though true enough) misses our point entirely. We have not yet defined the process of counting; but when we do so, our definition will involve equivalent sets. Thus we cannot use counting at this time to establish the equivalence of two sets.

Actually the concept of equivalent sets is much more fundamental than that of counting. We can establish equivalence even though we know nothing of numbers, for equivalence requires only the existence of a one-to-one correspondence. For instance, suppose that all the seats in a theater are occupied and everyone in the audience has a seat. Since there is then an obvious one-to-one correspondence, we conclude that the set of seats is equivalent to the set of people in the audience. It would be foolish to try to establish this equivalence by counting the elements of these two sets.

4.6 Finite and Infinite Sets

We showed you in Section 4.2 that the set of natural numbers is equivalent to the set of even numbers, for we established the one-to-one correspondence

$$\{1 \quad 2 \quad 3 \quad 4 \quad \cdots \quad n \quad \cdots\}$$
$$\updownarrow \quad \updownarrow \quad \updownarrow \quad \updownarrow \qquad \updownarrow$$
$$\{2 \quad 4 \quad 6 \quad 8 \quad \cdots \quad 2n \quad \cdots\}$$

This shows that a set may be equivalent to one of its proper subsets. Yet, this is disturbing; for it does not seem to be true for a set such as $\{a, b, c, d\}$, which is certainly not equivalent to any of its proper subsets. What is the difference between these two examples? Perhaps you have observed that the set of natural numbers is "infinite" and that the set $\{a, b, c, d\}$ is "finite", whatever these terms may mean.

We can use this piece of intuition to give a definition of "infinite" and "finite".

INFINITE SET   DEFINITION. A set A is called *infinite* if and only if it is equivalent to at least one of its proper subsets. Otherwise, it is called *finite*.

Thus $\{2, 4, 6, 8, \ldots\}$ is infinite, for it is equivalent to its proper subset $\{4, 8, 12, 16, \ldots\}$. This equivalence is established by the following one-to-one correspondence:

$$\{2, \quad 4, \quad 6, \quad 8, \quad \ldots, 2n, \ldots\}$$
$$\updownarrow \quad \updownarrow \quad \updownarrow \quad \updownarrow \qquad \updownarrow$$
$$\{4, \quad 8, \quad 12, 16, \ldots, 4n, \ldots\}$$

On the other hand, $\{1, 2, 3\}$ is finite; for $\{1, 2, 3\}$ is not equivalent to any of its proper subsets: $\varnothing$, $\{1\}$, $\{2\}$, $\{3\}$, $\{1, 2\}$, $\{1, 3\}$, $\{2, 3\}$.

4.7 Nonequivalent Sets

In general, if A and B are two sets, we cannot expect $A \sim B$. For example, if

$$A = \{a, b, c\} \qquad B = \{x, y, z, w\}$$

then $A \nsim B$ (read "A is not equivalent to B"). We would like to investigate what can happen in this case.

In our example, we see that there are proper subsets of B which are equivalent to A:

$$A = \left\{\begin{matrix} a \\ b \\ c \end{matrix}\right\} \sim \left\{\begin{matrix} x \\ y \\ z \end{matrix}\right\} \subset B$$

or

$$A = \left\{\begin{matrix} a \\ b \\ c \end{matrix}\right\} \sim \left\{\begin{matrix} x \\ z \\ w \end{matrix}\right\} \subset B$$

and so on.

This situation is, in fact, the general one.

THEOREM 4. Given any two sets A and B, if $A \nsim B$, then either
(a) There is a proper subset $C \subset B$ such that $A \sim C$.
or
(b) There is a proper subset $D \subset A$ such that $B \sim D$.

Unfortunately, technical (logical) difficulties make a formal proof of this statement very complicated. However, we can give the following informal argument.

If A and B are two sets, we can start constructing a one-to-one correspondence by picking an element a_1 from A, an element b_1 from B, and forming the pair $a_1 \leftrightarrow b_1$. Then we pick another $a_2 \varepsilon A$ (of course, $a_2 \neq a_1$), $b_2 \varepsilon B (b_2 \neq b_1)$, and form $a_2 \leftrightarrow b_2$. We continue in this way until we have used up all the elements in A, or in B, or in both. If this process pairs all the elements of A with all the elements of B, then we have constructed a one-to-one correspondence between A and B, so $A \sim B$. Otherwise, if we have exhausted A but some elements of B remain unmatched, then those elements of B which we have used form a proper subset $C \subset B$, and we have $A \sim C$. Similarly, if we have exhausted B but some elements of A remain unmatched, then we have constructed a proper subset $D \subset A$ such that $B \sim D$.

There is a useful partial converse to this theorem.

NONEQUIVALENT SETS

THEOREM 5. If A and B are any finite sets and A is equivalent to a proper subset C of B, then A and B are not equivalent.

Proof. We shall use a method called "indirect proof". Let us suppose that $A \sim B$. Then from the hypothesis that $A \sim C$, it follows that $B \sim C$.

81

However, by hypothesis C is a proper subset of B. Hence B is infinite according to our definition of an infinite set. But this is a contradiction, since we assumed that B is finite. Therefore, our assumption that $A \sim B$ cannot be true, and so $A \nsim B$.

This theorem gives us a practical means for showing the nonequivalence of two finite sets. All that you need to do is to show that one is equivalent to a proper subset of the other. As an example, why are the sets

$$\{a, b, c, d\} \quad \text{and} \quad \{x, y, z\}$$

not equivalent? Answer : $\{x, y, z\} \sim \{a, b, c\}$ and $\{a, b, c\} \subset \{a, b, c, d\}$.

---

1. Certain information concerning each student at I. O. University is recorded on his personal data card. The set of students and the set of data cards so used are _equivalent_ sets.

equivalent

2. Each post office box at I.O.U. is designated by a different number. Is the set of numbers so used equivalent to the set of post office boxes? _yes_
(yes, no)

Yes.

3. Each student is issued a post office box and its number is recorded on his data card. Is the set of post office boxes equivalent to the set of students? _Not Necessarily_
(yes, no)

Not enough information is given to answer the question. Two or more students may share the same box and/or all of the boxes may not have been assigned.

4. If the set of students and the set of P.O. box numbers are equivalent, and the set of students and the set of data cards are equivalent, what do we then know about the set of P.O. box numbers and the set of data cards? They are _equivalent_ sets.

equivalent

5. What property of equivalence is exhibited in frame 4? _Transitivity_

Transitivity.

6. Some instructors check attendance by assigning each student a distinct seat and observing which seats are unoccupied. The procedure is a check on the equivalence of the following sets: (a) the set of students in the class, (b) the set of their names, (c) the set of their assigned seats, (d) the set of occupied seats. If all four sets are equivalent, are all the students present? DON'T KNOW,

> Maybe—the correct number of persons is.

7. To prove that the sets $A = \{a, b, c, d, e\}$ and $B = \{x, y, z\}$ are not equivalent, we must find a proper subset of A which is equivalent to B. Such a subset is ――――――――.

> Many answers, for example $\{a, b, d\}$.

8. Is there a proper subset of $A = \{a, b, c, d, e\}$ which is equivalent to $B = \{v, w, x, y, z\}$? NO
> (yes, no)

> No.

9. Is the set of even numbers $A = \{2, 4, 6, 8, \ldots, 2n, \ldots\}$ infinite? Yes ―――― Justify your answer. It can go on & on to larger
> (yes, no)
numbers indefinitely.

> Yes. $\{2, 4, 6, 8, \ldots, 2n, \ldots\} \sim \{4, 8, 12, 16, \ldots, 4n, \ldots\}$, which is a proper subset of A.

10. The set $A = \{a, b, c\}$ is a proper subset of $B = \{a, b, c, d\}$. Is A equivalent to B? NO ―――― Would you call B finite or infinite? FINITE
> (yes, no)

> No.   Finite.

11. The set $A = \{3, 6, 9, \ldots\}$ is a proper subset of $B = \{1, 2, 3, 4, 5, 6, \ldots\}$. Is A equivalent to B? Yes ―――― Is B finite or infinite? INFINITE
> (yes, no)

> Yes.   Infinite.

12. Can a finite set be equivalent to an infinite set? To answer this question work frames 12 through 15. Let us suppose that A is finite and B is infinite and that $A \sim B$. Since B is infinite there is a set C which is a proper subset of B such that $B \sim C$.

> proper subset $B \sim C$

13. Continuing the discussion in frame 12 we see that since $A \backsim B$ there is a <u>one-to-one</u> between the elements of A and those of B. This pairing identifies a set of elements of A which are paired with the elements of C in B. The set D of such elements of A is a <u>proper subset</u> of A and D <u>is equal to</u> C.

> one-to-one correspondence (or pairing) proper subset is equivalent to

14. In frames 12 and 13 $A \sim B$, $B \sim C$, and $C \sim D$. Therefore A <u>is equivalent to</u> D. Why? <u>transitive theory</u>. Since D is a proper subset of A, A is <u>infinite</u>.

> is equivalent to transitive law of equivalence infinite

15. In frame 12 we assumed that A was finite and in frame 14 we proved it to be infinite. Now answer the question: can a finite set be equivalent to an infinite set? <u>No</u>
(yes, no)

> No.

4.8 Equivalence Relations

The concept of the equivalence of two sets is an example of a broader notion of equivalence which is fundamental to many parts of mathematics. We shall meet it regularly when we discuss various number systems in Part IV and in connection with geometry in Part V.

We suppose that there is a relationship between two mathematical objects of the same type which we shall write

$$a \approx b$$

Read "a is related to b".

EXAMPLES
1. Equivalence of sets: $A \sim B$, where A and B are sets.
2. Equality of numbers: $a = b$, where a and b are numbers.
3. Parallelism of lines: $l \parallel m$, where l and m are lines in the plane.
4. Proper inclusion of sets: $A \subset B$, where A and B are sets.
5. Inequality of numbers: $a < b$, where a and b are numbers.

EQUIVALENCE RELATION　　DEFINITION. A relation of this type is called an *equivalence relation* if and only if
(a) It is *reflexive*: For all a, $a \approx a$.

84

(b) It is *symmetric*: For all a and b, if $a \approx b$, then $b \approx a$.

(c) It is *transitive*: For all a, b, and c, if $a \approx b$, and $b \approx c$, then $a \approx c$.

Since we showed in Section 4.4 that the equivalence of sets has these three properties, we conclude that the *equivalence of sets is an equivalence relation*.

It is not true that every relation is an equivalence relation. For example, consider the inequality of numbers, $a < b$.

(a) $a < b$ is not reflexive, for it is false that $a < a$.

(b) $a < b$ is not symmetric, for if $a < b$ it is false that $b < a$.

(c) It is true, however, that $a < b$ is transitive. For if $a < b$ and $b < c$, then $a < c$.

---

1. Consider the equality of numbers, $a = b$.

(a) Is $a = a$? ___Yes___

(b) If $a = b$, is $b = a$? ___Yes___

(c) If $a = b$ and $b = c$, is $a = c$? ___Yes___

(d) Is the equality of numbers an equivalence relation? ___Yes___

> (a) Yes.   (b) Yes.   (c) Yes.   (d) Yes.

2. Consider the parallelism of lines in a plane, where we agree that a line is parallel to itself.

(a) Is parallelism reflexive? ___Yes___

(b) Is parallelism symmetric? ___Yes___

(c) Is parallelism transitive? ___Yes___

(d) Is parallelism an equivalence relation? ___Yes___

> (a) Yes.   (b) Yes.   (c) Yes.   (d) Yes.

3. In order that a relation be an equivalence relation, it is required that the relation be (a) ___Reflexive___, (b) ___symmetric___, and (c) ___transitive.___

> reflexive   symmetric   transitive

4. Is the proper inclusion of sets, $A \subseteq B$ an equivalence relation? ___No___ Why? _____

> No.   Neither reflexive nor symmetric.

5. Consider the relation of perpendicularity of lines in a plane: $l \perp m$. Is this reflexive? ___No___ Is this symmetric? ___Yes___ Is this transitive? ___No___ Is it an equivalence relation? ___No___

> No.   Yes.   No.   No.

In this chapter we have introduced the terms

one-to-one correspondence
equivalent sets and the corresponding notation $A \sim B$
finite set
infinite set
equivalence relation

We showed that

$A \sim A$ (reflexive).
If $A \sim B$, then $B \sim A$ (symmetric).
If $A \sim B$ and $B \sim C$, then $A \sim C$ (transitive).

Hence the equivalence of sets is an equivalence relation.

To test your understanding of this material, work through the Post Test that follows. **Do not** *refer back to the text while working the test. Work the whole test before checking your answers.*

POST TEST

In this test A, B, and C are names for sets.

1. Consider the sets A and B and the pairing shown

$$A = \{a \quad b \quad c \quad d\}$$
$$B = \{x \quad y \quad z \quad w\}$$

(a) Does this pairing establish the equivalence of sets A and B? __No__
(yes, no)

(b) Are sets A and B equivalent? __Yes__
(yes, no)

2. Set up one-to-one correspondences between the following pairs of sets when this is possible:

(a) $\{1, 2, 3, 5\}$

$\{1, 2, 6, 7\}$ possible __Yes__
(yes, no)

(b) $\{x, y, z\}$

$\{a, b, c, d\}$ possible __No__
(yes, no)

3. State whether the following pairs of sets are equivalent : (a) $\{3, 4, 6, ☆\}$; $\{1, 2, 3, \infty\}$. __Yes__ (b) $\{1, 2, 3, \ldots\}$; $\{1, 2, 3\}$. __No__
(yes, no)   (yes, no)

4. How many distinct one-to-one correspondences can be established between the sets $\{u, v\}$ and $\{r, s\}$? __Two__

5. Does the following define a one-to-one correspondence?
$$A = \{10, 20, 30\}$$

$$B = \{40, 50, 60\} \quad \underline{No}$$
(yes, no)

(b) Is A equivalent to B? $\underline{Yes}$
(yes, no)

6. If $A = B$, is $A \sim B$? $\underline{yes}$
(yes, no, maybe)

7. If $A \sim B$, is $A = B$? $\underline{Maybe}$
(yes, no, maybe)

8. If $A \sim B$ and $B \sim C$, why is $A \sim C$? $\underline{TRANSITIVE\ LAW}$

9. Is the set $\{\delta, \varepsilon, \delta, \varepsilon, \delta, \varepsilon, \ldots\}$ finite or infinite? $\underline{infinite}$ Why? $\underline{\text{equivalent to } \{\delta, \delta, \delta, \delta, \ldots\} \text{ and } \{\varepsilon, \varepsilon, \varepsilon, \varepsilon, \ldots\}}$

10. Is the set $\{\infty\}$ finite or infinite? $\underline{finite}$

11. Why are $S = \{a, b\}$ and $T = \{1, 2, 3, 4\}$ not equivalent?
$\underline{\text{they don't have one-to-one correspondence}}$

12. Is the set inclusion $A \subseteq B$ an equivalence relation. $\underline{No}$

13. Is the set equality $A = B$ an equivalence relation? $\underline{yes}$

14. Find the fallacy in the following "proof" that the number of married couples is infinite.

1. In a monogamous society there is a one-to-one correspondence between the set of married couples, A, and the set of married men, B.

2. This is a one-to-one correspondence between the set A and one of its proper subsets, B.

3. Therefore, by the definition of an infinite set, A is infinite.
$\underline{\text{B isn't a subset of A, not one-to-one!}}$

15. If it is true that there are more dogs than there are hairs on any one dog, it is inevitable that at least two dogs have the same number of hairs? (Assume that no hairless dogs exist.) $\underline{yes}$

1. (a) No. (b) Yes.
2. (a) Yes. (b) No.
3. (a) Yes. (b) No.
4. Two.
5. (a) No. (b) Yes.
6. Yes.
7. Maybe.
8. Transitivity of set equivalence.
9. Infinite. The given set is equivalent to its proper subset $\{\delta, \delta, \delta, \ldots\}$ and also to its proper subset $\{\varepsilon, \varepsilon, \varepsilon, \ldots\}$.
10. Finite. It is a singleton set.
11. $\{a, b\} \sim \{1, 2\}$ and $\{1, 2\} \subset \{1, 2, 3, 4\}$.
12. No.
13. Yes.

14. *B* is not a subset of *A*. (No married man is a married couple.)

15. Yes. In trying to match each dog with the number of his hairs, the set of available numbers will be completely used up before the set of dogs is.

If you made mistakes on the Post Test, reread the relevant parts of Chapter 4 until you are sure of the correct answers. Then proceed to the Readiness Test for Chapter 5.

5

Whole Numbers and Counting

This chapter depends heavily on Chapter 4, which you should have completed by now. You should be familiar with the following ideas:
  sets and subsets
  equivalence of sets
  the empty set
Test yourself on the Readiness Test below before beginning the chapter.

If you are now ready, read Sections 5.1 and 5.2 and do the corresponding exercises.

5.1 Introduction

When sets A and B are equivalent, our intuition tells us that there are *as many* elements in A as there are in B. So far, however, we have no way of finding just *how many* elements there are in each of these sets. This process of finding *how many* is that of *counting*. In raising this question we have assumed that a set does have some *number* of elements. We call this number the *cardinal number* of the set.

CARDINAL NUMBER

NUMBER PROPERTY

Our task, then in this chapter, is to answer the following questions:

(1) How is the cardinal number of a set defined?

(2) How can we find the cardinal number of a set; that is, how do we count?

The definition of a cardinal number which follows must agree, of course, with our intuition. We therefore ask that the concept of cardinal number have the following properties:

(1) Every finite set A has a unique whole number as its cardinal number. We write the cardinal number of A in the notation $n(A)$.

(2) Given any whole number, w, there is at least one finite set A for which $n(A) = w$.

one number

(3) If finite sets A and B are equivalent, then $n(A) = n(B)$.

(4) If for any two finite sets A and B, $n(A) = n(B)$, then $A \sim B$.

According to our definition of the cardinal number of a set which follows, a cardinal number is a whole number that is associated with a set in a particular fashion. Let us see how to do this.

5.2 Standard Sets

We begin our discussion of cardinal numbers by defining a sequence of sets called *standard sets.*

STANDARD SETS

DEFINITION. The *sequence of standard sets,* named $S(0), S(1), \ldots,$ $S(w), \ldots,$ is the sequence

$$S(0) = \varnothing \qquad\qquad S(4) = \{1, 2, 3, 4\}$$

$$S(1) = \{1\}$$
$$\qquad\qquad\qquad\qquad \ldots$$
$$S(2) = \{1, 2\}$$

$$S(3) = \{1, 2, 3\} \qquad S(w) = \{1, 2, 3, 4, \ldots, w\}$$

This sequence of standard sets has a number of properties which we shall find useful:

(1) There is a unique standard set corresponding to each whole number.

(2) Each set in this sequence is a proper subset of all those which follow it. For example,

$$S(3) \subset S(6) \qquad \text{since } \{1, 2, 3\} \subset \{1, 2, 3, 4, 5, 6\}$$

(3) Given any two standard sets, $S(a)$ and $S(b)$, then precisely one of the following statements is true:

$$S(a) \subset S(b) \qquad S(a) = S(b) \qquad S(a) \supset S(b)$$

(4) Each standard set is a finite set. Although this statement is intuitively clear, its proof is extremely difficult. We therefore assume it without proof.

(5) No two distinct standard sets are equivalent. For if $S(a) \neq S(b)$, by property (3) either $S(a) \subset S(b)$ or $S(a) \supset S(b)$. If $S(a) \sim S(b)$, then one of the sets $S(a)$ and $S(b)$ is equivalent to one of its proper subsets. This implies that $S(a)$ or $S(b)$ is infinite, but according to (4) they are both finite. Therefore, $S(a)$ cannot be equivalent to $S(b)$.

---

1. Is $4 \varepsilon S(4)$? ___yes___
   (yes, no)

Yes.

2. List the elements of $S(4)$. ___{1, 2, 3, 4}___

{1, 2, 3, 4}

3. Is $0 \, \varepsilon \, S(0)$? ___No___
(yes, no)

No; $S(0) = \emptyset$, and the empty set has no elements.

4. List all of the subsets of $S(3)$. $\emptyset, \{1\}, \{2\}, \{3\}, \{1,2\}, \{2,3\}, \{1,3\}, \{1,2,3\}$

$\emptyset, \{1\}, \{2\}, \{3\}, \quad \{1, 2\}, \{1, 3\}, \{2, 3\}, \{1, 2, 3\}$.

5. Which of the subsets of $S(3)$ (answer to frame 4) are themselves standard sets? $\emptyset, \{1\}, \{1,2\}, \{1,2,3\}$

$\emptyset, \{1\}, \{1, 2\}, \{1, 2, 3\}$.

6. Is it true that every standard set is a proper subset of some other standard set? ___yes___
(yes, no)

Yes; each standard set is a proper subset of all succeeding standard sets.

7. Is it true that every subset of a standard set is itself a standard set? ___No___
(yes, no)

No, see frames 4 and 5.

8. For each pair of the following standard sets, write a statement indicating which is a proper subset of the other: $S(1)$, $S(3)$, $S(5)$.
$S(1) \subset S(3), S(1) \subset S(5), S(3) \subset S(5)$

$S(1) \subset S(3), S(1) \subset S(5), S(3) \subset S(5)$.

9. If $S(a)$ and $S(b)$ are standard sets and both of the statements $S(a) \supset S(b)$ and $S(a) = S(b)$ are false, what relation must exist between $S(a)$ and $S(b)$? $S(a) \subset S(b)$

$S(a) \subset S(b)$.

10. If $S(a) \sim S(b)$, what other relation must exist between $S(a)$ and $S(b)$? $S(a) = S(b)$

$S(a) = S(b)$.

5.3 Cardinal Numbers

If we remember that intuitively the cardinal number of a set is to be the number of elements in this set, it is now easy to define the cardinal number of a standard set.

CARDINAL NUMBER OF A STANDARD SET
 DEFINITION. The *cardinal number of the standard set, S(w)*, is the whole number w. If we write $n(A)$ to represent the cardinal number of a set A, then $n(S(w)) = w$.
  For example,

$$n(\varnothing) = 0 \qquad n\{1, 2, 3\} = 3$$
$$n\{1\} = 1 \qquad \cdots$$
$$n\{1, 2\} = 2 \qquad n\{1, 2, \ldots, w\} = w$$
$$\cdots$$

Now we turn to the definition of the cardinal numbers of other sets A. If we consider an arbitrary set A, it may or may not be equivalent to a standard set. For example, $\{\bigcirc, \triangle, \star, \square\} \sim \{1, 2, 3, 4\}$, but the set of all whole numbers is not equivalent to any standard set. It seems reasonable to conclude that any *finite* set is equivalent to some standard set. Although this conclusion is true, its proof is also too difficult to present here. Since no two standard sets are equivalent, every finite set is therefore equivalent to one and only one standard set.

Now we are in a position to define the cardinal number of any finite set A. Our definition is based upon our intuitive requirement (3) of Section 5.1: If sets A and B are equivalent, then $n(A) = n(B)$.

CARDINAL NUMBER OF ANY FINITE SET
 DEFINITION. The *cardinal number of a finite set A* is, by definition, the cardinal number of the unique standard set, $S(w)$, equivalent to A. Thus $n(A)$ is by definition $n(S(w)) = w$.

 EXAMPLE. Find the cardinal number of $\{\bigcirc, \triangle, \star, \square\}$.

 Solution. Since $\{\bigcirc, \triangle, \star, \square\} \sim \{1, 2, 3, 4\} = S(4)$,

$$n\{\bigcirc, \triangle, \star, \square\} = n\{1, 2, 3, 4\} = n(S(4)) = 4$$

 EXAMPLE. Find the cardinal number of $\{2, 6, 8, 11, 13, 15\}$.

 Solution. Since $\{2, 6, 8, 11, 13, 15\} \sim \{1, 2, 3, 4, 5, 6\} = S(6)$,

$$n\{2, 6, 8, 11, 13, 15\} = n\{1, 2, 3, 4, 5, 6\} = n(S(6)) = 6$$

In summary, how do we find the number of elements in a finite set A; that is, how do we count? Answer: We find the unique standard set $S(w)$ which is equivalent to A. Then we say that "A has w elements".

This discussion permits us to look at finite sets in a new way. The finite sets are just those sets which we can count by the use of the whole numbers. (We cannot count the number of elements in an infinite set.) Thus we can represent an arbitrary finite set, A, by a symbol such as

$$A = \{a_1, a_2, \ldots, a_n\}$$

where the notation implies that A has n elements.

We now find that the properties of cardinal numbers which we required in Section 5.1 are now satisfied. For convenience in referring to these, we state them as theorems:

THEOREM 1. Every finite set A has a unique cardinal number $n(A)$.

(See the definition just above.)

THEOREM 2. Given any cardinal number, w, there is at least one set A for which $n(A) = w$. For example, $A = S(w)$ is such a set.

THEOREM 3. If two finite sets A and B are equivalent, then $n(A) = n(B)$.

Proof
1. There is some standard set $S(w)$ such that $A \sim S(w)$ and $n(A) = w$.
2. There is some standard set $S(v)$ such that $B \sim S(v)$ and $n(B) = v$.
3. Since $A \sim B$, by the transitive law of set equivalence, $S(w) \sim S(v)$.
4. Since no two different standard sets are equivalent, $S(w) = S(v)$, or $w = v$.
5. Hence $n(A) = n(B)$.

THEOREM 4. If for any two finite sets A and B, $n(A) = n(B)$, then $A \sim B$.

Proof
1. There is some standard set $S(w)$ such that $A \sim S(w)$ and $n(A) = w$.
2. There is some standard set $S(v)$ such that $B \sim S(v)$ and $n(B) = v$.
3. Since $n(A) = n(B)$, $w = v$.
4. Hence $A \sim S(w)$ and $B \sim S(w)$.
5. By the transitive property of set equivalence, $A \sim B$.

Theorems 3 and 4 can be combined into a single statement which is the most important theorem in this chapter:

FUNDAMENTAL THEOREM **THEOREM 5.** Two finite sets A and B are equivalent *if and only if* $n(A) = n(B)$.

93

1. Which of the following are *not* standard sets? (a) $\{\varnothing\}$. (b) $\{1, 2, 3\}$. (c) $\{\varnothing, 1, 2\}$. (d) $\varnothing$. *∅, ∅, ∅, 1, 2 ∅* [handwritten]

(a) and (c).

2. What is the cardinal number of each of the sets in frame 1? _____
1, 3, 3, 0 [handwritten]

(a) 1, (b) 3, (c) 3, (d) 0.

3. What is $n\{a, b, c, d, e\}$? *5* [handwritten]

5

4. What is $n\{1, 2, 3, \ldots, m\}$? *m* [handwritten]

m

5. What is $n\{0, 1, 2, 3, 4\}$? *5* [handwritten]

5

6. Is the set $\{0, 1, 2, 3, \ldots, w\}$ finite or infinite? *FINITE* [handwritten]

Finite.

7. Is the set $\{1, 2, 3, \ldots, n, \ldots\}$ finite or infinite? *INFINITE* [handwritten]

Infinite.

8. For any finite sets A and B, if $n(A) = n(B)$, what can we conclude about A and B? *EQUIVALENT SETS* [handwritten]

They are equivalent sets.

9. For any finite sets A and B such that $A \sim B$, what is the relationship between $n(A)$ and $n(B)$? *$n(A) = n(B)$* [handwritten]

$n(A) = n(B)$.

10. For any standard sets $S(w)$ and $S(v)$, if $n(S(w)) = n(S(v))$ what can we conclude about $S(w)$ and $S(v)$? *=* [handwritten]

They are equal. (They are, therefore, also equivalent.)

11. For any sets A and B, if $A \sim B$, and $n(A) = m$, then $n(B) = $ *M* [handwritten].

m

12. What is the standard set that is equivalent to $\{u, v, w, x, y, z\}$?
2 3, 4, 5, 6, 7, 8 3

$\{1, 2, 3, 4, 5, 6\}$.

13. What standard set is equivalent to $\{1, 2, 3, \ldots\}$? _____

There is none.

14. How do we find the cardinal number of a finite set A? Follow these steps:
(a) Find the unique standard set $S(w)$ which is ___ = to A ___.
(b) The cardinal number of $S(w)$ is $n(S(w)) =$ ___ w ___.
(c) Since $A \sim S(w)$, $n(A)$ ___ = ___ $n(S(w)) =$ ___ W ___.

(a) equivalent to A (b) w (c) $= : w$

5.4 Methods for Finding Cardinal Numbers

There is an easy way of finding the cardinal number of any nonempty, finite set by using the number line. First we construct the number line to represent the whole numbers. To do this we draw a horizontal line starting at a fixed point on the left and extending indefinitely to the right (Figure 5.1).

FIGURE 5.1. *Number line.*

Then we write the numerals for the whole numbers, equally spaced in their proper order, along this line.

Now consider the set $\{a, b, c, d, e, f\}$. Take its elements and place them successively (but in any order) above the numbers on the number line, beginning at 1 (see Figure 5.2). In this way you have constructed a one-to-one

FIGURE 5.2. *Use of number line to find the cardinal number of $\{a, b, c, d, e, f\}$.*

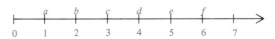

correspondence with the standard set $\{1, 2, 3, 4, 5, 6\}$, and so $n\{a, b, c, d, e, f\} = 6$.

INTERMEDIATE SET   Another method of finding the cardinal number of a set is to use an intermediate set whose cardinal number is known. The use of ballots in voting is a good example of this technique. Suppose that we wish to know the

95

number of voters who favor higher taxes for schools. Theoretically, we could get those in favor to stand along a number line and use the procedure above. Everyone would object to this clumsy procedure. So we have the voters mark ballots and count the ballots. Since the set of favorable voters is equivalent to the set of ballots marked "yes", they have the same cardinal numbers. By counting the ballots, we find the number of favorable voters.

When a child counts on his fingers, he is using an intermediate set. Similarly, we are using an intermediate set when we count seconds by means of a stopwatch.

---

1. The use of an intermediate set depends on the ___TRANSITIVE___ property of equivalence.

> transitive

2. To find the cardinal number of a nonempty set we attempt to establish a _one-to-one correspondence_ between this set and one of the _standard sets_

> one-to-one correspondence   standard sets

3. What intermediate set is involved when a college registrar counts names to determine how many students are enrolled? _SET OF NAMES_

> The set of names.

4. Many measuring devices use intermediate sets. A forester uses the set of growth rings of a tree to count _No. of YEARS._ .

> The number of years the tree was alive.

5. The set of revolutions of a wheel in a water meter is used as an _INTERMEDIATE_ set to count the number of gallons of water used.

> intermediate

6. Does the order in which a set of objects is counted affect the cardinal number of the set? _NO_ .
   (yes, no)

> No.

5.5 Counting Difficulties of Primitive Tribes

Studies of primitive tribes have found instances in which our concept of cardinal number is only partially understood. For example, it is quite common for an Australian aborigine to count "one, two, many." He has understood the notion of one-to-one correspondence for sets having one or two elements, but he assumes that all larger sets are mutually equivalent and gives each of them the cardinal number "many." Thus these aborigines failed to observe that if the cardinal numbers of two sets are equal, then the sets must be equivalent.

A more curious departure from our ideas occurs in the language of the Tsimschian Indians, a tribe on the northwest coast of British Columbia. According to the observations of Franz Boas, this tribe believed that the cardinal number of a set depends upon the nature of the objects in the set. As shown in Table 1, there are seven classes of cardinal numbers: (1) abstract, (2) flat objects or animals, (3) round objects and intervals of time, (4) men, (5) long objects, (6) canoes, and (7) measures. So these tribes failed to observe that if two sets are equivalent, then their cardinal numbers must be equal.

TABLE 1. Numerals used by the Tsimschian Indians†

No.	Counting	Flat Objects	Round Objects	Men	Long Objects	Canoes	Measures
1	gyāk·	gāk·	g'ɛ'rɛl	k·âl	k·'ā'wutsk·an	k·'amä'et	k·'al
2	t'ɛpqā't	t'ɛpqā't	gō'upɛl	t'ɛpqadâ'l	g·â'opsk·an	g·alpē'eltk	gu'lbɛl
3	gua'nt	gua'nt	gutlē'	gulâ'l	g·a'ltsk·an	g·altsk·ā'ntk	gulē'ont
4	tqālpq	tqālpq	tqālpq	tqālpqdâ'l	tqā'apsk·an	tqālpqsk	tqalpqalo'nt
5	kctonc	kctōnc	kctōnc	kcɛnɛcâ'l	k·'ɛtō'ɛntsk·an	kctō'onsk	kctōnsilo'nt
6	k·'âlt	k·'âlt	k·'âlt	k·'aldâ'l	k·'â'oltsk·an	k·'âltk	k·'âldɛlo'nt
7	t'ɛpqâ'lt	t'ɛpqâ'lt	t'ɛpqâ'lt	t'ɛpqaldâ'l	t'ɛepqâltsk·an	t'ɛpqâ'ltk	t'ɛpqâldɛlo'nt
8	guandâ'lt	yuktâ'lt	yuktâ'lt	yuktlēadâ'l	ēk'tlaɛdsk·an	yuktâ'ltk	yuktâldɛlo'nt
9	kctɛmâ'c	kctɛmâ'c	kctɛmâ'c	kctɛmacâ'l	kctɛmä'etsk·an	kctɛmâ'ck	kctɛmâsilo'nt
10	gy'ap	gy'ap	k·'pē'el	k·'pâl	k·'pē'etsk·an	gy'apsk	k·'pēo'nt
11	gyāk·	—	—	—	—	—	—
12	t'ɛpqā't	—	—	k·'pâl tɛ t'ɛpqadâ'l	—	—	—

† Reproduced from Schulenburg, A. C. Graf v. d., *Die Sprache der Zimschian-Indianer*, Sattler, Braunschweig, 1894.

Boas's work was published in 1889 and represented the situation at that time. Recent conversations with students at the University of Alaska indicate that traces of this custom still persist in some native languages of the region.

1. It is doubtful whether any tribe that used the "one, two, many" system could have actually engaged in arithmetic, but if they did, what would be the sum of one and two? _Many_

Many.

2. What would be the sum of two and two? __Many__

> Many.

3. What would be the sum of many and many? __Many__

> Many.

4. Each pair of "numbers" would have a unique sum, but how many possible "numbers" would there be for "many minus many?" __4__

> Four (none, one, two, many).

5.6 Whole Numbers

Since the concept of the cardinal number of a set is based upon that of a whole number, we should discuss the question: What are the whole numbers? In other words, what is the number "two", the number "three", and so forth? Whole numbers are so familiar to everyone that there may seem to be nothing much to say about them. Why not just apply our intuition and forget about defining them? If you like, you can do this, but a mathematician would be very unhappy with such a procedure. Since the whole numbers are of the utmost importance in mathematics, a mathematician insists that they be based upon a solid logical foundation. It is just here that the trouble arises: It is far from easy to find such a foundation for the whole numbers. A goodly number of the leading mathematicians and logicians of the past hundred years have written on this matter and have proposed several different approaches.

FREGE APPROACH TO
CARDINAL NUMBERS

We shall begin with the most intuitive of these, an approach published by Gottlob Frege in 1893. This is based upon the general notion of an *equivalence class* generated by an equivalence relation. Here we shall illustrate this concept in terms of the equivalence of sets, and later we shall apply it to other situations.

Suppose that we are given a large (possibly infinite) collection, U, of sets. Some of these will be singleton sets which are all equivalent to the set $\{a\}$. Let us put all these together as elements of the set

$$\big\{\{a\}, \{x\}, \{\varnothing\}, \{\bigcirc\}, \{\star\}, \{\text{John}\}, \{\text{Paris}\}, \ldots\big\}$$

Since, for instance, $\{\bigcirc\} \sim \{a\}$ and $\{\text{John}\} \sim \{a\}$, the transitive property of set equivalence tells us that $\{\bigcirc\} \sim \{\text{John}\}$. Further, from the symmetric property $\{\text{John}\} \sim \{\bigcirc\}$; and from the reflexive property $\{\bigcirc\} \sim \{\bigcirc\}$. Thus each element of the above set is equivalent to every other element. This is an illustration of an *equivalence class* of sets, according to the following definition:

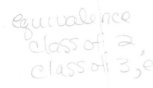

equivalence
class of 2,
class of 3, etc

DEFINITION. An *equivalence class of sets* is a collection of sets each of whose members is equivalent to every other member.

In the same way we can choose the sets in our large collection U which are equivalent to $\{a, b\}$, and form the equivalence class

$$\left\{\{a, b\}, \{x, y\}, \{\varnothing, \infty\}, \{\star, \diamond\}, \{\text{John, Mary}\}, \ldots\right\}$$

We note that no element of the class

$$\left\{\{a\}, \{x\}, \{\varnothing\}, \{\bigcirc\}, \{\star\}, \{\text{John}\}, \{\text{Paris}\}, \ldots\right\}$$

is equivalent to any element of the class

$$\left\{\{a, b\}, \{x, y\}, \{\varnothing, \infty\}, \{\star, \diamond\}, \{\text{John, Mary}\}, \ldots\right\}$$

If there are any sets in U which are not members of one of the above equivalence classes, we can continue this process and define more and more equivalence classes. After a possibly infinite number of such steps, we will have assigned each member U to one and only one equivalence class, and the process stops.

Now what have we accomplished? We have *partitioned* our original collection of sets U into a number of equivalence classes such that

(1) Every set in U belongs to one and only one equivalence class.

(2) The elements of an equivalence class are all mutually equivalent.

(3) No element of one equivalence class is equivalent to any element of a different equivalence class.

At this point we are ready for Frege's definition of a cardinal number. Let the given collection of sets U be the collection of *all* sets. Carry out the partitioning of U into equivalence classes as just described. Then, according to Frege, we have the definitions:

DEFINITION. The *cardinal number* of a set A is the equivalence class to which A belongs.

DEFINITION. A *whole number* is the cardinal number of a finite set.

Next we have the problem of giving names to these equivalence classes. Since the class

$$\left\{\{a\}, \{x\}, \{\varnothing\}, \{\bigcirc\}, \{\star\}, \{\text{John}\}, \{\text{Paris}\}, \ldots\right\}$$

is uniquely determined by any one of its elements we could name it by any one of these, say $\{x\}$, and write, for instance,

$$\langle\{x\}\rangle = \left\{\{a\}, \{x\}, \{\varnothing\}, \{\bigcirc\}, \{\star\}, \{\text{John}\}, \{\text{Paris}\}, \ldots\right\}$$

where $\langle\{x\}\rangle$ is the name of the equivalence class determined by $\{x\}$. This, however, is too complicated for the purposes of arithmetic; so we invent special symbols to be names for these equivalence classes.

Thus we write

$$1 = \Big\{\{a\}, \{x\}, \ldots\Big\}$$
$$2 = \Big\{\{a, b\}, \{x, y\}, \ldots\Big\}$$
$$3 = \Big\{\{a, b, c\}, \{x, y, z\}, \ldots\Big\}$$

and so forth.

The whole number zero is something of a special case, for it should be associated with the empty set. Since the empty set is unique, its equivalence class contains only the set $\varnothing$. Thus

$$0 = \{\varnothing\}$$

The difficulty with this approach is the concept of "the collection of *all* sets equivalent to A". This concept is vague, for objects and ideas are being created continuously, and so the "collection of *all* sets" is not a fixed entity. Thus the definition of a whole number appears to vary with time. But even worse than this, logical difficulties have arisen with the whole concept of the "collection of *all* sets", and these are so serious that Frege's approach fails to meet current standards of mathematical rigor. For this reason, we must look further for a sounder treatment.

---

1. According to Frege the cardinal number of a set A is the _____ *equivalence class* of sets to which A belongs.

equivalence class

2. According to Frege a whole number is the cardinal number of a *finite* set.

finite

3. According to Frege, the numeral "2" is the name for the equivalence class of sets to which the set $\{c, d\}$ belongs.

$\{a, b\}, \{x, y\}$, or any other set equivalent to these.

4. According to Frege, the numeral "3" is a name for the equivalence class of sets having ___*3*___ distinct elements.

three

5. According to Frege, the whole number "zero" is the equivalence class of sets whose only member is the set ___$\varnothing$___.

$\varnothing$

5.7 Von Neumann Approach to Whole Numbers

This approach, which was published by John von Neumann in 1923, does not involve the logical difficulties of the Frege approach but is somewhat more sophisticated. The idea is to define each whole number as a particular set, instead of as a collection of sets as in the Frege approach. The problem is how to do this in a satisfactory fashion.

If we look at the whole numbers as they are represented on the number line, we see that they have the three important properties:

(1) The set of whole numbers is an infinite set.

(2) There is a first whole number, namely zero.

(3) Each whole number is followed by a unique whole number called its *successor*. Thus the successor of 0 is 1, the successor of 1 is 2, and so forth.

In summary, the set of whole numbers is an infinite sequence beginning with zero.

If we are to define each whole number as a particular set, we therefore need a sequence of sets that has the above three properties. Let us try to find such a sequence. We might begin with the sequence of sets

$$\varnothing, \{a\}, \{a, b\}, \{a, b, c\}, \ldots$$

The trouble with this is that before long we will run out of letters of the alphabet and be in doubt as to how to continue.

Alternatively, we might think that we could use the sequence of standard sets

$$\varnothing, \{1\}, \{1, 2\}, \{1, 2, 3\}, \ldots$$

The trouble here is that this sequence is described in terms of the whole numbers themselves and hence is of no help in *defining* the whole numbers.

We might even use the sequence of sets

$$\varnothing, \{/\}, \{//\}, \{///\}, \ldots$$

which one employs in tallying a vote. This is closer to our needs, but still raises questions as to how it is to be continued to the right.

Von Neumann hit upon a sequence like these which encounters none of these difficulties. Its basic element is the empty set $\varnothing$, a concept that does not depend upon anything else in our culture. The first set in his sequence is $\varnothing$. The next set is the set $\{\varnothing\}$, a singleton set whose only element is the set $\varnothing$. To simplify notation we shall rename this as "1". The next set is the set $\{\varnothing, 1\}$, which we rename "2". Continuing in this way we obtain the sequence of sets

$$\varnothing$$
$$\{\varnothing\} = 1$$
$$\{\varnothing, 1\} = 2$$
$$\{\varnothing, 1, 2\} = 3$$
$$\{\varnothing, 1, 2, 3\} = 4$$
$$\cdots$$
$$\{\varnothing, 1, 2, 3, \ldots, w\} = w^+$$
$$\cdots$$

where w^+ is the name of the set that is the successor of the set w in this sequence.

The definition is inductive in the following sense: The set 1 is defined in terms of $\varnothing$; then 2 is defined in terms of $\varnothing$ and 1; 3 is defined in terms of $\varnothing$, 1, and 2; and w^+ is defined in terms of all the sets before it in the sequence; $\varnothing$, 1, 2, ..., w. In this way the possible appearance of circular reasoning is avoided.

We observe that this sequence of sets has the three required properties and that its definition is clear to anyone who understands the meaning of $\varnothing$. Now we can define the whole numbers:

VON NEUMANN WHOLE NUMBERS

DEFINITION. The *whole number* 0 is the set $\varnothing$. The whole numbers 1, 2, 3, ... are the sets $\{\varnothing\}, \{\varnothing, 1\}, \{\varnothing, 1, 2\}, ...$ described above. The successor w^+ of any whole number w is the set $\{\varnothing, 1, 2, 3, ..., w\}$.

Thus we have defined the infinite sequence of whole numbers

SUCCESSOR, w^+

$$0, 1, 2, 3, ..., w, w^+, ...$$

in which each whole number, w, has a unique *successor*, w^+, on its right.

REMARK

The numerals, such as 1, 2, 3, ..., appearing in this definition are particular names for the corresponding sets. Of course, other names can be used, such as

one, two, three, four, ...
I, II, III, IV, ...
eins, zwei, drei, vier, ...
un, deux, trois, quatre, ...

1. What is the name of the set $\{\varnothing, 1\}$? _____

2.

2. Each whole number after the first is defined in terms of its predecessor. Which whole number has no predecessor? _____

0 (or $\varnothing$).

3. A number immediately following a given number is called the _____ of the given number.

successor

4. The symbol for the successor of w is w^+. What is 5^+? _____

6.

5. What is 0^+? _____

1.

6. If $a^+ = 27$, what is a? _____

26.

7. If $a^+ = 0$, what is a? _____

There is no whole number a such that $a^+ = 0$.

8. A portion of the number line is shown. On it indicate 75^+, $(75^+)^+$, and a, if $a^+ = 75$.

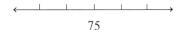

75

a = 74 75 76 77

9. According to von Neumann, the whole number 3 is the set _____
_____.

$\{\emptyset, 1, 2\}$

10. According to von Neumann, the whole number 0 is the set _____.

$\emptyset$

11. According to von Neumann, the whole number w^+ is the set
_____.

$\{\emptyset, 1, 2, \ldots, w\}$

12. What is the English name for the whole number $\{\emptyset, 1, 2, 3, 4\}$?
_____

Five.

13. What numeral represents the whole number $\{\emptyset, 1, 2, 3, 4, 5\}$?
_____

6.

14. The whole number 3 is the set _____. The standard set $S(3)$ is the set _____. Are these two sets equivalent? _____.
Are they equal? _____
(yes, no)   (yes, no)

> $\{\varnothing, 1, 2\}$ $\{1, 2, 3\}$ Yes   No.

15. What is the relationship between the whole number 0 (a set) and the standard set $S(0)$? _____
$(=, \subset, \sim)$

> Both sets are the empty set $\varnothing$, hence $=$ and $\sim$.

16. For what whole numbers w (expressed as sets) is $w \sim S(w)$? (See frames 14 and 15.) _____.

> All whole numbers w.

17. For what whole numbers w (expressed as sets) is $w = S(w)$? _____

> Only $w = \varnothing$.

18. Draw a diagram representing the whole numbers $0, 1, 2, 3, \ldots, w, w^+, \ldots$, on the number line.

5.8 Peano Postulates (optional)

Our final way of looking at the whole numbers is the axiomatic approach. We can abandon any hope of defining these numbers, and merely state how they behave. In this approach, the whole numbers are undefined symbols and their properties are described by a collection of axioms. In order to avoid circular reasoning every mathematical theory must begin in this way with a set of undefined terms and a collection of axioms. Perhaps you have seen this done at the start of your study of geometry.

Actually Peano's axioms are for the natural numbers rather than for the whole numbers. But if we have the natural numbers we can get the whole numbers by joining zero to them, so Peano's approach meets all our needs. According to Peano, we have

PEANO POSTULATES
(1) A set A of undefined elements including a specific element called 1. A is called the set of natural numbers.

(2) An undefined operation called "forming the successor" which applies to each natural number and gives another natural number.

(3) The axioms

    (a) 1 is a natural number.

    (b) If a is a natural number, then it has a successor a^+ which is a natural number.

    (c) There is no natural number a such that $a^+ = 1$.

    (d) If a and b are natural numbers such that $a^+ = b^+$, then $a = b$.

    (e) If S is a set of natural numbers such that

        (1) 1 is in S, and

        (2) if n is in S, then n^+ is in S,

        then S is the set of natural numbers, A.

You observe that the natural numbers as we have defined them satisfy these axioms. Peano's contribution (1889) was the proof that the entire theory of the natural numbers follows from these axioms provided that suitable definitions of addition and multiplication are given. We cannot present any of this proof here; if you are interested you can find it in other books.

The following exercises are proposed only for those interested in a follow-up to the Peano axioms.

1. To get our usual arithmetic how should we define $a + 1$ in terms of the successor operation? For all natural numbers a, $a + 1 =$ _____.

> a^+

2. Similarly, to get our usual arithmetic, we should define $a + b^+$ as follows: For all natural numbers a and b, $a + b^+ =$ _____.

> $(a + b)^+$

3. Since every natural number except 1 is of the form b^+ (see frame 9), addition is thus uniquely defined for _____ of natural numbers.

> every pair

4. Show that for every two natural numbers, a and b, $(a + b) + 1 = a + (b + 1)$.

Proof
1. $(a + b) + 1 = $ _____ (frame 1).
2. $a + (b + 1) = $ _____ (frame 1).
3. $a + (b + 1) = a + b^+ = $ _____ (frame 2).

$(a + b)^+$ $a + b^+$ $(a + b)^+$

5. Define 2 as 1^+. Then show that for every two natural numbers, a and b,

$$(a + b) + 2 = a + (b + 2)$$

Proof
1. $(a + b) + 2 = (a + b) + 1^+ = $ _____ (frame 2).
2. $= $ _____ (frame 4).
3. $= a + (b + 1)^+. $ _____
4. $= a + (b + 1^+). $ _____
5. $= a + (b + 2).$

$[(a + b) + 1]^+$ $[a + (b + 1)]^+$ Frame 2.   Frame 1.

6. A continuation of the process begun in frames 4 and 5 would show that for every three natural numbers, a, b, and c, $(a + b) + c = $ _____ .

$a + (b + c)$

7. In a manner similar to that in frames 1 and 2, we should define the product $a \cdot b$ of two natural numbers as follows: For all natural numbers a, $a \cdot 1 = $ _____ and for all natural numbers a and b, $a \cdot b^+ = $ _____ .

a $(a \cdot b) + a$

8. Since every natural number except 1 is of the form b^+ (see frame 9), multiplication is thus uniquely defined for _____ of natural numbers.

every pair

9. Prove that every natural number except 1 is of the form b^+.

Proof
1. Consider the set S of natural numbers whose elements are 1 and all natural numbers of the form b^+.
2. $1 \, \varepsilon \, S.$ _____
3. For all c: if $c \, \varepsilon \, S$, then $c^+ \, \varepsilon \, S.$ _____
4. Therefore, S is the set of all natural numbers. Axiom _____ .

Step (1).	Step (1).	(e)

10. The set of natural numbers is therefore the set whose elements are

$$1, 2 = 1^+, 3 = 2^+, 4 = \underline{\hspace{1cm}}, 5 = \underline{\hspace{1cm}}, \ldots$$

3^+ 4^+

REFERENCES

Beaumont, R. A., and R. S. Pierce, *The Algebraic Foundations of Mathematics*, Addison-Wesley, Reading, Mass., 1963. See Chapter 3 for a more detailed exposition of the contents of this chapter.

Henkin, Leon, W. N. Smith, V. J. Varineau, and M. J. Walsh, *Retracing Elementary Mathematics*, Macmillan, New York, 1962. See Chapter 2 for an equivalent version of the Peano axioms and later chapters for their consequences.

Russell, Bertrand, "Definition of Number", reprinted in *World of Mathematics*, Simon and Schuster, New York, 1956, pp. 537–543. This is an account of the Frege–Russell approach to cardinal numbers.

————, "My Mental Development", *ibid.*, pp. 381–401; especially bottom of p. 388 for comment on the Frege approach. Frege's comment in German can be translated "Arithmetic has received a staggering blow".

Wilder, R. L., *Introduction to the Foundations of Mathematics*, Wiley, New York, 1952. See pp. 62–71 for a discussion of various definitions of finite and infinite sets.

In this chapter we have defined the following terms:

  standard set
  cardinal number of a set
  whole number

and have shown you how to find cardinal numbers and how to count.

Now test yourself on the Post Test that follows. Do not *refer to the text while working this test. Check your answers with the key after you have completed the entire test.*

POST TEST

1. Write the standard set $S(3)$ in set notation. $\{1, 2, 3\}$
2. If $S(a)$ and $S(b)$ are standard sets, and both of $S(a) \subset S(b)$ and $S(b) \subset S(a)$ are false, what relation must exist between a and b? $a = b$

3. The cardinal number of $S(5)$ is ___5___.

4. If $A \sim S(w)$, then $n(A) =$ ___w___.

5. To find the cardinal number of a finite set A: (a) Find w such that $A \sim$ ___$S(w)$___. (b) Then $n(A) =$ ___w___.

6. What standard set is equivalent to $\varnothing$? $S(0) = \varnothing$

7. What is $n(\varnothing)$? ___0___

8. What standard set is equivalent to $\{a, b, x, q\}$? $S(4) = \{1,2,3,4\}$

9. If A and B are any finite sets and $A \sim B$, what is the relationship between $n(A)$ and $n(B)$? $n(A) = n(B)$

10. If A and B are any finite sets and $n(A) = n(B)$, what is the relationship between A and B? $A \sim B$

11. Draw a diagram showing how to use the number line to find $n\{x, y, z\}$. _____ $n\{x,y,z\} = 3$

12. What intermediate set is used when a child counts his toys by matching them with his fingers and then counts his fingers? HIS FINGERS _____

13. The Tsimschian Indians used different cardinal numbers for the sets of three trees and of three men. What principle of this chapter did this usage violate? $A \sim B$, then $n(A) = n(B)$

14. According to Frege the whole number 2 is ___Equivalence___ CLASS to which $\{x, y\}$ belong.

15. According to von Neumann, a whole number is a _____.

16. According to von Neumann, the whole number 5 is the set _____ _____.

17. According to von Neumann, the whole number 0 is the set _____.

18. What numeral represents the von Neumann whole number $\{\varnothing, 1, 2, 3\}$? _____

19. According to von Neumann, the whole number w^+ is the set _____ _____.

20. If $a = 6$, what is a^+? _____ What is $(a^+)^+$? _____

21. What is the relationship between the von Neumann whole number 3 (a set) and the standard set $S(3)$? _____

$(=, \sim, \subset, \supset)$

22. For what von Neumann whole numbers w is $w = S(w)$? _____

1. $\{1, 2, 3\}$.
2. $a = b$.
3. 5
4. w
5. (a) $S(w)$. (b) w
6. $S(0) = \varnothing$.
7. 0.
8. $S(4) = \{1, 2, 3, 4\}$, 4.

9. $n(A) = n(B)$.
10. $A \smile B$.
11.
$$\xrightarrow[\;0\quad 1\quad 2\quad 3\;]{\overset{x\qquad y\qquad z}{\rule{4cm}{0.4pt}}}, \qquad n\{x, y, z\} = 3.$$

12. His fingers.
13. If $A \smile B$, then we must have $n(A) = n(B)$.
14. The equivalence class of sets to which $\{a, b\}$ belongs.
15. Set
16. $\{\varnothing, 1, 2, 3, 4\}$
17. $\varnothing$
18. 4.
19. $\{\varnothing, 1, 2, \ldots, w\}$
20. $7 \,; 8$.
21. $\smile$.
22. Only $w = \varnothing$.

If you had difficulty with the Post Test, review Chapter 5 (and possibly Chapter 4) to find the source of your trouble. When you have mastered the ideas of this chapter, proceed to Chapter 6 and answer the questions in its Readiness Test.

6

Union, Intersection, and Complement of Sets

Chapter 6 concerns operations with sets—using given sets to form others. To study it meaningfully you should have a good understanding of the ideas and notations of earlier chapters. If you successfully completed the Post Test for Chapter 3, frames 1 through 3 should constitute an adequate Readiness Test for this chapter.

R E A D I N E S S   T E S T

1. For the universal set consisting of the *first ten letters* of the alphabet list within curly brackets:
   (a) The elements of the set

   $$A = \{x|x \text{ is a vowel}\}$$

   (b) The elements of the set

   $$B = \{x|x \text{ is used in spelling the word "arithmetic"}\}$$

   (c) The elements of the set

   $$C = \{y|y \text{ is used in spelling the word "mathematics"}\}$$

   (a) $A = \{a, e, i\}$ (in any order).   (b) $B = \{a, c, e, h, i\}$ (in any order).
   (c) $C = \{a, c, e, h, i\}$ (in any order).

2. Among the answers to frame 1 are there any sets that are subsets of others? _Yes_____. If so, use set-inclusion symbols to list the ones that are.
   $A \subseteq B, A \subseteq C, C \subseteq B, B \subseteq C$

   Yes. $A \subseteq B, A \subseteq C, C \subseteq B, B \subseteq C$.

3. What is meant by the empty set, $\varnothing$? _NO MEMBERS_____

   The set with no members or elements.

If you missed questions 1 or 3, review Section 3.4. If you missed question 2 review Section 3.5. After this review, or if you have answered all three questions correctly, you should now read Sections 6.1 through 6.3. Frames 1 through 13, which follow the text, are designed to supplement it.

6.1 Introduction

In this chapter we shall discuss three operations on sets, called *union*, *intersection*, and *complementation*, which are essential for our discussions of addition and subtraction in later chapters. We assume that we have a given universal set U and various of its subsets, $A, B, C, \ldots$. As in Chapter 3, each of these subsets may be defined either by listing its elements or by stating that its elements are those members of U that have a given property in common. Out of these sets $A, B, C, \ldots$ it is possible to generate new sets, which are also subsets of U. We shall consider three methods of defining such new subsets in this chapter. These are

(1) Given A and B, we can form the set whose elements are elements of *both* A and B. We call this set the *intersection* of A and B.

(2) Given A and B, we can form the set whose elements are elements of A or of B (or both). We call this the *union* of A and B.

(3) Given U and A, we can form the set whose elements are those in U which are *not* in A. We call this the *absolute complement of A*. Later we shall assume that B is a subset of A and form the set of those elements in A which are not in B. We call this the *complement of B relative to A*.

In Chapter 3 we have already shown you examples of the first two procedures when our subsets were defined in terms of the common properties of their elements.

(1) The *intersection* of two sets, A and B, contains precisely those elements which have *both* of the properties that were used to define A and B separately.

(2) The *union* of A and B contains those elements which have *either or both* of the properties that were used to define A and B separately.

The purpose of this chapter is to develop these ideas in greater detail.

6.2 Definitions and Illustrations

INTERSECTION **(1) INTERSECTION**

DEFINITION. The *intersection* of A and B is the set whose elements are members of both A and B. We use the symbol $A \cap B$ to denote the intersection of A and B.

This can be considered as an application of the notion of the conjunction of two open sentences as defined in Chapter 2. Recall that $P = \{x|p_x\}$ is the set of elements x in U for which p_x is true, and that $Q = \{x|q_x\}$ is the set of elements x in U for which q_x is true. Hence $P \cap Q$ is the set of elements x in U for which *both* p_x and q_x are true. That is

$$P \cap Q = \{x|p_x \text{ and } q_x\}$$

ILLUSTRATIONS
1. Let $A = \{a, b, c, d\}$ and $B = \{a, c, e, f\}$. Then $A \cap B = \{a, c\}$.
2. Let A be the set of letters in the word "engineer" and B be the set of vowels in the alphabet. Then $A \cap B = \{e, i\}$.
3. Let

$$U = \text{set of students in your university}$$
$$A = \{x|x \text{ belongs to a fraternity}\}$$
$$B = \{x|x \text{ is a football player}\}$$

Then

$$A \cap B = \{x|x \text{ belongs to a fraternity } and \text{ is a football player}\}$$

4. Let U be the set of citizens of the United States, A be the set of citizens less than 21 years of age, and B be the set of U.S. Senators. Then $A \cap B = \emptyset$.

5. $U \cap A = A$.

6. For any set A, $A \cap \emptyset = \emptyset$, since $\emptyset$ has no elements and hence A and $\emptyset$ have no elements in common.

DISJOINT SETS   **DEFINITION.** A and B are said to be *disjoint* if and only if $A \cap B = \emptyset$.

ILLUSTRATIONS

1. $\{a, b, c\}$ and $\{d, e, f\}$ are disjoint.

2. Let A be the set of vowels in the word *arithmetic* and B be the set of its consonants. Then A and B are disjoint.

3. If A is any set and $B = \emptyset$, then A and B are disjoint, that is, $A \cap \emptyset = \emptyset$ for all A. For, since $\emptyset$ does not contain any elements, there are no elements that belong to both A and B.

4. Let A be any set and B be the set of elements of U that are not members of A. Then A and B are disjoint.

UNION   **(2) UNION**

DEFINITION.   The *union* of A and B is the set whose elements are members of A or of B (or of both). We use the symbol $A \cup B$ to denote the union of A and B.

This is an application of the concept of the disjunction of two open sentences as defined in Chapter 2. Let $P = \{x|p_x\}$ and $Q = \{x|q_x\}$. Then $P \cup Q$ is the set of elements x in U for which either p_x is true or q_x is true. That is,

$$P \cup Q = \{x|p_x \text{ or } q_x\}$$

where *or* is used in its inclusive sense.

ILLUSTRATIONS

1. Let $A = \{a, b, c, d\}$ and $B = \{a, c, e, f\}$. Then $A \cup B = \{a, b, c, d, e, f\}$.

2. Let A be the set of letters in the word "engineer", B be the set of vowels (excluding y) in the alphabet. Then $A \cup B = \{a, e, i, o, u, n, g, r\}$.

3. Let $A = \{x|x \text{ is white}\}$ and $B = \{x|x \text{ is large}\}$. Then $A \cup B = \{x|x \text{ is white } or \text{ large}\}$.

4. Let U be the set of students in your university, A be the set of athletes, and B be the set of varsity football players. Then $A \cup B$ is the set of athletes, and $A \cup B = A$.

5. Let A be any set and B be the set of elements of U that are not members of A. Then $A \cup B = U$.

6. Let A be any set. Then $A \cup \emptyset = A$.

7. Let A be any set. Then $A \cup U = U$.

6.3 Venn Diagrams

VENN DIAGRAMS

FIGURE 6.1. *The universal set.*

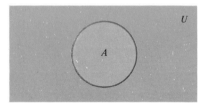

FIGURE 6.2. *Set A.*

We can help you with your understanding of these ideas by introducing a geometrical representation of sets, called *Venn diagrams*. Although this is symbolic only, it reflects these notions rather well and will help you develop intuition regarding operations with sets. First, we represent the universal set, *U*, by the points in the interior of a rectangle (Figure 6.1). Further, we represent a set *A* that is a subset of *U* by the points in the interior of a circle drawn inside this rectangle (Figure 6.2).

When we have two sets, *A* and *B*, they may take a variety of positions, such as those drawn in Figure 6.3.

Now we can illustrate the ideas of intersection and union geometrically. In each part of Figure 6.4 we have put the regions that are common to *A* and *B* in the darker shade of color. Thus in each rectangle we have shown the set $A \cap B$ by the darker color. This should help you to understand why we use the term *intersection* for this idea.

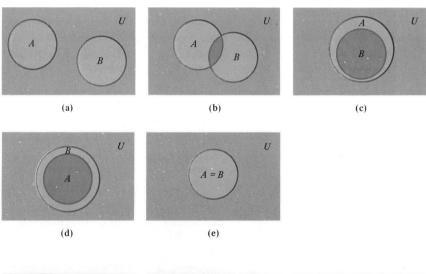

(a)   (b)   (c)

FIGURE 6.3. *Possible positions of sets A and B.*

(d)   (e)

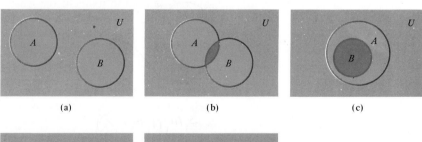

(a)   (b)   (c)

FIGURE 6.4. $A \cap B$ *is the colored region.*

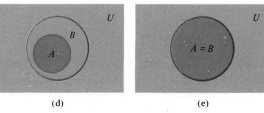

(d)   (e)

In each part of Figure 6.5 we have colored the regions that belong to A or B or to both A and B. Thus in each rectangle we have shown the set $A \cup B$ in color.

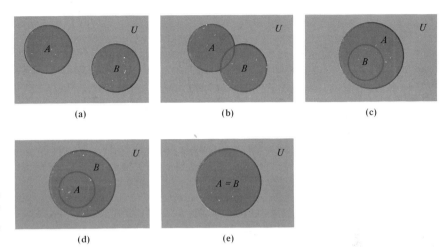

FIGURE 6.5. $A \cup B$ *is the colored region.*

1. Recall (Section 6.2) that for two sets A and B, their intersection denoted by $A \cap B$, is the set consisting of all elements that belong to both A and B. If

$$C = \{a, b, c, d, e\}$$
$$D = \{a, e, i, o, u\}$$
$$E = \{u, v, w, x, y, z\}$$

(a) What is $C \cap D$? $\underline{\{a, e\}}$
(b) What is $D \cap E$? $\underline{\{u\}}$
(c) What is $C \cap E$? $\underline{\varnothing}$

(a) $\{a, e\}$.   (b) $\{u\}$.   (c) $\varnothing$.

2. Let the universal set be the set of all living creatures and let $A = \{x|x$ is an insect$\}$, $B = \{y|y$ has the ability to fly$\}$, and $C = \{z|z$ is a bird$\}$. Describe in words: (a) $A \cap B$. $\underline{\text{All insect that can fly}}$
(b) $B \cap C$. $\underline{\text{All birds that can fly}}$ (c) $A \cap C$. $\underline{\varnothing}$

(a) All insects capable of flight.   (b) All birds capable of flight.
(c) The empty set.

3. For the universal set U and any subset A, $U \cap A = \underline{A}$.

A

115

4. Two sets A and B are said to be disjoint if $A \cap B =$ *Ø*

$\varnothing$

5. Let the universal set be the set of all triangles. If A is the set of all isosceles triangles and B is the set of all right triangles, what is $A \cap B$?
SET OF ALL ISOSCELES RIGHT $\triangle$.

The set of all isosceles right triangles.

6. The union of two sets A and B, denoted by $A \cup B$, is the set of all elements that belong to A or to B (inclusive use of "or", that is, elements that belong to A or to B or to both A and B). If

$$C = \{2, 3, 4, 5\}$$
$$D = \{0, 1, 2, 3\}$$
$$E = \{7, 8, 9\}$$

(a) What is $C \cup D$? *{0, 1, 2, 3, 4, 5}*
(b) What is $C \cup E$? *{2, 3, 4, 5, 7, 8, 9}*

(a) $\{0, 1, 2, 3, 4, 5\}$ (in any order).   (b) $\{2, 3, 4, 5, 7, 8, 9\}$ (in any order).

7. If A is any set, what is $A \cup \varnothing$? *A*

A.

8. If A is any set, what is $A \cap \varnothing$? *Ø*

$\varnothing$.

9. Let the universal set be the letters of the alphabet. If

$$A = \{x|x \text{ is used in spelling "arithmetic"}\}$$
$$B = \{y|y \text{ is used in spelling "mathematics"}\}$$

what is $A \cup B$? *{a, i, t, h, m, e, r, s}*

$\{a, c, e, h, i, m, r, s, t\}$ (in any order).

10. For the Venn diagram shown, U is the set of all letters of the alphabet. List the elements of

(a) set *A.* $\{a, b, c, d, e, f\}$
(b) set *B.* $\{e, f, g, h, i, j\}$
(c) *A ∩ B.* $\{e, f\}$
(d) *A ∪ B.* $\{a, b, c, d, e, f, g, h, i, j\}$

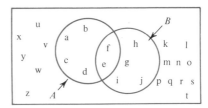

(a) $A = \{a, b, c, d, e, f\}.$
(b) $B = \{e, f, g, h, i, j\}.$
(c) $A \cap B = \{e, f\}.$
(d) $A \cup B = \{a, b, c, d, e, f, g, h, i, j\}.$

11. For the Venn diagram shown, list the elements of

(a) set *C* $\{a, b, c, d, e, f, g, h\}$
(b) set *D* $\{a, b, c\}$
(c) *C ∩ D* $\{a, b, c\}$
(d) *C ∪ D* $\{a, b, c, d, e, f, g, h\}$

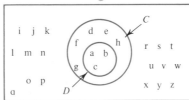

(a) $C = \{a, b, c, d, e, f, g, h\}.$
(b) $D = \{a, b, c\}.$
(c) $C \cap D = \{a, b, c\} = D.$
(d) $C \cup D = \{a, b, c, d, e, f, g, h\} = C.$

12. Let *U* be the set of the first ten letters of the alphabet. In the outline shown, complete a Venn diagram by listing the elements and circling the sets described by

$$A = \{a, e, i\}$$

$$B = \{a, c, e, h, i\}$$

$$C = \{a, e, i, c, h\}$$

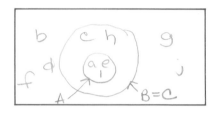

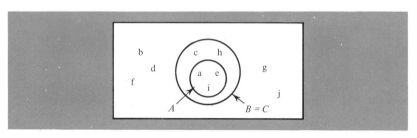

13. Let the universal set be the set of all letters of the alphabet and

$$A = \{x|x \text{ appears in the word "alphabet"}\}$$

$$B = \{a, e, i, o, u\}$$

$$C = \{p, q, r, s, t\}$$

(a) What is $A \cap B$? $\{a, e\}$
(b) What is $A \cup B$? $\{a, b, e, h, i, l, o, p, t, u\}$
(c) What is $A \cap C$? $\{p, t\}$
(d) What is $A \cup C$? $\{a, p, l, h, q, b, r, es, t\}$
(e) What is $B \cap C$? $\emptyset$
(f) What is $B \cup C$? $\{a, e, i, o, u, p, q, r, s, t\}$

(g) In the outline shown, complete a Venn diagram by listing the elements and circling the sets A, B, and C described above.

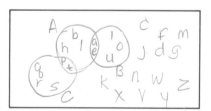

(a) $\{a, e\}$.
(b) $\{a, b, e, h, i, l, o, p, t, u\}$.
(c) $\{p, t\}$.
(d) $\{a, b, e, h, l, p, q, r, s, t\}$.
(e) $\emptyset$.
(f) $\{a, e, i, o, p, q, r, s, t, u\}$.

118

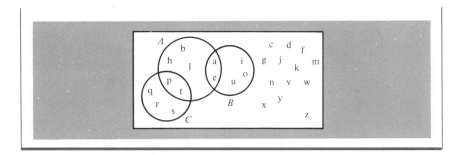

6.4 Truth Tables

We can conveniently use the truth tables of Chapter 2 to help us keep these relationships in mind. This method is clearer in some ways than the use of a Venn diagram, and it is certainly easier to put on paper. We shall use it later on in this book in the proofs of some needed facts about these operations.

As in Chapter 2, we first construct an elementary truth table. We suppose that we have a universal set U and two subsets of it, A and B. Let x be an arbitrary member of U. Then it can belong to (1) both A and B, (2) A and not B, (3) B and not A, or (4) neither A nor B. There are no other possibilities. We describe this situation in the elementary truth table, Table 1.

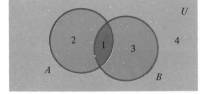

FIGURE 6.3b. (Repeat) The numbered regions correspond to lines in Table 1.

TABLE 1. Elementary Truth Table

Line	$x \varepsilon A$	$x \varepsilon B$
1	T	T
2	T	F
3	F	T
4	F	F

To relate this to the Venn diagrams, let us consider part (b) of Figure 6.3. The region labeled 1 in this figure corresponds to line 1 of the table. Similarly, the numbering of the other regions corresponds to the corresponding lines of the table. If we try to make the same correspondence with other parts of Figure 6.3, we find that some of the numbered regions are missing. As an example here is part (a) of Figure 6.3, where there is no region 1.

We can represent the intersection $A \cap B$ by adding a column to this table, as in Table 2.

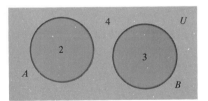

FIGURE 6.3a. (Repeat) There is no region 1.

INTERSECTION   TABLE 2. $A \cap B$

$x \varepsilon A$	$x \varepsilon B$	$x \varepsilon (A \cap B)$
T	T	T
T	F	F
F	T	F
F	F	F

We constructed the right-hand column of Table 2 from the definition of $A \cap B$. Note that the entries in this table are identical with those in the truth table for a conjunction (Table 2) of Chapter 2.

Similarly, we can represent the union $A \cup B$ by Table 3. Note that this table is equal to the table for a disjunction in Chapter 2, Table 4.

UNION TABLE 3. $A \cup B$

$x \varepsilon A$	$x \varepsilon B$	$x \varepsilon (A \cup B)$
T	T	T
T	F	T
F	T	T
F	F	F

6.5 Multiple Intersections and Unions

We can extend the concepts of intersection and union to collections of three or more subsets of the universal set U.

DEFINITIONS. Let A, B, and C be any subsets of U. Then

$A \cap B \cap C$ 1. The set $A \cap B \cap C$ contains just those elements which are elements of all of A, B, and C.

$A \cup B \cup C$ 2. The set $A \cup B \cup C$ contains those elements which belong to one or more of A, B, or C.

We can illustrate these concepts by the Venn diagrams of Figures 6.6 and 6.7.

The corresponding truth tables require eight lines. Table 4 is the one for $A \cap B \cap C$; the similar one for $A \cup B \cup C$ is proposed as a problem for you in the following frames.

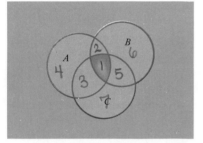

FIGURE 6.6. $A \cap B \cap C$ *is the dark colored region.*

TABLE 4. $A \cap B \cap C$

$x \varepsilon A$	$x \varepsilon B$	$x \varepsilon C$	$x \varepsilon (A \cap B \cap C)$
1. T	T	T	T
2. T	T	F	F
3. T	F	T	F
4. T	F	F	F
5. F	T	T	F
6. F	T	F	F
7. F	F	T	F
8. F	F	F	F

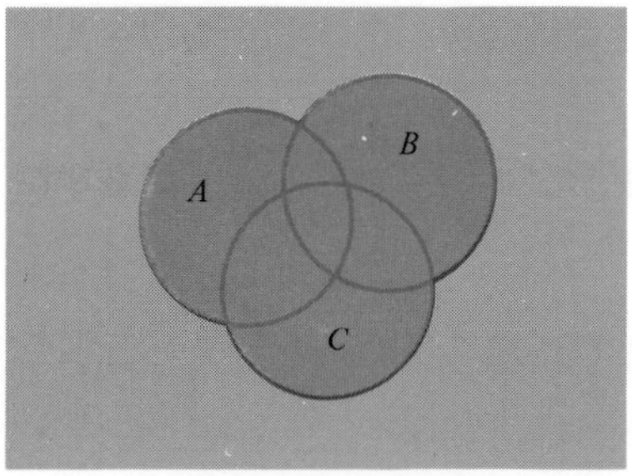

FIGURE 6.7. $A \cup B \cup C$ *is the dark colored region.*

6.6 Commutative Property of Intersections and Unions

When we were given two sets, A and B, we have written their intersection as $A \cap B$, but we could also have considered the intersection $B \cap A$. The question before us at this time is whether it is true that

$$A \cap B = B \cap A$$

Clearly the answer to this question is "yes", for each side of the above equality represents the set of elements common to both A and B.

If the plain English of the last sentence does not convince you that $A \cap B = B \cap A$, you may be convinced by examining the truth tables of Table 5.

TABLE 5. Proof that for all sets A and B: $A \cap B = B \cap A$

TABLE 5(a)

$x \, \varepsilon \, A$	$x \, \varepsilon \, B$	$x \, \varepsilon \, (A \cap B)$
T	T	T
T	F	F
F	T	F
F	F	F

TABLE 5(b)

$x \, \varepsilon \, B$	$x \, \varepsilon \, A$	$x \, \varepsilon \, (B \cap A)$
T	T	T
F	T	F
T	F	F
F	F	F

To form these tables, we fill in the first two columns of Table 5(a) to indicate all possible positions of x. From these we use the definition of intersection (Table 2) to fill in the third column of Table 5(a). In Table 5(b) we fill in the first two columns with precisely the same letters that we used for the columns with the same headings in Table 5(a). This amounts to interchanging these columns of Table 5(a), since sets A and B are now interchanged. Then using Table 2 with care we fill in the third column of Table 5(b).

Finally, we observe that the third columns of Tables 5(a) and 5(b) are identical. This tells us that in every situation the sets $A \cap B$ and $B \cap A$ have identical elements. This proves that for all sets A and B: $A \cap B = B \cap A$. Since the interchange of A and B does not affect the meaning of the set $A \cap B$, we say that set intersection is *commutative*, a word derived from "commute", one of whose meanings is "to exchange or interchange". Thus we have proved the following theorem:

COMMUTATIVE PROPERTY

Applies to addition and multiplication

union & intersection are commutative

THEOREM 1. For every pair of sets, A and B, $A \cap B = B \cap A$. That is, the operation of forming the intersection of two sets is *commutative*.

Similarly, we can consider unions of sets. We form Table 6, in which we have saved space by writing it as a single table rather than as the two tables of Table 5.

By means of the same argument used for intersections, we arrive at the following theorem:

121

TABLE 6. Commutativity of Unions

$x \varepsilon A$	$x \varepsilon B$	$x \varepsilon (A \cup B)$	$x \varepsilon (B \cup A)$
T	T	T	T
T	F	T	T
F	T	T	T
F	F	F	F

THEOREM 2. For every pair of sets, A and B, $A \cup B = B \cup A$. That is, the operation of forming the union of two sets is commutative.

A similar procedure shows that in a multiple intersection, such as $A \cap B \cap C$, we can change the order of the sets A, B, and C without changing the meaning of the expression. That is,

$$A \cap B \cap C = A \cap C \cap B$$
$$= B \cap A \cap C$$
$$= C \cap A \cap B$$

GENERALIZED COMMUTATIVE PROPERTY

and so on. These equalities are examples of the *generalized commutative property* of set intersection. Since set union behaves in the same fashion, we can state the following result:

THEOREM 3. *Generalized Commutative Properties.* The intersection of any finite number of sets, $A_1, \ldots, A_n$, that is, $A_1 \cap A_2 \cap \cdots \cap A_n$, is independent of the order in which these sets appear in this expression. The same conclusion holds true for the multiple union $A_1 \cup A_2 \cup \cdots \cup A_n$.

---

1. A Venn diagram is a pictorial representation of sets. The elements within a boundary belong to the set under consideration, and those outside the boundary do not. A truth table shows the same thing by means of a T (true) or F (false) response to the statement "These elements belong to this set". The table contains all possibilities for membership, while a Venn diagram may not.

Complete the truth table for the Venn diagram shown.

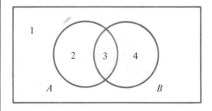

Region	$x \varepsilon A$	$x \varepsilon B$
1	F	F
2	T	F
3	T	T
4	F	T

122

Region	x ε A	x ε B
1	F	F
2	T	F
3	T	T
4	F	T

2. In frame 1 what region has no members if (a) A and B are disjoint? REGION 3 (b) $B \subset A$? REGION 4 .

(a) Region 3.   (b) Region 4.

3. Those elements for which the responses to "It belongs to set A" and "It belongs to set B" are both "true" belong to what set? A∩B, A∪B _____ Those elements for which at least one of the responses is "true" belong to what set? A∪B

$A \cap B$ and $A \cup B$. $A \cup B$.

4. Write the truth table for $A \cup B \cup C$. See Table 4.

x ε A	x ε B	x ε C	x ε (A ∪ B ∪ C)
T	T	T	T
T	T	F	T
T	F	T	T
T	F	F	T
F	T	T	T
F	T	F	T
F	F	T	T
F	F	F	F

x ε A	x ε B	x ε C	x ε (A ∪ B ∪ C)
T	T	T	T
T	T	F	T
T	F	T	T
T	F	F	T
F	T	T	T
F	T	F	T
F	F	T	T
F	F	F	F

5. Let

> U be the set of living creatures
>
> A be the set of worms
>
> B be the set of small creatures
>
> C be the set of green creatures

Then $A \cap B \cap C$ is the set of SMALL GREEN WORMS.

small, green worms

6. Using the sets in frame 5, $A \cup B \cup C$ is the set of creatures whose members are worms or small or green.

either worms, or small, or green

7. Interchanging the order in which the two questions "Does it belong to A?" and "Does it belong to B?" are asked produces the same truth table entries in $A \cap B$ and in $A \cup B$, and hence the two operations $\cap$ and $\cup$ are Commutative

commutative

8. To illustrate the commutativity of $\cap$, let us consider a set of data cards for the students at I.O. University. Suppose that there are 100 men and 100 women in each class—freshman, sophomore, junior, senior—800 students in all, and that each has one data card. If we wish to find the cards for all the sophomore women, we can have a sorter (human or electronic) examine each card, placing those for women in one pile and those for men in another. How many cards would be examined? 800

800.

9. We could then ask the sorter to examine all the women's cards, placing those for the sophomores in one pile and those for the other classes in another. How many cards would be examined? 400

400.

10. Had we made the separations in the other order, sophomore's cards first and then women's, how many would be examined in each operation? 800 by class and 200 by sex.

800   200

124

11. What elements of U are members of $(A \cap B) \cap C$? _Elements of U that are members of all A, B, & C._

> Those elements of U which are members of all of A, B, and C.

12. From frame 11 and Section 6.5, how can $(A \cap B) \cap C$ be expressed in a different fashion? $(A \cap B) \cap C = $ _A ∩ B ∩ C_

> $A \cap B \cap C$

13. What elements of U are members of $A \cap (B \cap C)$? _Elements of U that are members of all A, B, & C._

> Those elements of U which are members of all of A, B, and C.

14. From frames 12 and 13, what is the relation among the sets $(A \cap B) \cap C$, $A \cap (B \cap C)$, and $A \cap B \cap C$? _They are equal_

> They are equal.

15. What is the relation among the sets $(A \cup B) \cup C$, $A \cup (B \cup C)$, and $A \cup B \cup C$? _=_

> They are equal.

16. In the Venn diagram shown, indicate $A \cup B$ by shading the appropriate area.

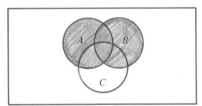

> Answer in frame 17.

$(A \cup B) \cup C$

17. The answer to frame 16 is shown. On it indicate $(A \cup B) \cup C$ by shading the appropriate area.

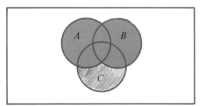

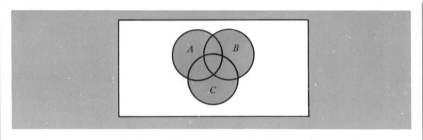

18. In two steps shade $A \cup (B \cup C)$ in the Venn diagram shown.

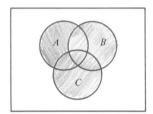

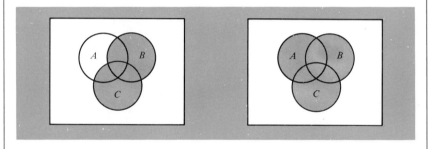

19. What relationship do the two Venn diagrams in frames 17 and 18 seem to indicate for this case? $(A \cup B) \cup C = A \cup (B \cup C)$

$(A \cup B) \cup C = A \cup (B \cup C)$.

20. Again, the Venn diagram involved in frames 16 to 18 is a special case. To include all possibilities complete the truth table.

$x \varepsilon A$	$x \varepsilon B$	$x \varepsilon C$	$x \varepsilon A \cup B$	$x \varepsilon (A \cup B) \cup C$	$x \varepsilon B \cup C$	$x \varepsilon A \cup (B \cup C)$
T	T	T	T	T	T	T
T	T	F	T	T	T	T
T	F	T	T	T	T	T
T	F	F	T	T	F	T
F	T	T	T	T	T	T
F	T	F	T	T	T	T
F	F	T	F	T	T	T
F	F	F	F	F	F	F

$x \varepsilon A$	$x \varepsilon B$	$x \varepsilon C$	$x \varepsilon A \cup B$	$x \varepsilon (A \cup B) \cup C$	$x \varepsilon B \cup C$	$x \varepsilon A \cup (B \cup C)$
T	T	T	T	T	T	T
T	T	F	T	T	T	T
T	F	T	T	T	T	T
T	F	F	T	T	F	T
F	T	T	T	T	T	T
F	T	F	T	T	T	T
F	F	T	F	T	T	T
F	F	F	F	F	F	F

21. Observe that the table includes all possibilities for the location of elements. By comparing the columns headed $x \varepsilon (A \cup B) \cup C$ and $x \varepsilon A \cup (B \cup C)$ we note that the entries are ___the same___ $(A \cup B) \cup C = A \cup (B \cup C)$ and hence conclude that, for all sets A, B, and C _____.

> identical or the same $\quad (A \cup B) \cup C = A \cup (B \cup C)$

6.7 Absolute Complement

We now turn to the third operation of this chapter, that of forming complements.

Previously (Section 6.2) we have encountered examples of two disjoint sets, A and B, whose union is the universal set. For example, let

$$U = \text{the set of natural numbers}$$

$$A = \text{the set of even numbers}$$

$$B = \text{the set of odd numbers.}$$

Then $A \cap B = \varnothing$ and $A \cup B = U$.

This suggests the idea of the absolute *complement* of a set (usually simply called *the* complement) whose definition is as follows:

ABSOLUTE COMPLEMENT

FIGURE 6.8. *A′ is the dark colored region.*

DEFINITION. The *absolute complement* of a set A contained in a universal set U is the set consisting of those elements of U that are *not* members of A. We write the complement of A as the set $\mathbf{A'}$.

In a Venn diagram A' is represented by the region in U outside the region represented by A (Figure 6.8). The truth table for A' is simply given by Table 7.

You will notice that $x \varepsilon A'$ and $x \not\varepsilon A$ have identical meanings. Thus the notion of the complement of a set is an application of our treatment of the *negation* of an open sentence in Chapter 2. It is, therefore, no coincidence that the truth tables for negation and complement have the same entries.

TABLE 7. Complement

$x \, \varepsilon \, A$	$x \, \varepsilon \, A'$
T	F
F	T

THEOREM 4. The complement of A', namely, $(A')'$, is A. This follows from the definition of complement, from the Venn diagram, Figure 6.8, or from the truth table, Table 8.

TABLE 8. $(A')' = A$

$x \, \varepsilon \, A$	$x \, \varepsilon \, A'$	$x \, \varepsilon \, (A')'$
T	F	T
F	T	F

EXAMPLES

1. Let $U = \{a, b, c, d, e, f, g\}$ and $A = \{a, c, e, g\}$. Then $A' = \{b, d, f\}$ and $(A')' = \{a, c, e, g\} = A$.

2. Let U be the set of undergraduates at your university, and

$$A = \{x | x \text{ is a sophomore}\}$$

Then

$$A' = \{x | x \text{ is a freshman, junior, or senior}\}$$

3. Let $A = \{x | p_x\}$. Then $A' = \{x | \text{ not } p_x\}$.
4. $\emptyset' = U$.
5. $U' = \emptyset$.

From this definition of complement, we can immediately see the truth of the following theorem:

THEOREM 5. For all A, $A \cap A' = \emptyset$ and $A \cup A' = U$.

6.8 Relative Complement

A related idea is that of *relative complement*. This, indeed, will be the foundation of our treatment of subtraction. Here we are given two sets A and B in U where $B \subseteq A$. Then we make the following definition:

DEFINITION. Given sets A and B in U where $B \subseteq A$. The *complement of B relative to A* is the set consisting of those elements of A that are *not* members of B. We write this as the set $A \setminus B$, read "A less B".

RELATIVE COMPLEMENT

FIGURE 6.9. *The relative complement $A \setminus B$ is the dark colored region.*

This definition of relative complement is illustrated by the Venn diagram in Figure 6.9. The corresponding truth table is given in Table 9. In this table

TABLE 9. Relative Complement, $A \setminus B$

$x \, \varepsilon \, A$	$x \, \varepsilon \, B$	$x \, \varepsilon \, (A \setminus B)$
T	T	F
T	F	T

we omit the lines where $x \, \varepsilon \, A$ is false, for we are only considering those x which are elements of A.

Three easy theorems can now be proved.

THEOREM 6. For all A and B where $B \subseteq A$,

$$B \cup (A \setminus B) = A \quad \text{and} \quad B \cap (A \setminus B) = \varnothing$$

The proof follows at once from Figure 6.9 or Table 9.

THEOREM 7. For all A and B where $B \subseteq A$,

$$A \setminus B = A \cap B'$$

To prove this, let us use the corresponding truth tables for $A \setminus B$ and $A \cup B'$ as shown in Table 10.

TABLE 10. Proof that $A \setminus B = A \cap B'$ when $B \subseteq A$

$x \, \varepsilon \, A$	$x \, \varepsilon \, B$	$x \, \varepsilon \, (A \setminus B)$	$x \, \varepsilon \, B'$	$x \, \varepsilon \, (A \cap B')$
T	T	F	F	F
T	F	T	T	T

As a special case let $A = U$. Then from Theorem 7 we conclude the following result:

THEOREM 8. For all B: $U \setminus B = B'$.

For $U \setminus B = U \cap B'$ from Theorem 7. But we have previously seen that $U \cap B' = B'$.

Thus we have two notations for the absolute complement of B: $U \setminus B$ and B'. We shall use whichever of these is most convenient for our purposes.

The fact that these operations of union and intersection are commutative raises the question: Is the operation of forming the relative complement $A \setminus B$ commutative? That is, is $A \setminus B = B \setminus A$ for all sets A and B? The answer is clearly "no", for $A \setminus B$ is defined only when $B \subseteq A$, and $B \setminus A$ is defined only when $A \subseteq B$. But $B \subseteq A$ and $A \subseteq B$ cannot both be true unless $A = B$. Therefore, $A \setminus B$ is not equal to $B \setminus A$ for *every* pair of sets A and B, and the operation of forming the relative complement is *not commutative*.

Union, Intersection, and Complement of Sets

1. In Sections 6.7 and 6.8 two kinds of derived sets are discussed: complements and relative complements. What is the symbol for the complement of the set A? _A'_

A'.

2. For the universal set $= \{0, 1, 2, 3, 4, 5, 6, 7, 8, 9\}$, if $A = \{0, 2, 4, 6\}$, what is A'? $\{1,3,5,7,8,9\}$

$\{1, 3, 5, 7, 8, 9\}$.

3. For the sets of frame 2 what is $A \cap A'$? _$\emptyset$_

$\emptyset$.

4. For the sets of frame 2 what is $A \cup A'$? $\{0,1,2,3,4,5,6,7,8,9\}$

$\{0, 1, 2, 3, 4, 5, 6, 7, 8, 9\}$.

5. The word "complement" is related to other English words. Note that it has nothing to do with compliments and is spelled differently. Can you complete another word that starts with the same letters? c o m p l e t e

Complete.

6. A set and its complement complete the _universal_ set.

universal

7. Symbolically, $A \cup$ _A'_ $= U$.

A'.

8. If $A = \{a \,(\text{shoes})|a \text{ is a right shoe}\}$, then $A' = \{a|a \text{ is } \underline{a \text{ left shoe}}\}$.

a left shoe

9. If U is the set of students enrolled in Psych 1 and C is the set of those students in Psych 1 who are passing, then C' is _the set of students in Psych 1 who are not passing_.

the set of students in Psych 1 who are not passing

10. Complete the truth table. Remember that if $x \varepsilon A$, $x \notin A'$.

$x \varepsilon A$	$x \varepsilon B$	$x \varepsilon (A \cup B)$	$x \varepsilon (A \cup B)'$	$x \varepsilon A'$	$x \varepsilon B'$	$x \varepsilon A' \cap B'$
T	T	T	F	F	F	F
T	F	T	F	F	T	F
F	T	T	F	T	F	F
F	F	F	T	T	T	T

$x \varepsilon A$	$x \varepsilon B$	$x \varepsilon (A \cup B)$	$x \varepsilon (A \cup B)'$	$x \varepsilon A'$	$x \varepsilon B'$	$x \varepsilon A' \cap B'$
T	T	T	F	F	F	F
T	F	T	F	F	T	F
F	T	T	F	T	F	F
F	F	F	T	T	T	T

11. Compare the columns headed $x \varepsilon (A \cup B)'$ and $x \varepsilon A' \cap B'$ in frame 10. What relationship has been shown? $(A \cup B)' = A' \cap B'$

$(A \cup B)' = A' \cap B'$ for all sets A and B.

12. On a separate sheet of paper make a truth table to prove for all sets A and B that $(A \cap B)' = A' \cup B'$.

$x \varepsilon A$	$x \varepsilon B$	$x \varepsilon (A \cap B)$	$x \varepsilon (A \cap B)'$	$x \varepsilon A'$	$x \varepsilon B'$	$x \varepsilon A' \cup B'$
T	T	T	F	F	F	F
T	F	F	T	F	T	T
F	T	F	T	T	F	T
F	F	F	T	T	T	T

13. In the text the complement of B relative to A is defined only on the condition that both are in the universal set and $B \subseteq A$.

$B \subseteq A$

14. If U is the set of all living persons, A is the set of all school teachers, and B is the set of all female school teachers, then $A \setminus B$ is set of all male school teachers.

the set of all male school teachers

15. If $A = B$, then $A \setminus B = \varnothing$.

$\varnothing$ (or the empty set)

16. If $B = \varnothing$, then $A \setminus B =$ ___A___.

A

17. In the Venn diagrams shade (a) B', (b) $A \cap B'$, (c) $A \setminus B$.

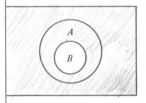 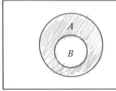 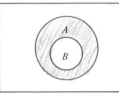

(a) (b) (c)

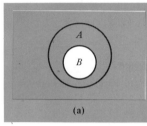 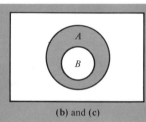

(a) (b) and (c)

18. If $U = \{a, b, c, d, e, f\}$, $A = \{a, c, e\}$, and $B = \{a\}$, $A' = \{$ ___b, d, f___ $\}$, $B' = \{$ ___b, c, d, e, f___ $\}$, $A \setminus B = \{$ ___c, e___, ___ $\}$.

$\{b, d, f\}$ $\{b, c, d, e, f\}$ $\{c, e\}$

19. On a separate sheet of paper make a truth table to show that $(B \cup A) \cap (B \cup A') = B$ for all sets A and B.

$x \,\varepsilon\, A$	$x \,\varepsilon\, B$	$x \,\varepsilon\, (B \cup A)$	$x \,\varepsilon\, A'$	$x \,\varepsilon\, (B \cup A')$	$x \,\varepsilon\, (B \cup A) \cap (B \cup A')$
T	T	T	F	T	T
T	F	T	F	F	F
F	T	T	T	T	T
F	F	F	T	T	F

20. On a separate sheet of paper make a truth table to show that $A' \cup (A \setminus B) = B'$ for all sets A and B for which $B \subseteq A$. (Note that since $B \subseteq A$ there are no elements in B that are not in A.)

$x \,\varepsilon\, A$	$x \,\varepsilon\, B$	$x \,\varepsilon\, A'$	$x \,\varepsilon\, A \setminus B$	$x \,\varepsilon\, A' \cup (A \setminus B)$	$x \,\varepsilon\, B'$
T	T	F	F	F	F
T	F	F	T	T	T
F	F	T	F	T	T

Post Test

In this chapter we have introduced the following concepts:

intersection, $A \cap B$
disjoint sets, $A \cap B = \varnothing$
union, $A \cup B$
multiple intersections and unions,

$$A \cap B \cap C = (A \cap B) \cap C = A \cap (B \cap C)$$

$$A \cup B \cup C = (A \cup B) \cup C = A \cup (B \cup C)$$

commutative property of intersection and union
absolute complement, A' or $U \setminus A$
relative complement, $A \setminus B$ when $B \subseteq A$

You should now review this chapter to be certain that you understand these ideas and can apply them in various situations. When your review is complete, test your knowledge of the chapter by working the following Post Test. Do not *refer to the text while working this test. Check your answers after you have completed the entire test.*

POST TEST

1. Find the intersections of the following sets : (a) The set of letters in "union" and the set of letters in "intersection". $\{i, o, n\}$ (b) $\{x, y, z\}$ and $\varnothing$. $\varnothing$

2. Are the sets $\{1, 2, 3\}$ and $\{x, y, z\}$ disjoint? yes

3. Use set-builder notation to write the intersection of the sets $\{x|x$ is high$\}$; $\{x|x$ is round$\}$. $\{x|x$ is high & round$\}$

4. Find the unions of the sets (a) $\{a, b, c\}$; U. U (b) $\{a, b, c\}$; $\varnothing$. a, b, c

5. Using set-builder notation write the union of the sets $\{x|p_x\}$; $\{x|q_x\}$. $\{x| p_x$ & $q_x\}$

6. Shade the region in the diagram which represents $A \cup B$.

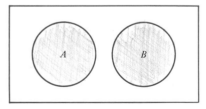

7. Write the truth table for $A \cap B$. Use a separate piece of paper. $\varnothing$

8. The statement that for all sets A and B, $A \cup B = B \cup A$ is called the commutative property of set union.

Union, Intersection, and Complement of Sets

9. The sets $A \cap B \cap C$ and $B \cap A \cap C$ are equal because each set contains just those elements that belong to __all__ of the sets A, B, and C.

10. Write a symbol for the shaded region in the diagram. $A \cap B \cap C$

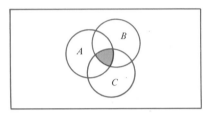

11. For

$$A = \{0, 1, 2, 5, 6, 7, 8, 9\}$$

$$B = \{0, 2, 4, 6, 8\}$$

$$C = \{0, 1, 2, 3, 4\}$$

(a) What is $A \cap (B \cup C)$? $\{0, 1, 2, 6, 8\}$ (b) What is $(A \cap B) \cup (A \cap C)$? $\{0, 1, 2, 6, 8\}$

12. In this drawing the colored region could be represented by which of the following symbols? (a) $U - A$. (b) $U \setminus A$. (c) A'. (d) $A \cap U$. (e) $A \setminus A'$. __b, c,__

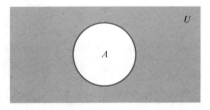

13. Let the universal set be the set of natural numbers that are multiples of 10. Let A be the subset of U consisting of all the even numbers in U. Then the complement of A is __∅__.

14. If $Y \subseteq Z'$, which of these statements are true: (a), (b), or both or neither? (a) $Z \subseteq Y'$. (b) $Y \cap Z = \emptyset$. __a, b__

15. If X represents the set of undergraduates at Exodus College and S represents the set of freshmen and sophomores there, what are the elements of $X \setminus S$? __set of junior & seniors__

16. For all sets A and B, where $B \subseteq A$, $B \cup (A \setminus B) =$ __A__.

17. Under what condition(s) is the notation $A \setminus B$ meaningless? __$B \not\subseteq A$__

18. If $R \subseteq S$, then $(S \setminus R) \cap R =$ __∅__.

134

1. (a) {i, o, n}. (b) ∅.
2. Yes.
3. $\{x|x$ is high and round$\}$.
4. (a) U. (b) $\{a, b, c\}$.
5. $\{x|p_x$ or $q_x\}$.
6.

7.

$x \, \varepsilon \, A$	$x \, \varepsilon \, B$	$x \, \varepsilon \, (A \cap B)$
T	T	T
T	F	F
F	T	F
F	F	F

8. Commutative
9. All
10. $A \cap B \cap C$.
11. Each is equal to $\{0, 1, 2, 6, 8\}$.
12. (b) and (c).
13. ∅ (The set of odd multiples of 10 is empty.)
14. Both are true.
15. The juniors and seniors at Exodus College.
16. A
17. If $B \nsubseteq A$.
18. ∅

If you made mistakes on the Post Test, reread the relevant parts of Chapter 6 until you are sure of the correct answers. Then go to the beginning of Chapter 7.

Chapter 7 discusses Cartesian products of sets. You should be familiar with the basic material on sets covered in Chapters 3, 4, and 6. Here is a short test that will enable you to determine whether you are prepared to study Chapter 7.

READINESS TEST

This diagram applies to the first four questions.

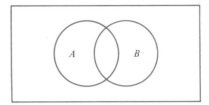

1. In this Venn diagram shade the region corresponding to $A \cap B$.

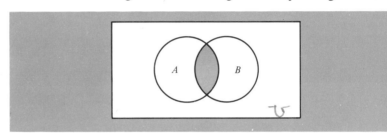

2. The interior of the rectangle corresponds to set U, the _universal_ _____ set.

universal

3. $A \subset U$ and $B \subset U$, so we say each is a ___subset___ of U.

subset (or proper subset)

4. Complete the truth table.

$x \, \varepsilon \, A$	$x \, \varepsilon \, B$	$x \, \varepsilon \, A \cup B$
T	T	T
T	F	T
F	T	T
F	F	F

$x \varepsilon A$	$x \varepsilon B$	$x \varepsilon A \cup B$
T	T	T
T	F	T
F	T	T
F	F	F

5. If sets P and Q are disjoint, then $P \cap Q = $ _____ .

$\emptyset$ (or the empty set)

6. True or false: "If $R = \{a, b, c\}$ and $S = (1, 2, 3\}$, then $R = S$".

F.

7. For all sets A and B, $A \cup B$, $= B \cup A$. This is known as the _commutative_ property of set union.

commutative

8. For *all* sets A, $A \cup \emptyset = $ _A_ .

A

9. The statement $A \sim B$ means that there is a _one to one_

one-to-one correspondence

10. If $A \sim B$, then A and B are said to be _equivalent_.

equivalent

11. If $B = \{5\}$ and $A \subseteq B$, then what set or sets may A equal? _B_

$A = B$ or $\emptyset$.

12. If $S = \{3\}$ and $R \subset S$, then what set or sets may R equal? _$\emptyset$_

$R = \emptyset$.

If you missed any of these questions, review Chapters 3, 4, and 6 until you see your errors and understand how the correct answer was arrived at. Having done this, or if all your answers were correct, read Sections 7.1 through 7.4.

7.1 Introduction

As background for our discussion of binary operations (Chapter 8) and our treatment of the multiplication of whole numbers (Chapter 11) we must introduce one last idea from set theory. This is the *Cartesian product, A × B,* of two sets, *A* and *B*. In order to define such a product of two sets, we must introduce the concept of an *ordered pair*.

7.2 Ordered Pairs

ORDERED PAIRS

To define an ordered pair we choose two elements of the universal set, *a* and *b*, which may be distinct or equal. Then we write the symbol (*a, b*), which we call an ordered pair. By "ordered" we mean that *a* is the first element of the pair and that *b* is the second element. Thus we distinguish the ordered pair (*a, b*) from the ordered pair (*b, a*) unless *a = b*.

You are probably familiar with such ordered pairs, for ordered pairs (*x, y*), where *x* and *y* are real numbers, are commonly used to represent the coordinates of a point in the plane (Figure 7.1).

As additional examples of ordered pairs, we can write (3, 4), (4, 3), (5, 5), (Mary, John), and (chemistry, physics).

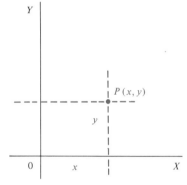

FIGURE 7.1. *Cartesian coordinate system.*

REMARKS

1. You must not confuse the *ordered pair* (*a, b*) with the set {*a, b*}. For in (*a, b*) the order is essential, and moreover *a* can be equal to *b*. But in {*a, b*} the order is immaterial and *a* and *b* are understood to be distinct.

2. We shall say that two ordered pairs, (*a, b*) and (*c, d*) are equal if and only if *a = c* and *b = d*. Thus (3, 4) ≠ (4, 3), but $(2^2, 3^2) = (4, 9)$.

3. We can consider sets whose elements are ordered pairs. As an example, we can write

$$\{(2, 4), (6, 3), (4, 2), (1, 1)\}$$

7.3 Cartesian Products

Suppose that we have two sets,

$$A = \{a, b, c\} \quad \text{and} \quad B = \{p, q\}$$

We shall now define the *Cartesian product, A × B,* as a set whose elements are ordered pairs. According to the definition each element of the set *A × B* is an ordered pair whose first element is a member of *A* and whose second element is a member of *B*. Indeed, every ordered pair that can be formed in this way is an element of the set *A × B*. Thus, for the example above,

$$A \times B = \{(a, p), (b, p), (c, p), (a, q), (b, q), (c, q)\}$$

For convenience in keeping things straight we shall frequently represent the set *A × B* by the array

$A \times B$

	a	*b*	*c*
p	(a, p)	(b, p)	(c, p)
q	(a, q)	(b, q)	(c, q)

In this array we write the elements of the first factor, A, horizontally and those of the second factor, B, vertically. Then we fill in the rectangle with the corresponding ordered pairs.

The general definition of a Cartesian Product is as follows:

CARTESIAN PRODUCT

DEFINITION. The *Cartesian product*, $A \times B$, of two sets, A and B, is the set whose elements are all possible ordered pairs of the form (a, b), where $a \, \varepsilon \, A$ and $b \, \varepsilon \, B$.

In this definition, we put no conditions on A and B. They may have elements in common or may indeed be identical. Either or both sets may be empty.

Examples of Cartesian products are not uncommon in daily life. Let A be the set of girls {Jane, Mary, Sue} and B the set of boys {John, Richard, Edward}. Then $A \times B$ can represent the set of all possible dates that can be arranged among these two sets of young people.

$A \times B$

	Jane	*Mary*	*Sue*
John	(Jane, John)	(Mary, John)	(Sue, John)
Richard	(Jane, Richard)	(Mary, Richard)	(Sue, Richard)
Edward	(Jane, Edward)	(Mary, Edward)	(Sue, Edward)

REMARK

It should be observed that the Cartesian product differs from set intersection, union, and complementation in one important aspect. If A and B are subsets of a universal set U, then $A \cap B$, $A \cup B$, A', and $A \setminus B$ (when it is defined) are subsets of U. The Cartesian product $A \times B$, however, is not necessarily a subset of U. For this reason we cannot draw a Venn diagram to illustrate $A \times B$.

cross

7.4 Special Cases of Cartesian Products

There are some important special cases of Cartesian products.

(1) $A \times \emptyset$ and $\emptyset \times B$. When we try to put $A \times \emptyset$ in the rectangular form, we are in trouble. Let $A = \{a_1, a_2, \ldots, a_n\}$. Then we have the following array:

7.4 Special Cases of Cartesian Products

$A \times \emptyset = \emptyset$

	a_1	a_2 $\cdots$ a_n
$\emptyset$	$(a_1, ?)$	$(a_2, ?) \cdots (a_n, ?)$

We can list the elements of A along the horizontal axis as before, but what can we do about the elements of $\emptyset$ on the vertical axis? There just aren't any. In fact, there is no way of writing an ordered pair $(a, ?)$ with an element of A as the first element and an element of $\emptyset$ as the second element. The inescapable conclusion is that there are no such ordered pairs. Hence

$A \times \emptyset = \emptyset$

$$\text{For all } A : A \times \emptyset = \emptyset.$$

A similar proof shows that

$$\text{For all } B : \emptyset \times B = \emptyset.$$

(2) $A \times B$, where $B = \{b\}$. This is the special case where B contains only a single element. Let A have elements $a_1, a_2, \ldots, a_n$.

$A \times B$

	a_1	a_2 $\cdots$ a_n
b	(a_1, b)	$(a_2, b) \cdots (a_n, b)$

The rectangle has reduced to a single row.

---

1. The adjective "Cartesian" comes from the name of a philosopher and mathematician, René Decartes, who lived 1596–1650. He invented the coordinate system described in the text for graphing points in a plane. You probably remember enough about graphing from high school algebra to know that the point whose coordinates are (3, 2) is not the point whose coordinates are (2, 3). The order of the coordinates is important. Ordinary two-digit numbers are ordered pairs of digits. Is 42 the same as 24? ___No___

No.

2. Fractions are also ordered pairs of numbers. Give an example of a fraction in which the order of the terms makes a difference. ___3/4___

Any fraction in which the numerator and denominator are different is an example.

141

3. The ordered pair (x, y) equals the ordered pair $(3, 5)$ if and only if $x = 3, y = 5$.

> $x = 3$ and $y = 5$

4. Which of the following is equal to $(4, 5)$? $(5, 4)$. _No_
(yes, no)
$(\sqrt{16}, \sqrt{25})$. _Yes_ $\{4, 5\}$. _No_ — *Is a set.*
(yes, no)   (yes, no)

> No.   Yes.   No.

5. Now let's see if we have understood the concept of Cartesian product. If $A = \{MG, FIAT, XKE\}$ and $B = \{see, drive\}$, then $A \times B =$ *{(MG, see), (FIAT, see), (XKE, see), (MG, drive), (FIAT drive) (XKE, drive*

> $\begin{Bmatrix} (MG, see) & (FIAT, see) & (XKE, see) \\ (MG, drive) & (FIAT, drive) & (XKE, drive) \end{Bmatrix}$

6. If $A = \{chocolate, pecan, strawberry\}$ and $B = \{dish, cone, sundae\}$, then $A \times B$ has _9_ elements?
(how many)

> 9

7. In frames 7 through 11 let $A = \{\rightarrow, *, \varepsilon\}$ and $B = \{\Sigma, 0, ?\}$. Is $(*, ?)$ an element of $A \times B$? _Yes_

> Yes.

8. With the same sets A and B, is $(\Sigma, *)$ an element of $A \times B$? _No_

> No.   *WRONG ORDER*

9. To what Cartesian product does $(\Sigma, *)$ belong? *B $\times$ A*

> $B \times A$.

10. Is $(\rightarrow, \rightarrow)$ an element of $A \times B$? _No_

> No.

11. What Cartesian product contains $(\rightarrow, \rightarrow)$? *A $\times$ A*

> $A \times A$.

12. Under what conditions does $S \times T$ contain a single element? *If they are both singleton.*

If S and T are both singletons.

13. The text proved that $A \times \varnothing = \varnothing$. Now try your hand at proving that, for all A, $\varnothing \times A = \varnothing$. *A cannot be crossed with $\varnothing$ because there is not a one-to-one correspondence.*

$\varnothing \times A$ consists by definition of ordered pairs with first element a member of $\varnothing$. But $\varnothing$ has no members. Hence no such ordered pairs can be found and $\varnothing \times A$ has no members. Hence $\varnothing \times A = \varnothing$.

$\varnothing \times \varnothing = \varnothing$

14. Now try to prove $\varnothing \times \varnothing = \varnothing$. Use, if you can, the facts that have just been proved. *$A \times \varnothing = \varnothing$, therefore $\varnothing \times \varnothing = \varnothing$*

It has been proved that $A \times \varnothing = \varnothing$ for all A. This includes the case where $A = \varnothing$. Hence $\varnothing \times \varnothing = \varnothing$.

Now return to the text and read carefully Section 7.5. When you have finished, continue with the excerises following Section 7.5.

7.5 Properties of the Cartesian Product

At this point it is reasonable to ask: Is the Cartesian product commutative? To answer this question, take as an example $A = \{a_1, a_2, a_3\}$ and $B = \{b_1, b_2\}$, where A and B are *disjoint*. Then we have

A × B

	a_1	a_2	a_3
b_1	(a_1, b_1)	(a_2, b_1)	(a_3, b_1)
b_2	(a_1, b_2)	(a_2, b_2)	(a_3, b_2)

and

B × A

	b_1	b_2
a_1	(b_1, a_1)	(b_2, a_1)
a_2	(b_1, a_2)	(b_2, a_2)
a_3	(b_1, a_3)	(b_2, a_3)

Are these sets $A \times B$ and $B \times A$ equal? If they are, each must contain exactly the same elements as the other. Let us check one. In $A \times B$, we find the element (a_1, b_1). Is this an element of $B \times A$? We might be tempted to say "yes", for (b_1, a_1) is an element of $B \times A$, but the answer is really "no" for the *ordered* pair (a_1, b_1) is quite different from the ordered pair (b_1, a_1). By examining the other elements of $B \times A$ in turn, we see that (a_1, b_1) is not the equal to any of them because of our assumption that A and B are disjoint. Hence we conclude that in this case $A \times B \neq B \times A$.

This is, indeed, a special case, but it is sufficient to prove that the Cartesian product $A \times B$ is not commutative. For, the assertion that $A \times B$ is commutative means that $A \times B = B \times A$ for all A and B. Since we have one example where this is false, the operation is not commutative. Hence we have the following theorem:

$A \times B \neq B \times A$ **THEOREM 1.** The operation of forming the Cartesian product $A \otimes B$ is _not_ commutative.

To make this doubly clear let us again consider the sets

$$A = \{\text{Jane, Mary, Sue}\}$$

$$B = \{\text{John, Richard, Edward}\}$$

Suppose that we are interested in the set of possible dates on which the boy invites the girl. In our ordered pairs, we shall write the guest first and the host second. Then the appropriate set of dates is

$$A \text{ (guest)} \times B \text{ (host)}$$

This gives the set we illustrated earlier.

Now suppose that it is leap year and the girls invite the boys. We continue to write the guest first and the host second. Then the set of dates is

$$B \text{ (guest)} \times A \text{ (host)}$$

Are these the same sets? They certainly contain the same unordered pairs, but if finances are taken into account (as they are on these dates) they are surely very different.

Although the Cartesian product is not commutative, the relation of the equivalence of sets is more general than that of set equality, and it might be true that $(A \times B) \sim (B \times A)$. To examine this possibility let us start with an example. Suppose that

$$A = \{a, b, c\} \qquad B = \{x, y\}$$

then

$$A \times B = \left\{ \begin{array}{l} (a, x), (b, x), (c, x) \\ (a, y), (b, y), (c, y) \end{array} \right\}$$

On the other hand,

$$B \times A = \begin{cases} (x, a), (y, a) \\ (x, b), (y, b) \\ (x, c), (y, c) \end{cases}$$

Can we construct a one-to-one correspondence between these two sets? *yes* We see immediately that each element in $A \times B$ has a "natural" counterpart in $B \times A$, the pair written in reverse order. So the one-to-one correspondence we desire is

$$\begin{array}{cccccc} \{(a, x) & (b, x) & (c, x) & (a, y) & (b, y) & (c, y)\} \\ \updownarrow & \updownarrow & \updownarrow & \updownarrow & \updownarrow & \updownarrow \\ \{(x, a) & (x, b) & (x, c) & (y, a) & (y, b) & (y, c)\} \end{array}$$

Since such a correspondence always exists, we formalize this as a theorem:

$A \times B \sim B \times A$

THEOREM 2. If A and B are any two sets, then $(A \times B) \sim (B \times A)$.

Proof. First suppose that neither A nor B is empty. We must construct a one-to-one correspondence between $A \times B$ and $B \times A$. Our example suggests that to each pair (a, b) in $A \times B$ we should associate the pair (b, a) in $B \times A$. So we define the correspondence to be

$$S : (a, b) \leftrightarrow (b, a)$$

It is evident from its definition that this correspondence is one-to-one.

Then consider $A \times \emptyset = \emptyset \times A$. Since both of these sets are equal to $\emptyset$, $(A \times \emptyset) \sim (\emptyset \times A)$.

Finally, we would like to look at a special case of particular interest in later developments. Suppose A is any nonempty set, and let B be a set consisting of a single element. What can we say about $A \times B$? As always, we start by considering an example: If

$$A = \{a, b, c, d, e\} \qquad \text{and} \qquad B = \{x\}$$

then

$$A \times B = \{(a, x), (b, x), (c, x), (d, x), (e, x)\}$$

We see immediately that $(A \times B) \sim A$, by virtue of the one-to-one correspondence

$$\begin{array}{cccccc} \{(a, x) & (b, x) & (c, x) & (d, x) & (e, x)\} \\ \updownarrow & \updownarrow & \updownarrow & \updownarrow & \updownarrow \\ \{ a & b & c & d & e \} \end{array}$$

This suggests the following theorem:

$A \times \{x\} \sim A$

THEOREM 3. If A is any set, and B is any set containing a single element (say $B = \{x\}$), then
{mice, dogs} (rabbits, dogs)
$$\{mice, dogs\} (rabbits, dogs)$$
$$(A \times B) \sim A$$

one-to-one correspondence is established, because
ordered pair is considered one unit.

Proof. First, suppose that A is nonempty. Then, since $B = \{x\}$, we have

$$A \times B = \{(a, x) | a \; \varepsilon \; A\}$$

Thus two pairs in $A \times B$ are different if and only if their left-hand entries are different. To establish a one-to-one correspondence, S, between $A \times B$ and A, then, we need only match the pair $(a, x) \; \varepsilon \; A \times B$ with the element $a \; \varepsilon \; A$. That is, we choose the correspondence

$$S : (a, x) \longleftrightarrow a$$

Therefore, in this case $(A \times B) \sim A$.

On the other hand, if $A = \varnothing$, we have proved that $\varnothing \times B = \varnothing$. Hence in this case $A \times B = A$ and so $(A \times B) \sim A$.

---

1. If $R = \{1, 2, 3\}$ and $S = \{10, 20, 30\}$, then $R \times S = \{(1, 10), (1, 20), (1, 30), (2, 10), (2, 20), (2, 30), (3, 10), (3, 20), (3, 30)\}$ and $S \times R =$ {(10, 1), (10, 2), (10, 3), (20, 1), (20, 2), (20, 3), (30, 1), (30, 2), (30, 3)}

$\{(10, 1), (10, 2), (10, 3), (20, 1), (20, 2), (20, 3), (30, 1), (30, 2), (30, 3)\}$

2. Is $R \times S = S \times R$ in this case? **No**

No.

3. If $F = \{$Earl, Truman, Alexander$\}$ and $G = \{$Boyd, Brewster, Frank$\}$, is $F \times G = G \times F$? **No**

No.

4. If $F = \{$Earl, Alexander, Brewster$\}$ and $G = \{$Alexander, Brewster, Earl$\}$, is $F \times G = G \times F$? **Yes**

Yes.

5. Then, in general, $A \times B \neq B \times A$ and the operation of forming the Cartesian product is not **commutative**

commutative

6. Are the sets in frame 3 equivalent? **Yes**

Yes.

7. Are the sets in frame 4 equivalent? **Yes**

Yes.

8. For all A and B is $A \times B$ equivalent to $B \times A$? _Yes_

> Yes.

9. To prove the correctness of your response to frame 8, you must set up a one-to-one correspondence between $A \times B$ and $B \times A$. If neither A nor B is empty, what element of $B \times A$ is matched with the element (a_i, b_j) of $A \times B$? _(b_j, a_i)_

> (b_j, a_i).

10. $A \times B = B \times A$ if $A = B$, for $A \times A$ must equal $A \times A$. Is it true that $A \times B = B \times A$ implies that $A = B$? (Be careful: Consider $B = \varnothing$). _No_

> No. Although $A \times \varnothing = \varnothing \times A$, A need not be equal to $\varnothing$.

11. If $A \neq \varnothing$ and $B \neq \varnothing$ and $A \times B = B \times A$, does $A = B$? _Yes_

> Yes.

A comment on frame 11: To see that if $A \neq \varnothing$ and $B \neq \varnothing$, then $A \times B = B \times A$ implies $A = B$, consider the set of first elements of the ordered pairs which compose $A \times B$ and the set of first elements of the ordered pairs which compose $B \times A$. Since $A \times B$ and $B \times A$ are identical, these sets of first elements are identical. But by definition of $A \times B$ and $B \times A$, one of these sets of first elements is A and the other is B. Hence $A = B$.

12. We have seen that if A and B are nonempty sets, then $A \times B = B \times A$ implies $A = B$. Can we go further and say that if A, B, C, and D are all nonempty sets and $A \times B = C \times D$, then $A = C$ and $B = D$? _Yes_

> Yes.

The reasoning given for frame 11 will apply equally well for the set of "second elements".

13. If X, Y, R, and S are all nonempty and $X \times Y = R \times S$, then _$X = R$, $Y = S$_.

> $X = R$ and $Y = S$

7.6 Multiple Cartesian Products

If we begin with three sets A, B, and C, there are three types of multiple Cartesian products that can be formed: (1) $A \times B \times C$, (2) $(A \times B) \times C$, and (3) $A \times (B \times C)$. Let us examine these in turn.

(1) In order to discuss $A \times B \times C$, we must first generalize the notion of an ordered pair (a, b) to that of an ordered triple (a, b, c). Two ordered triples (a, b, c) and (x, y, z) are *equal* if and only if $a = x$, $b = y$, and $c = z$. Then $A \times B \times C$ is defined as follows:

$A \times B \times C$

DEFINITION. $A \times B \times C$ is the set of all ordered triples (a, b, c), where $a \, \varepsilon \, A$, $b \, \varepsilon \, B$, and $c \, \varepsilon \, C$.

In this product, the order in which A, B, and C are written is important, for as in the case of $A \times B$ we can show that in general $A \times B \times C \neq B \times A \times C \neq C \times B \times A$, and so on. That is, *the generalized commutative property is not true.*

On the other hand, our proof in the case of two sets can be generalized to establish the result:

$(A \times B) \times C$

THEOREM 4. For all sets A, B, and C,

$$A \times B \times C \sim B \times A \times C \sim C \times B \times A, \ldots$$

(2) In order to discuss the product $(A \times B) \times C$, let us consider the special case where

$$A = \{a_1, a_2, a_3\}$$
$$B = \{b_1, b_2\}$$
$$C = \{c_1, c_2\}$$

We have seen that $A \times B$ can be written

$$A \times B = \{(a_1, b_1), (a_2, b_1), (a_3, b_1), (a_1, b_2), (a_2, b_2), (a_3, b_2)\}$$

Now we must form $(A \times B) \times C$. The elements of this set are new ordered pairs, where the first element is already an ordered pair of the form (a_i, b_j) and whose second element is either c_1 or c_2. Thus a typical element of $(A \times B) \times C$ is

$$((a_3, b_1), c_2)$$

Continuing in this way we find that

$$\begin{aligned}
(A \times B) \times C = \{ &((a_1, b_1), c_1), ((a_2, b_1), c_1), ((a_3, b_1), c_1), \\
&((a_1, b_2), c_1), ((a_2, b_2), c_1), ((a_3, b_2), c_1), \\
&((a_1, b_1), c_2), ((a_2, b_1), c_2), ((a_3, b_1), c_2), \\
&((a_1, b_2), c_2), ((a_2, b_2), c_2), ((a_3, b_2), c_2)\}
\end{aligned}$$

148

Thus, in general, an element of $(A \times B) \times C$ is an ordered pair of the form $((a, b), c)$ whose first element is itself an ordered pair of the form (a, b).

It is immediately clear that (if A, B, and C are nonempty) $A \times B \times C \neq (A \times B) \times C$; for the elements of $A \times B \times C$ are ordered *triples* of the form (a, b, c), whereas the elements of $(A \times B) \times C$ are ordered *pairs* of the form $((a, b), c)$. On the other hand, the following theorem is true:

THEOREM 5. For all sets A, B, and C,

$$A \times B \times C \sim (A \times B) \times C$$

Proof. To prove this theorem we must establish a one-to-one correspondence between the two given sets. Let

$$A = \{a_1, a_2, \ldots, a_r\}$$
$$B = \{b_1, b_2, \ldots, b_s\}$$
$$C = \{c_1, c_2, \ldots, c_t\}$$

Then a typical element of $A \times B \times C$ is (a_i, b_j, c_k), where a_i, b_j, and c_k are arbitrary members of A, B, and C, respectively. Similarly, a typical element of $(A \times B) \times C$ is $((a_i, b_j), c_k)$.

A one-to-one correspondence between $A \times B \times C$ and $(A \times B) \times C$ is then established by the pairing

$$S : (a_i, b_j, c_k) \leftrightarrow ((a_i, b_j), c_k)$$

for all possible subscripts i, j, and k.

$A \times (B \times C)$ (3) The treatment of $A \times (B \times C)$ is quite similar. In the special case where

$$A = \{a_1, a_2, a_3\}$$
$$B = \{b_1, b_2\}$$
$$C = \{c_1, c_2\}$$

we find that

$$
\begin{aligned}
A \times (B \times C) = \{ &(a_1, (b_1, c_1)), (a_1, (b_1, c_2)), (a_1, (b_2, c_1)), \\
&(a_1, (b_2, c_2)), (a_2, (b_1, c_1)), (a_2, (b_1, c_2)), \\
&(a_2, (b_2, c_1)), (a_2, (b_2, c_2)), (a_3, (b_1, c_1)), \\
&(a_3, (b_1, c_2)), (a_3, (b_2, c_1)), (a_3, (b_2, c_2)) \}
\end{aligned}
$$

So, in general, an element of $A \times (B \times C)$ is an ordered pair of the form $(a, (b, c))$ whose second element is itself an ordered pair of the form (b, c). Thus we see that the sets $A \times B \times C$, $(A \times B) \times C$, and $A \times (B \times C)$ have quite different natures and so are unequal unless they are empty. As in the previous argument, however, we can show that they are all *equivalent*. An important special case, which we shall need for the next chapter, is stated in our final theorem.

THEOREM 6. For any nonempty sets *A*, *B*, and *C* it is false that

$$(A \times B) \times C = A \times (B \times C)$$

but it is true that

$$(A \times B) \times C \sim A \times (B \times C)$$

$(A \times B) \times C \sim A \times (B \times C)$

If any of *A*, *B*, or *C* is empty, $(A \times B) \times C$ and $A \times (B \times C)$ are equal as well as equivalent, for each is the empty set.

---

1. Let us look at an example to illustrate multiple Cartesian products. If

$$A = \{Jim, Joe\}$$
$$B = \{May, June\}$$
$$C = \{Black, White\}$$

then $A \times B =$ {(Jim, May), (Jim, June), (Joe, May), (Joe, June)}

{(Jim, May), (Jim, June), (Joe, May), (Joe, June)}

2. Let *A*, *B*, and *C* be as in frame 1. Then $(A \times B) \times C =$ {((Jim, May), Black); ((Jim, May), White); ((Jim, June), Black); ((Jim, June), White); ((Joe, May), Black); ((Joe, May), White); ((Joe, June), Black; (Joe, June), white.

((Joe, May), Black)   ((Joe, May), White)   ((Joe, June), Black)
((Joe, June), White)

3. Let *A*, *B*, and *C* be as in frame 1. Then $B \times C =$ {(May, Black); (May, White); (June, Black); (June, White)}.

(May, Black)   (May, White)   (June, Black)   (June, White)

4. Let *A*, *B*, and *C* be as in frame 1. Then $A \times (B \times C) =$ {(Jim, (May, Black)); (Jim, (May, White)); (Jim, (June, Black)); (Jim, (June, White)); (Joe, (May, Black)); (Joe, (May, White)); (Joe, (June, Black)); (Joe, (June, White)}.

(Jim, (June, Black))   (Jim, (June, White))   (Joe, (May, Black))
(Joe, (May, White))   (Joe, (June, Black))   (Joe, (June, White))

5. Is the set $(A \times B) \times C$ in frame 2 equal to the set $A \times (B \times C)$ in frame 4? No

No.

150

6. Since we have at least one example where $(A \times B) \times C \neq A \times (B \times C)$, what is the truth value of the proposition "For all sets, A, B, and C, $(A \times B) \times C = A \times (B \times C)$"? _F_

F.

7. Is the set $(A \times B) \times C$ in frame 2 equivalent to the set $A \times (B \times C)$ in frame 4? _Yes_

Yes.

8. For all A, B, and C is $(A \times B) \times C$ equivalent to $A \times (B \times C)$? _Yes_

Yes.

9. To prove the correctness of your response to frame 8 suppose that none of A, B, and C is empty. You must then set up a one-to-one correspondence between $(A \times B) \times C$ and $A \times (B \times C)$. A typical element of $(A \times B) \times C$ is $[(a_i, b_j), c_k]$. A typical element of $A \times (B \times C)$ is $[a_i, (b_j, c_k)]$. To establish the required correspondence we match $[(a_i, b_j), c_k]$ with _$[a_i, (b_j, c_k)]$_

$[a_i, (b_j, c_k)]$

10. If one or more of A, B, and C is $\varnothing$, then $(A \times B) \times C =$ _$\varnothing$_ and $A \times (B \times C) =$ _$\varnothing$_. Since _$\varnothing$_ is equivalent to _$\varnothing$_, it follows that in this case $(A \times B) \times C$ is equivalent to _$A \times (B \times C)$_. This completes the proof of Theorem 6.

$\varnothing$ $\varnothing$ $\varnothing$ $\varnothing$ $A \times (B \times C)$

In this chapter we have introduced the following concepts:

ordered pair
ordered triple
Cartesian product of two sets
multiple Cartesian product

The notation "$\otimes$" is used for the Cartesian product.
It was shown that the following statements are false:

For all sets A and B: $A \times B = B \times A$.
For all sets A, B, and C: $A \times B \times C = (A \times B) \times C = A \times (B \times C)$.

However, it was shown that the following statements are true:

For all sets A and B: $A \times B \sim B \times A$.
For all sets A, B, and C: $A \times B \times C \sim (A \times B) \times C \sim A \times (B \times C)$.

You may wish to review some of the material. Then proceed to answer the following questions as well as you can.

POST TEST

The following information applies to questions 1 and 2:

$$A = \{a_1, a_2\} \text{ and } B = \{b_1, b_2\}$$

Consider the list $(a_1, b_1), (a_2, b_1), (b_1, b_2), (a_2, b_2)$.

1. At least one of the ordered pairs in the list is not an element of $A \times B$. Which? *(b, b₂)*

2. Give any elements of $A \times B$ not shown in the list of ordered pairs. *(a, b₂)*

3. True or false: For all sets A and B; $A \times B = B \times A$. *F*

4. True or false: For all sets A and B; $A \times B \sim B \times A$. *T*

5. True or false. For all sets A, B, and C; $A \times (B \times C) = (A \times B) \times C$. *F*

6. True or false: For all sets A, B, and C; $A \times (B \times C) \sim (A \times B) \times C$. *T*

7. If $A = \{1, 2, 3, 4, 5\}$ and $B = \{b\}$, then $A \times B = \{$ *(1, b)(2, b)(3, b) (4, b)(5, b)* $\}$.

8. If the ordered pair $(r, s) = (1, 0)$, then $r = $ *1* and $s = $ *0*.

9. If $(3, 4)$ is an element of $(A \times B)$, then 3 is an element of *A*.

10. A simpler way of writing the set $\emptyset \times A$ is *∅*.

11. True or false: For all sets A, B, and C: $A \cap B \cap C = A \cap C \cap B$. *T*

12. True or false: For all sets A, B, and C: $A \times B \times C = A \times C \times B$. *F*

---

1. (b_1, b_2).
2. (a_1, b_2).
3. F.
4. T.
5. F.
6. T.
7. $\{(1, b), (2, b), (3, b), (4, b), (5, b)\}$
8. 1, 0
9. A
10. $\emptyset$
11. T.
12. F.

This concludes Part I of this book. Before proceeding to Part II use the following Summary Test to help you to review Part I. Your instructor will tell you how to handle this test.

Summary Test for Part I

A

Circle the number of every true statement in this section.

1. For all sets A and B, if $n(A) = n(B)$, then $A \sim B$.
2. $\{x|x$ is a U.S. Senator$\} \sim \{x|x$ is a state of the U.S.$\}$
3. For all sets A, B, and C, if $A \sim B$, then $A \cup C \sim B \cup C$.
4. For all sets A and B, if $A \sim B$ and $B \subset A$, then A is infinite.
5. $n\{1, 2, 4, 5\} = 5$.
6. For all sets A and B, $A \cup (A \cap B) = A$.
7. For all sets A, B, and C, if $A \sim B$, and $B \sim C$, then $A \sim C$.
8. For all sets A and B, if $A \subseteq B$, then $(A \cup B) \cap (A \cap B) = B$.
9. For all sets A, if $A \sim \varnothing$, then $A = \varnothing$.
10. For all sets A, B, C, and D, if $A \sim B$, and $C \sim D$, then $A \sim D$.
11. For all sets A and B, $A \subseteq A \cup B$.
12. For all nonempty standard sets A, the cardinal number of A is an element of A.
13. For all sets A and B, if $B \subseteq A$, then $A \sim B$.
14. $n\{\varnothing\} = 1$.
15. For all sets A, if $A \sim \{1, 2, 3, \ldots, n, \ldots\}$, then A is infinite.
16. For all sets A and B, if $A \sim B$, then more than one one-to-one correspondence exists between A and B.
17. No two distinct standard sets are equivalent.
18. For all sets A and B such that $B \subseteq A$, $A \setminus B = B' \cap A$.
19. For all sets A and B, $(A \cup B)' = A' \cup B'$.
20. The ordered pair $(0, 1)$ equals the ordered pair $(1, 0)$.
21. $x = 5$ is an open sentence.
22. For all sets A and B, $A \times B = B \times A$.
23. For all sets A, B, and C, $A \times (B \times C) \sim (A \times B) \times C$.
24. If $A = \{a, e, i, o, u\}$ and $B = \{a, b, c, d, e\}$, then $A = B$.
25. $[4 = 3 + 1$ or $7 = 9]$ and $[1 \cdot 0 = 1$ or $6 \div 3 = 2]$.

B

26. Sets A and B are said to be disjoint if _____.
27. If a one-to-one correspondence between sets A and B can be established, the sets are said to be _____.
28. Label each of the following as either (a) an open sentence, (b) a proposition, or (c) neither:
   (i) $x + 5 = 7$. _____
   (ii) Stop the bus. _____
   (iii) Some men are richer than others. _____
   (iv) $7 + 2 = 8 - 1$. _____
   (v) For all whole numbers x and y: $x^2 - y^2 = (x + y)(x - y)$.
   _____
   (vi) $x + x = 2x$. _____

29. Fill in the third column of the truth table.

p_x	q_x	p_x or q_x
T	T	
T	F	
F	T	
F	F	

30. Complete the Venn diagram to illustrate sets A, B, and C, such that $A \cap B \neq \emptyset$, $A \cap C \neq \emptyset$, $B \cap C \neq \emptyset$.

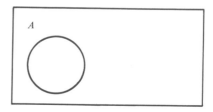

31. Write the converse of the proposition "For all whole numbers x, if $x = 1$, then $x^2 = x$". _____

32. Write the negation of "3 is a prime number". _____

33. Complete the truth table for the open sentence "p_x and (not p_x)".

p_x	not p_x	p_x and (not p_x)

34. For all sets A, $A \cup \emptyset =$ _____.

35. List the elements of $X \cap Y$ where $X = \{$a, e, i, o, u$\}$; $Y = \{$a, b, c, d, e, f, g, h, i, j$\}$. _____

36. Form the contrapositive of "If a woman is older than her husband, then she conceals here age". _____

37. Let $A = \{1, 2, 3, 4\}$. Which is correct, (a) or (b)? (a) $5 \varepsilon A$. (b) $5 \notin A$. _____

38. Let $A = \{1, 2, 3, \ldots\}$. Which is correct, (a) or (b)? (a) $5 \varepsilon A$. (b) $5 \notin A$. _____

39. How many elements are in the set $\emptyset$? _____

40. For all sets A, $A \cup A' =$ _____.

41. For all sets A, $A \times \emptyset =$ _____.

42. For all sets A, $A \setminus \emptyset =$ _____.

43. For all sets A, $A \cap A' =$ _____.

44. After each of the symbols listed in the left-hand column put (a), (b), or (c) if the symbol represents the corresponding item in the right column. If it does not correspond to any item of the right-hand column, do not fill in the blank.

(1) $U \setminus A.$ _____   (a) absolute complement of A
(2) $A \setminus U.$ _____   (b) complement of A relative to B
(3) $A'.$ _____   (c) complement of B relative to A
(4) $A \setminus B.$ _____
(5) $B \setminus A.$ _____

45. If $A = \{a, e, i, o, u\}$ and $B = \{a, b, c, d, e\}$, which of the following are elements of $A \times B$? (1) (a, c). (2) (d, c). (3) (e, g). (4) (c, o). (5) (a, a).

_____

46. The complement of A relative to B is defined in our text only for the case where (a) $A \subset U$ and $B \subset U$. (b) $A \subseteq B$. (c) $B \subseteq A$. (d) $A \cap B = \emptyset$.

_____

47. What conclusion can be drawn if, given two sets R and S, we know that $R \subseteq S$ and $S \subseteq R$? _____

48. In the universe of the whole numbers, the complement of the set of odd numbers is _____.

49. Use a listing in brackets to indicate the set of natural numbers.

_____

50. $U' =$ _____.

51. If A and B are sets, define: A is a subset of B. _____
_____

52. List the elements of the set indicated by $\{x | x + 3 = 5\}$.

_____.

53. If the universal set is $\{1, 3, 5, 7, 9\}$, list the elements of the set denoted by $\{x | x < 5\}$. _____

54. Which of the following are not members of the set of whole numbers? $-1, 0, \frac{1}{2}, 1.$ _____

55. Find a counterexample to the false proposition "For all whole numbers $x : x^2 + 2x + 1 = 3$". _____

56. The cardinal number of a finite set A is defined to be _____
_____
_____.

57. An equivalence relation must have what three properties:

(1) _____, (2) _____, and
(3) _____.

58. What is the whole number 2?

(a) According to Frege. _____
_____

(b) According to Von Neumann. _____
_____

When you have finished this Summary Test you may proceed to Chapter 8, Binary Operations.

PART II

Fundamentals of the Arithmetic of Whole Numbers

Chapters 8 through 12

8

Binary
Operations

Before beginning this chapter you should review Chapter 6: Union, Intersection, and Complement; and Chapter 7: Cartesian Products. As a measure of your comprehension of these chapters, try the following Readiness Test.

READINESS TEST

1. The commutative property of set intersection states that for all subsets A and B of a universal set U: __$A \cap B = B \cap A$__

> $A \cap B = B \cap A$

2. If A and B are subsets of U, $A \cap B$ is a __subset__ of U.

> subset

3. If A, B, and C are any subsets of U, what is the relation among the sets $A \cap B \cap C$, $(A \cap B) \cap C$, and $A \cap (B \cap C)$? __equal__

> They are equal.

4. The statement that for all subsets A, B, and C of U the multiple intersection $A \cap B \cap C$ is the same for all orderings of A, B, and C is called the __commutative property__

> generalized commutative property

5. If A and B are any sets, the Cartesian product $A \times B$ is the set of __ordered pairs__ (a, b), where a is an element of __A__ and b is an element of __B__.

> ordered pairs A B

6. If A and B are any subsets of U, is $A \times B$ always a subset of U? __No__

> No. ϕ could be subset

7. Which of the following are true for all sets A and B?
(a) $A \times B = B \times A$.   (b) $A \times B \sim B \times A$.
(c) $A \times B \times C = C \times B \times A$.   (d) $(A \times B) \times C = A \times (B \times C)$.
(e) $(A \times B) \times C \sim A \times (B \times C)$.   b & e

> (b) and (e) only.

If you missed any of these questions, review Chapters 6 or 7 as needed and then proceed to the text and exercises of Chapter 8.

8.1 Introduction

The usual operations of arithmetic and set theory combine *two* given numbers or sets and produce a third number or set. Examples of such operations are

$$
\begin{array}{ll}
2 + 5 & 3 \times 4 \\
5 - 2 & 6 \div 3 \\
A \cup B & A \cap B \\
A \setminus B & A \times B
\end{array}
$$

Since *two* elements occur in each of these expressions, the operations may be called *binary*.

The operation of forming the absolute complement of A, A', involves just *one* set A. Hence it is called *unary*.

The multiple intersections, unions, and Cartesian products

$$
A \cap B \cap C \qquad A \cup B \cup C \qquad A \times B \times C
$$

each involve three elements, and so are called *ternary*.

In this chapter we shall be concerned only with *binary* operations. We shall define them carefully, develop their properties, and consider examples of them.

8.2 Binary Operations on a Set

The intuitive idea of a binary operation can be grasped if you imagine that we have some kind of a machine (Figure 8.1) into which we insert two

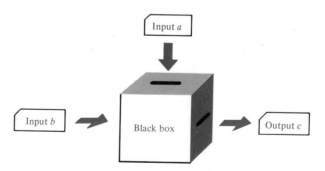

FIGURE 8.1. *Binary operation.*

objects a and b (in that order) and obtain an output c. To add 3 and 7 we insert 3 in input a and 7 in input b. The machine (here an adding machine) grinds away and produces as output the number 10.

Each binary operation requires different machinery in the black box, but the schematic diagram in Figure 8.1 is the same for all of them. For example, for unions we have the "union machine", Figure 8.2.

160

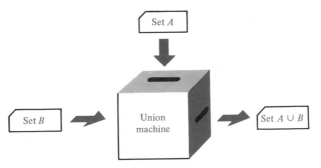

FIGURE 8.2. *Union machine.*

BINARY OPERATION ON A SET

In order for a binary operation to be defined on a set we need the following items:

(1) A set $S = \{a, b, c, \ldots\}$ whose elements may be numbers, sets, or anything else.

(2) The set of ordered pairs (a, b), where a and b are elements of S. We recall that this set is the Cartesian product $S \times S$.

(3) An assignment (as in our machines): $(a, b) \to c$ which assigns a unique element c of S to each ordered pair (a, b) in $S \times S$.

Thus the operation of addition of whole numbers assigns to every ordered pair (a, b) of whole numbers the whole number $a + b$, or

$$(a, b) \to (a + b)$$

Similarly, the operation of multiplying two whole numbers can be written in the form

$$(a, b) \to (a \cdot b)$$

We shall denote a general binary operation by $*$ and thus write it as

$$(a, b) \to (a * b)$$

Thus we have the following general definition of a binary operation on a set:

DEFINITION. Let $S = \{a, b, c, \ldots\}$ be any set. The operation $*$ is a *binary operation on S* if and only if to every ordered pair (a, b) in $S \times S$ there is assigned a unique element $a * b$ of S. Addition + Multiplication are binary operations on whole nos. Division is operation on rational numbers. + natural nos.

There are several delicate points to observe in this definition:

(1) The order of a and b in $a * b$ may be important, for (a, b) is an *ordered pair*. Thus we may have $a * b \neq b * a$.

(2) The operation must be defined for *every* ordered pair (a, b) in $S \times S$.

(3) The "output" $a * b$ must be an element of S.

Let us now look at some familiar examples of binary operations.

EXAMPLES OF BINARY OPERATIONS

(1) *Intersection of sets.* Here S is the set of all subsets of a universal set U. If A and B are any elements of S, $A \cap B$ is also a subset of U. So

$$(A, B) \to (A \cap B)$$

is a binary operation on the set S.

(2) *Union of sets.* Similarly, if S is as in (1),

$$(A, B) \rightarrow (A \cup B)$$

is a binary operation on S.

(3) *Addition of whole numbers.* Let S be the set of whole numbers. In the next chapter we shall define addition and show that the sum of every two whole numbers is a whole number (a fact that you undoubtedly know already!). Then if a and b are whole numbers,

$$(a, b) \rightarrow (a + b)$$

is a binary operation on the set of whole numbers.

(4) *Multiplication of whole numbers.* Similarly, if S is the set of whole numbers, the operation

$$(a, b) \rightarrow (a \cdot b)$$

will be shown to be a binary operation on S.

(5) *Cartesian products of sets.* If we are willing, for the moment, to ignore the logical problems involved in discussing *the set of all sets*, we can show that the Cartesian product is a binary operation. Let S be the set of all sets. Then

$$(A, B) \rightarrow (A \times B)$$

is a binary operation on S.

Several familiar operations on certain sets, however, do not fulfill our definition of a binary operation on a set.

OPERATIONS NOT BINARY
ON CERTAIN SETS

(6) *Subtraction.* If S is the set of whole numbers, subtraction *is not* a binary operation on S, for $a - b$ is not a whole number if $a < b$. On the other hand, if S is the set of integers (positive, negative, or zero), we shall show later that $a - b$ is defined for every (a, b). Thus

$$(a, b) \rightarrow (a - b)$$

is a binary operation on the set of *integers*.

(7) *Division.* If S is the set of whole numbers, division *is not* a binary operation on S, for $(1, 2) \rightarrow (1 \div 2)$ does not result in a whole number. If, however, S is the set of all nonzero *rational numbers*, we shall see later that

$$(a, b) \rightarrow (a \div b)$$

is a binary operation on the set of *nonzero rational numbers*.

(8) *Relative complement of sets.* $A \setminus B$. Recall that $A \setminus B$ is defined only when $B \subseteq A$. Since $A \setminus B$ is not defined for every A and B which are subsets of U, the operation of forming relative complements *is not* a binary operation on the set of all subsets of U.

---

1. A binary operation involves ⟶ two ⟵ inputs.

two

---

2. Why is $A \cap B \cap C$ not a binary operation? _This involves 3 inputs._

It involves three sets or inputs.

3. A binary operation $*$ on a set S assigns a unique element of S, _$a * b$_, to each ordered pair (a, b), where a and b are elements of _S_.

$a * b$ S

4. In general, is $a * b = b * a$? _No_

No.

5. In a binary operation $*$ on a set S, $a * b$ is an element of _S_.

S

6. If $*$ is a binary operation on S, the notation $(a, b) \rightarrow (a * b)$ means that the element _$a * b$_ of S is assigned to the ordered pair _(a, b)_ of $S \times S$.

$a * b$ (a, b)

7. The binary operation of addition on the whole numbers assigns what whole number to the ordered pair $(5, 7)$? _12_

$5 + 7 = 12$.

8. Why is subtraction not a binary operation on the set of whole numbers? _$a - b$ may not be whole no. if $b > a$._

$a - b$ is not a whole number if $a < b$.

9. Subtraction is a binary operation on what set? _Set of integers_

The set of integers.

10. Why is division not a binary operation on the set of whole numbers? _$a \div b$ may not be a whole no._

For some ordered pairs (a, b), $a \div b$ is not a whole number.

11. Division is a binary operation on what set? <u>Set of nonzero rational numbers</u>

> The set of nonzero rational numbers.

12. What set operations are binary operations on the set *S* of all subsets of a universal set *U*? <u>∩ , ∪</u>

> Intersection and union.

☆ 13. Why is the Cartesian product *not* a binary operation on the set *S* of all subsets of a universal set *U*? _____

> If *A* and *B* are subsets of *U*, *A* × *B* is not in general a subset of *U*.

8.3 Commutative Binary Operations

We have already observed that since $A \cap B = B \cap A$ and $A \cup B = B \cup A$, set intersection and union are commutative. Similarly, the binary operations of addition and multiplication of whole numbers are commutative. There are, however, a number of familiar binary operations which are not commutative, for example Cartesian product of sets, subtraction on the set of integers, and division on the set of nonzero rational numbers.

In general, we shall define the commutativity of a binary operation in the following way:

COMMUTATIVE BINARY OPERATION

DEFINITION. A binary operation * on a set *S* is *commutative* if and only if for every two elements *a* and *b* of *S*,

$$a * b = b * a$$

+ or ×

Frequently, as in the cases of addition and multiplication of whole numbers, a binary operation can be defined by a table. Table 1 is a part of such an addition table for the whole numbers, where the entries in the

TABLE 1. Partial Addition Table for the Whole Numbers

+	0	1	2	3	4	5
0	0	1	2	3	4	5
1	1	2	3	4	5	6
2	2	3	4	5	6	7
3	3	4	5	6	7	8
4	4	5	6	7	8	9
5	5	6	7	8	9	10

164

table are the sums of the numbers designating the corresponding columns and rows. The commutativity of addition is illustrated by the fact that this table is symmetrical about its main diagonal, which is printed in color.

Nonfamiliar binary operations may also be defined by tables like Table 1. For example, let $\triangle$ be the operation defined by Table 2. Since $3 \triangle 2 = 3$

TABLE 2. Table for $a \triangle b$ where a and b are elements of $S = \{1, 2, 3, 4\}$

$\triangle$	1	2	3	4
1	1	2	3	4
2	1	2	3	4
3	1	2	3	4
4	1	2	3	4

one variable cancels out the other.

and $2 \triangle 3 = 2$, this operation is not commutative. You will observe that the table is not symmetrical about its main diagonal.

1. A binary operation $*$ on a set S is commutative if and only if for all elements a, b of S, ___$a * b = b * a$___ .

$a * b = b * a$

2. What binary operations of set theory are commutative?
___$\cap, \cup$___

Intersection and union.

3. What binary operation of set theory is not commutative? ___CARTESIAN PRODUCT___

Cartesian product.

4. What binary operations of arithmetic are commutative? ___$+, \times$___

Addition and multiplication.

5. What binary operations of arithmetic are not commutative? ___
___$-, \div$___

Subtraction and division.

6. The binary operation $\otimes$ is defined on the set $\{1, 2, 3\}$ by the table. Is this operation commutative? ___No___

$\otimes$	1	2	3
1	1	2	3
2	3	1	2
3	2	3	1

No.

7. Justify your response to frame 6. _$2 \otimes 3 = 3$_

A counterexample is $3 \otimes 2 = 2$, $2 \otimes 3 = 3$.

8. Let us consider an operation $\triangle$ defined thus: For all whole numbers a and b, $a \triangle b = a + 2b$. To find $2 \triangle 3$ we replace a by 2 and b by 3. What is $2 \triangle 3$? _8_

8.

9. For the operation $\triangle$ of frame 8 what is $3 \triangle 2$? _7_

7.

10. From the evidence in frames 8 and 9 we can conclude that the operation $\triangle$ is _not commutative_

not commutative

11. If the operation $\square$ is defined for all whole numbers a and b by $a \square b = a + b + ab$, what is $2 \square 3$? _11_

$2 + 3 + 2 \times 3 = 11$.

12. For the operation $\square$ of frame 11 what is $3 \square 2$? _11_

11.

13. From the evidence in frames 11 and 12 can we conclude that the operation $\square$ is commutative? _No_

No. (One example doesn't prove a general statement.)

166

14. Why *is* the operation □ of frame 11 commutative? For all whole numbers *a* and *b*: $a + b + ab = \underline{b + a + ba}$ since addition and multiplication are commutative.

> $b + a + ba$

15. If the operation ∘ is defined for all whole numbers *a* and *b* by $a \circ b = a$, show that ∘ is not commutative. _____

> Any differing values of *a* and *b* will suffice. For example, put $a = 2$ and $b = 1$. Then $2 \circ 1 = 2$, while $1 \circ 2 = 1$, so $2 \circ 1 \neq 1 \circ 2$.

8.4 Associative Binary Operations

A binary operation on a set *S* permits us to combine *two* members of *S* and thus obtain a third element of *S*. But it does not tell us how to combine *three* elements of *S*, such as $a * b * c$. In this section we shall introduce the associative property of a binary operation and show that if the operation satisfies this property, then we can give a meaning to the symbol $a * b * c$.

To introduce the concept of associativity let us take the addition of whole numbers as an illustration. If we write the whole numbers 2, 5, and 8 in this order, we wish to find the value of

$$2 + 5 + 8$$

Since addition is a binary operation, we can add only two numbers at a time and so we seem to be in difficulty. We can, however, compute $2 + 5 + 8$ by introducing the grouping

$$(2 + 5) + 8$$

Now add $2 + 5 = 7$, and then add $7 + 8 = 15$. So it appears that

$$2 + 5 + 8 = 15$$

Another grouping is possible,

$$2 + (5 + 8) = 2 + 13 = 15$$

This suggests that the two groupings will always give the same result. As a matter of fact, we shall prove later that for all whole numbers *a*, *b*, and *c*,

$$(a + b) + c = a + (b + c)$$

This is an illustration of the associative property for the binary operation of addition.

The general definition of an associative binary operation is the following:

DEFINITION. The binary operation $*$ on a set S is *associative* if and only if for every triple, a, b, and c, of elements of S,

$$(a * b) * c = a * (b * c)$$

We can illustrate this in terms of our machines in Figures 8.3 and 8.4.

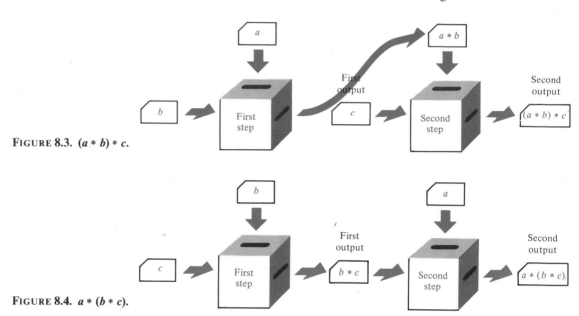

FIGURE 8.3. $(a * b) * c.$

FIGURE 8.4. $a * (b * c).$

When the second outputs, $(a * b) * c$ and $a * (b * c)$, are identical for all a, b, and c, we say that the operation $*$ is associative.

To give one more illustration of this idea, let us construct our machines when the operation is ordinary addition. We shall be concerned with the situation where

$$(4 + 6) + 5 = 4 + (6 + 5)$$

For the left-hand side we have Figure 8.5.

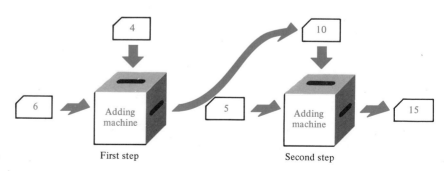

FIGURE 8.5. $(4 + 6) + 5 = 15.$

For $4 + (6 + 5)$, we have Figure 8.6.

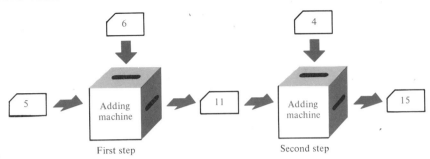

FIGURE 8.6. *4 + (6 + 5) = 15.*

First step   Second step

Although many familiar operations are associative, you must not assume this to be true without verification. Let us turn to the various binary operations so far discussed and discover which have the associative property.

EXAMPLES OF ASSOCIATIVE OPERATIONS

(1) *Intersection of sets.* In Chapter 6 we introduced the multiple intersection $A \cap B \cap C$ and showed that the sets $A \cap B \cap C$, $(A \cap B) \cap C$, and $A \cap (B \cap C)$ are all equal. Hence set intersection is associative. We can verify this in another fashion by considering the two series of Venn diagrams in Figures 8.7 and 8.8. Since the two sets $(A \cap B) \cap C$ in Figure 8.7(c)

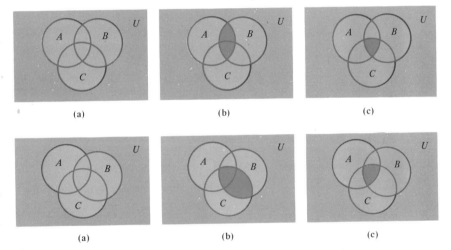

FIGURE 8.7. (*b*) $A \cap B$ *is in heavy color.*
(*c*) $(A \cap B) \cap C$ *is in heavy color.*

(a)   (b)   (c)

FIGURE 8.8. (*b*) $B \cap C$ *is in heavy color.*
(*c*) $(A \cap (B \cap C))$ *is in heavy color.*

(a)   (b)   (c)

and $A \cap (B \cap C)$ in Figure 8.8(c) are identical, we conclude that

$$(A \cap B) \cap C = A \cap (B \cap C)$$

and that the operation of forming intersections is associative. Strictly speaking, we have shown this to be true only for the sets A, B, and C in our diagram. To complete the proof, we should consider all possible positions for these sets and obtain the result in each case. Since this cannot be done conveniently, we do not do so here. This difficulty is, in fact, a deficiency of the method of Venn diagrams.

Finally, we can establish this result using a truth table, Table 3. Now we need eight rows to cover all possible positions for an element of U. Since the columns headed $x \, \varepsilon \, [(A \cap B) \cap C]$ and $x \, \varepsilon \, [A \cap (B \cap C)]$ are identical

TABLE 3. $(A \cap B) \cap C = A \cap (B \cap C)$

$x \varepsilon A$	$x \varepsilon B$	$x \varepsilon C$	$x \varepsilon (A \cap B)$	$x \varepsilon (A \cap B) \cap C$	$x \varepsilon (B \cap C)$	$x \varepsilon A \cap (B \cap C)$
T	T	T	T	T	T	T
T	F	T	F	F	F	F
F	T	T	F	F	T	F
F	F	T	F	F	F	F
T	T	F	T	F	F	F
T	F	F	F	F	F	F
F	T	F	F	F	F	F
F	F	F	F	F	F	F

for every triple of sets, A, B, and C, we conclude that this operation is associative.

THEOREM 1. For every triple of sets, A, B, and C,

$$(A \cap B) \cap C = A \cap (B \cap C)$$

That is, the operation of forming the intersection of sets is *associative*.

(2) *Union of sets.* The parallel discussion for unions is left to the problems. There you will show that for all A, B, and C,

$$(A \cup B) \cup C = A \cup (B \cup C)$$

so that this operation is associative.

THEOREM 2. For every triple of sets, A, B, and C,

$$(A \cup B) \cup C = A \cup (B \cup C)$$

That is, the operation of forming the unions of sets is associative.

(3) *Addition of whole numbers.* Later we shall prove that for any three whole numbers,

$$(a + b) + c = a + (b + c)$$

and so the addition of whole numbers is associative.

(4) *Multiplication of whole numbers.* Again we shall prove that for any three whole numbers,

$$(a \cdot b) \cdot c = a \cdot (b \cdot c)$$

OPERATIONS NOT ASSOCIATIVE ON CERTAIN SETS

and so the multiplication of whole numbers is associative.

(5) *Cartesian product of sets.* In Chapter 7 we discussed the Cartesian products $(A \times B) \times C$ and $A \times (B \times C)$ and showed that these two sets are generally different. Therefore, the Cartesian product of sets is *not* associative.

We remind you, however, that a weaker statement is true: For all sets A, B, and C,

$$(A \times B) \times C \sim A \times (B \times C)$$

170

(6) *Subtraction on the set of integers.* This binary operation is *not* associative, for the statement: For all a, b, and c,

$$(a - b) - c = a - (b - c)$$

is false. As a counterexample take $a = 10$, $b = 4$, and $c = 2$. Then

$$(10 - 4) - 2 = 6 - 2 = 4$$

$$10 - (4 - 2) = 10 - 2 = 8$$

(7) *Division on the set of nonzero rationals.* Again this binary operation is *not* associative, for the statement: For all a, b, and c,

$$(a \div b) \div c = a \div (b \div c)$$

is false. As a counterexample, take $a = 12$, $b = 6$, and $c = 2$. Then

$$(12 \div 6) \div 2 = 2 \div 2 = 1$$

$$12 \div (6 \div 2) = 12 \div 3 = 4$$

Now that you understand the meaning of the associative property, let us return to our original problem, namely to give meaning to the expression $a * b * c$, where a, b, and c are elements of the set S on which $*$ is defined as a binary operation. If $*$ is associative, it is reasonable to define $a * b * c$ to be equal to either of the equal expressions $(a * b) * c$ and $a * (b * c)$.

The formal definition is the following:

MEANING OF $a * b * c$ **DEFINITION.** Let $*$ be an associative binary operation on a set S, and let a, b, and c be any elements of S, written in the *order a, b, c*. Then by definition the expression $a * b * c$ is equal to either of the two equal expressions $(a * b) * c$ and $a * (b * c)$.

REMARK

The definition of $a * b * c$ depends on the order in which a, b, and c are written. Thus we do not assert that $a * b * c = b * a * c$, although this may be true in special cases.

---

1. A binary operation on a set S is associative if and only if for all a, b, and c in S, $(a * b) * c = a * (b * c)$

$(a * b) * c = a * (b * c)$

2. When $*$ is associative on S we define $a * b * c$ (for a, b, and c, in this order) to be equal to either of the expressions $(a * b) * c$ _____ and $a * (b * c)$.

$(a * b) * c \qquad a * (b * c)$

3. What binary operations of set theory are associative? $\cup, \cap$ _____

> Union and intersection.

4. What binary operation of set theory is not associative? CARTESIAN PRODUCT

> Cartesian product.

5. What binary operations of arithmetic are associative? $+, \times$ _____

> Addition and multiplication.

6. What binary operations of arithmetic are not associative? _____
$-, \div$

> Subtraction and division.

7. Let the operation $\triangle$ be defined by

$$a \triangle b = a + 2b \qquad \text{for all whole numbers } a \text{ and } b$$

What is $(1 \triangle 2) \triangle 3$? $1+4=5, 5+6=11$

> 11 $(1 \triangle 2 = 1 + 4 = 5, 5 \triangle 3 = 5 + 6 = 11)$.

8. For the same operation, what is $1 \triangle (2 \triangle 3)$? 17

> 17 $(2 \triangle 3 = 8, 1 \triangle 8 = 17)$.

9. Is the operation $\triangle$ associative? No

> No.

10. Let the operation $\circ$ be defined by $a \circ b = a$ for all a and b in a set S. What is $(a \circ b) \circ c$? a

> a.

11. For the operation $\circ$ of frame 10 what is $a \circ (b \circ c)$? a

> a.

172

12. Is the operation ∘ associative? _Yes_

Yes.

13. Is the operation ∘ commutative? _No_

No.

14. What is $a \circ b \circ c$? _a_

a.

15. What is $b \circ a \circ c$? _b_

b.

16. Is $a \circ b \circ c$ equal to $b \circ a \circ c$? _No_

No.

8.5 Generalized Commutative Property

For set intersection and union it has been shown that the *generalized commutative property* holds: that for all A, B, and C,

$$A \cap B \cap C = B \cap A \cap C = C \cap A \cap B = \cdots$$
$$A \cup B \cup C = B \cup A \cup C = C \cup A \cup B = \cdots$$

But, on the contrary, for the operation ∘ defined by $a \circ b = a$ (see frames 10 to 16 of the last section), this property is not true. So, for some binary operations the generalized commutative property is true and for others it is false. Is there any direct means of proving this property to be true without examining the operation in great detail? Fortunately there is such a means, and we state it as a theorem:

GENERALIZED COMMUTATIVE PROPERTY

THEOREM 3. If ∗ is a binary operation on a set S which is *both* commutative and associative, then the generalized commutative property is true for ∗. That is, for all a, b, and c in S, the six expressions

$$a * b * c \qquad b * a * c \qquad c * a * b$$
$$a * c * b \qquad b * c * a \qquad c * b * a$$

are defined and are equal.

173

Binary Operations

Proof. The full proof of this theorem requires us to show that $a * b * c$ is equal to each of the other five listed expressions. To avoid the tedium of doing so, we shall illustrate the method by proving that, for example,

$$a * b * c = c * b * a$$

1. $a * b * c = (a * b) * c$ Since * is associative.
2. $= (b * a) * c$ Since * is commutative.
3. $= c * (b * a)$ Since * is commutative.
4. $= c * b * a$ Since * is associative.

The other four cases can be proved in a similar fashion.

---

1. As in the proof of Theorem 3, show that $a * b * c = b * c * a$.

Proof.
1. $a * b * c =$ $a * (b * c)$
2. $= (b * c) * a$
3. $= b * c * a$

1. $a * b * c = a * (b * c)$ Associative.
2. $= (b * c) * a$ Commutative.
3. $= b * c * a$ Associative.

2. What binary operations of set theory are both commutative and associative? $\cap, \cup$

Intersection and union.

3. What binary operation of set theory is not both commutative and associative? CARTESIAN PRODUCT

Cartesian Product.

4. Hence the generalized commutative property is true for what binary operations of set theory? $\cap, \cup$

Intersection and union.

5. Although the generalized commutative property is not true for Cartesian products, what weaker but similar relation is true between $A \times B \times C$ and $C \times B \times A$? $\sim$

They are equivalent.

6. For what binary operations of arithmetic is the generalized commutative property true? $+ \times$. Why? Both are commutative & associative

> Addition and multiplication.   They are both commutative and associative.

8.6   Remarks on "Closure"

It is possible that you have seen statements such as

(1) Addition is closed on the set of whole numbers.
(2) Subtraction is not closed on the set of whole numbers.

Statement (1) means that the sum of every pair of whole numbers is a whole number, and statement (2) means that there are pairs of whole numbers whose difference is not a whole number. This notion of closure is not used in this book because it is redundant. According to the definition of a binary operation on a set S, any binary operation on S is automatically closed on S, so why introduce the superfluous notion of closure?

Closure, however, does have a useful meaning when it is applied to subsets of S. For example, the binary operation of addition on the whole numbers is closed on the subset of even numbers, since the sum of two even numbers is even. But it is not closed on the subset of odd numbers or on the subset of primes.

In Chapter 8 we have introduced the following concepts:

> binary operation on a set
> commutative binary operation *– 3 elements*
> associative binary operation
> generalized commutative property of a binary operation

We have illustrated the application of these ideas to a variety of situations in set theory and in arithmetic.

After you have reviewed this chapter, you should check your mastery of it by working the following Post Test.

P O S T   T E S T

1. An operation is binary if it has _____ *2* _____ inputs.
2. In a binary operation $*$ on S, the output $a * b$ is an element of _____ *S* ____.
3. Intersection is a binary operation on S, where S is the set of _____ *subsets* _____ *of the universal set.*
4. Which operations of arithmetic are *not* binary operations on the *set of whole numbers*? _____
5. What binary operations of set theory and arithmetic are not commutative? _____ *÷, —, CARTESIAN PRODUCT*

6. If $a * b = b$ and $b * a = a$, is $*$ commutative? _No_

7. If $*$ is an associative binary operation on a set S, then for all elements of a, b, and c of S, $(a*b)*c = a*(b+c)$

8. What binary operations of set theory and arithmetic are not associative? _— ÷ CARTESIAN PRODUCT_

9. Give a counterexample to show that subtraction is not associative on the set of integers. _____

10. Although Cartesian product is not an associative operation, what weaker relation is true between $(A \times B) \times C$ and $A \times (B \times C)$? _____

11. If $*$ is an associative binary operation on S, how is $a * b * c$ defined? $a * b * c = \underline{(a*b)* C}$ or $\underline{a*(b*c)}$.

12. If $*$ is an associative binary operation on S, can we be sure that $a * b * c = b * a * c$? _No_

13. What properties of a binary operation $*$ imply that the generalized commutative property is true for $*$? _Commutative associative._

14. For what binary operations of set theory and arithmetic is the generalized commutative property true? _∩, ∪, + , ×_

_____

1. two
2. S
3. subsets of a universal set U
4. Subtraction and division.
5. Subtraction, division, and Cartesian product.
6. No.
7. $(a * b) * c = a * (b * c)$
8. Subtraction, division, and Cartesian product.
9. Many answers, such as $(14 - 10) - 2 \neq 14 - (10 - 2)$.
10. They are equivalent.
11. $(a * b) * c, a * (b * c)$
12. No.
13. Commutative and associative properties.
14. Intersection, union, addition, and multiplication.

If you missed any of these questions, recheck the relevant portions of the chapter to make sure that you see why you were wrong. Then proceed to Chapter 9, Addition.

You should have read Chapters 6 and 8 and completed their Post Tests before proceeding. In Chapter 9 we shall define the sum of two whole numbers and develop its properties.

Before reading Chapter 9 you should be familiar with the following ideas:

whole number
union of sets
disjoint sets
empty set
cardinal number of a set
binary operations on a set
commutative binary operation
associative binary operation

The following Readiness Test is designed to check your understanding of these topics.

R E A D I N E S S   T E S T

1. If $A = \{1, 2, 3\}$, then $n(A) = $ _____ 3 .

3

2. If $A = \{1, 2, 3\}$ and $B = \{4, 5\}$, then $A \cup B = $ _____ $\{1,2,3,4,5\}$.

$\{1, 2, 3, 4, 5\}$

3. If $A = \{1, 2, 3\}$ and $B = \{4, 5\}$, then $A \cap B = $ _____ $\varnothing$.

$\varnothing$

4. Two sets, A and B, are disjoint if and only if _____ $A \cap B = \varnothing$.

$A \cap B = \varnothing$

5. If A and B are finite sets and $A \sim B$, then what relationship holds between $n(A)$ and $n(B)$? _____ $n(A) = n(B)$

$n(A) = n(B)$.

6. If A is any set, $A \cup \varnothing = $ _____ A and $A \cap \varnothing = $ _____ $\varnothing$.

A $\varnothing$

---

7. If * is a binary operation on a set S, then $a * b$ must be an element of $\underline{}$.

handwritten: S

S

8. If * is a commutative binary operation on S, then for all elements a and b of S, $\underline{a * b = b * a}$.

*handwritten: a * b = b * a*

$a * b = b * a$

9. If * is an associative binary operation on a set S, then for all elements a, b, and c of S, $\underline{(a * b) * c = a * (b * c)}$.

*handwritten: (a * b) * c = a * (b * c)*

$(a * b) * c = a * (b * c)$

10. If the binary operation * is commutative and associative, then what further property of * is true? *handwritten: generalized Commutative*

generalized commutative property.

When you have completed your review, as indicated by your performance on this test, proceed to Sections 9.1 through 9.6 and work the program following Section 9.6.

9.1 Introduction

We now have enough background to discuss the subject of addition. Let us begin by thinking of how a child adds by counting blocks. To be specific, how does he decide that $2 + 3 = 5$? Doubtless there are many ways, including counting on his fingers. We choose the following for our discussion.

In order to add 2 to 3, the child will select a set of two blocks $\{\square \ \square\}$ and another set of three blocks $\{\square \ \square \ \square\}$. Then he puts them together and thus forms the set

$$\{\square \ \square \ \square \ \square \ \square\}$$

Finally, he counts the number of blocks in this set and discovers that this number is 5. Hence he says that "2 plus 3 equals 5". (Never say "2 *and* 3 equals 5"—*and* does not specify the operation involved.)

Counting on one's fingers amounts to the same thing. The child holds up two fingers and then three different fingers. Finally, he counts the lot and finds that five fingers are raised. Thus $2 + 3 = 5$.

NOT PROVING

9.2 Definition of Addition

The ideas of the previous section can now lead us to give a general definition of addition. First, let us translate the intuitive language of the above discussion into more usual mathematical terms. To show that $2 + 3 = 5$ we take the following steps:

(1) Choose a set A such that $n(A) = 2$. That is, we choose A to have two elements.

(2) Choose a set B such that $n(B) = 3$ and such that A and B are disjoint. That is, we choose B to have three elements, none of which is also a member of A.

(3) Form $A \cup B$.

(4) Find $n(A \cup B) = 5$.

(5) Then we define addition by the equality $a + b = n(A \cup B)$.

To be specific we may choose

(1) $A = \{1, 2\}$ so that $n(A) = 2$, and

(2) $B = \{3, 4, 5\}$ so that $n(B) = 3$.

Then

(3) $A \cup B = \{1, 2, 3, 4, 5\}$.

From Chapter 5 we conclude that

(4) $n(A \cup B) = 5$

or that

(5) $2 + 3 = 5$.

It is necessary that A and B be disjoint. Suppose we had chosen $A = \{1, 2\}$ and $B = \{1, 2, 3\}$. Then $A \cup B = \{1, 2, 3\}$ and $n(A \cup B) = 3$. So $2 + 3 = 3$. This is not the idea.

We could have used other sets for A and B. Let us see how this works. We choose

(1) $A = \{a, b\}$. This has two elements, since $\{a, b\} \sim \{1, 2\}$.

(2) $B = \{c, d, e\}$. This has three elements, since $\{c, d, e\} \sim \{1, 2, 3\}$. Moreover, $A \cap B = \varnothing$.

(3) $A \cup B = \{a, b, c, d, e\}$. This has five elements, since $\{a, b, c, d, e\} \sim \{1, 2, 3, 4, 5\}$.

Thus

(4) $n(A \cup B) = 5$, and

(5) $2 + 3 = 5$.

The general definition of the sum of two whole numbers follows the above lines.

DEFINITION OF ADDITION   **DEFINITION.** Let a and b be any two whole numbers, A and B be sets such that $a = n(A)$, $b = n(B)$, and $A \cap B = \varnothing$. Then by definition,

$$n(A) + n(B) = n(A \cup B)$$

or

$$a + b = n(A \cup B)$$

As a further illustration of how this definition can be applied, let us prove the following result:

THEOREM 1. For all whole numbers a, $a + 0 = a$. This result is called the "additive property of zero".

Proof
1. Choose A such that $n(A) = a$.
2. Choose $B = \varnothing$ so that $n(\varnothing) = 0$.
3. Then $A \cap \varnothing = \varnothing$, and the two sets are disjoint.
4. $A \cup \varnothing = A$.
5. $n(A \cup \varnothing) = n(A) = a$.
6. Therefore, $a + 0 = n(A \cup \varnothing) = a$.

REMARK

We have defined addition in terms of set union. Thus the proofs of the various properties of addition (to be given later in this chapter) must all be based on appropriate properties of set union and upon our definition of addition.

9.3 Remarks Concerning the Definition of Addition

There are three serious matters concerning the definition of addition that need discussion.

(1) First, in the definition we assumed that given two whole numbers a and b we could find sets A and B such that $a = n(A)$, $b = n(B)$, and $A \cap B = \varnothing$. Of course, we can find sets A and B with the first two properties, for we can choose them to be standard sets. The requirement that A and B be *disjoint* is more troublesome. Let us see how to handle this.

In particular cases, suitable choices for A and B are fairly obvious. For example, if $a = 3$ and $b = 4$, we can choose $A = \{1, 2, 3\}$ and $B = \{4, 5, 6, 7\}$. The choice $\{1, 2, 3, 4\}$ for B is clearly unsatisfactory since $\{1, 2, 3\}$ and $\{1, 2, 3, 4\}$ are not disjoint. It is necessary, however, for us to give a general procedure for choosing A and B which does not depend upon any special relationship between the numbers a and b. The procedure described below uses a low-down trick which you are not likely to have invented for yourselves. But when we use the trick, the result is very easy.

Let us suppose that $a \neq 0$ and $b \neq 0$. Then we write the corresponding standard sets, $\{1, 2, \ldots, a\}$ and $\{1, 2, \ldots, b\}$, which are clearly not disjoint. Now form the following sets whose elements are ordered pairs.

$$A = \{1, 2, \ldots, a\} \times \{1\} = \{(1, 1), (2, 1), \ldots, (a, 1)\}$$
$$B = \{1, 2, \ldots, b\} \times \{2\} = \{(1, 2), (2, 2), \ldots, (b, 2)\}$$

From Theorem 3, Chapter 7, it follows that

$$A \sim \{1, 2, \ldots, a\} \qquad \text{and} \qquad B \sim \{1, 2, \ldots, b\}$$

Hence $n(A) = a$ and $n(B) = b$. Moreover, A and B are disjoint, since no ordered pair of the form $(j, 1)$ can equal an ordered pair of the form $(k, 2)$, since $1 \neq 2$.

If $a = 0$, choose $A = \varnothing$, $B = \{1, 2, \ldots, b\}$. These are disjoint and $n(A) = 0$, $n(B) = b$. Similarly, if $b = 0$, choose $A = \{1, 2, \ldots, a\}$, $B = \varnothing$. If both are zero, choose $A = \varnothing$, $B = \varnothing$. Then $A \cap B = \varnothing \cap \varnothing = \varnothing$, so A and B are disjoint and $n(A) = 0$, $n(B) = 0$.

This discussion is summarized in the following theorem:

A AND *B* DISJOINT   **THEOREM 2.**   For any two whole numbers, a and b, there exist disjoint sets A and B such that $n(A) = a$ and $n(B) = b$.

(2) Second, our definition of $a + b$ conceivably depends upon our choices of the disjoint sets A and B such that $a = n(A)$ and $b = n(B)$. Suppose that we choose other disjoint sets C and D such that $a = n(C)$ and $b = n(D)$ and $C \cap D = \varnothing$. It would be horrible if $n(A \cup B)$ turned out to be different from $n(C \cup D)$, for then $a + b$ would have two or more different values.

As a matter of fact, this cannot happen and so we say that $a + b$ is *uniquely defined*. The expression *uniquely defined* is explained as follows:

UNIQUELY DEFINED   **DEFINITION.**   The statement that $a + b$ is *uniquely defined* means that in our definition of $a + b$ $[a + b = n(A \cup B)]$ the result is independent of our choice of the chosen sets A and B as long as $n(A) = a$, $n(B) = b$, and $A \cap B = \varnothing$.

So that we shall not interrupt the flow of ideas at this point, we shall postpone the proof that $a + b$ is uniquely defined to Section 9.8.

(3) Finally, we ask whether addition is a binary operation on the set of whole numbers. The only point at issue is whether $a + b$ (as we have defined it) is a whole number.

We have defined $a + b$ to be $n(A \cup B)$, where A and B are finite sets. So the question is: Is $n(A \cup B)$ a whole number? We recall that, according to Frege, a whole number is the cardinal number of a finite set, and so the question may be restated: If A and B are finite sets, is $A \cup B$ a finite set? We therefore need the following theorem:

THEOREM 3.   If A and B are finite sets, then $A \cup B$ is a finite set.

The truth of this theorem is intuitively evident, but its proof is too difficult to present in this text.

The above argument proves the following result, which we had anticipated in Chapter 8:

BINARY OPERATION   **THEOREM 4.**   Addition is a binary operation on the set of whole numbers.

9.4 Commutative and Associative Properties of Addition

(1) COMMUTATIVE PROPERTY

To establish this property we must show that for all pairs of whole numbers, a and b.

$$a + b = b + a$$

181

Since the addition of whole numbers is defined in terms of the union of sets, the proof of the commutative property of addition must be based upon the known commutative property of set union. The formal proof is as follows.

COMMUTATIVE

THEOREM 5. The addition of whole numbers is commutative.

Proof
(1) Choose disjoint sets A and B such that $n(A) = a$ and $n(B) = b$.
2. For any pairs of sets, A and $B : A \cup B = B \cup A$ (commutative property of set union).
3. $n(A \cup B) = n(B \cup A)$, for the cardinal number of a set does not depend upon the name used to describe it.
4. $a + b = n(A \cup B)$ and $b + a = n(B \cup A)$ (definition of addition).
5. From 3 and 4 it follows that

$$a + b = b + a$$

ASSOCIATIVE

(2) ASSOCIATIVE PROPERTY OF ADDITION

As in the case of the commutative property, our proof of this refers back to the associative property of set union. The formal proof is as follows.

THEOREM 6. The addition of whole numbers is associative. That is, for any three whole numbers a, b, and c,

$$(a + b) + c = a + (b + c)$$

Proof
1. Choose mutually disjoint sets A, B, and C such that

$$n(A) = a \qquad n(B) = b \qquad n(C) = c$$

2. For every three sets A, B, and C,

$$(A \cup B) \cup C = A \cup (B \cup C)$$

(associative property of set union).
3. $n[(A \cup B) \cup C] = n[A \cup (B \cup C)]$.
4. $n[(A \cup B) \cup C] = n(A \cup B) + n(C)$ (definition of addition).
$\qquad\qquad\qquad = [n(A) + n(B)] + n(C)$
$\qquad\qquad\qquad = (a + b) + c.$
5. $n[A \cup (B \cup C)] = n(A) + n(B \cup C)$ (definition of addition).
$\qquad\qquad\qquad = n(A) + [n(B) + n(C)]$
$\qquad\qquad\qquad = a + (b + c).$
6. From steps 3, 4, and 5,

$$(a + b) + c = a + (b + c)$$

Since addition is associative, we can define the triple sum $a + b + c$ to be equal to either of the equal expressions $(a + b) + c$ or $a + (b + c)$.

GENERALIZED COMMUTATIVE

(3) GENERALIZED COMMUTATIVE PROPERTY

Since addition is both commutative and associative, the generalized commutative property is also true for addition. We state this as Theorem 7:

182

THEOREM 7.   For any three whole numbers a, b, and c the following six expressions are equal:

$$a + b + c \qquad b + a + c \qquad c + a + b$$
$$a + c + b \qquad b + c + a \qquad c + b + a$$

9.5 Caution

In this chapter we have developed the *addition* of whole numbers in terms of the *unions* of corresponding pairs of disjoint sets. Do not confuse these two ideas.

 We *add* numbers; we do *not* add sets.†
 We take *unions* of sets; we do *not* take unions of numbers.
 When we *add* numbers, we take *unions* of corresponding disjoint sets.
 These remarks should clarify the difficulties one encounters with statements like

(1)   5 apples + 3 apples = 8 apples

Some people permit the use of a statement of this kind, but it is basically incorrect, for this statement uses addition for sets rather than for numbers. It is certainly correct to write $5 + 3 = 8$, but the statement (1) should more properly be phrased

 "The union of a set of 5 apples with a set of 3 apples is a set of 8 apples".

There are even worse troubles with sentences like

(2)   5 pears + 3 lemons = 8 pieces of fruit

for "you can't add pears to lemons". Of course not, but one can say correctly,

 "The union of a set of 5 pears with a set of 3 lemons is a set of eight pieces of fruit".

Similarly, we must not use "union" when we mean "plus". The statement

(3) $5 \cup 9 = 14$

is nonsense. Clearly what is meant is "$5 + 9 = 14$".

9.6 Property of Equality

There is an old saying in mathematics to the effect that: If equals are added to equals, the sums are equal. Let us see what this means and how it is justified. We are concerned with the theorem:

† This statement is true in almost all cases, but there are exceptions. For example, in the von Neumann definition of whole numbers, we have defined 1 to be the set $\{\emptyset\}$ and 2 to be the set $\{\emptyset, 1\}$. According to our definition of the addition of whole numbers, we could therefore write

$$\{\emptyset\} + \{\emptyset, 1\} = \{\emptyset, 1, 2\}$$

and similarly define the sum of pairs of sets of this particular type. These, however, are very special cases; the sum of two *arbitrary* sets is *not* defined.

THEOREM 8. If a, b, and c are any whole numbers and if $a = b$, then $a + c = b + c$.

Proof
1. The hypothesis says that a and b are names for the same number.
2. $a + c$ is a symbol representing the sum of the number whose name is a (or b) and the number whose name is c.
3. $b + c$ is a symbol representing the sum of the number whose name is b (or a) and the number whose name is c.
4. Therefore, $a + c$ and $b + c$ are two different names for the sum of the same two numbers.
5. Because of this we write $a + c = b + c$.

COROLLARY. If a, b, c, and d are whole numbers, and if $a = b$ and $c = d$, then $a + c = b + d$.

CANCELLATION LAW   **CANCELLATION LAW FOR ADDITION**
A useful theorem is the converse of Theorem 8, as follows:

THEOREM 9. If a, b, and c are any whole numbers and if $a + c = b + c$, then $a = b$.

We could prove this theorem using various theorems in set theory, but the proof is much easier if we know how to subtract. So we postpone the proof of Theorem 9 to Chapter 10, Subtraction.

---

1. If a and b are whole numbers, then $a + b$, called a _plus_ b is a whole number.

plus

2. Thus $a + b$ is a numeral and, for example, $4 + 3$ is a numeral. When you are asked to find the value of $4 + 3$ or "evaluate $4 + 3$", you are to find the usual numeral representing the same whole number that $4 + 3$ does. In this case, the usual numeral is __7__ and we then write $4 + 3 =$ __7__.

7	7

3. To show that $4 + 3 = 7$, we might proceed as follows:
Let $A = \{a, b, c, d\}$ and $B = \{e, f, g\}$. Then $n(A) = $ __4__ , $n(B) = $ __3__ , and $A \cap B = $ __$\emptyset$__ . Hence $n(A) + n(B) = n(A \cup B)$; that is, $4 + 3 = n(A \cup B)$. Now $A \cup B = $ __$\{a, b, c, d, e, f, g\}$__ so $n(A \cup B) = $ __7__ .
Thus $4 + 3 = 7$.

184

4	3	$\varnothing$	$\{a, b, c, d, e, f, g\}$	7

4. Using the same sets as in frame 3, show that $3 + 4 = 7$, in the same style as the proof in frame 3. Use a separate piece of paper.

Let $B = \{e, f, g\}$ and $A = \{a, b, c, d\}$. Then $n(B) = 3$, $n(A) = 4$, and $B \cap A = \varnothing$. Hence $n(B) + n(A) = n(B \cup A)$; that is, $3 + 4 = n(B \cup A)$. Now $B \cup A = \{e, f, g, a, b, c, d\}$, so $n(B \cup A) = 7$. Thus $3 + 4 = 7$.

5. Using the definition of addition of whole numbers, find the value of $2 + 4$. Use a separate piece of paper.

Let $A = \{a, b\}$ and $B = \{c, d, e, f\}$. Then $n(A) = 2$, $n(B) = 4$, and $A \cap B = \varnothing$. Hence $n(A) + n(B) = n(A \cup B)$; that is, $2 + 4 = n(A \cup B)$. But $A \cup B = \{a, b, c, d, e, f\}$, so $n(A \cup B) = 6$. Thus $2 + 4 = 6$. (*Note:* You may have used sets other than those given here.)

6. In order to define the sum of two whole numbers, a and b, we need to find two sets, A and B, such that $n(A) = a$, $n(B) = b$, and $A \cap B = \varnothing$. Then $a + b = n(A \cup B)$.

$n(B) = b$	$A \cap B = \varnothing$	$n(A \cup B)$

7. Why do the sets required in frame 6 exist? Theorem __2__.

2. For every pair of whole numbers, a and b, there exist disjoint sets, A and B, such that $n(A) = a$ and $n(B) = b$.

8. Using the definition of addition of whole numbers, evaluate $3 + 0$. Use a separate piece of paper.

Let $A = \{a, b, c\}$ and $B = \varnothing$. Then $n(A) = 3$, $n(B) = 0$, and $A \cap B = \varnothing$. Hence $n(A) + n(B) = n(A \cup B)$; that is, $3 + 0 = n(A \cup B)$. But $A \cup B = \{a, b, c\}$ and $n(A \cup B) = 3$. Hence $3 + 0 = 3$. (*Note:* You could have used a set other than the set A given here.)

9. What is the error in the following incorrect proof that $1 + 4 = 4$? Let $A = \{a\}$ so that $n(A) = 1$; $B = \{a, b, c, d\}$ so that $n(B) = 4$. Then $A \cup B = \{a, b, c, d\}$ and $n(A \cup B) = 4$. Therefore, $1 + 4 = 4$. Sets A & B aren't disjoint.

The sets A and B are not disjoint.

10. If you prove that $3 + 4 = 7$ by using sets $A = \{a, b, c\}$ and $B = \{d, e, f, g\}$ and someone else correctly uses different sets $A_1 = \{x, y, z\}$ and $B_1 = \{p, q, r, s\}$, you observe that $n(A \cup B) = n(A_1 \cup B_1)$. This is an example of the fact that the sum of any whole numbers is *uniquely de*.

> uniquely defined

11. Let a and b be any whole numbers and A and B be sets (not necessarily disjoint) such that $n(A) = a$ and $n(B) = b$. Define $a * b$ by

$$a * b = n(A \cap B)$$

Is $a * b$ uniquely defined? *No* Why? *a AND b could be such that the equation wouldnt make sens*

> No.   For example, let $a = 2$ and $b = 3$. If we let $A = \{a, b\}$ and $B = \{c, d, e\}$ we would have $a * b = 0$. If we let $A_1 = \{a, b\}$ and $B_1 = \{a, b, c\}$, then we would have $a * b = 2$. Thus the value of $a * b$ would be ambiguous, its value depending on the particular sets chosen.

12. If A and B are finite sets, then $A \cup B$ is a *finite* set. Therefore, if a and b are whole numbers, $a + b = n(A \cup B)$ is a *whole numbe*
(finite, infinite)

> finite   whole number

13. If a and b are any two whole numbers, then $a + b$ is a whole number given by $a + b = n(A \cup B)$, where A and B are any two sets such that *$n(A) = a, n(B) = b$ and $A \cap B = \emptyset$*

> $n(A) = a$, $n(B) = b$, and $A \cap B = \varnothing$

14. For any two whole numbers, a and b, $a + b = b + a$. This is called the *commutative* property of addition.

> commutative

15. For any triple of whole numbers, a, b, and c, $(a + b) + c = a + (b + c)$. This is called the *associative* property of addition.

> associative

16. If a is any whole number, $a + 0 = $ *a* by the additive property of zero.

> a

17. What theorem justifies the statement $2 + 3 = 3 + 2$? Theorem ____.

[handwritten: 5]

> 5 (commutative property of addition).

18. What theorem justifies the statement $2 + (3 + 4) = (2 + 3) + 4$?

[handwritten: Associative prop. of +.]

> Associative property of addition.

19. What theorem justifies the statement $2 + 0 = 2$?

[handwritten: Additive prop. of zero.]

> Additive property of zero.

20. For each of the following statements, give the property of addition justifying the statement:
  (a) $(3 + 2) + 0 = 3 + 2.$ *[handwritten: Additive prop. of 0.]*
  (b) $(2 + 3) + 4 = 4 + (2 + 3).$ *[handwritten: Comm. prop. of addition]*
  (c) $3 + 4 = 4 + 3.$ *[handwritten: Comm. prop. of addition]*
  (d) $(5 + 3) + 1 = 5 + (3 + 1).$ *[handwritten: Assoc. prop. of addition]*

> (a) Additive property of zero.
> (b) Commutative property of addition.
> (c) Commutative property of addition.
> (d) Associative property of addition.

21. Let us prove the corollary to Theorem 8. If a, b, c, and d are whole numbers, and if $a = b$ and $c = d$, then $a + c = b + d$.

Proof
1. By Theorem ____ *[handwritten: 8]*, if $a = b$, then $a + c = b + c$.
2. Similarly, by Theorem ____ *[handwritten: 8]*, if $c = d$, then $c + b = d + b$.
3. But $c + b = b + c$ and $d + b = b + d$ because of *[handwritten: Comm. prop. of addition]* Hence $b + c = b + d$.
4. From steps 1 and 3 we have that $a + c = b + c$ and $b + c = b + d$, so the symbols $a + c$ and $b + d$ represent the same number, $b + c$, so $a + c = b + d$.

> 8   8   commutative property of addition

22. Justify each of the following statements:
(a) If $a = b$, then $a + 5 = b + 5$. Theorem ____ *[handwritten: 8]*.
(b) If $b + 7 = c + 7$, then $b = c$. Theorem ____ *[handwritten: 9]*.

> (a) 8   (b) 9 (cancellation for addition)

23. If a, b, and c are natural numbers, as in Theorem 2, put $A = \{(1, 1), (2, 1), \ldots, (a, 1)\}$, $B = \{(1, 2), (2, 2), \ldots, (b, 2)\}$. Then $n(A) = $ _____ *a* and $n(B) = $ _____ *b* and A and B are _____ *disjoint*. Now find a set C such that $n(C) = c$ and A, B, and C are mutually disjoint. $C = $ _____ *{(1,3)(2,3)(3,3)...(c,3)}* _____ .

> a b disjoint $\{(1, d), (2, d), \ldots, (c, d)\}$, where you may choose d to be any number except 1 or 2

24. Since a number ending with a zero is easy to work with in addition, a child might find $28 + 7$ by saying, "Since $7 = 2 + 5$, I'll add the 2 to 28 and get 30. Then $30 + 5 = 35$". More formally, this is the sequence of steps:

$$28 + 7 = 28 + 2 + 5 = 30 + 5 = 35$$

What theorem justifies this procedure? _____ *generalized comm. prop* _____

> generalized commutative property.

25. What theorem justifies the following statement? To find $3 + 6 + 8$, it doesn't matter whether you find $3 + 6$ and add 8 to this sum or whether you find $6 + 8$ and add this sum to 3. _____ *Assoc. prop. of +.* _____

> Associative property of addition.

26. To find $7 + 8 + 3$, a student might say, "I'll find $7 + 3$ and get 10, then $8 + 10 = 18$". More formally, here are the steps:

$$(7 + 8) + 3 = (8 + 7) + 3 = 8 + (7 + 3) = 8 + 10 = 18$$

(a) What theorem justifies the first equality? _____ *Commutative* _____
(associative, commutative

_____
properties)
(b) What theorem justifies the second equality? _____ *Associative* _____
(associative, commutative

_____
properties)

> (a) Commutative property of addition ($7 + 8 = 8 + 7$).
> (b) Associative property of addition.

27. Using only the definition of a triple sum and the commutative and associative properties of addition, but not the generalized commutative property, prove that

$$2 + 4 + 8 = 8 + 2 + 4$$

Give the reasons for each step.

Proof
1. 2 + 4 + 8 = (2+4)+8   Definition of triple sum.
2.   = 8+(2+4)   Comm. prop.
3.   = 8 + 2 + 4   Definition of triple sum.

1. (2 + 4) + 8   Definition of triple sum.
2. 8 + (2 + 4)   Commutative property.
3.

28. Correct the following misleading statement: 6 sheep + 5 goats = 11 animals. The union of the set of 6 sheep and set of 5 goats is the set of 11 animals.

The union of a set of 6 sheep and a set of 5 goats is a set of 11 animals.

29. Correct the following nonsensical statement: 12 ∪ 18 = 30. _____
12 + 18 = 30

12 + 18 = 30.

FIGURE 9.1. $n(A) = 15$ $n(B) = 10$
$n(A \cap B) = 4$ $n(A \cup B) = 21$
$A) + n(B) = n(A \cap B) + n(A \cup B) = 25.$

9.7 Extension of an Earlier Formula

If A and B are disjoint, we defined addition by the formula

$$n(A) + n(B) = n(A \cup B)$$

How should this formula be altered if A and B are no longer disjoint? In order to guess the correct result, consider the case illustrated in Figure 9.1. In this figure A and B overlap so that $A \cap B \neq \varnothing$. Suppose that $n(A) = 15$, $n(B) = 10$, $n(A \cap B) = 4$; what is $n(A \cup B)$? From the figure we see that region on the left contains $15 - 4 = 11$ elements and that region on the right contains $10 - 4 = 6$ elements. The total number of elements in $A \cup B$ is the sum of the numbers of elements in the three regions, respectively. Hence

$$n(A \cup B) = 11 + 4 + 6 = 21$$

On the other hand,

$$n(A) + n(B) = 15 + 10 = 25$$

What do we do to get a correct equation involving $n(A)$, $n(B)$, $n(A \cap B)$, and $n(A \cup B)$? You should see that it is

$$15 + 10 = 4 + 21$$

or that

$$n(A) + n(B) = n(A \cap B) + n(A \cup B)$$

Having guessed this formula, we must now prove it correct in all cases.

189

Addition

THEOREM 10. For any pair of sets, *A* and *B*,

$$n(A) + n(B) = n(A \cap B) + n(A \cup B)$$

Proof. Let

$$A = \{a_1, a_2, \ldots, a_r, c_1, c_2, \ldots, c_s\}$$
$$B = \{b_1, b_2, \ldots, b_t, c_1, c_2, \ldots, c_s\}$$

where *A* and *B* are not disjoint. Then

$$A \cup B = \{a_1, a_2, \ldots, a_r, b_1, b_2, \ldots, b_t, c_1, c_2, \ldots, c_s\}$$
$$A \cap B = \{c_1, c_2, \ldots, c_s\}$$

Thus $n(A) = r + s$, $n(B) = t + s$, $n(A \cap B) = s$ and $n(A \cup B) = r + s + t$. Therefore,

$$n(A) + n(B) = (r + s) + (t + s) = r + t + 2s$$
$$n(A \cap B) + n(A \cup B) = s + (r + s + t) = r + t + 2s$$

Hence

$$n(A) + n(B) = n(A \cap B) + n(A \cup B)$$

We can use this formula to solve problems such as the following:

PROBLEM. Suppose that in a group of 20 students who are enrolled in mathematics, history, or both

15 take mathematics
10 take history

How many take both mathematics and history?

Solution

1. Let *A* be the set of students taking mathematics. Then $n(A) = 15$.
2. Let *B* be the set of students taking history. Then $n(B) = 10$.
3. The set $A \cup B$ is the set of all the students in this group, so $n(A \cup B) = 20$.
4. We want $x = n(A \cap B)$.
5. From the above formula,

$$15 + 10 = x + 20$$

So $x = 5$.

Another method of solution is obtained from a Venn diagram, Figure 9.2. In this figure we first write x in $A \cap B$. Then the remainder of *A* contains $15 - x$ elements, and the remainder of *B* contains $10 - x$ elements. The total number of elements in the three regions is 20, so

$$(15 - x) + x + (10 - x) = 20$$
$$25 - x = 20$$
$$x = 5$$

More complicated problems of this type are best solved by Venn diagrams:

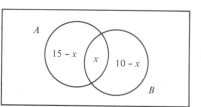

FIGURE 9.2. $n(A) = 15$ $n(B) = 10$
$n(A \cap B) = x$ $n(A \cup B) = 20$
$15 + 10 = x + 20$, so $x = 5$.

9.7 Extension of an Earlier Formula

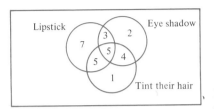

FIGURE 9.3. *In view of the given data the total number of girls in the group is 27.*

PROBLEM. Each of a group of girls uses at least one of the kinds of makeup below.

> 20 use lipstick
> 14 use eye shadow
> 15 tint their hair
> 8 use lipstick and eye shadow
> 10 use lipstick and tint their hair
> 9 use eye shadow and tint their hair
> 5 use lipstick and eye shadow and tint their hair

How many girls are there in the group? We draw the Venn diagram, Figure 9.3.

Solution. Using the information given we put numbers in the corresponding regions. We put 5 in the intersection of all three sets. Then there are 3 who use lipstick and eye shadow but do not tint their hair. Proceeding in this way we fill in numbers in all the regions. Then the total number in the group is the sum of the numbers in the diagram, or 27.

How many use eye shadow but not lipstick? The answer is $2 + 4 = 6$.

---

1. Draw a Venn diagram for the sets $A = \{a, b, c, d, e, f\}$ and $B = \{b, d, f, g, h\}$ and then illustrate Theorem 10. Use a separate sheet of paper.

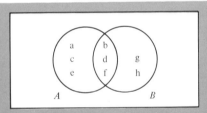

$n(A) = 6$, $n(B) = 5$, $n(A \cup B) = 8$, $n(A \cap B) = 3$. Since $6 + 5 = 8 + 3$, we have $n(A) + n(B) = n(A \cap B) + n(A \cup B)$.

2. A pair of dice was rolled 100 times. A number greater than 6 turned up 70 times and a number less than 8 turned up 65 times. How many times did the 7 turn up? __35__

Let A be the set of tosses in which a number greater than 6 turned up. Then $n(A) = 70$. Let B be the set of tosses in which a number less than 8 turned up. Then $n(B) = 65$. Then $A \cup B$ is the set of all tosses, so $n(A \cup B) = 100$. $A \cap B$ is the set of tosses in which a number greater than 6 and less than 8 turned up, that is, the set of tosses in which the 7 turned up. We wish to find $n(A \cap B)$. Using Theorem 10, $n(A) + n(B) = n(A \cap B) + n(A \cup B)$. $70 + 65 = n(A \cap B) + 100$, so $n(A \cap B) = 35$.

191

3. Of 100 people drinking coffee in a restaurant, 40 drank their coffee black. Of the remaining 60, 52 used cream and 47 used sugar. How many people used both cream and sugar? _39_

Let A be the set of people using cream. Then $n(A) = 52$. Let B be the set of people using sugar. Then $n(B) = 47$. $A \cup B$ is the set of people using cream or sugar, so $n(A \cup B) = 60$. $A \cap B$ is the set of people using cream and sugar, so we want $n(A \cap B)$. By Theorem 10, $n(A) + n(B) = n(A \cap B) + n(A \cup B)$. $52 + 47 = n(A \cap B) + 60$. So $n(A \cap B) = 39$.

4. In a certain group of students,

> 53 do not smoke
> 37 smoke cigarettes
> 25 smoke pipes
> 12 smoke cigars
> 18 smoke cigarettes and pipes
> 7 smoke cigarettes and cigars
> 6 smoke pipes and cigars
> 3 smoke cigarettes, pipes, and cigars

(a) How many students are there in the group? _____ (b) How many smoke pipes but not cigars? _____

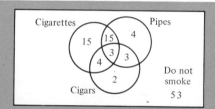

From the Venn diagram, in which the numbers are determined by starting with the intersection of all 3 sets of smokers, we find that (a) the total number in the group is 99 and (b) the number who smoke pipes but not cigars is $4 + 15$, or 19.

9.8   Proof That Addition Is Uniquely Defined (Optional)

Here we present the proof of Theorem 11.

UNIQUELY DEFINED   **THEOREM 11.**   The addition of whole numbers is uniquely defined.

Since this proof is rather complicated, it is given only to make you honest so that you will not rely on unproved theorems. You are not expected to be able to reproduce this proof.

Recall the purpose of this theorem. Suppose that whole numbers a and b are given, and that we find disjoint sets A and B such that $n(A) = a$ and $n(B) = b$. Then $a + b = n(A \cup B)$. We can also find other disjoint sets C and D such that $n(C) = a$ and $n(D) = b$. So $a + b = n(C \cup D)$. The essence of the theorem is that

$$n(A \cup B) = n(C \cup D)$$

To examine this matter let us start with some examples:
Let

$$A = \{a, b, c, d\} \qquad C = \{m, n, o, p\}$$
$$B = \{i, j\} \qquad D = \{x, y\}$$

Then $A \sim C$ and $B \sim D$, since we have (for example) the following one-to-one correspondences:

$$
\begin{array}{cc}
S & T \\
A = \{a \quad b \quad c \quad d\} & B = \{i \quad j\} \\
\updownarrow \updownarrow \updownarrow \updownarrow & \updownarrow \updownarrow \\
C = \{m \quad n \quad o \quad p\} & D = \{x \quad y\}
\end{array}
$$

Moreover,

$$A \cup B = \{a, b, c, d, i, j\}$$
$$C \cup D = \{m, n, o, p, x, y\}$$

We easily see how the one-to-one correspondences between A and C and between B and D define the following one-to-one correspondence between $A \cup B$ and $C \cup D$:

$$
\begin{array}{c}
V \\
A \cup B = \{a \quad b \quad c \quad d \quad i \quad j\} \\
\updownarrow \updownarrow \updownarrow \updownarrow \updownarrow \updownarrow \\
C \cup D = \{m \quad n \quad o \quad p \quad x \quad y\}
\end{array}
$$

Before we jump to the conclusion that we have a theorem here, let us try another example:

$$A = \{a, b, c, d\} \qquad C = \{m, n, o, p\}$$
$$B = \{a, j\} \qquad D = \{x, y\}$$

$$
\begin{array}{cc}
S & T \\
A = \{a \quad b \quad c \quad d\} & B = \{a \quad j\} \\
\updownarrow \updownarrow \updownarrow \updownarrow & \updownarrow \updownarrow \\
C = \{m \quad n \quad o \quad p\} & D = \{x \quad y\}
\end{array}
$$

Also

$$A \cup B = \{a, b, c, d, j\}, \quad C \cup D = \{m, n, o, p, x, y\}$$

193

But now we see that $(A \cup B) \sim (C \cup D)$, since $(A \cup B) \sim \{m, n, o, p, x\}$, which is a proper subset of $C \cup D$. What is the difference between this example and the preceding one? It does not take long to realize that in the first example, we had $A \cap B = \emptyset$, $C \cap D = \emptyset$. But in the second example, this fails, since $A \cap B = \{a\}$. On the basis of this experience, we formulate the following theorem:

THEOREM 12. For any sets A, B, C, and D, if $A \sim C$ and $B \sim D$, and if $A \cap B = \emptyset$ and $C \cap D = \emptyset$, then

$$(A \cup B) \sim (C \cup D)$$

Proof. Our hypotheses imply the existence of one-to-one correspondences S and T, the first between A and C, the second between B and D. We must construct a one-to-one correspondence V between $A \cup B$ and $C \cup D$. To do this, we proceed as follows: Let x be any element of $A \cup B$. Since $A \cap B = \emptyset$, then either $x \varepsilon A$ or $x \varepsilon B$, but x cannot belong to both A and B. Thus, under the correspondences S and T, x is paired with exactly one element in $C \cup D$. Moreover, since $C \cap D = \emptyset$, two different elements of $A \cup B$ cannot be paired to the same element in $C \cup D$, because each $y \varepsilon C \cup D$ occurs in only one of the correspondences S and T. So we see, as in our first example, that V does define a one-to-one correspondence between $A \cup B$ and $C \cup D$.

Now we can prove Theorem 11.

Proof of Theorem 11
1. Let sets A, B, C, D be chosen so that $n(A) = a$, $n(C) = a$, $n(B) = b$, $n(D) = b$, $A \cap B = \emptyset$, $C \cap D = \emptyset$.
2. Then $A \sim C$ and $B \sim D$.   Theorem 4, Chapter 5.
3. $A \cup B \sim C \cup D$ Theorem 12.
4. $n(A \cup B) = n(C \cup D)$ Theorem 3, Chapter 5.
5. Therefore, the sum $a + b$ is uniquely defined.

In Chapter 9 we have defined the addition of two whole numbers and have discussed the following properties of addition:

    addition is a binary operation on the set of whole numbers
    additive property of zero
    commutative property
    associative property
    if $a = b$, then $a + c = b + c$
    cancellation law
    uniquely defined —when you follow the defintion of +, only one
    We also proved that for any finite sets A and B, unique answer.

$$n(A) + n(B) = n(A \cap B) + n(A \cup B)$$

Now check your mastery of this material by working the following Post Test. Do not *refer to the text while doing this test. Complete the whole test before checking your answers.*

194

POST TEST

1. If a and b are whole numbers, $a + b = n(A \cup B)$, where A and B are sets such that $n(A) = a$, $n(B) = b$, $A \cap B = \emptyset$

2. Using the definition of addition, show that $3 + 3 = 6$. Use a separate piece of paper.

3. Justify each of the following statements:
   (a) $5 + 17 = 17 + 5$. *Commutative*
   (b) $1 + (2 + 3) = (1 + 2) + 3$. *Associative*
   (c) $3 + 0 = 3$. *Additive prop. of zero*
   (d) $8 + (3 + 2) = 8 + (2 + 3)$. *Commutative*
   (e) If a and b are whole numbers and $a + 6 = b + 6$, then $a = b$. *cancellation*
   (f) $5 + (3 + 1) = (3 + 1) + 5$. *Commutative*

4. There are many pairs of disjoint sets A and B such that $n(A) = a$ and $n(B) = b$. Does the sum $a + b$ depend upon your choice of A and B with the above properties? *No* Your answer illustrates the fact that the addition of whole numbers is *uniquely defined*.

5. Addition is a binary operation on the set of whole numbers because
   (a) There are *two* inputs.
   (b) $a + b$ is defined for *every* ordered pair (a, b) of whole numbers.
   (c) The sum $a + b$ is a *whole* number.

6. The proof of the commutative property of the addition of whole numbers uses what theorem in set theory? *Commutative prop of set union*

7. Since addition is associative, how is the sum $a + b + c$ defined?
   $(a+b)+c$

8. The generalized commutative property of addition states that the sum $a + b + c$ is independent of the *order* in which these numbers are written.

9. Correct the misleading statement 4 pens + 6 pens = 10 pens. *The $\cup$ of 4 pens & 6 pens = 10 pens*

10. If $a = b$ and $c = d$, what relation is true between $a + c$ and $b + d$?
    They are equal.

11. If $4 + x = 10$ and $4 + y = 10$, why is $x = y$? *Cancellation law*

12. In the Venn diagram

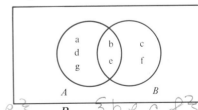

A

B

$A = \{a, d, g, b, e\}$, $B = \{b, e, c, f\}$, $n(A) = 5$,
$n(B) = 4$, $n(A \cap B) = 4$, $n(A \cup B) = 7$. Hence verify in this case that

$$n(A) + n(B) = n(A \cap B) + n(A \cup B)$$
$$5 + 4 = 7 + 2$$

13. Each of a group of people had at least one initial T. Five had their first initial T and seven had their last initial T. Three had both initials T. How many people were in the group? ___Nine___.

1. $n(A) = a$, $n(B) = b$, and $A \cap B = \varnothing$.
2. Let $A = \{1, 2, 3\}$ and $B = \{4, 5, 6\}$. Then $n(A) = 3$, $n(B) = 3$, and $A \cap B = \varnothing$. Hence $3 + 3 = n(A \cup B)$. But $A \cup B = \{1, 2, 3, 4, 5, 6\}$, so $n(A \cup B) = 6$. Thus $3 + 3 = 6$.
3. (a) Commutative property. (b) Associative property. (c) Additive property of zero. (d) Commutative property. (e) Cancellation law. (f) Commutative property.
4. No; uniquely defined
5. (a) two. (b) every. (c) whole
6. Commutative property of set union.
7. As either $(a + b) + c$ or $a + (b + c)$.
8. order
9. The union of a set of 4 pens and a set of 6 pens is a set of 10 pens.
10. They are equal.
11. Cancellation law.
12. $\{a, d, g, b, e\}$; $\{b, e, c, f\}$; 5; 4; 2; 7. So $5 + 4 = 2 + 7$.
13. Nine.

If you were successful in this Post Test, proceed to Chapter 10, Inequality and Subtraction.

10

Inequality and Subtraction

Before beginning this chapter, you should have completed Chapters 6, 8, and 9. In Chapter 10 we define the concepts of "greater than" and "less than" for pairs of whole numbers. Then we apply these ideas and the set-theoretic concept of relative complement to define subtraction and to develop its properties.

You will need to recall the following definitions:

    standard set
    cardinal number of a set
    relative complement
    binary operation on a set
    commutative property of a binary operation
    associative property of a binary operation

as well as certain properties of addition. The following Readiness Test will test your comprehension of these ideas.

R E A D I N E S S   T E S T

1. Let $A = \{1, 2, 3, 4\}$ and $B = \{1, 2, 3, 4, 5, 6\}$. Label the following statements true or false.

(a) $A \subseteq A$. _T_   (b) $A \subseteq B$. _T_

(c) $A \subset A$. _F_   (d) $A \subset B$. _T_

(e) $B \subset A$. _F_   (f) $B \subseteq A$. _F_

> (a) T.   (b) T.   (c) F.   (d) T.   (e) F.   (f) F.

2. Let $A = \{1, 2, 3, 4\}$ and $B = \{1, 2, 3, 4, 5, 6\}$.

(a) State whether each of the following sets is defined: $A \setminus B$. _No_
$B \setminus A$. _Yes_ $B \setminus B$. _Yes_

(b) Find those sets in (a) which are defined. $B \setminus A = \{5, 6\}, B \setminus B = \emptyset$

> (a) No; Yes; Yes.   (b) $B \setminus A = \{5, 6\}, B \setminus B = \emptyset$.

3. If A and B are finite sets, $n(A \cup B) = n(A) + n(B)$ if $A \cap B = \emptyset$.

> $A \cap B = \emptyset$ (or A and B are disjoint)

4. Find the sets A and B such that $n(A) = 4$, $n(B) = 2$, and $B \subseteq A$.
$A = \{1, 2, 3, 4\}$, $B = \{3, 4\}$.

> $A = \{1, 2, 3, 4\}, B = \{1, 2\}$ is one of many possible answers.

5. (a) The standard set $S(3) = \{1, 2, 3\}$, (b) $n[S(3)] = 3$.

> (a) $\{1, 2, 3\}$ (b) 3

---

6. In a binary operation $*$ on a set S, $a * b$ must be an *element of S*

element of S

7. A binary operation $*$ on a set S must be defined for every *ordered pair* in $S \times S$.

ordered pair

You should now be ready to begin Chapter 10.

10.1 Introduction

The notion of subtraction is based upon the operation that children call "take away". If we have a set A consisting of 7 objects and a subset B of A consisting of 4 objects, how many objects are left if we take B away from A? Obviously 3. Hence we write $7 - 4 = 3$.

Our definition of subtraction is motivated by this idea. We shall base it upon the properties of the relative complement $A \setminus B$ discussed in Chapter 6. We shall also need some additional properties of the whole numbers, which are given in the next section. Then we return to our discussion of subtraction.

10.2 Inequalities between Whole Numbers

Our intuition tells us that the whole number b is smaller than the whole number a if the standard set $S(b)$ contains fewer elements than the standard set $S(a)$, or if $S(b) \subset S(a)$. We use this intuition to define inequality as follows:

$b < a$ **DEFINITION.**   Let a and b be two whole numbers. We say that "b is less than a" (written $b < a$) if and only if $S(b) \subset S(a)$.

$b > a$ Also, "b is greater than a" (written $b > a$) if and only if $S(b) \supset S(a)$.

From this definition it is clear that the statements $b < a$ and $a > b$ have the same meaning; for the statements $S(b) \subset S(a)$ and $S(a) \supset S(b)$ are just two ways of saying the same thing.

In Chapter 5 we saw that for two given standard sets $S(a)$ and $S(b)$, precisely one of the following is true:

$$S(b) \subset S(a) \qquad S(b) = S(a) \qquad S(b) \supset S(a)$$

Using the definition of inequality above, we obtain the following result:

198

10.2 Inequalities between Whole Numbers

LAW OF TRICHOTOMY

THEOREM 1. LAW OF TRICHOTOMY. For any pair of whole numbers precisely one of the following is true:

$$b < a \qquad b = a \qquad b > a$$

Moreover, we have at once the following theorem:

THEOREM 2. If a and b are any two whole numbers with $b < a$, then there exist sets A and B such that $n(A) = a$, $n(B) = b$, and $B \subset A$.

For $A = S(a)$ and $B = S(b)$ have the required properties.

Inequality between whole numbers can also be represented on the number line (Figure 10.1). The numbers are ordered along this line so that $S(b) \subset S(a)$ if and only if b is to the left of a on the line. Hence we have the interpretation of inequality:

FIGURE 10.1. *Number line.*

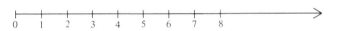

THEOREM 3. Let a and b be any two whole numbers. Then b is to the left of a on the number line if and only if $b < a$. Similarly, b is to the right of a if and only if $b > a$.

Theorem 4 is the most important theorem about inequalities, for it will be used to prove the rest of the theorems on inequality and will be basis for our approach to subtraction.

FUNDAMENTAL THEOREM

THEOREM 4. Let a and b be any two whole numbers. Then $b < a$ if and only if there is a whole number c $(\neq 0)$ such that $a = b + c$.

Proof
(a) *If $b < a$, then there is a whole number $c(\neq 0)$ such that $a = b + c$.*
1. Since $b < a$, $S(b) \subset S(a)$ Definition of $<$.
2. Therefore, $S(a) \setminus S(b)$ is defined and is not empty.
3. $S(a) = S(b) \cup [S(a) \setminus S(b)]$ Theorem 6, Chapter 6.
   $S(b) \cap [S(a) \setminus S(b)] = \varnothing$
4. Hence $n[S(a)] = n[S(b)] + n[S(a) \setminus S(b)]$ Definition of $+$.
5. Now $n[S(a)] = a$ and $n[S(b)] = b$. Let $n[S(a) \setminus S(b)] = c(\neq 0)$. Then from 4,

$$a = b + c$$

Thus the required number is $c = n[S(a) \setminus S(b)]$.
(b) *If there is a whole number c $(\neq 0)$ such that $a = b + c$, then $b < a$.*
1. Since $a = b + c$,

$$S(a) = S(b + c) = \{1, 2, \ldots, b, b + 1, \ldots, b + c\}$$

2. Since $S(b) = \{1, 2, \ldots, b\}$ and $c \neq 0$, it follows that $S(b) \subset S(a)$.
3. Therefore, $b < a$ Definition of $<$.

199

The following theorems are consequences of Theorem 4.

TRANSITIVE PROPERTY

THEOREM 5. For any three whole numbers: If $a < b$ and $b < c$, then $a < c$. This result is called the *transitive property* of inequalities.

Proof
1. Since $a < b$, there is a whole number x ($\neq 0$) such that $b = a + x$.
2. Since $b < c$, there is a whole number y ($\neq 0$) such that $c = b + y$.
3. From (1) and (2),

$$c = b + y = (a + x) + y = a + (x + y)$$

where $x + y \neq 0$
4. Therefore, by Theorem 4, $a < c$.

THEOREM 6. For any three whole numbers a, b, and c: if $b < a$, then $b + c < a + c$.

Proof
1. Since $b < a$, there is a whole number x ($\neq 0$) such that $a = b + x$ Theorem 4.
2. Therefore, $a + c = (b + x) + c = (b + c) + x$.
3. So $b + c < a + c$ Theorem 4.

We can also define the symbols $b \leq a$ and $b \geq a$ as follows:

$b \leq a$ AND $b \geq a$

DEFINITION. We say that "b is less than or equal to a" (written $b \leq a$) if and only if $S(b) \subseteq S(a)$.
Similarly, "b is greater than or equal to a" (written $b \geq a$) if and only if $S(b) \supseteq S(a)$.

Theorems 2, 4, 5, and 6 have almost exact parallels in terms of these new symbols. We shall state them as Theorems 2′, 4′, 5′, and 6′ and omit the proofs, for the proofs are almost identical to those of Theorems 2 to 6.

THEOREM 2′. If a and b are any two whole numbers with $b \leq a$, then there exist sets A and B such that $n(A) = a$, $n(B) = b$, and $B \subseteq A$.

THEOREM 4′. Let a and b be any two whole numbers. Then $b \leq a$ if and only if there is a whole number c such that $a = b + c$. (The possibility that $c = 0$ is included.)

THEOREM 5′. For any three whole numbers a, b, and c, if $a \leq b$ and $b \leq c$, then $a \leq c$.

THEOREM 6′. For any three whole numbers a, b, and c, if $b \leq a$, then $b + c \leq a + c$.

200

1. The inequality $b < a$ is true if and only if what relation is true between the standard sets $S(b)$ and $S(a)$? $S(b)$ ___⊂___ $S(a)$.

> ⊂

2. The inequality $b \geq a$ is true if and only if what relation is true between the standard sets $S(b)$ and $S(a)$? $S(b)$ ___⊇___ $S(a)$.

> ⊇

3. If $b < a$, then on the number line b is to the __left__ of a.

> left

4. The inequality $b \leq a$ is true if and only if there is a whole number c such that __$a = b + c$__.

> $a = b + c$

5. The whole number c of frame 4 is the cardinal number of what set derived from $S(a)$ and $S(b)$? __$c = n[S(a) \setminus S(b)]$__

> $c = n[S(a) \setminus S(b)]$.

6. Using standard sets prove that $3 < 7$ by following these steps:
(a) $S(3) = \{$__1, 2, 3__$\}$. (b) $S(7) = \{$__1 2 3 4 5 6 7__$\}$.
(c) Thus $S(3)$ ___⊂___ $S(7)$. (d) $3 < 7$. __Definition of $<$__
 (<, ⊂, =, ⊃) (reason)

> (a) $\{1, 2, 3\}$ (b) $\{1, 2, 3, 4, 5, 6, 7\}$ (c) ⊂ (d) Definition of $<$.

7. Since $3 < 7$ and $7 < 10$, then 3 ___<___ 10. Which law of in-
$\phantom{7. Since 3 < 7 and}$ (<, =, >)
equalities have you used? __Transitive of inequalities__

> < Transitive law of inequalities.

8. Since $3 < 7$, $3 + 4$ ___<___ $7 + 4$.
$\phantom{8. Since 3 < 7, 3 + 4}$ (<, =, >)

> <

9. *Prove:* For any four whole numbers, if $a < b$ and $c < d$, then $a + c < b + d$.

Proof

1. If $a < b$, then $a + c$ ___< ___ $b + c$ by Theorem __6__.
$$(<, =, >)$$

2. If $c < d$, then $b + c$ ___< ___ $b + d$ by Theorem __6__.
$$(<, =, >)$$

3. Then $a + c$ ___< ___ $b + c$ and $b + c$ ___< ___ $b + d$, so $a + c < b + d$ by Theorem __5__.

$<$; 6	$<$; 6	$<, <, 5$ (or transitive law)

10. There is a cancellation law of inequalities for addition which is the converse of Theorem 6.

Prove: For any three whole numbers, if $a + c < b + c$, then $a < b$.

Proof

1. Suppose a is not less than b. Then, by the law of trichotomy, either $a = b$ or __$a > b$__.

2. If $a = b$, then by Theorem 8, Chapter 9, $a + c$ ___= ___ $b + c$.
$$(<, =, >)$$

3. If $a > b$, and hence $b < a$, then by Theorem 6, $b + c$ ___< ___ $a + c$,
$$(<, =, >)$$

so $a + c$ ___> ___ $b + c$.
$$(<, =, >)$$

4. Thus we have shown, for any three whole numbers, if a is not less than b, then $a + c$ is not less than $b + c$. Then the contrapositive of this statement, for any 3 whole numbers, if $a+c <$ $b+c$, then $a < b$. ___, is true.

$a > b$	$=$	$<$ $>$	For any three whole numbers, if
			$a + c < b + c$, then $a < b$

10.3 Definition of Subtraction

In view of Theorem 4' we can now define subtraction as follows:

EQUAL

$a - b = c$ ~~EQUIVALENT~~
TO $a = b + c$

DEFINITION. Let a and b be any whole numbers such that $b \leq a$. Then $a - b$ is defined to be that whole number c such that $a = b + c$.

In the expression $a - b$, the number a is called the "minuend", the number b is called the "subtrahend", and $a - b$ is called the "difference".

REMARKS

1. Note that $a - b$ is defined only when $b \leq a$.
2. The subtraction statement "$a - b = c$" is equivalent to the addition

statement "$a = b + c$". This observation will be the basis of the proofs of most of our theorems about subtraction.

3. The difference, c, which is equal to $a - b$ by the definition, is the cardinal number of the set $S(a) \setminus S(b)$.

As was noted in Remark 3, the difference $a - b$ is the cardinal number of $S(a) \setminus S(b)$. We can, however, use other sets to find $a - b$. The relevant theorem is the following:

$a - b = n(A \setminus B)$ **THEOREM 7.** Let a and b be any two whole numbers with $b \leq a$. Then the difference $a - b$ can be obtained in the following fashion:

Choose any sets A and B with $n(A) = a$ and $n(B) = b$ and such that $B \subseteq A$. This is possible because of Theorem 2'. Then $a - b = n(A \setminus B)$.

Proof
1. Since $B \subseteq A$, $A \setminus B$ is defined. Let $A \setminus B = C$, and $n(C) = c$.
2. $A = B \cup (A \setminus B)$ and $B \cap (A \setminus B) = \emptyset$ Chapter 6.
or $A = B \cup C$ and $B \cap C = \emptyset$.
3. $n(A) = n(B) + n(C)$ Definition of addition.
4. Hence $a = b + c$ or $a - b = c$ Definition of subtraction.
5. Therefore, $a - b = n(C) = n(A \setminus B)$.

10.4 Properties of Subtraction

Many of the properties of addition fail to have analogs in subtraction, but there are several cases in which addition and subtraction do have parallel properties. Let us consider them one by one.

(1) *Binary Operation.* Subtraction is *not* a binary operation on the set of whole numbers, for $a - b$ is defined only when $b \leq a$ and not for *every* ordered pair (a, b).

We shall prove later that subtraction *is* a binary operation on the set of integers.

(2) *Commutativity.* Subtraction is not commutative, for $7 - 2 \neq 2 - 7$.

(3) *Associativity.* Since $(10 - 4) - 1 = 5$ and $10 - (4 - 1) = 7$, it is clear that subtraction is not associative.

(4) *Property of zero.* Since $a = 0 + a$, it follows from the definition of subtraction that $a - 0 = a$.

(5) *Property of equality.* As in the case of addition (Theorem 8, Chapter 9) we have the following theorem:

THEOREM 8. If a, b, and c are any whole numbers such that $a = b$, $c \leq a$, and $c \leq b$, then
$$a - c = b - c.$$

The proof is almost identical to that of Theorem 8, Chapter 9, and is left to the exercises.

As an application of this theorem, we can now prove the *cancellation law of addition.*

CANCELLATION LAWS

THEOREM 9. For any three whole numbers,

$$\text{If } a + c = b + c, \text{ then } a = b.$$

Proof
1. Since $(a + c) = (b + c)$, it follows from Theorem 8 that $(a + c) - c = (b + c) - c$.
2. Since $a + c = a + c$, it follows from the definition of subtraction that

$$(a + c) - c = a.$$

3. Since $b + c = b + c$, it is also true that

$$(b + c) - c = b.$$

4. From steps 1, 2, and 3,

$$a = b$$

The *cancellation law of subtraction* can be proved as follows:

THEOREM 10. For any three whole numbers a, b, and c such that $c \leq a$ and $c \leq b$,

$$\text{If } a - c = b - c, \text{ then } a = b.$$

Proof
1. Let $a - c = d$; then $a = c + d$.
2. Since $a - c = b - c$, it is also true that $b - c = d$, or $b = c + d$.
3. Therefore, $a = b$.

10.5 Addition and Subtraction on the Number Line

The operations of addition and subtraction can be easily performed by counting on the number line. For example, to add $2 + 4$ we consider the disjoint sets $\{1, 2\}$ and $\{3, 4, 5, 6\}$, where $n\{1, 2\} = 2$ and $n\{3, 4, 5, 6\} = 4$. Then

$$2 + 4 = n[\{1, 2\} \cup \{3, 4, 5, 6\}]$$

$$= n\{1, 2, 3, 4, 5, 6\}$$

$$= 6$$

USE OF NUMBER LINE

This can be simplified to the procedure shown in Figure 10.2. Starting at 0 draw an arrow of length 2 pointing to the right. From the end of this arrow draw a second arrow of length 4 pointing to the right. The end point of this second arrow is at 6, so $2 + 4 = 6$.

FIGURE 10.2. *Addition on the number line.*

204

To do subtraction we reverse the procedure. Consider the problem of finding $7 - 4$. We start from the standard set $A = \{1, 2, 3, 4, 5, 6, 7\}$, where $n(A) = 7$. Then we choose $B \subseteq A$ to be $B = \{4, 5, 6, 7\}$, where $n(B) = 4$. Therefore, $A \setminus B = \{1, 2, 3\}$. So $7 - 4 = n\{1, 2, 3\} = 3$. This can be accomplished on the number line as shown in Figure 10.3. Starting at 0

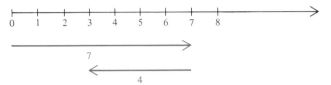

FIGURE 10.3. *Subtraction on the number line.*

draw an arrow of length 7 pointing to the right. From the end of this arrow, draw a second arrow of length 4 pointing to the *left*. The end of the second arrow is at 3, so $7 - 4 = 3$.

1. In the set of whole numbers, if $a \leq b$, which difference is defined: ___b - a___?
   $(a - b, b - a)$

   > $b - a$

2. Why is $3 - 7$ not defined in the set of whole numbers?
   _____

   > $7 > 3$, not $7 \leq 3$ as required.

3. In the set of whole numbers, $c - d$ is defined if and only if ___d ≤ c___.
   $(c \leq d, c = d, d \leq c)$

   > $d \leq c$

4. Show that $2 \leq 6$. $S(2) = \{1, 2\}$, $S(6) = \{1, 2, 3, 4, 5, 6\}$. $S(2) \subseteq S(6)$. Hence $2 \leq 6$.

   > $\{1, 2\}$ $\{1, 2, 3, 4, 5, 6\}$ $\subseteq$ $2 \leq 6$

5. Since $2 \leq 6$, ___6 - 2___ is defined in the set of whole numbers.
   $(2 - 6, 6 - 2)$

   > $6 - 2$

6. The subtraction statement $6 - 4 = 2$ is equivalent to the addition statement $6 = 4 + 2$. Since $6 = 4 + 2$ is true, it follows that $6 - 4 = 2$ is true.

> $6 = 4 + 2$ 2

7. Use Theorem 7 to show that $6 - 4 = 2$. We might let $A = \{5,6,7,8,9,10\}$ and $B = \{5,7,8,10\}$. Then $n(A) = 6$, $n(B) = 4$, and $B \subseteq A$ ($\subseteq$ or $\supseteq$?). Hence, by definition of subtraction, $n(A) - n(B) = n(A \setminus B)$; that is, $6 - 4 = n(A \setminus B)$. But $A \setminus B = \{6, 9\}$ so $n(A \setminus B) = 2$. Hence

> 6   4 $\subseteq$ $\{6, 9\}$ 2

8. Use Theorem 7 to show that $5 - 5 = 0$. Write your argument on a separate piece of paper.

> Let $A = \{1, 2, 3, 4, 5\}$ and $B = \{1, 2, 3, 4, 5\}$. Thus $n(A) = 5$, $n(B) = 5$, and $B \subseteq A$. Thus, by the definition of subtraction, $n(A) - n(B) = n(A \setminus B)$; that is, $5 - 5 = n(A \setminus B)$. But $A \setminus B = \emptyset$, so $n(A \setminus B) = 0$. Hence $5 - 5 = 0$.

9. Why is subtraction *not* a binary operation on the set of whole numbers? $a - b$ might be a negative number or an integer.

> $a - b$ is not defined for *every* ordered pair (a, b) of whole numbers.

10. Why is subtraction not commutative (even on the set of integers)? A counterexample is $5 - 2 \neq 2 - 5$.

> Many answers, such as $8 - 3 \neq 3 - 8$.

11. Why is subtraction not associative? A counterexample is $(10 - 4) - 3 \neq 10 - (4 - 3)$.
$6 - 3 \neq 9$

> Many answers, such as $(8 - 5) - 3 \neq 8 - (5 - 3)$.

12. If a and b are whole numbers such that $b \leq a$, then $a - b$ is defined, and if $a - b = c$ we call a the minuend, b the subtrahend, and c the difference. Thus, for example, in the expression $6 - 4 = 2$, __6__ is the minuend, __4__ the subtrahend, and __2__ the difference.

> 6   4   2

13. On a separate piece of paper prove Theorem 8: If a, b, and c are any whole numbers such that $a = b$, $c \leq a$, and $c \leq b$, then $a - c = b - c$. Model your proof on Theorem 8, Chapter 9.

> **Proof**
> 1. Since $c \leq a$ and $c \leq b$, then $a - c$ and $b - c$ exist.
> 2. The hypothesis says that a and b are names for the same number.
> 3. $a - c$ is a symbol representing the difference of the number whose name is a (or b) and the number whose name is c.
> 4. $b - c$ is a symbol representing the difference of the number whose name is b (or a) and the number whose name is c.
> 5. Therefore, $a - c$ and $b - c$ are two different names for the difference of the same two numbers.
> 6. Because of this we write $a - c = b - c$.

14. The cancellation law of addition states that for any three whole numbers a, b, and c, if $a + c = b + c$, then ___$a = b$___.

> $a = b$

15. The cancellation law for subtraction states that for any three whole numbers a, b, and c, where $c \leq a$ and $c \leq b$, if $a - c = b - c$, then ___$a = b$___.

> $a = b$

16. To perform the addition $a + b$ on the number line we start at ___0___ and draw an arrow of length ___a___ to the right. From the end of this arrow we draw a second arrow of length ___b___ to the right. The end of the second arrow is at the point labeled ___$a + b$___.

> $0 \quad a \quad b \quad a + b$

17. To perform the subtraction $a - b$ on the number line we start at ___0___ and draw an arrow of length ___a___ to the ___right___. From the end of this arrow we draw a second arrow of length ___b___ to the ___left___. The end of the second arrow is at the point labeled ___$a - b$___.

> $0 \quad a \quad$ right $\quad b \quad$ left $\quad a - b$

10.6 Theorems about Subtraction

There are quite a few theorems about subtraction that are needed in arithmetic. All of these are proved in the same way:

BASIC STRATEGY OF PROOF. Convert all subtraction statements such as $a - b = c$ into the corresponding addition statements $a = b + c$. Then use the properties of addition.

As illustrations of this method, we shall prove two theorems which are the basis for the usual computational methods of subtraction. You are then expected to use similar procedures to prove other theorems.

THEOREM 11. For all whole numbers, a, b, c, and d, where $a \geq b$ and $c \geq d$,

$$(a + c) - (b + d) = (a - b) + (c - d)$$

Proof
1. Let $a - b = f$; then $a = b + f$ Basic strategy.
2. Let $c - d = g$; then $c = d + g$.
3. $a + c = (b + f) + (d + g)$
   $\quad\quad = (b + d) + (f + g).$
4. $(a + c) - (b + d) = f + g$
   $\quad\quad\quad\quad\quad\quad = (a - b) + (c - d).$

THEOREM 12. For all whole numbers a, b, and c, where $a \geq b$,

$$a - b = (a + c) - (b + c)$$

Proof
1. Let $a - b = d$, then $a = b + d$ Basic strategy.
2. $a + c = (b + d) + c$
   $\quad\quad = (b + c) + d.$
3. $(a + c) - (b + c) = d$
   $\quad\quad\quad\quad\quad\quad = a - b.$

In the following frames prove (on separate pieces of paper) the stated theorems using the methods described in this section.

1. For any whole number a, $a - a = 0$.

   Proof. $a - a = 0$ is equivalent to the true addition statement $a = a + 0$.

2. For all whole numbers a and b

   $$(a + b) - b = a$$

   Proof
   1. $a + b = a + b.$
   2. $(a + b) - b = a$ Definition of subtraction.

3. For all whole numbers a and b, where $b \leq a$,

$$(a - b) + b = a$$

Proof
1. $a - b = a - b$.
2. $(a - b) + b = a$ Definition of subtraction.

4. For all whole numbers a, b, and c, where $b \geq c$,

$$(a + b) - c = a + (b - c)$$

Proof
1. Let $b - c = d$. Then $b = c + d$ Definition of subtraction.
2. $a + b = a + (c + d)$
    $= (a + d) + c$.
3. $(a + b) - c = a + d$ Definition of subtraction.
    $= a + (b - c)$.

5. For all whole numbers a, b, and c, where $(b + c) \leq a$,

$$a - (b + c) = (a - b) - c$$

Proof
1. Let $a - (b + c) = d$.
    Then $a = (b + c) + d$ Definition of subtraction.
2. $a = b + (c + d)$.
3. $a - b = c + d$ Definition of subtraction.
4. $(a - b) - c = d$ Definition of subtraction.
    $= a - (b + c)$.

In this chapter we have introduced the notations $a < b$, $a > b$, $a \leq b$, $a \geq b$, and $a - b$.

We have discussed the following concepts:

inequality (greater than, less than)
trichotomy law of inequality
transitive law of inequality
subtraction of whole numbers
properties of subtraction

The following Post Test will check your comprehension of these new ideas.

POST TEST

1. Use standard sets to show that $4 < 6$. $S(4) =$ {1,2,3,4} ,
$S(6) =$ {1,2,3,4,5,6}, $S(4)$ ⊂ $S(6)$; thus 4<6 .

2. If $S(a)$ and $S(b)$ are standard sets corresponding to the whole numbers a and b, then $a \leq b$ if and only if $S(a)$ ⊆ $S(b)$.

3. The transitive law of inequalities says: For any three whole numbers, if $a < b$ and $b < c$, then a<c .

4. If a and b are whole numbers and if $a = b$ is false and $a > b$ is false, what relation between a and b is true? a<b

5. If $a < b$ find sets A and B such that $n(A) = a$, $n(B) = b$, and $A \subset B$. Do *not* choose special values for a and b, but give an answer that applies to any whole numbers a and b. _____

6. If $b \leq a$, there exists a whole number c such that a=b+c .

7. If a and b are whole numbers and $a < b$, then $a + 7$ < $b + 7$.
$(<, =, >)$

8. If a is any whole number, then, since $2 < 7$, $2 + a$ < $7 + a$.
$(<, =, >)$

9. Show that the following is *not* true. For any four whole numbers $a, b, c,$ and d, if $a < b$ and $c < d$, and if $c < a$ and $d < b$, then $a - c < b - d$. A counterexample is $a =$ 10 , $b =$ 6 , $c =$ 5 , $d =$ 3 .

10. If $b \leq a$, then $a - b$ is defined to be the whole number c such that a=b+c .

11. Why is $6 - 2 = 4$? 6=2+4

12. If $b \leq a, n(A) = a, n(B) = b$, and $B \subseteq A$, then $a - b = n($ A\B).

13. On the set of whole numbers, subtraction is not a binary
$(is, is not)$
operation, subtraction is not commutative, and subtraction is
$(is, is not)$ $(is,$
not associative.
is not)

14. On a separate piece of paper prove: For all whole numbers a, $a - a = 0$.

15. On a separate piece of paper prove: For all whole numbers $a, b,$ and c such that $b \leq a$, $a - b = (a + c) - (b + c)$.

1. $\{1, 2, 3, 4\}$; $\{1, 2, 3, 4, 5, 6\}$; $\subset$; $4 < 6$
2. $\subseteq$
3. $a < c$
4. $a < b$.
5. $A = S(a)$, $B = S(b)$. Answers like $A = \{1, 2\}$, $B = \{1, 2, 3\}$ are not acceptable.
6. $a = b + c$
7. $<$
8. $<$

9. For example, $a = 3$, $b = 5$, $c = 1$, $d = 4$. For $3 < 5$ and $1 < 4$ where $1 < 3$ and $4 < 5$. But $3 - 1$ is not less than $5 - 4$.

10. $a = b + c$

11. $6 - 2 = 4$ is equivalent to $6 = 2 + 4$.

12. $(A \setminus B)$

13. is not; is not; is not

14. (See Section 10.6, frame 1.)

15. (See Section 10.6, Theorem 12.)

If you made mistakes in this test review the chapter until you understand why you went wrong. Then proceed to Chapter 11.

11

Multiplication and Division

Before starting this chapter you should review Chapter 7, Cartesian Products. In Chapter 11 we first define the multiplication of whole numbers and discuss the properties of this operation. Then we define division in terms of multiplication.

You should be familiar with the following concepts:

Cartesian product of sets
equivalence of sets
union of sets
cardinal number of a set
commutative property of a binary operation
associative property of a binary operation
inequality: "less than", "greater than"

To check your comprehension of these concepts, work through the following Readiness Test.

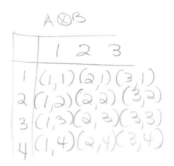

READINESS TEST

1. Let $a = 3$ and $b = 4$.
(a) Find a set A such that $n(A) = 3$.
(b) Find a set B such that $n(B) = 4$.
(c) Show the elements of $A \times B$ in an array in the usual manner.
(d) Find $n(A \times B)$.

Among many possible answers:
(a) $A = \{1, 2, 3\}$.
(b) $B = \{1, 2, 3, 4\}$.
(c)

$A \times B$

	1	2	3
1	(1, 1)	(2, 1)	(3, 1)
2	(1, 2)	(2, 2)	(3, 2)
3	(1, 3)	(2, 3)	(3, 3)
4	(1, 4)	(2, 4)	(3, 4)

(d) 12.

2. If S and T are finite sets such that $S \sim T$, then $n(S)$ _____ $n(T)$.

=

3. For any set S, $S \times \varnothing =$ _____.

$\varnothing$

4. Label the following statements true or false. ~~T~~
(a) For all sets S and T, if $S = T$, then $S \sim T$. ___T___
(b) For all sets S and T, if $S \sim T$, then $S = T$, ___F___
(c) For all sets S and T, $S \cup T = T \cup S$. ___T___
(d) For all sets S and T, $S \cap T = T \cap S$. ___T___

Is this ⊗ or ×? ⊛ — (e) For all sets S and T, $S \times T = T \times S$. ___

> (a) T.   (b) F.   (c) T.   (d) T.   (e) F.

5. If $*$ is a binary operation on the set of whole numbers,
(a) $*$ is commutative if and only if ___for every pair of whole nos. a & b a * b = b * a___
(b) $*$ is associative if and only if ___for every triple of whole no. a, b, & c, (a*b)*c = a*(b*c)___.

> (a) for every pair of whole numbers a and b, $a * b = b * a$
> (b) for every triple of whole numbers a, b, and c, $(a * b) * c = a * (b * c)$

6. If $a < b$, then $a + c$ ___<___ $b + c$.

> $<$

7. If $S(a) \supset S(b)$, where $S(a)$ and $S(b)$ are standard sets, then a ___>___ b.
$(<, =, >)$

> $>$

8. $A \times B \neq B \times A$ but $A \times B$ ___$\sim$___ $B \times A$.

> $\sim$ (equivalent)

9. $(A \times B) \times C \neq A \times (B \times C)$ but $(A \times B) \times C$ ___$\sim$___ $A \times (B \times C)$.

> $\sim$ (equivalent)

When you are satisfied that you are prepared for this chapter, read Sections 11.1 through 11.4 and work the program following Section 11.4.

11.1 Multiplication

One approach to multiplication is to regard it as being repeated addition. Accordingly, we write

$$3 \cdot 5 = 5 + 5 + 5 = 15$$

$$5 \cdot 3 = 3 + 3 + 3 + 3 + 3 = 15$$

Although this method is completely sound for the product of two natural numbers, it runs into difficulty when we try to apply it to $0 \cdot 5$. How do we add 5 to itself zero times and conclude that the result is zero? There is no trouble of this sort, however, when we write

$$5 \cdot 0 = 0 + 0 + 0 + 0 + 0 = 0$$

In this chapter we shall not follow this approach, and shall introduce by contrast a definition of the multiplication of whole numbers that is based on our earlier discussion of the Cartesian product of two sets.

11.2 Definition of Multiplication

The definition to be given later in this section is based upon intuition which a child can obtain by using a pegboard or similar devices. To multiply $3 \cdot 5$, he can put pegs into holes so that he has three columns, each containing five pegs (Figure 11.1). By counting the total number of pegs he finds that $3 \cdot 5 = 15$. To compute $5 \cdot 3$ he makes five columns, each containing three pegs (Figure 11.2) and again reaches the result: $5 \cdot 3 = 15$.

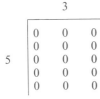

3

	0	0	0
	0	0	0
5	0	0	0
	0	0	0
	0	0	0

FIGURE 11.1

5

	0	0	0	0	0
3	0	0	0	0	0
	0	0	0	0	0

FIGURE 11.2

After a number of exercises of this type, he has developed an effective, though possibly tedious, method of multiplying. Moreover, he is aware that multiplication is commutative. Our task here is to capitalize on this intuition and to give a formal definition of multiplication on the basis of which we can prove its important properties.

Let us be given any two whole numbers, a and b. We wish to define their product $a \cdot b$. The rectangular array on the pegboard suggests that we base this on the known concept of the Cartesian product of two corresponding sets, A and B. We choose A such that $a = n(A)$ and B such that $b = n(B)$. Then we form $A \times B$ (the rectangle of the pegboard) and count its elements to find $n(A \times B)$. Put formally, the definition is as follows:

MULTIPLICATION

DEFINITION. The product, $a \cdot b$ of any pair of whole numbers a and b is defined to be

$$a \cdot b = n(A \otimes B)$$

where A and B are any sets such that $n(A) = a$ and $n(B) = b$.

When there is no risk of confusion we shall write $a \cdot b$ simply as ab, where juxtaposition indicates the product. It is also common to use the cross, $\times$, to indicate multiplication of numbers. We have not done so here to prevent confusion between the Cartesian product of sets and the product of two numbers. When there is no risk of such confusion, the $\times$ is an excellent notation for the multiplication of numbers, and we shall adopt this notation in later chapters.

This definition should raise the following questions in your mind about ab:
(1) Is it uniquely defined?
(2) Is it a binary operation on the set of whole numbers?
(3) Is it commutative?
(4) Is it associative?
We answer these in the next section.

215

11.3 Properties of Multiplication

(1) MULTIPLICATION IS UNIQUELY DEFINED

The question before us is whether the product ab depends upon our choice of sets A and B such that $n(A) = a$ and $n(B) = b$. Suppose that we choose other sets, C and D, such that $n(C) = a$ and $n(D) = b$. Then we have another formula for ab: $ab = n(C \times D)$. The question before us is the truth of the equality:

$$n(A \times B) = n(C \times D)$$

Our intuition says that this is correct, and it is. We, therefore, say that multiplication is *uniquely defined*, for the definition of $a \cdot b$ does not depend upon your personal choice of the sets A and B used in finding $a \cdot b$. Thus we have our first theorem:

UNIQUELY DEFINED

THEOREM 1. The multiplication of whole numbers is uniquely defined. – one answer,

The proof of this theorem is somewhat long, and so (as in the case of the corresponding theorem for addition) we postpone its proof to Section 11.10.

BINARY OPERATION

(2) MULTIPLICATION IS A BINARY OPERATION ON THE SET OF WHOLE NUMBERS

Multiplication is clearly binary and it is surely defined for every ordered pair (a, b) of whole numbers. The only delicate question is whether $a \cdot b$ is a whole number. By definition $a \cdot b = n(A \times B)$, where A and B are finite sets. Thus $a \cdot b$ is a whole number if the Cartesian product $A \times B$ of two finite sets is a finite set. Although this fact should be almost self-evident, its proof is too complicated to present here.

In view of these remarks we conclude that the following theorem is true:

THEOREM 2. Multiplication is a binary operation on the set of whole numbers.

COMMUTATIVE

(3) MULTIPLICATION IS COMMUTATIVE

We must show that for every pair of whole numbers a and b,

$$ab = ba$$

From the definition of multiplication, this amounts to proving that for every pair of sets, A and B:

$$n(A \times B) = n(B \times A)$$

The proof is harder than the corresponding theorem in addition—that

$$n(A \cup B) = n(B \cup A)$$

for we have shown that in general $A \times B \neq B \times A$, whereas in the earlier case $A \cup B = B \cup A$. All that is required for our conclusion, however, is that

216

we demonstrate that for all A and B,

$$(A \times B) \sim (B \times A)$$

This was proved in Theorem 2, Chapter 7.

The formal argument is the following:

THEOREM 3. For every pair of whole numbers, a and b, $ab = ba$. That is, the multiplication of whole numbers is commutative.

Proof

1. Given a and b, choose sets A and B such that $n(A) = a$ and $n(B) = b$.
2. Then $ab = n(A \times B)$; $ba = n(B \times A)$.
3. $(A \times B) \sim (B \times A)$ Theorem 2, Chapter 7
4. $n(A \times B) = n(B \times A)$ Theorem 3, Chapter 5.
5. $ab = ba$ Definition of product.

ASSOCIATIVE

(4) MULTIPLICATION IS ASSOCIATIVE

The problem here is to demonstrate that for any triple of whole numbers

$$a(bc) = (ab)c$$

In view of our detailed discussion of the commutativity of multiplication and the results of Chapter 7, we proceed immediately to the formal proof.

THEOREM 4. For any triple of whole numbers, a, b, and c,

$$a(bc) = (ab)c$$

That is the multiplication of whole numbers is associative.

Proof

1. Given a, b, and c, choose sets A, B, and C such that $n(A) = a$, $n(B) = b$, and $n(C) = c$.
2. Then $bc = n(B \times C)$
   $$a(bc) = n[A \times (B \times C)]$$
   $$(ab)c = n[(A \times B) \times C].$$
3. We know that $A \times (B \times C) \neq (A \times B) \times C$, but we have proved that for any sets A, B, and C,

$$[A \times (B \times C)] \sim [(A \times B) \times C] \quad \text{Theorem 6, Chapter 7.}$$

4. Therefore,

$$n[A \times (B \times C)] = n[(A \times B) \times C]$$

5. Hence

$$a(bc) = (ab)c$$

GENERALIZED COMMUTATIVE

(5) GENERALIZED COMMUTATIVE PROPERTY

Since multiplication is associative, we can define the triple product $a \cdot b \cdot c$ as being equal to either of the equal expressions: $(ab)c$ or $a(bc)$.

Since multiplication is both commutative and associative, the *generalized commutative property* is true.

THEOREM 5. For all whole numbers, *a*, *b*, and *c* the following six expressions are equal:

$$a \cdot b \cdot c \qquad b \cdot a \cdot c \qquad c \cdot a \cdot b$$

$$a \cdot c \cdot b \qquad b \cdot c \cdot a \qquad c \cdot b \cdot a$$

CANCELLATION LAW **(6) CANCELLATION LAW**

As in the cases of addition and subtraction, there is a *cancellation law for multiplication.*

THEOREM 6. For any whole numbers *a* and *b* and any whole number $c \, (\neq 0)$:

$$\text{If } a \cdot c = b \cdot c, \text{ then } a = b.$$

The proof of this theorem is postponed until we have considered division.

REMARK

The hypothesis $c \neq 0$ in Theorem 6 is essential; for from $3 \cdot 0 = 7 \cdot 0$ we cannot conclude that $3 = 7$.

11.4 Special Products — identity property of X.

$a \cdot 1 = a$ (1) $a \cdot 1 = a$ for any whole number *a*. In order to apply the definition choose *A* such that $n(A) = a$. If we then choose any singleton set $\{x\}$, we have $n\{x\} = 1$. From Theorem 3, Chapter 7, we know that for any set *A*,

$$(A \times \{x\}) \sim A$$

Therefore,

$$n(A \times \{x\}) = n(A)$$

or

$$a \cdot 1 = a$$

Since multiplication is commutative, we also have $1 \cdot a = a$.

$a \cdot 0 = 0$ (2) $a \cdot 0 = 0$ for any whole number *a*. Here again we choose *A* such that $n(A) = a$. We also recall that $n(\varnothing) = 0$. So we must compute $n(A \times \varnothing)$. From Section 7.4 we know that $A \times \varnothing = \varnothing$. Thus

$$a \cdot 0 = n(A \times \varnothing)$$

$$= n(\varnothing)$$

$$= 0$$

Since multiplication is commutative it also follows that $0 \cdot a = 0$.

We are now in a position to prove the following important theorem:

THEOREM 7. If a and b are any two whole numbers and if $ab = 0$, then at least one of the numbers a and b is zero.

IF $a \cdot b = 0, a = 0$ or $b = 0$

Proof. We must consider a number of possibilities, which are exhibited in the table.

Line	a	b	ab
1	0	0	
2	0	$\neq 0$	
3	$\neq 0$	0	
4	$\neq 0$	$\neq 0$	

Filling the third column we obtain:

Line	a	b	ab	
1	0	0	0	Section 11.4(2).
2	0	$\neq 0$	0	Section 11.4(2).
3	$\neq 0$	0	0	Section 11.4(2)
4	$\neq 0$	$\neq 0$	$\neq 0$	If $A \neq \emptyset$ and $B \neq \emptyset$, then $A \times B \neq \emptyset$.

Since we assume that $ab = 0$, we must exclude line 4, and so one of the first three lines is true. But this shows that $a = 0$, $b = 0$, or both a and $b = 0$.

---

1. The product, ab, is defined to be $n(\underline{A \times B})$, where $\underline{n(A)} = a$ and $\underline{n(B)} = b$.

$A \times B$	$n(A)$	$n(B)$

2. If $A = \{a, b\}$ and $B = \{a, b, c\}$, show the elements of $A \times B$ in an array in the usual manner.

$A \times B$	a	b
a	(a, a)	(b, a)
b	(a, b)	(b, b)
c	(a, c)	(b, c)

3. To show by definition of product that $2 \cdot 3 = 6$, we might proceed as follows: Let $A = \{a, b\}$ and $B = \{a, b, c\}$. Then $n(A) = \underline{2}$, and $n(B) = \underline{3}$. Now $(A \times B) = \{(a, a), (a, b), (a, c), (b, a), (b, b), (b, c)\}$ so $n(A \times B) = \underline{6}$. Thus, since $n(A) \cdot n(B) = n(A \times B)$, we have $2 \cdot 3 = 6$.

2	3	6

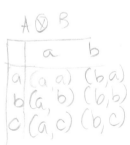

4. Show by definition of product that $3 \cdot 2 = 6$. Use a separate piece of paper.

> Let $A = \{a, b, c\}$ and $B = \{a, b\}$. Then $A \times B = \{(a, a), (a, b), (b, a), (b, b), (c, a), (c, b)\}$ and $n(A) = 3$, $n(B) = 2$, $n(A \times B) = 6$. Since $n(A) \cdot n(B) = n(A \times B)$ we have $3 \cdot 2 = 6$. (*Note*: You may have used different sets than the sets A and B given above, as long as their cardinalities were 3 and 2, respectively.)

5. Let a and b be any whole numbers and A and B be sets so that $n(A) = a$ and $n(B) = b$. Then $ab = n(A \times B)$ and $ba = n(B \times A)$. For the proof that multiplication is commutative—that $ab = ba$—we needed to show that $n(A \times B) = n(B \times A)$. Now it is not true that for all sets A and B, $A \times B = B \times A$, but we do know from Chapter 7 that for all sets A and B, $A \times B \sim B \times A$. Hence $n(A \times B) = n(B \times A)$ so $ab = ba$.

> $ab = ba \qquad \sim \qquad =$

6. Similarly, for the proof of associativity of multiplication, let a, b, and c be any whole numbers and A, B, C be sets such that $n(A) = a$, $n(B) = b$, and $n(C) = c$. We wanted to show that $(ab)c = a(bc)$. Now, by definition of product,

$$(ab)c = n(A \times B) \cdot n(C)$$
$$= n[(A \times B) \times C]$$

and similarly,

$$a(bc) = n(A) \cdot n(B \times C)$$
$$= n[A \times (B \times C)]$$

Now, it is *not* true that for all sets A, B, and C, $(A \times B) \times C = A \times (B \times C)$, but again from Chapter 7 we know that $(A \times B) \times C \sim A \times (B \times C)$, so that $n[(A \times B) \times C] = n[A \times (B \times C)]$, so we have $(ab)c = a(bc)$ for all whole numbers a, b, and c.

> $a(bc) \qquad n[A \times (B \times C)] \qquad \sim \qquad = \qquad =$

7. What theorem about Cartesian products is used to prove that the multiplication of whole numbers is commutative? $A \times B \sim B \times A$

> $A \times B \sim B \times A$.

8. What theorem about Cartesian products is used to prove that the multiplication of whole numbers is associative? $(A \times B) \times C \sim A \times (B \times C)$

> $(A \times B) \times C \sim A \times (B \times C)$.

9. The statement that $a \cdot b$ is *uniquely defined* means that the value of $a \cdot b$ (as computed from its definition) does not depend upon your _choice_ of sets A, B as long as _$n(A)$_ $= a$ and _$n(B)$_ $= b$.

| choice | $n(A)$ | $n(B)$ |

10. Show by definition of product that $5 \cdot 0 = 0$. Use a separate piece of paper.

> Let $A = \{a, b, c, d, e\}$ and $B = \emptyset$. Then $n(A) = 5$ and $n(B) = 0$. Moreover, $A \times B = \emptyset$ so $n(A \times B) = 0$. So we have $n(A) \cdot n(B) = n(A \times B)$; that is, $5 \cdot 0 = 0$.

11. Show by definition of product that $5 \cdot 1 = 5$. Use a separate piece of paper.

> Let $A = \{a, b, c, d, e\}$ and $B = \{x\}$. Then $n(A) = 5$, $n(B) = 1$, $A \times B = \{(a, x), (b, x), (c, x), (d, x), (e, x)\}$ and $n(A \times B) = 5$. Thus, since $n(A) \cdot n(B) = n(A \times B)$, we have $5 \cdot 1 = 5$.

12. Justify each of the following statements by naming a theorem or property about whole numbers.
 (a) $3 \cdot 18 = 18 \cdot 3$. _Commutative_
 (b) $5 \cdot (2 \cdot 4) = (5 \cdot 2) \cdot 4$. _Associative_
 (c) $5 \cdot 0 = 0$. _property of zero._
 (d) $1 \cdot 15 = 15$. _property of one_
 (e) $5[2 \cdot (3 + 6)] = (5 \cdot 2) \cdot (3 + 6)$. _Associative_
 (f) $6(3 + a) = (3 + a) \cdot 6$, where a is a whole number. _Commutative_
 (g) $0 \cdot (6 + 5) = 0$. _property of zero_
 (h) $3 \cdot 7 \cdot 5 = 5 \cdot 3 \cdot 7$. _General, commutative property_

> (a) Commutative property of multiplication.
> (b) Associative property of multiplication.
> (c) Multiplicative property of zero.
> (d) Multiplicative property of 1 [Section 11.4(1)].
> (e) Associative property of multiplication.
> (f) Commutative property of multiplication.
> (g) Multiplicative property of zero.
> (h) Generalized commutative property for multiplication.

13. On another sheet of paper, prove: If a, b, and c are whole numbers and if $a = b$, then $ac = bc$. (*Hint*: Similar theorems were proved for addition and subtraction.)

> 1. By hypothesis, a and b are names for the same number.
> 2. ac is a symbol representing the product of the number whose name is a (or b) and the number whose name is c.
> 3. bc is a symbol representing the product of the number whose name is b (or a) and the number whose name is c.
> 4. Therefore, ac and bc are two different names for the product of the same two numbers.
> 5. Because of this we write $ac = bc$.

14. An immediate result of frame 13 is: If a, b, c, and d are whole numbers and if $a = b$ and $c = d$, then $ac = bd$.

Proof
1. Since a, b, and c are whole numbers and $a = b$, then $ac = bc$ by frame 13.
2. Similarly, by frame 13, since b, c, and d are whole numbers and $c = d$, then $cb = \underline{db}$.
3. But by the commutative law of multiplication $cb = \underline{bc}$ and $db = \underline{bd}$, so $bc = bd$.
4. Hence we have $ac = bc$ and $bd = bc$, so ac and bd are symbols representing the same number, $\underline{bc}$.
5. Because of this we write $ac = bd$.

db	bc	bd	bc

15. *Prove*:

THEOREM 8. If $a < b$ and $c \neq 0$, then $ac < bc$.

Proof
1. Since $a < b$, $S(a) \underline{\subseteq} S(b)$.
2. Let C be such that $n(C) = c$. Since $C \neq \varnothing$, $S(a) \times C \underline{\subseteq} S(b) \times C$.
3. $n[S(A) \times C] = \underline{ac}$; $n[S(b) \times C] = \underline{bc}$.
4. Therefore, $ac \underline{<} bc$.

$\subset$	$\subset$	$ac \,; bc$	$<$

16. Prove a partial converse of Theorem 8:

THEOREM 9. If $ac < bc$ and $c \neq 0$, then $a < b$.
Using indirect proof assume a not less than b.

Proof
1. Then $a \underline{=} b$ or $a \underline{>} b$.
2. Assume $a = b$. Then $ac \underline{=} bc$ Frame 13.
3. Assume $a > b$. Then $ac \underline{>} bc$ Frame 15.

4. Since steps 2 and 3 contradict the hypothesis $ac < bc$ it follows that $a < b$.

| $=; >$ | $=$ | $ac > bc$ | $ac < bc; a < b$ |

When you have completed this program, read Sections 11.5 through 11.8 and work the program following Section 11.8.

11.5 Division

The process of division is the reverse of that of multiplication. For reasons to be explained later we must exclude zero at this point and deal only with the natural numbers.

DIVISION   **DEFINITION.** Let a, d, and q be natural numbers. Then $a \div d = q$ if and only if $a = qd$. We read $a \div d$ as "a divided by d". The number a is called the dividend, d the divisor, and q the quotient.

We carry out division on the pegboard (Section 11.2) by reversing the scheme for multiplication. To divide 15 by 3 we start with 15 pegs and arrange them in rows of 3 (Figure 11.1). Then we find that there are 5 rows. Hence $15 \div 3 = 5$.

11.6 Properties of Division

(1) Since the division $a \div d$ is defined only when there is a natural number q such that $a = qd$, division is not defined for all pairs (a, d) of natural numbers. Hence division is *not a binary operation* on the set of natural numbers. For example, $5 \div 2$ is not defined, since there is no natural number q such that $5 = 2q$.

We shall prove later that division *is* a binary operation on the set of non-zero rational numbers.

(2) Since $12 \div 3 = 4$ and $3 \div 12$ is not defined, division on the natural numbers is *not commutative.*

(3) Since

$$(12 \div 6) \div 2 = 2 \div 2 = 1$$

$$12 \div (6 \div 2) = 12 \div 3 = 4$$

division on the natural numbers is *not associative.*

223

11.7 Difficulties with Division by Zero

DIVISION BY ZERO

It is natural for you to wonder what to do about expressions such as

$$a \div 0 \qquad 0 \div 0 \qquad 0 \div a$$

where $a \neq 0$, which we have so far excluded from our discussion. Let us examine these in turn.

If $a \div 0$ (where $a \neq 0$) is equal to a whole number b, then it must be true that $0 \cdot b = a$. But $0 \cdot b = 0$ (Section 11.4). Since $a \neq 0$, this is a contradiction. Hence the expression $a \div 0$ is not sensible and will not be defined.

If $0 \div 0$ is equal to a whole number b, then it must be true that $0 \cdot b = 0$. This, however, is true (Section 11.4) for every b. So $0 \div 0$ can be anything. A result of this kind is very unsatisfactory, for a symbol in mathematics is inconvenient unless it has a unique meaning. Therefore, we do not give any meaning to $0 \div 0$ and call it undefined.

If $0 \div a$ (where $a \neq 0$) is equal to a whole number b, then $ab = 0$. By Theorem 7 we conclude that $b = 0$. Hence $0 \div a = 0$.

These remarks enable us to extend our definition of division to the set of whole numbers as follows:

DEFINITION. Let a, d, and q be *whole* numbers such that $d \neq 0$. Then $a \div d = q$ if and only if $a = qd$. Division by zero is not defined.

11.8 Theorems about Division

In proving theorems about division we use a strategy similar to that for proving theorems about subtraction:

STRATEGY OF PROOF

BASIC STRATEGY. In proving a theorem concerning the division $a \div b = c$, convert this statement into the equivalent multiplication statement $a = bc$, and then use the properties of multiplication.

Here are a few samples of such theorems. In the exercises you are asked to prove others by a similar method.

THEOREM 10. For all whole numbers a and b, where $b \neq 0$ and such that $a \div b$ is defined,

$$(a \div b) \cdot b = a$$

Proof
1. Let $a \div b = c$. Then $a = cb$.
2. Substituting $a \div b$ for c in $cb = a$ we have

$$(a \div b) \cdot b = a$$

THEOREM 11. For all whole numbers a and b, where $b \neq 0$,

$$(a \cdot b) \div b = a$$

224

Proof

1. Let $a \cdot b = c$. Then $a = c \div b$.
2. Substituting $a \cdot b$ for c in $a = c \div b$, we have

$$a = (a \cdot b) \div b$$

A theorem of a different kind is the analog of similar theorems for addition, subtraction, and multiplication.

THEOREM 12. For all whole numbers a, b, and c, where $a \div c$ and $b \div c$ are defined, if $a = b$, then $a \div c = c = b \div c$.

The proof is almost identical to those given earlier for Theorem 8, Chapter 9; Theorem 8, Chapter 10; and frame 13, Section 11.4.

Now we can prove the cancellation laws of multiplication and division as follows:

CANCELLATION LAWS

THEOREM 6 (See Section 11.3). **CANCELLATION LAW FOR MULTIPLICATION.** For any whole numbers a and b and for any whole number c ($\neq 0$): If $a \cdot c = b \cdot c$, then $a = b$.

Proof

1. Since $a \cdot c = b \cdot c$, we have from Theorem 12 that

$$(a \cdot c) \div c = (b \cdot c) \div c$$

2. Hence from Theorem 11, $a = b$.

THEOREM 13. CANCELLATION LAW FOR DIVISION. For any three whole numbers a, b, and c such that $a \div c$ and $b \div c$ are defined:

$$\text{If } a \div c = b \div c, \text{ then } a = b.$$

Proof

1. Since $a \div c = b \div c$, we have from frame 13, Section 11.4, that $(a \div c) \cdot c = (b \div c) \cdot c$.
2. Hence, from Theorem 10, $a = b$.

---

1. By definition of division, $12 \div 3 = 4$ because $12 = 4 \cdot 3$.

$12 = 4 \cdot 3$

2. $3 \div 12$ is not defined because no whole number a such that $3 = 12a$.

not defined
there is no whole number a such that $3 = 12a$.

225

3. $0 \div 7 =$ ___0___.

0

4. $7 \div 0$ is _undefined_

undefined

5. Show that if a, b, and c are natural numbers, and if $a \div b = c$, then $a \div c = b$. Use a separate piece of paper.

If $a \div b = c$, then $a = cb$
$cb = bc$
$a = bc$
$a \div c = b$

1. If $a \div b = c$, then $a = cb$.
2. By commutativity of multiplication, $cb = bc$.
3. Hence $a = bc$, so, by definition of division, $a \div c = b$.

6. Why is division not a binary operation on the set of whole numbers? The symbol $a \div d$ is not defined for _all_ ordered pairs (a, d).

all

7. Give a counterexample to show that division on the set of whole numbers is not commutative. _$10 \div 2 = 5$, but $2 \div 10$ is not defined._

For example, $8 \div 2 = 4$, but $2 \div 8$ is not defined.

8. Give a counterexample to show that division on the set of whole numbers is not associative. $(16 \div 4) \div 2 = 2$, $16 \div (4 \div 2) = 8$

For example, $(24 \div 4) \div 2 = 3$, $24 \div (4 \div 2) = 12$.

9. It is true that $(24 \div 6) \div 1 = 24 \div (6 \div 1) = 4$. Does this prove that division is associative? _No_

No.

10. Prove that $a \div 1 = a$. $a = a \cdot 1$

This is true since $a = a \cdot 1$.

11. *Prove:*

THEOREM 14. For all whole numbers a, b, and c, if $a < b$ and $a \div c$ and $b \div c$ are both defined, then $a \div c < b \div c$.

226

Proof
1. Let $a \div c = d$. Then $a =$ ___cd___ .
2. Let $b \div c = e$. Then $b =$ ___ce___ .
3. $cd < ce$. Why? ___a < b by the hypothesis___
4. $d < e$. Why? ___Theorem 9___

| cd | ce | $a < b$ by hypothesis. | Theorem 9. |

---

12. *Prove*:

THEOREM 15. If $a \div c$ and $b \div c$ are both defined and $a \div c < b \div c$, then $a < b$.

Proof
1. Let $a \div c = d$. Then $a =$ ___cd___ .
2. Let $b \div c = e$. Then $b =$ ___ce___ .
3. $d < e$. Why? ___Hypothesis___
4. Then cd ___<___ ce. Theorem 8.
5. Hence $a < b$.

| cd | ce | Hypothesis. | $<$ |

---

13. *Prove*:

THEOREM 16. If $a < b$, $c \neq 0$, and $c \div a$ and $c \div b$ are both defined, then $c \div b < c \div a$.

Proof
1. Let $c \div a = d$. Then $c =$ ___ad___ .
2. Then $cb =$ ___adb___ .
3. So $cb \div ab =$ ___d___ .
4. Let $c \div b = e$. Then $c =$ ___be___ .
5. Then $ca =$ ___abe___ .
6. So $ca \div ab =$ ___e___ .
7. Since $a < b$ by hypothesis, ca ___<___ cb.
8. Dividing by ab (since both quotients are defined) we have $ca \div ab$ ___<___ $cb \div ab$. Hence from steps (3) and (6), ___e < d___ .
9. Therefore, from steps (1) and (4), ___c ÷ b < c ÷ a___

| ad | abd | d | be | abe | e | $<$ | $e < d$ |
| $c \div b < c \div a$ | | | | | | | |

---

14. *Prove*:

THEOREM 17. $(ab) \div d = b(a \div d)$.

Proof
1. Let $a \div d = e$. Then $a = ed$.
2. So $ab = edb$.
3. $(ab) \div d = eb$
4. $\qquad = b(a \div d)$.

Now complete the chapter by reading Section 11.9 and working its program.

11.9 Division with Remainder

3

0	0	0
0	0	0
0		

Figure 11.3

When $a \div d$ $(d \neq 0)$ is not defined by the process above, it is possible to save the situation by defining division with remainder.

Let us consider the use of the pegboard to see what happens if we try to divide 7 by 3. We take 7 objects and try to arrange them in rows of 3. The result is an array like that in Figure 11.3. Ordinary division is not defined, for we have two full rows and one row with only one peg in it. We can state this result as $7 \div 3 = 2$ with a remainder of 1. Notice that $7 = 3 \cdot 2 + 1$.

DIVISION WITH REMAINDER

DEFINITION. Let a, d, q, and r be whole numbers such that $a = qd + r$ and $r < d$. Then $a \div d = q$ with a remainder of r.

It is very important to known that division with remainder is always possible. This is proved in the next theorem.

THEOREM 18. If a and d are any whole numbers with $d \neq 0$, there exist whole numbers q and r with $r < d$ such that

$$a = qd + r$$

Before proving this theorem let us examine two illustrations of it. First let $a = 17$ and $d = 5$. Then it is clear that $q = 3$ and $r = 2$, since

$$17 = 3 \cdot 5 + 2 \qquad \text{and} \qquad 2 < 3$$

To suggest the general procedure for other examples, let us do this a more systematic way. On the number line mark off the multiples of the divisor 5: $0 \cdot 5, 1 \cdot 5, 2 \cdot 5, 3 \cdot 5, 4 \cdot 5, \ldots$ as in Figure 11.4. Then mark the point corresponding to 17. It lies between $3 \cdot 5 = 15$ and $4 \cdot 5 = 20$. So the quotient $q = 3$. The remainder $r = 17 - 3 \cdot 5 = 2$.

FIGURE 11.4. *Scheme for dividing 17 by 5.*

Second, let $a = 20$ and $d = 5$. Then $q = 4$ and $r = 0$. To do this on the number line, mark off the multiples of 5 as in Figure 11.5. Then mark the point corresponding to 20. It is exactly the same as the point $4 \cdot 5$, so $q = 4$ and $r = 0$.

FIGURE 11.5. *Scheme for dividing 20 by 5.*

To generalize this procedure in the case of general a and d mark the multiples of d on the number line as in Figure 11.6. Then find the point corresponding to a. If this is one of the points already marked, say qd, then the quotient is q and $r = 0$. If a lies between two of these points, say qd and

FIGURE 11.6. *Scheme for dividing a by d.*

$(q + 1)d$ as in Figure 11.7, then the quotient is q. The remainder, $r = a - qd$, is the distance from a to qd, which from Figure 11.7 is less than d. This completes the proof.

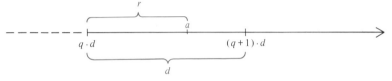

FIGURE 11.7. *The quotient is q and the remainder is* $r < d$*.*

EXACT DIVISION

When $r = 0$, we say that the division is *exact*. In this case we use "divides" in a technical sense and say that "d divides a" (evenly). When this is true, we are back at the situation described in Section 11.5.

---

1. Since $17 = 6 \cdot 2 + 5$ and $5 < 6$ we say that $17 \div \underline{6} = \underline{2}$ with a remainder of $\underline{5}$.

> 6   2   5

2. $17 \div 2 = \underline{8}$ with a remainder of $\underline{1}$ because $17 = 2 \cdot 8 + 1$ _____.

> 8   1 $17 = 2 \cdot 8 + 1$ and $1 < 2$

3. $18 \div 25 = \underline{0}$ with a remainder of $\underline{18}$ because $18 = 25 \cdot 0 + 18$ _____.

> 0   18 $18 = 25 \cdot 0 + 18$ and $18 < 25$

4. If a and d are whole numbers where $d \neq 0$, d divides a if and only if there is a whole number q such that $a = qd +$ ___0___.

0

5. If a and d are whole numbers with $d \neq 0$ and d divides a, then there is a whole number q such that $a = qd + 0$. Hence we have $a \div d =$ ___q___.

q

6. Conversely, if a, d, and q are whole numbers, $d \neq 0$ and if $a \div d = q$, then $a = qd +$ ___0___. Hence $a \div d = q$ with a remainder of ___0___, so we say d _divides_ a.

0   0   divides

11.10 Multiplication Is Uniquely Defined (optional)

UNIQUELY DEFINED

Here we present the proof of Theorem 1 which was omitted in Section 11.3.

THEOREM 1. *The multiplication of whole numbers is uniquely defined.*

Recall that we are given two whole numbers a and b and sets A and B such that $n(A) = a$ and $n(B) = b$. We also have two other sets C and D such that $n(C) = a$ and $n(D) = b$. The result to be proved is that

$$n(A \times B) = n(C \times D)$$

Our intuition says that this is correct. How do we prove it? The standard method of proving that the cardinal numbers of two sets are equal is to show that the sets can be put into a one-to-one correspondence. That is, we must prove that

$$(A \times B) \sim (C \times D)$$

Before trying to prove this let us start with an example. If

$$A = \{a, b, c\}, \; B = \{m, n,\}, \; C = \{x, y, z\}, \; D = \{r, s\}$$

then

$$A \times B = \begin{Bmatrix} (a, m), & (b, m), & (c, m) \\ (a, n), & (b, n), & (c, n) \end{Bmatrix}$$

$$C \times D = \begin{Bmatrix} (x, r), & (y, r), & (z, r) \\ (x, s), & (y, s), & (z, s) \end{Bmatrix}$$

Moreover, we have the following equivalences (as indicated by the displayed one-to-one correspondences):

$$A \sim C \qquad\qquad B \sim D$$

$$S: \begin{matrix} \{a & b & c\} \\ \updownarrow & \updownarrow & \updownarrow \\ \{x & y & z\} \end{matrix} \qquad T: \begin{matrix} \{m & n\} \\ \updownarrow & \updownarrow \\ \{r & s\} \end{matrix}$$

Using these we can immediately write the one-to-one correspondence

$$(A \times B) \sim (C \times D)$$

$$V: \begin{matrix} \{(a,m) & (b,m) & (c,m) & (a,n) & (b,n) & (c,n)\} \\ \updownarrow & \updownarrow & \updownarrow & \updownarrow & \updownarrow & \updownarrow \\ \{(x,r) & (y,r) & (z,r) & (x,s) & (y,s) & (z,s)\} \end{matrix}$$

As a generalization, we state the following theorem:

THEOREM 19. If A, B, C, and D are any sets satisfying $A \sim C$ and $B \sim D$, then

$$(A \times B) \sim (C \times D)$$

Proof. We first suppose that none of A, B, C, and D is empty and pattern our argument on the previous example. Since $A \sim C$ and $B \sim D$, there are two one-to-one correspondences, say S and T, between A and C and between B and D, respectively. Now to prove our theorem, we must construct a one-to-one correspondence, V, between $A \times B$ and $C \times D$. But a pair from $A \times B$, say (a, b), includes an element from A and an element from B. The element $a \varepsilon A$ is paired (via S) with a unique element $c \varepsilon C$, and the element $b \varepsilon B$ is paired (via T) with a unique element $d \varepsilon D$. These two elements define an element of $C \times D$, (c, d). So we define

$$V: (a, b) \leftrightarrow (c, d)$$

where a and c are paired in S and where b and d are paired in T, and our theorem is proved for this case.

If any of the sets A, B, C, and D is empty, both $A \times B$ and $C \times D$ are empty and hence equivalent. This completes the proof of our theorem.

Proof of Theorem 1

1. Given two whole numbers a and b, choose sets A, B, C, and D such that

$$a = n(A) = n(C) \qquad b = n(B) = n(D)$$

2. Then $A \sim C$ and $B \sim D$ Theorem 4, Chapter 5.
3. $(A \times B) \sim (C \times D)$ Theorem 19.
4. $n(A \times B) = n(C \times D)$ Theorem 3, Chapter 5.

When two sets are equivalent, their cardinal numbers are equal.

You have now completed your introduction to multiplication and division. The most important ideas in this chapter are
    definition of multiplication

properties of multiplication:
    uniquely defined
    a binary operation
    commutative
    associative
    $a \cdot 1 = a; a \cdot 0 = 0$
    cancellation law
definition of division: $a \div d = q$ provided $a = qd$
properties of division:
    not a binary operation
    not commutative
    not associative
    division by zero not defined
    cancellation law
division with remainder

To check your comprehension of these ideas, work the Post Test that follows. Do not refer to the text while working this test. Check your answers after you have completed the entire test.

	1	2	3
1	(1,1)	(2,1)	(3,1)
2	(1,2)	(2,2)	(3,2)
3	(1,3)	(2,3)	(3,3)
4	(1,4)	(2,4)	(3,4)

POST TEST

1. Use the definition of multiplication to compute $3 \cdot 4$. Use a separate piece of paper. $n(A \otimes B) \supseteq 12$

2. The statement "The product of two whole numbers is uniquely defined" means _There is only one answer that can be reached by multiplying 2 whole numbers._

3. What theorem about Cartesian products is used to prove that the multiplication of whole numbers is commutative? $A \otimes B \sim B \otimes A$

4. The law of cancellation for the multiplication of whole numbers states that: _For all whole no. a, b, c, where c ≠ 0: If a·c = b·c, then a = b._

5. Prove that for any whole number $a, a \cdot 0 = 0$ $n(A) = a, n(B) = \emptyset$ $A \otimes \emptyset = \emptyset, n(A \otimes B) = 0, so a \cdot 0 = 0$

6. Label the following true or false.
(a) For every whole number $a, a \cdot 1 = a$. _T_
(b) For every whole number $a, a \cdot 0 = 0$. _T_
(c) For every pair of whole numbers, a and $b, a \div b = b \div a$. _F_
(d) For every pair of whole numbers, a and $b, ab = ba$. _T_
(e) For every triple of whole numbers, a, b, and $c, a(bc) = (ab)c$. _T_
(f) For every triple of whole numbers, a, b, and $c, a \div (b \div c) = (a \div b) \div c$. _F_
(g) For all whole numbers $a, b,$ and c, if $a < b$, then $ac < bc$. _F_

It is not stated that c ≠ 0.

7. Justify each of the following statements.
(a) $2 \cdot 3 = 3 \cdot 2$. _commutative_
(b) $2 \cdot (3 + 4) = (3 + 4) \cdot 2$. _commutative_
(c) $2 \cdot (3 + 4) = 2 \cdot (4 + 3)$. _commutative_
(d) $2 \cdot (3 \cdot 4) = (2 \cdot 3) \cdot 4$. _associative_
(e) $2 \cdot (3 \cdot 4) = (3 \cdot 4) \cdot 2$. _commutative_

8. If a, d, and q are whole numbers and $d \neq 0$, then $a \div d$ is defined to be equal to q if and only if _$a = qd$_.

9. If $a \neq 0$, why must we call $a \div 0$ undefined? _If $a \div 0 = b$ then $a = 0 \times b$, $a = 0$, but if $a \neq 0$ then there is no b._

10. If $a \div c < b \div c$, what is the relation between a and b? _$a < b$_

11. The statement "b divides c" means that _b is exact._

12. $19 \div 5 =$ _3_ with a remainder of _4_ because _$5 \cdot 3 + 4 = 19$_.

13. *Prove*: For any natural number a, $a \div a = 1$. _$a = 1 \cdot a$ therefore $a \div a = 1$._

14. *Prove*: If a and b are whole numbers and $a \div b$ is defined, then $(a \div b) \cdot b = a$. _$a \div b = c$ then $a = cb$ substituting $(a \div b)$ for c in $cb = a$, we get $(a \div b) \cdot b = a$._

15. If a and b are whole numbers, and $ab = 0$, and $a \neq 0$, then b _$= 0$_.

16. $0 \div 0$ is _undefined_. $1 \div 0$ is _undefined_. $0 \div 1$ is _0_.

17. Show that the following statement is not true: If a, b, c, and r are natural numbers and $c \div a = b$ with a remainder of r, then $c \div b = a$ with a remainder of r. _$20 \div 3 = 6 \, r \, 2$, $20 \div 6 = 3 \, r \, 2$_

1. Let $A = \{a, b, c\}$, $B = \{x, y, z, w\}$. Then $A \times B =$

	a	b	c
x	(a, x)	(b, x)	(c, x)
y	(a, y)	(b, y)	(c, y)
z	(a, z)	(b, z)	(c, z)
w	(a, w)	(b, w)	(c, w)

and $n(A \times B) = 12$.

2. The product $a \cdot b$ does not depend upon the choice of sets A and B used in the computation provided $n(A) = a$ and $n(B) = b$.

3. $A \times B \sim B \times A$.

4. For all whole numbers a, b, and c where $c \neq 0$: If $a \cdot c = b \cdot c$, then $a = b$.

5. Let A be such that $n(A) = a$, and let $B = \emptyset$. Then $A \times B = A \times \emptyset = \emptyset$. So $n(A \times B) = 0$ and $a \cdot 0 = 0$.

6. (a) T. (b) T. (c) F. (d) T. (e) T. (f) F. (g) F.

7. (a) Commutativity of multiplication.
   (b) Commutativity of multiplication.
   (c) Commutativity of addition.
   (d) Associativity of multiplication.
   (e) Commutativity of multiplication.

8. $a = qd$.

9. If $a \div 0 = b$, then $a = 0 \cdot b$. Hence $a = 0$. But $a \neq 0$ by hypothesis. So no such b exists.

10. $a < b$.

11. the division of c by b is exact (no remainder)

12. $3 ; 4 ; 19 = 5 \cdot 3 + 4$

13. For any natural number a, $a = 1 \cdot a$. Hence, by definition of division, $a \div a = 1$.

14. (See Theorem 10.)

15. $= 0$

16. undefined ; undefined ; 0

17. For example, $19 \div 5 = 3$ with a remainder of 4, $19 \div 3 = 6$ with a remainder of 1.

If you were successful in this test, proceed to the Readiness Test for Chapter 12.

12

The Distributive Law

You should have completed the Post Test to Chapter 11 before starting this chapter. In Chapter 12 we discuss the Distributive Law, which gives a connection between addition and multiplication. To follow this chapter you must have previously mastered the chapters on addition (Chapter 9) and multiplication (Chapter 11). The following Readiness Test will determine whether you are prepared to proceed.

READINESS TEST

1. If $n(A) = a$ and $n(B) = b$, then $n(A \times B) =$ _____ (in terms of a and b).

> $a \cdot b$

2. If $n(A) = a$ and $n(B) = b$ and $A \cap B = \varnothing$, then $n(A \cup B) =$ _____ (in terms of a and b).

> $a + b$

3. What operations of arithmetic are commutative? _____

> Addition and multiplication.

4. If $b \leq a$, then $a - b$ is defined to be the whole number c such that _____ .

> $a = b + c$

5. If $a = qd$, then $a \div d =$ _____.

> q

6. When is $a \div b$ defined? _____

> When $b \neq 0$ and there is an integer c such that $a = bc$.

7. How is $a + b + c$ defined? _____

> It is equal to either of $(a + b) + c$ or $a + (b + c)$.

If you believe that you are ready, read the material in this chapter, completing the programs as they occur. Refer to the text as necessary while working these programs.

12.1 Introduction

As they have been defined in Chapters 9 and 11, addition and multiplication appear as quite separate binary operations. Given two whole numbers a and b, we find sets A and B such that $n(A) = a$ and $n(B) = b$. For addition we must choose A and B disjoint; for multiplication they may be disjoint or not as we will. Then

$$a + b = n(A \cup B)$$

$$a \cdot b = n(A \times B)$$

Actually, these two processes are not as independent of each other as these definitions may suggest. Indeed, we may regard multiplication of natural numbers as repeated addition.

When we turn to the addition and multiplication of other kinds of numbers (fractions and negative numbers) in later chapters, we shall find that we can no longer regard multiplication as repeated addition. For in expressions such as

$$\tfrac{1}{2} \cdot \tfrac{3}{5}$$

we certainly cannot "add $\tfrac{3}{5}$ to itself one half of a time". Nevertheless, for all our types of numbers there is a close connection between addition and multiplication. This is given by the *distributive law*, which is stated: For all whole numbers a, b, and c,

$$a(b + c) = ab + ac.$$

For the natural numbers, this law is equivalent to the statement that "multiplication is repeated addition". For other number systems, however, the distributive law remains true, whereas "multiplication is repeated addition" becomes nonsense.

Our purpose in this chapter is twofold: (1) to state and prove the distributive law for whole numbers, and (2) to prepare the way for its generalization to other number systems. We have reserved an entire chapter for this law, for it lies at the heart of arithmetic and algebra. It plays an essential role in (1) the justification of the usual procedures for adding and multiplying whole numbers, (2) the rules for multiplying signed numbers, (3) the processes of removing parentheses and factoring in arithmetic and algebra, and (4) the proofs of numerous special and useful results in arithmetic. It is, therefore, a law of the greatest importance, whose value may not be appreciated at first sight because of its simplicity.

12.2 Distributive Property of Cartesian Product over Set Union

The logical foundation of the distributive law is a similar property involving Cartesian products and the union of sets. It has the following statement:

12.2 Distributive Property of Cartesian Product over Set Union

CARTESIAN PRODUCT OVER UNION

THEOREM 1. DISTRIBUTIVE PROPERTY OF CARTESIAN PRODUCT OVER SET UNION. For all sets A, B, and C,

$$A \times (B \cup C) = (A \times B) \cup (B \times C)$$

As a first attempt at establishing this result let us suppose that

$$A = \{a_1, a_2\}$$
$$B = \{b_1, b_2, b_3\}$$
$$C = \{c_1, c_2\}$$

Then $B \cup C = \{b_1, b_2, b_3, c_1, c_2\}$.

Next form the product $A \times (B \cup C)$:

$A \times (B \cup C)$

	a_1	a_2
b_1	(a_1, b_1)	(a_2, b_1)
b_2	(a_1, b_2)	(a_2, b_2)
b_3	(a_1, b_3)	(a_2, b_3)
c_1	(a_1, c_1)	(a_2, c_1)
c_2	(a_1, c_2)	(a_2, c_2)

Immediately we see that the set that is above the dashed line in this array is the set $A \times B$, and that the set below the dashed line is the set $A \times C$. Since these two sets have no elements in common, it follows that the complete set of pairs in this array is their union, that is,

$$A \times (B \cup C) = (A \times B) \cup (A \times C)$$

This is a special case, for we have chosen particular sets A, B, and C. The result, however, is true in all cases. The details of the general proof are given in the exercises below.

There is an analogous property involving Cartesian products and set intersection:

CARTESIAN PRODUCT OVER INTERSECTION

THEOREM 2. DISTRIBUTIVE PROPERTY OF CARTESIAN PRODUCT OVER SET INTERSECTION. For all sets A, B, and C,

$$A \times (B \cap C) = (A \times B) \cap (A \times C)$$

This property may be verified by choosing particular sets just as was done in connection with Theorem 1.

---

1. Let us consider another example to illustrate Theorem 1. Let $A = \{x, y, z\}$, $B = \{a, b\}$, $C = \{p, q, r\}$. Then $B \cup C = \{$_____$\}$ and

237

The Distributive Law

$A \times (B \cup C) =$

	x	y	z
a			
b			
p			
q			
r			

Also $A \times B =$

	x	y	z
a			
b			

and $A \times C =$

	x	y	z
p			
q			
r			

Then $A \times (B \cup C) =$ _____.

$B \cup C = \{a, b, p, q, r\}$

$A \times (B \cup C) =$

	x	y	z
a	(x, a)	(y, a)	(z, a)
b	(x, b)	(y, b)	(z, b)
p	(x, p)	(y, p)	(z, p)
q	(x, q)	(y, q)	(z, q)
r	(x, r)	(y, r)	(z, r)

$A \times B =$

	x	y	z
a	(x, a)	(y, a)	(z, a)
b	(x, b)	(y, b)	(z, b)

$A \times C =$

	x	y	z
p	(x, p)	(y, p)	(z, p)
q	(x, q)	(y, q)	(z, q)
r	(x, r)	(y, r)	(z, r)

$A \times (B \cup C) = (A \times B) \cup (A \times C)$.

2. Consider the proof of Theorem 1 : $A \times (B \cup C) = (A \times B) \cup (A \times C)$. The set $A \times (B \cup C)$ is a set of ordered pairs of the following types: (a, b), where b is in B but not in C; (a, c), where c is in C but not in B; and (a, d), where d is in both B and C.

Proof
1. The set $A \times B$ consists of those pairs above which are of the types _____ or _____.
2. The set $A \times C$ consists of those pairs above which are of the types _____ or _____.
3. The set $(A \times B) \cup (A \times C)$ consists of those pairs above which are of the types _____ or _____ or _____.
4. Therefore, $A \times (B \cup C) =$ _____.

(a, b); (a, d) (a, c); (a, d) (a, b); (a, c); (a, d)
$(A \times B) \cup (A \times C)$

3. For the sets of frame 1,

$$A = \{x, y, z\} \qquad B = \{a, b\} \qquad C = \{p, q, r\}$$

is it true that

$$(B \cup C) \times A = (B \times A) \cup (C \times A)?$$

Let us see.

$(B \cup C) \times A =$

	a	b	p	q	r
x					
y					
z					

$B \times A =$

	a	b
x		
y		
z		

$C \times A =$

	p	q	r
x			
y			
z			

Is $(B \cup C) \times A = (B \times A) \cup (C \times A)$? _____

$(B \cup C) \times A =$

	a	b	p	q	r
x	(a, x)	(b, x)	(p, x)	(q, x)	(r, x)
y	(a, y)	(b, y)	(p, y)	(q, y)	(r, y)
z	(a, z)	(b, z)	(p, z)	(q, z)	(r, z)

$B \times A =$

	a	b
x	(a, x)	(b, x)
y	(a, y)	(b, y)
z	(a, z)	(b, z)

$C \times A =$

	p	q	r
x	(p, x)	(q, x)	(r, x)
y	(p, y)	(q, y)	(r, y)
z	(p, z)	(q, z)	(r, z)

Yes, they are equal.

4. Let us look at an example to illustrate Theorem 2:

$$A \times (B \cap C) = (A \times B) \cap (A \times C)$$

If we take

$$A = \{\text{Ada, Edie, Ida}\}$$
$$B = \{\text{Smith, Johnson, Brown}\}$$
$$C = \{\text{Smith, Jones, Brown}\}$$

then

$(B \cap C) = \{\text{Smith, Brown}\}$ and $A \times (B \cap C) = \{(\text{Ada, Smith}),$ (Ada, Brown), (Edie, Smith), (Edie, Brown), (Ida, Smith), (Ida, Brown)\}.

$A \times B = \{(\text{Ada, Smith}),$ (Ada, Johnson), (Ada, Brown), (Edie, Smith), (Edie, Johnson), (Edie, Brown), _____, _____, _____\}

(Ida, Smith)   (Ida, Johnson)   (Ida, Brown)

5. Let A, B, and C be as in frame 4. Which of the ordered pairs in $A \times B$ will also be found in $A \times C$? _____

All except those containing "Johnson" [i.e., exactly the six ordered pairs that compose the set $A \times (B \cap C)$].

240

6. Using the notations of frame 2, let us prove Theorem 2, $A \times (B \cap C) = (A \times B) \cap (A \times C)$.

Proof

1. The set $A \times (B \cap C)$ consists of pairs of the type _____ .
2. The set $A \times B$ consists of pairs of the types _____ or _____ .
3. The set $A \times C$ consists of pairs of the types _____ or _____ .
4. The set $(A \times B) \cap (A \times C)$ consists of pairs of the type _____ .
5. Therefore, $A \times (B \cap C) =$ _____ .

(a, d) $(a, b); (a, d)$ $(a, c); (a, d)$ (a, d)
$(A \times B) \cap (A \times C)$

12.3 Distributive Property of Multiplication over Addition

Although we previously called this *the distributive law*, there are other relations like those of Section 12.2 which are also distributive. So, to be definite, we use the more explicit language: *distributive property of multiplication over addition*. This property is stated in Theorem 3:

MULTIPLICATION OVER ADDITION

THEOREM 3. DISTRIBUTIVE PROPERTY OF MULTIPLICATION OVER ADDITION. For every three whole numbers a, b, and c,

$$a(b + c) = (ab) + (ac)$$

Proof

1. As usual, choose sets A, B, and C such that $n(A) = a$, $n(B) = b$, and $n(C) = c$. Moreover, choose B and C so that $B \cap C = \varnothing$.
2. From Theorem 1,

$$A \times (B \cup C) = (A \times B) \cup (A \times C)$$

3. Therefore,

$$n[A \times (B \cup C)] = n[(A \times B) \cup (A \times C)]$$

4. From the definition of multiplication

$$n[A \times (B \cup C)] = n(A) \cdot n(B \cup C)$$
$$= a \cdot n(B \cup C)$$

5. From the definition of addition and our assumption that $B \cap C = \varnothing$,

$$n(B \cup C) = n(B) + n(C)$$
$$= b + c$$

241

6. Therefore,

$$n[A \times (B \cup C)] = a(b + c)$$

7. Now, working on the right side of the equality in step 3, we must consider

$$n[(A \times B) \cup (A \times C)]$$

First we must show that $(A \times B)$ and $(A \times C)$ are disjoint. This follows from Theorem 2 and the assumption that $B \cap C = \varnothing$. For

$$(A \times B) \cap (A \times C) = A \times (B \cap C) = A \times \varnothing = \varnothing.$$

8. Hence from the definition of addition,

$$n[(A \times B) \cup (A \times C)] = n(A \times B) + n(A \times C)$$

9. Using the definition of multiplication, we derive the formulas

$$n(A \times B) = ab \quad \text{and} \quad n(A \times C) = ac$$

so that

$$n[(A \times B) \cup (A \times C)] = (ab) + (ac)$$

10. Finally, substituting the results of steps 6 and 9 into the equality in step 3, we obtain the desired statement:

$$a(b + c) = (ab) + (ac)$$

12.4 Illustrations and Extensions

The most elementary illustrations of the distributive property of multiplication over addition are similar to the following:

$$3 \cdot (4 + 6) = (3 \cdot 4) + (3 \cdot 6)$$

or

$$3 \cdot 10 = 12 + 18$$

and each side is equal to 30. Thus we can obtain the result by using either side of this equation, the choice being made on the basis of simplicity and convenience. In certain cases the use of this law permits us to multiply with great ease. For example,

$$23 \cdot 11 = 23(10 + 1) = 230 + 23 = 253$$

This method is more striking in the case of

$$28 \cdot 9 = 28(10 - 1) = 280 - 28 = 252$$

Since this involves subtraction rather than addition, it assumes the true fact that multiplication is distributive over subtraction. We shall prove this later in this chapter.

In algebra we use this law to remove parentheses, as in the examples

$$5 \cdot (x + y) = 5x + 5y$$

$$7 \cdot (2x + 6y) = 14x + 42y$$

Using the law from right to left, we can "remove a common factor" as follows:

$$4x + 4y = 4 \cdot (x + y)$$

$$8x + 12y = 4 \cdot (2x + 3y)$$

Since multiplication is commutative, the distributive property of multiplication over addition can also be written

$$(b + c)a = (ba) + (ca)$$

Therefore, we can use it as in the example

$$4a + 7a = (4 + 7)a = 11a$$

This illustration again raises the thorny question of what we mean by statements such as

$$4 \text{ apples} + 7 \text{ apples} = 11 \text{ apples}$$

At first sight you might think that this is an application of the distributive law such as

$$4 \text{ apples} + 7 \text{ apples} = (4 + 7) \text{ apples}$$

$$= 11 \text{ apples}$$

but surely this is a misunderstanding. In the distributive law

$$(4 \cdot a) + (7 \cdot a) = (4 + 7) \cdot a = 11 \cdot a$$

the dot refers to multiplication. Surely the expression "4 apples" does not mean "4 times apples". So this is certainly not an application of the distributive law.

The distributive law can be extended in the following fashion:

EXTENDED DISTRIBUTIVE PROPERTY

THEOREM 4. EXTENDED DISTRIBUTIVE PROPERTY OF MULTIPLICATION OVER ADDITION. For any whole numbers a and $b_1, \ldots, b_n$,

$$a(b_1 + b_2 + \cdots + b_n) = (ab_1) + (ab_2) + \cdots + (ab_n)$$

Let us suggest how this can be derived from the ordinary distributive property for the case $n = 3$. We must prove that

$$a(b_1 + b_2 + b_3) = (ab_1) + (ab_2) + (ab_3)$$

We know that

$$b_1 + b_2 + b_3 = (b_1 + b_2) + b_3$$

243

so

$$a \cdot (b_1 + b_2 + b_3) = a \cdot [(b_1 + b_2) + b_3]$$
$$= a(b_1 + b_2) + ab_3$$
$$= (ab_1 + ab_2) + ab_3$$
$$= ab_1 + ab_2 + ab_3$$

By continuing this process step by step we can prove the extended form of the law given above.

Another important application of the distributive law is the expansion of products of the form

$$(a + b)(c + d)$$

Let us see how this goes:

$$(a + b)(c + d) = (a + b)c + (a + b)d$$
$$= (ac + bc) + (ad + bd)$$
$$= ac + bc + ad + bd$$

That is, $(a + b)(c + d)$ is equal to the sum of the products obtained by multiplying each term of $a + b$ by each term of $c + d$. This result is the basis for the usual procedure of long multiplication of natural numbers. For example, $23 \cdot 45 = (20 + 3)(40 + 5)$. Using the result above,

$$23 \cdot 45 = (20 + 3)(40 + 5)$$
$$= (20 \cdot 40) + (20 \cdot 5) + (3 \cdot 40) + (3 \cdot 5)$$
$$= 800 + 100 + 120 + 15$$
$$= 1035$$

12.5 "Multiplication Is Repeated Addition"

REPEATED ADDITION From our definition of addition we know that $3 = 2 + 1$ and that $2 = 1 + 1$. So $3 = (1 + 1) + 1 = 1 + 1 + 1$. Also, $4 = 3 + 1$, so $4 = (1 + 1 + 1) + 1 = 1 + 1 + 1 + 1$. Let us use this result to express $5 \cdot 4$ as a sum. To do so we use the extended distributive law:

$$5 \cdot 4 = 5 \cdot (1 + 1 + 1 + 1)$$
$$= (5 \cdot 1) + (5 \cdot 1) + (5 \cdot 1) + (5 \cdot 1)$$
$$= 5 + 5 + 5 + 5$$

---

1. For every triple of whole numbers $a, b,$ and $c, a(b + c) = $ _____ .

$(ab) + (ac)$

2. As an example, by using the distributive law,

$$3 \cdot (5 + 4) = (\quad \cdot \quad) + (\quad \cdot \quad)$$
$$= \underline{\quad} + \underline{\quad}$$
$$= \underline{\quad}$$

$3 \cdot 5 + 3 \cdot 4 \qquad 15 + 12 \qquad 27$

3. Using the distributive law,

$$16 \cdot 99 = 16 \cdot (100 - \underline{\quad})$$
$$= (\quad \cdot \quad) - (\quad \cdot \quad)$$
$$= \underline{\quad} - \underline{\quad}$$
$$= \underline{\quad}$$

$16 \cdot (100 - 1) \qquad (16 \cdot 100) - (16 \cdot 1) \qquad 1600 - 16 \qquad 1584$

4. Using a consequence of the distributive law,

$$18 \cdot 12 = (10 + 8) \cdot (10 + 2)$$
$$= (\quad \cdot \quad) + (\quad \cdot \quad) + (\quad \cdot \quad) + (\quad \cdot \quad)$$
$$= \underline{\quad} + \underline{\quad} + \underline{\quad} + \underline{\quad}$$
$$= \underline{\quad}$$

$(10 \cdot 10) + (10 \cdot 2) + (8 \cdot 10) + (8 \cdot 2) \qquad 100 + 20 + 80 + 16 \qquad 216$

5. Because of commutativity of multiplication, we have for any triple of whole numbers,

$$(a + b) \cdot c = (\quad \cdot \quad) + (\quad \cdot \quad)$$

$(a \cdot c) + (b \cdot c)$

6. Thus, for example, by the distributive law,

$$(12 + 14) \cdot 4 = (\quad \cdot \quad) + (\quad \cdot \quad)$$
$$= \underline{\quad} + \underline{\quad}$$
$$= \underline{\quad}$$

$(12 \cdot 4) + (14 \cdot 4) \qquad 48 + 56 \qquad 104$

7. Reversing the sides of the equality in the distributive law, we have, for any triple of whole numbers a, b, and c,

$$(ab) + (ac) = \underline{\hspace{2cm}}$$

$a(b + c)$

8. Likewise, for any triple of whole numbers a, b, and c,

$$(ac) + (bc) = \underline{\hspace{2cm}}$$

$(a + b)c$

9. Thus, if x and y are whole numbers,

$$(5x) + (5y) = \underline{\hspace{2cm}}$$
$$(3x) + (12y) = (3 \cdot x) + (3 \cdot (4y)) = \underline{\hspace{2cm}}$$

$5 \cdot (x + y)$ $3 \cdot (x + 4y)$

10. Use the distributive law on each of the following, assuming a, b, and c are whole numbers; with $c < b$,

$3(a + c) = \underline{\hspace{2cm}}$ $2(b - c) = \underline{\hspace{2cm}}$

$(b + 3) \cdot 2 = \underline{\hspace{2cm}}$ $ab - ac = \underline{\hspace{2cm}}$

$(2 \cdot b) + (2 \cdot c) = \underline{\hspace{2cm}}$ $5b - 5c = \underline{\hspace{2cm}}$

$a(b + 3) = \underline{\hspace{2cm}}$ $5a + 30b = \underline{\hspace{2cm}}$

$(3a) + (3c)$	$(2b) - (2c)$
$2b + 6$	$a(b - c)$
$2(b + c)$	$5 \cdot (b - c)$
$ab + 3a$	$5(a + 6b)$

11. By using the extended distributive law, if a, b, c, and d are whole numbers,

$$2(a + b + c + d) = \underline{\hspace{2cm}}$$

$2a + 2b + 2c + 2d$

12. If x and y are whole numbers,

$$2x + 6y + 8 = 2x + 2(3y) + 2 \cdot 4$$
$$= \underline{\hspace{2cm}}$$

$2(x + 3y + 4)$

13. Using the distributive law,

$$50 + 30 + 70 = (\underline{\quad} + \underline{\quad} + \underline{\quad}) \cdot 10$$
$$= \underline{\quad} \cdot 10$$
$$= \underline{\quad}$$

$(5 + 3 + 7) \cdot 10 \qquad 15 \cdot 10 \qquad 150$

14. Using the distributive law,

$$8(247) = 8 \cdot (200 + 40 + 7)$$
$$= (\underline{\quad \cdot \quad}) + (\underline{\quad \cdot \quad}) + (\underline{\quad \cdot \quad})$$
$$= \underline{\quad} + \underline{\quad} + \underline{\quad}$$
$$= \underline{\quad}$$

$(8 \cdot 200) + (8 \cdot 40) + (8 \cdot 7) \qquad 1600 + 320 + 56 \qquad 1976$

15. Use the extended distributive law and the fact that $5 = 1 + 1 + 1 + 1 + 1$ to express the product $7 \cdot 5$ as a sum.

$$7 \cdot 5 = \underline{\hspace{3cm}}$$

$$7 \cdot 5 = 7 \cdot (1 + 1 + 1 + 1 + 1)$$
$$= (7 \cdot 1) + (7 \cdot 1) + (7 \cdot 1) + (7 \cdot 1) + (7 \cdot 1)$$
$$= 7 + 7 + 7 + 7 + 7$$

12.6 Other Distributive Properties

In the distributive properties considered so far we have established a relationship between two binary operations on a particular set. Similar distributive properties are true in other parts of mathematics where we deal with binary operations on other basic sets. The general definition of a distributive property is given below:

* OVER   **DEFINITION.** Let $*$ and $\diamond$ be two binary operations on a set S. Then $*$ *is a distributive over* $\diamond$ if and only if for all elements a, b, and c of S,

$$a * (b \diamond c) = (a * b) \diamond (a * c)$$

EXAMPLES

1. When $*$ is multiplication and $\diamond$ is addition, this becomes the distributive property of multiplication over addition:

$$a(b + c) = (ab) + (ac)$$

247

2. When $*$ is Cartesian product and $\diamond$ is set union, it becomes the distributive property of Cartesian product over set union.

3. When $*$ is Cartesian product and $\diamond$ is set intersection, it becomes the distributive property of Cartesian product over set intersection.

These examples naturally raise the question: What other pairs of binary operations satisfy the distributive property?

4. First let us consider multiplication over subtraction. In this case the following theorem is true:

THEOREM 5. DISTRIBUTIVE PROPERTY OF MULTIPLICATION OVER SUBTRACTION. For all whole numbers a, b, and c with $c \leq b$,

$$a(b - c) = (ab) - (ac)$$

MULTIPLICATION OVER SUBTRACTION

Proof

1. Since $c \leq b$, $b - c$ is a whole number. Let $b - c = d$.
2. By the definition of subtraction, $b = c + d$.
3. Therefore, $ab = a(c + d) = ac + ad$.
4. So $ab - ac = ad$.
5. That is, $ab - ac = a(b - c)$.

Moreover, since multiplication is commutative, it is also true that

$$(b - c)a = (ba) - (ca)$$

5. Next consider addition over multiplication. If addition is distributive over multiplication, it must be true that for all whole numbers a, b, and c,

$$a + (b \cdot c) = (a + b) \cdot (a + c)$$

It turns out that this statement is false. A counterexample is $a = 1$, $b = 2$, $c = 3$, for then it must be true that

$$1 + (2 \cdot 3) = (1 + 2) \cdot (1 + 3)$$

$$1 + 6 = 3 \cdot 4$$

$$7 = 12 \quad \text{which is false}$$

Hence *addition is not distributive over multiplication*. Similarly, *subtraction is not distributive over multiplication*.

12.7 Distributive Properties Involving Division

In the distributive properties considered so far, it was possible to apply the commutative property to derive a second formulation of a distributive property.

Thus from $a(b + c) = ab + ac$ we derived $(b + c)a = ba + ca$. And from $a(b - c) = ab - ac$ we derived $(b - c)a = ba - ca$. These are therefore called *two-sided* distributive properties, since a can be written on either side of the expression in parentheses.

12.7 Distributive Properties Involving Division

DIVISION OVER ADDITION

In the case of division (which is not commutative) we must consider the *left-distributive property* and the *right-distributive property*.

RIGHT-DISTRIBUTIVE PROPERTY

THEOREM 6. RIGHT-DISTRIBUTIVE PROPERTY OF DIVISION OVER ADDITION. Let a, b, and c be whole numbers such that $b \div a$ and $c \div a$ are defined. Then

$$(b + c) \div a = (b \div a) + (c \div a)$$

Proof
1. Let $b \div a = d$ and $c \div a = e$.
2. Then $b = ad$ and $c = ae$.
3. So $b + c = ad + ae$
   $= a(d + e)$.
4. Therefore, $(b + c) \div a = d + e$
   $= (b \div a) + (c \div a)$.

The statement of the corresponding left-distributive property is: Let a, b, and c be whole numbers such that $a \div b$ and $a \div c$ are defined. Then

$$a \div (b + c) = (a \div b) + (a \div c)$$

Unfortunately, this is false. As a counterexample choose $a = 24, b = 2, c = 4$. Then it must be true that

$$24 \div (2 + 4) = (24 \div 2) + (24 \div 4)$$

or

$$24 \div 6 = (24 \div 2) + (24 \div 4)$$

or

$$4 = 12 + 6 \qquad \text{which is false}$$

Therefore, division is *right* but not *left* distributive over addition. A similar statement is true concerning division over subtraction.

---

1. Which of the following distributive properties are true?
(a) Multiplication over addition.
(b) Addition over multiplication.
(c) Multiplication over subtraction.
(d) Subtraction over multiplication.
(e) Division over addition (right-distributive).
(f) Division over addition (left-distributive).
(g) Division over subtraction (right-distributive).
(h) Division over subtraction (left-distributive).
(i) Cartesian product over set union.
(j) Cartesian product over set intersection.

(a), (c), (e), (g), (i), and (j).

The Distributive Law

2. For those parts of frame 1 that are true write the appropriate formula.

(a) _____

(c) _____

(e) _____

(g) _____

(i) _____

(j) _____

(a) $a(b + c) = ab + ac$.
(c) $a(b - c) = ab - ac$.
(e) $(b + c) \div a = (b \div a) + (c \div a)$.
(g) $(b - c) \div a = (b \div a) - (c \div a)$.
(i) $A \times (B \cup C) = (A \times B) \cup (A \times C)$.
(j) $A \times (B \cap C) = (A \times B) \cap (A \times C)$.

3. Which true distributive properties of frame 1 are *two-sided*?

_____

(a), (c), (i), and (j).

4. Why can we not prove the left-distributive property of division over addition directly from the corresponding right-distributive property?

_____

Division is not commutative.

5. *Prove*: If a, b, and c are whole numbers such that $b \leq a$ and $a \div c$ is defined and $b \div c$ is defined, then $(a - b) \div c = (a \div c) - (b \div c)$. Use a separate piece of paper.

Proof
1. Let $a \div c = d$ and $b \div c = e$.
2. Then $a = dc$ and $b = ec$ Definition of division.
3. $a - b = dc - ec$.
4. $a - b = (d - e)c$ Distributive law.
5. $(a - b) \div c = d - e$;   Definition of division.
   that is, $(a - b) \div c = (a \div c) - (b \div c)$.

6. For all whole numbers a and b, let us define the operations $a * b$ and $a \oplus b$ by

$$a * b = (a \cdot b) + b \qquad \text{and} \qquad a \oplus b = (a + b) \cdot b$$

Thus, for example, $3 * 2 =$ _____ and $3 \oplus 2 =$ _____.

8     $[((3 \cdot 2) + 2)]$ 10 $[((3 + 2) \cdot 2)]$

250

7. For the operations $*$ and $\oplus$ in frame 6, prove that the distributive property: For all whole numbers a, b, and c,

$$a * (b \oplus c) = (a * b) \oplus (a * c)$$

is not true. Use a separate piece of paper.

> Since the statement says: "For all whole numbers a, b, and c..." we need only exhibit any three whole numbers for which the statement is not true. For example, let $a = 1$, $b = 2$, and $c = 3$. Then
>
> $$a * (b \oplus c) = 1 * (2 \oplus 3)$$
> $$= 1 * 15$$
> $$= 30$$
>
> but
>
> $$(a * b) \oplus (a * c) = (1 * 2) \oplus (1 * 3)$$
> $$= 4 \oplus 6$$
> $$= 60$$

8. Show also that the distributive property: For all whole numbers a, b, and c,

$$a \oplus (b * c) = (a \oplus b) * (a \oplus c)$$

is not true. Use a separate piece of paper.

> Again, taking $a = 1$, $b = 2$, and $c = 3$,
> $$a \oplus (b * c) = 1 \oplus (2 * 3) = 1 \oplus 9 = 90$$
> but
> $$(a \oplus b) * (a \oplus c) = (1 \oplus 2) * (1 \oplus 3) = 6 * 12 = 84$$
> Thus, it is not true that for *all* whole numbers a, b, and c,
> $$a \oplus (b * c) = (a \oplus b) * (a \oplus c)$$

9. Let the binary operations $\circ$ and $\triangle$ be defined as follows: For all whole numbers a, b, and c,

$$a \circ b = b$$
$$a \triangle b = 2 \cdot a \cdot b$$

Thus, for example, $2 \circ 5 = $ _____ and $2 \triangle 5 = $ _____.

> 5   20

10. For the operations $\circ$ and $\triangle$ defined in frame 9, a possible distributive property is: For all whole numbers a, b, and c,

$$a \circ (b \triangle c) = (a \circ b) \triangle (a \circ c)$$

Joe Zilch attempted to prove the property *not* true and obtained: For $a = 1, b = 2$, and $c = 3$,

$$a \circ (b \triangle c) = 1 \circ (2 \triangle 3) = 1 \circ 12 = 12$$

$$(a \circ b) \triangle (a \circ c) = (1 \circ 2) \triangle (1 \circ 3) = 2 \triangle 3 = 12$$

Can he then conclude that the theorem is true? _____
(yes, no)

No. To prove that the theorem is true, it must be shown that for all triples of whole numbers a, b, and c, the equality holds. (He may simply have chosen a particular triple for which the equality holds while there may be other triples for which the equality doesn't hold. Or maybe the property is true; all we know so far is that there exists a triple for which the equality holds.)

11. See if the triple $a = 2, b = 3, c = 5$ will prove that the distributive property of problem 10 is not true. _____
(does, does not)

Does not. For $a = 2, b = 3, c = 5$,

$$a \circ (b \triangle c) = 2 \circ (3 \triangle 5) = 2 \circ 30 = 30$$

$$(a \circ b) \triangle (a \circ c) = (2 \circ 3) \triangle (2 \circ 5) = 3 \triangle 5 = 30$$

Thus, from this, we cannot conclude that the property is not true.

12. After a few such trials, we might suspect that the property holds. Let's try to prove: For any triple of whole numbers a, b, and c,

$$a \circ (b \triangle c) = (a \circ b) \triangle (a \circ c)$$

(where $\circ$ and $\triangle$ are as defined in frame 9).

Proof

$$a \circ (b \triangle c) = a \circ (2 \cdot b \cdot c)$$

$$= \underline{\hspace{3cm}}$$

$$(a \circ b) \triangle (a \circ c) = b \triangle c$$

$$= \underline{\hspace{3cm}}$$

$2 \cdot b \cdot c \qquad 2 \cdot b \cdot c$
Thus, $a \circ (b \triangle c) = (a \circ b) \triangle (a \circ c)$ for all whole numbers a, b, and c.

13. Another possible distributive property for the operations ∘ and △ is: For all whole numbers a, b, and c,

$$a \triangle (b \circ c) = (a \triangle b) \circ (a \triangle c)$$

You investigate, decide whether the property is true or false, and prove your assertion. _____
(T, F)

> It is true for: For all whole numbers a, b, and c,
>
> $$a \triangle (b \circ c) = a \triangle c = 2 \cdot a \cdot c$$
> $$(a \triangle b) \circ (a \triangle c) = (2 \cdot a \cdot b) \circ (2 \cdot a \cdot c) = 2 \cdot a \cdot c$$
>
> Thus $a \triangle (b \circ c) = (a \triangle b) \circ (a \triangle c)$.

14. Determine whether the distributive property

$$(a \triangle b) \circ c = (a \circ c) \triangle (b \circ c)$$

for all whole numbers a, b, and c is true or false. _____
(T, F)

> It is false. For example, with $a = 1$, $b = 2$, and $c = 3$, we have
>
> $$(a \triangle b) \circ c = (1 \triangle 2) \circ 3 = 4 \circ 3 = 3$$
>
> but
>
> $$(a \circ c) \triangle (b \circ c) = (1 \circ 3) \triangle (2 \circ 3) = 3 \triangle 3 = 18$$

12.8 Evaluation of Arithmetic Expressions

The distributive law permits us to evaluate $2 \cdot (4 + 5)$ as either $2 \cdot 9 = 18$ or as $(2 \cdot 4) + (2 \cdot 5) = 8 + 10 = 18$. What meaning, however, is to be given to $2 \cdot 4 + 5$ where the parentheses are omitted? Does it mean

$$(2 \cdot 4) + 5 = 8 + 5 = 13$$

or

$$2 \cdot (4 + 5) = 2 \cdot 9 = 18$$

When parentheses are inserted the meaning is clear, but without parentheses $2 \cdot 4 + 5$ is apparently ambiguous. Nevertheless, expressions like this occur frequently in arithmetic, and so the ambiguity must be removed. This is done by adhering to the following convention:

CONVENTIONS OF ARITHMETIC

CONVENTION. In arithmetic expressions without parentheses such as $2 \cdot 4 + 5$, $18 - 12 \div 2$, and $12 - 2 \cdot 3$, first do the multiplications or divisions and then the additions or subtractions. Thus by this convention

$$2 \cdot 4 + 5 = 8 + 5 = 13$$

$$8 - 12 \div 2 = 8 - 6 = 2$$

$$12 - 2 \cdot 3 = 12 - 6 = 6$$

There is another convention which is also frequently employed in connection with chains of additions and subtractions:

CONVENTION. In an expression like

$$12 + 6 - 4 - 3 + 9 - 2$$

begin at the left and carry out each operation in turn. Thus

$$12 + 6 - 4 - 3 + 9 - 2 = 18 - 4 - 3 + 9 - 2$$
$$= 14 - 3 + 9 - 2$$
$$= 11 + 9 - 2$$
$$= 20 - 2$$
$$= 18$$

These conventions are sometimes a source of confusion and are easily forgotten. If there is any possibility of ambiguity, it is best to insert parentheses so that your meaning is completely clear.

1. Using the conventions of this section find the values of the following expressions:
   (a) $4 + 7 \cdot 6 =$ _____.
   (b) $36 - 12 \div 4 =$ _____.
   (c) $15 - 5 - 2 + 10 =$ _____.
   (d) $(5 + 6 \cdot 3) \cdot 4 - (10 \div 5 - 1) =$ _____.
   (e) $[(22 - 7 - 6 \div 2) \cdot 4] \div 6 =$ _____.

   (a) 46   (b) 33   (c) 18   (d) 91   (e) 8

12.9 Distributive Properties of Unions and Intersections (Optional)

In the set S of subsets of a universal set U, intersection and union are binary operations. There are two distributive properties connecting these.

THEOREM 7. DISTRIBUTIVE PROPERTY OF UNION OVER INTERSECTION. For all subsets A, B, and C of U,

UNION OVER INTERSECTION

$$A \cup (B \cap C) = (A \cup B) \cap (A \cup C)$$

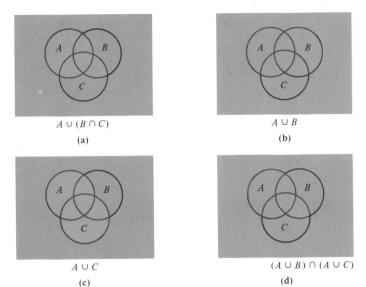

FIGURE 12.1. *Proof that*
$A \cup (B \cap C) = (A \cup B) \cap (A \cup C)$.

We may verify this by a sequence of Venn diagrams or prove it by a truth table. The appropriate Venn diagrams are given in Figure 12.1. The truth-table proof is given in Table 1.

TABLE 1. $A \cup (B \cap C) = (A \cup B) \cap (A \cup C)$

$x \varepsilon A$	$x \varepsilon B$	$x \varepsilon C$	$x \varepsilon (B \cap C)$	$x \varepsilon A \cup (B \cap C)$	$x \varepsilon (A \cup B)$	$x \varepsilon (A \cup C)$	$x \varepsilon (A \cup B) \cap (A \cap C)$
T	T	T	T	T	T	T	T
T	T	F	F	T	T	T	T
T	F	T	F	T	T	T	T
T	F	F	F	T	T	T	T
F	T	T	T	T	T	T	T
F	T	F	F	F	T	F	F
F	F	T	F	F	F	T	F
F	F	F	F	F	F	F	F

A related theorem interchanges $\cap$ and $\cup$:

THEOREM 8. DISTRIBUTIVE PROPERTY OF INTERSECTION
INTERSECTION OVER UNION   **OVER UNION.** For all subsets A, B, and C of U,

$$A \cap (B \cup C) = (A \cap B) \cup (A \cap C)$$

The proof is included in the exercises.

1. Why does Table 1 prove that $A \cup (B \cap C) = (A \cup B) \cap (A \cup C)$?

The columns labeled $x \varepsilon A \cup (B \cap C)$ and $x \varepsilon (A \cup B) \cap (A \cup C)$ are identical.

2. It has been mentioned that a Venn diagram may be misleading. In the one shown in (a) shade $(A \cap C) \cup B$. In the duplicate in (b) shade $(C \cup B) \cap A$. Do they appear to be the same? _____.

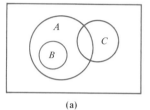

(a)

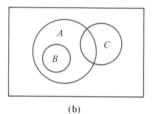

(b)

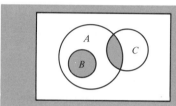

Yes.

3. They are, however, not equal in general. To show this complete the truth table.

$x \varepsilon A$	$x \varepsilon B$	$x \varepsilon C$	$x \varepsilon (A \cap C)$	$x \varepsilon (A \cap C) \cup B$	$x \varepsilon (C \cup B)$	$x \varepsilon (C \cup B) \cap A$
T	T	T				
T	T	F				
T	F	T				
T	F	F				
F	T	T				
F	T	F				
F	F	T				
F	F	F				

$x \varepsilon A$	$x \varepsilon B$	$x \varepsilon C$	$x \varepsilon (A \cap C)$	$x \varepsilon (A \cap C) \cup B$	$x \varepsilon (C \cup B)$	$x \varepsilon (C \cup B) \cap A$
T	T	T	T	T	T	T
T	T	F	F	T	T	T
T	F	T	T	T	T	T
T	F	F	F	F	F	F
F	T	T	F	T	T	F
F	T	F	F	T	T	F
F	F	T	F	F	T	F
F	F	F	F	F	F	F

4. Frame 3 shows that the proposition: For all sets A, B, and C, _____ is false.

$(A \cap C) \cup B = (C \cup B) \cap A$

5. Another useful theorem is that for all sets A, B, and C, $A \cap (B \cup C) = (A \cap B) \cup (A \cap C)$. In Venn diagram (a) mark A with lower left to upper right lines, and B and C with upper left to lower lines. In Venn diagram (b) shade $(A \cap B) \cup (A \cap C)$.

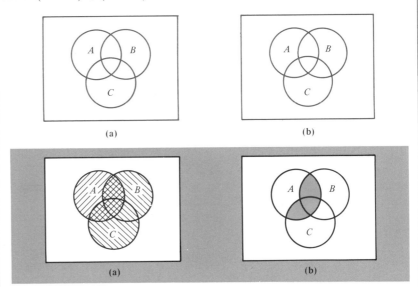

(a)　　　　　　　　　　　　　　　(b)

(a)　　　　　　　　　　　　　　　(b)

6. Again, for this particular case, they appear to be equal. On a separate sheet of paper construct a truth table with all possible cases to show that they are.

$x \varepsilon A$	$x \varepsilon B$	$x \varepsilon C$	$x \varepsilon B \cup C$	$x \varepsilon A \cap (B \cup C)$	$x \varepsilon A \cap B$	$x \varepsilon A \cap C$	$x \varepsilon (A \cap B) \cup (A \cap C)$
T	T	T	T	T	T	T	T
T	T	F	T	T	T	F	T
T	F	T	T	T	F	T	T
T	F	F	F	F	F	F	F
F	T	T	T	F	F	F	F
F	T	F	T	F	F	F	F
F	F	T	T	F	F	F	F
F	F	F	F	F	F	F	F

In this chapter we have defined the general distributive property of one binary operation over another. As special cases we have emphasized the following:

distributive property of multiplication over addition
distributive property of multiplication over subtraction
right-distributive properties of division over addition and subtraction
extended distributive property of multiplication over addition

The Distributive Law

In Chapters 14 and 16 we shall be applying these to justify the usual methods for addition and multiplication of natural numbers. To be sure that you are ready to proceed, work the following Post Test. Do not consult the text while obtaining your answers. Check your answers with the key after you have completed the entire test.

POST TEST

1. State the distributive property of Cartesian product over set union:
_____
_____

2. What theorem about $\times$ and $\cup$ is used to prove the distributive property of multiplication over addition? _____

3. On a separate piece of paper prove the distributive property of multiplication over addition.

4. Remove the common factor from $4a + 12b + 64c$. _____

5. The extended distributive property of multiplication over addition states that for all whole numbers $a, b_1, \ldots, b_n$, _____
_____ .

6. What theorem about whole numbers is used to rewrite the distributive property of multiplication over addition in the form: $(b + c)a = (ba) + (ca)$?
_____ .

7. Compute $4 \cdot 6$ by repeated addition. _____

8. If $\oplus$ and $\triangle$ are binary operations on a set S, then $\oplus$ is distributive over $\triangle$ if and only if: For all a, b, and c in S, _____ .

9. On a separate piece of paper prove that multiplication is distributive over subtraction.

10. Is addition distributive over multiplication? _____ Why?
_____

11. Is division left-distributive over addition? _____ Is division right-distributive over subtraction? _____

12. Let $*$ be defined by $a * b = a$ and $\circ$ be defined by $a \circ b = b$. State the distributive property of $*$ over $\circ$. _____
Show that for all a, b, and c this is true. $a * (b \circ c) =$ _____
_____ ; $(a * b) \circ (a * c) =$ _____ .

13. Evaluate $[25 - (4 + 3 \cdot 2) - 5] \cdot 2$. _____

14. State the distributive law of set intersection over set union. _____

---

1. For all sets A, B, and C, $A \times (B \cup C) = (A \times B) \cup (A \times C)$.
2. Distributive property of Cartesian product over set union.
3. (See the proof of Theorem 3.)
4. $4(a + 3b + 16c)$.

5. $a(b_1 + \cdots + b_n) = (ab_1) + \cdots + (ab_n)$
6. Commutative property.
7. $4 \cdot 6 = 6 + 6 + 6 + 6 = 24$.
8. $a \oplus (b \triangle c) = (a \oplus b) \triangle (a \oplus c)$
9. (See the proof of Theorem 5.)
10. No. A counterexample is $a = 1$, $b = 2$, $c = 4$ (many other possible answers).
11. No. Yes.
12. $a * (b \circ c) = (a * b) \circ (a * c)$. $a * (b \circ c) = a * c = a$; $(a * b) \circ (a * c) = a \circ a = a$
13. 20.
14. For all sets A, B, and C, $A \cap (B \cup C) = (A \cap B) \cup (A \cap C)$.

Summary of the Properties of the Whole Numbers

The statements given below are the most important properties of the whole numbers. All other properties of the whole numbers (except mathematical induction, which is not discussed in this book) can be derived from these. It is understood that each of these statements is to be prefixed by the phrase: "For all whole numbers a, b, c, d". Special exceptions are noted as necessary. When a symbol such as $a - b$ or $a \div b$ is written, it is understood that a and b are such that this symbol is defined.

EQUALITY

1. If $a = b$, then $a + c = b + c$.
2. If $a = b$, then $a - c = b - c$.
3. If $a = b$, then $ac = bc$.
4. If $a = b$ and $c \neq 0$, then $a \div c = b \div c$.

ADDITION

1. Addition is a binary operation. on the set of whole numbers.
2. $a + b = b + a$ Commutative property.
3. $(a + b) + c = a + (b + c)$ Associative property.
4. $a + 0 = a$ Additive property of zero.
5. If $a + c = b + c$, then $a = b$ Cancellation law.

SUBTRACTION

1. Subtraction is not a binary operation, and is neither commutative nor associative.
2. $a - b = c$ if and only if $a = b + c$ Definition.
3. $a - 0 = a$ Subtractive property of zero.
4. If $a - c = b - c$, then $a = b$ Cancellation law.

259

MULTIPLICATION

1. Multiplication is a binary operation. on the set of whole numbers.
2. $ab = ba$ Commutative property.
3. $(ab)c = a(bc)$ Associative property.
4. $a \cdot 1 = a$ Multiplicative property of 1.
5. If $ac = bc$ and $c \neq 0$, then $a = b$ Cancellation law.

DIVISION

1. Division is *not* a binary operation, and is neither commutative nor associative.
2. $a \div b = c$ if and only if $a = bc$ Definition.
3. If $a \div c = b \div c$, then $a = b$ Cancellation law.

DISTRIBUTIVE PROPERTIES

1. $a(b + c) = ab + ac$.
2. $a(b - c) = ab - ac$.
3. $(a + b) \div c = (a \div c) + (b \div c)$.

INEQUALITY

1. Exactly one of the following is true: Trichotomy law.

$$a < b \qquad a = b \qquad a > b$$

2. If $a < b$ and $b < c$, then $a < c$ Transitive property.
3. If $a < b$, then $a + c < b + c$ Additive property.
4. If $a < b$ and $c \neq 0$, then $ac < bc$ Multiplicative property.

Chapters 8 through 12 have laid the foundations of the arithmetic of whole numbers. In Chapters 13 through 17 we shall show you how these principles are used to justify the various computational procedures in use. Before starting these chapters review Chapters 8 through 12 and work the following Summary Test, which covers them.

Summary Test for Part II

A

Circle the number of every true statement in this section.

1. Addition is a binary operation on the set of whole numbers.
2. Subtraction is a commutative binary operation on the set of integers.
3. Division is an associative binary operation on the set of nonzero rational numbers.
4. Multiplication is an associative binary operation on the set of whole numbers.
5. For every whole number $a, a \cdot 1 = 1$.
6. For every whole number $a, a \div 0 = 0$.
7. For all finite sets A and B, $n(A) + n(B) = n(A \cup B)$.
8. For all whole numbers a, b, and c where all quotients are defined, $(a + b) \div c = (a \div c) + (b \div c)$.
9. For all sets: set union is distributive over set intersection.
10. For all sets A and B, if $A \subseteq B$, then $n(A) < n(B)$.

B

11. Find a counterexample for the (false) proposition: For all whole numbers x, y, and z, if $xy = xz$, then $y = z$.

$$x = \underline{\hspace{2cm}}, y = \underline{\hspace{2cm}}, z = \underline{\hspace{2cm}}.$$

12. In a binary operation, the number of inputs is $\underline{\hspace{2cm}}$.
13. If the binary operation $a * b$ is commutative, then $a * b = \underline{\hspace{2cm}}$.
14. If $*$ is a binary operation on S and a and b are elements of S, then $a * b$ must be an $\underline{\hspace{2cm}}$ of S.
15. Cartesian products form a useful background for the study of the arithmetic operation of $\underline{\hspace{2cm}}$.

In questions 16 through 23 state what law or property justifies the given statement.

16. $5 \cdot (2 \cdot 3) = (5 \cdot 2) \cdot 3.$ $\underline{\hspace{5cm}}$
17. $5 \cdot (2 + 3) = (5 \cdot 2) + (5 \cdot 3).$ $\underline{\hspace{4cm}}$
18. $5 \cdot (2 + 3) = (2 + 3) \cdot 5.$ $\underline{\hspace{4cm}}$
19. $5 \cdot (2 + 3) = 5 \cdot (3 + 2).$ $\underline{\hspace{4cm}}$
20. $5 + (2 + 3) = (5 + 2) + 3.$ $\underline{\hspace{4cm}}$
21. $5 + (2 + 3) = (2 + 3) + 5.$ $\underline{\hspace{4cm}}$
22. If a and b are whole numbers and if $a < 7$ and $7 < b$, then $a < b$.
$\underline{\hspace{2cm}}$
23. If a and b are whole numbers and $a + 10 = b + 10$, then $a = b$.
$\underline{\hspace{2cm}}$

24. $12 \div 4 = \underline{\hspace{1cm}}$ because $\underline{\hspace{4cm}}$.
25. $19 \div 5 = \underline{\hspace{1cm}}$ with a remainder of $\underline{\hspace{1cm}}$ because $\underline{\hspace{2cm}}$.

26. If b is a whole number and $5b = 0$, then $b = $ _____.

27. The distributive property of multiplication over addition states that _____.

28. The distributive property of multiplication over subtraction states that _____.

29. Using the distributive property of multiplication over subtraction, complete the following steps:

$$12 \cdot 39 = 12(40 - \underline{\hspace{1cm}})$$

$$= \underline{\hspace{1cm}} - \underline{\hspace{1cm}}$$

$$= \underline{\hspace{1cm}}$$

30. If a and b are whole numbers, $9a + 6b + 21 = 3 \cdot ($_____$)$.

31. Use standard sets to show that $3 < 5$. _____

32. Use the definition of subtraction to show that $5 - 3 = 2$. _____

33. Use the definition of multiplication to find $2 \cdot 3$. _____

34. Use the definition of addition to find $2 + 3$. _____

Questions 35 through 40 refer to the following definition: For every pair of whole numbers a and b, an operation $*$ is defined by $a * b = a + 2b$.

35. Find $2 * 3$. _____

36. Find $2 * (3 * 4)$. _____

37. Show that $*$ is not commutative. _____

38. Show that $*$ is not associative. _____

39. Show that for every whole number x, $x * 0 = x$. _____

40. If x is a whole number, find $0 * x$. _____

When you have completed this test you may proceed to Chapter 13, Systems of Numeration.

PART III

Algorithms for the Arithmetic of Whole Numbers

Chapters 13 through 17

13

Systems of Numeration

With this chapter we begin a new unit in this course. This unit deals with the problems of expressing whole numbers in standard notations and then finding the practical rules for the arithmetic operations of addition, subtraction, multiplication, and division. In order to justify these rules we shall rely upon the properties of the whole numbers which were derived in Chapters 8 through 12.

Before beginning this chapter, answer the following Readiness Test.

READINESS TEST

1. If b is a whole number, $b \times b \times b \times b$ is what power of b? $\underline{b^4}$
_____ .

> The fourth power.

2. A symbol for a number is called a $\underline{numeral}$.

> numeral

3. There are many $\underline{numerals}$ for the same
    (numerals, numbers)
$\underline{number}$.
(numeral, number)

> numerals   number

4. $725 \div 256 = \underline{2}$ with a remainder of $\underline{213}$.

> 2   213

5. What is the largest power of 4 that is less than 265? $\underline{4^4}$

> $4^4 = 256$.

6. $265 \div 4^4 = \underline{1}$ with a remainder of $\underline{9}$.

> 1   9

If these ideas are clear to you, read Sections 13.1 and 13.2 and write your answers to the corresponding exercises.

13.1 Elementary Ideas

If we are to work with numbers, it is very clear that we must have some convenient and systematic way for naming them. This means that we must develop a set of symbols for our numbers, which we will call a system of numeration. Different civilizations have used various systems of numeration, but now nearly everyone uses the Hindu–Arabic system, with which we are so familiar. Let us see what is involved in developing such a system.

In the earliest days man could represent numbers by a row of pebbles, such as

$$\bigcirc\ \bigcirc\ \bigcirc\ \bigcirc \quad \text{or} \quad \bigcirc\ \bigcirc\ \bigcirc\ \bigcirc\ \bigcirc\ \bigcirc$$

Our word "calculus" means a pebble, and from this we derive familiar words, such as "calculate", which refer to the manipulation of sets of pebbles. Or he may have made marks on a clay tablet or cut notches on a stick and thus represented numbers by symbols:

$$|| \qquad ||| \qquad ||||| \qquad \text{etc.}$$

This is fine for small numbers, but it becomes awkward as the size of the number increases. So man invented new symbols for groups of these primitive marks. Thus he might write □ instead of |||||, and then □| instead of ||||||. The size of the group so designated, the symbol used for the group, and the fashion in which the various symbols were combined to represent larger numbers varied widely in different civilizations.

Since there are five fingers on a hand and ten fingers on two hands, groups of five and/or ten appear widely in early systems of numeration. There are also symbols for one hundred and one thousand, and higher powers of ten. The Romans mixed the five system and the ten system and wrote symbols for fifty and five hundred. A sample of the various grouping symbols that have been used is given in Table 1.

A common method for combining such symbols to represent larger numbers is that of addition. In this method the symbols are ordered from left to right (sometimes vertically) and their sum is then computed. For instance,

In the Roman system: III = 3; VI = 6.

In the Babylonian system:  = 4, = 23.

In the Egyptian system: ∩ ∩ ||| = 23.

There are, however, variations on this. The Roman system is a mixture of addition and subtraction methods. For

$$\text{IV} = 4 \qquad \text{XIV} = 14 \qquad \text{XL} = 40$$

In the Babylonian system there were multiplicative operations, such as: When a symbol for a number smaller than 100 is placed to the left of the symbol for 100, the two are to be multiplied. Thus

$$\begin{aligned} &= 10 \times 100 = 1{,}000 \\ &= 10 \times 1000 = 10{,}000 \end{aligned}$$

GROUPING SYMBOLS

TABLE 1. Grouping Symbols

System	Grouping Symbol	Corresponding Arabic Numeral
Babylonian	$\vee$	$1, 60, 60^2, \ldots, 60\text{I}, \ldots$
	$<$	10
	$\vee\!\!\succ$	100
Egyptian	$\cap$	10
	$\mathfrak{I}$	100
	$\mathfrak{l}$	1000
Early Greek	Π ⎫ first letters of	5
	Δ ⎬ corresponding	10
	H ⎭ words	100
	χ	1000
Roman	V	5
	X	10
	L	50
	C (earlier Θ)	100
	D	500
	M (earlier Φ)	1000
Mayan	—	5
	=	10

These methods sometimes lead to ambiguous symbols (such as the Roman IXC) and are not easily adapted to computation. A better system is that of positional notation, which is best exemplified by the Hindu–Arabic numerals, to be discussed in the next section.

ROMAN NUMERALS

1. A partial list of Roman numerals is given:

I = 1	VI = 6	XI = 11	L = 50
II = 2	VII = 7	⋮	XC = 90
III = 3	VIII = 8	XX = 20	C = 100
IV = 4	IX = 9	XXX = 30	D = 500
V = 5	X = 10	XL = 40	M = 1000

Write in Roman numerals each of the following: (a) 2532. MMDXXXII
(b) 876. DCCCLXXVI

(a) MMDXXXII   (b) DCCCLXXVI

2. Addition in Roman numerals is performed by the simple operation of placing all the symbols together and converting to more compact form any combinations for which this is possible. Using Roman numerals add the two numbers in the answer to frame 1. MMMCDVIII

MMMCCCCVIII (or MMMCDVIII).

267

3. A partial multiplication table for Roman numerals is given. Use it to find the product of XII and XVII. Recall the addition principle. XII means X + I + I. Thus the distributive property can be used. Write your response on a separate piece of paper.

	I	V	X	L
I	I	V	X	L
V	V	XXV	L	CCL
X	X	L	C	D
L	L	CCL	D	MMD

XVII
XII
XVII
XVII
CLXX
CCIV

4. The subtractive convention in Roman numeration can cause difficulty when multiplying. Find the product of IX and XV. (IX means X − I.) Write your response on a separate piece of paper.

XV   In subtracting XV from CL, change
IX   L to XXXXVV.
CL
−XV
CXXXV

13.2 Hindu–Arabic Numerals

These are our common numerals. They have two features which were not generally included in earlier systems of numeration: (1) There is a symbol for 0, and (2) the position notation is used. The basic features are the following:

FUNDAMENTAL SYMBOLS

(1) The symbol for any number is a combination of the *fundamental symbols*

$$0, 1, 2, 3, 4, 5, 6, 7, 8, 9$$

GROUP SIZES

(2) The *fundamental group size* is ten. Other group sizes are ten × ten = hundred, ten × ten × ten = thousand, and so on. We say that the *base* of the system is ten.

(3) The meaning of a fundamental symbol depends upon its position in the sequence of these symbols. Thus in the symbol 627, the 6 means 6 × hundred, the 2 means 2 × ten, and the 7 means 7 × one or 7. The general scheme is the following:

billion	hundred million	ten million	million	hundred thousand	ten thousand	thousand	hundred	ten	one
2	6	3	9	0	5	2	1	7	8

(4) A symbol such as 627 represents the sum of the numbers represented by the fundamental symbols taking into account their positions:

$$627 = (6 \times \text{hundred}) + (2 \times \text{ten}) + 7$$

Rather than writing ten, hundred, thousand, and so on, we prefer to use other symbols based on this notation. Thus

$$10 = (\text{one} \times \text{ten}) + (0 \times \text{one}) = \text{ten}$$
$$10^2 = 10 \times 10 = \text{hundred}$$
$$10^3 = 10 \times 10 \times 10 = \text{thousand}$$
$$10^4 = \text{ten thousand}$$
$$10^5 = \text{hundred thousand}$$
$$10^6 = \text{million}$$
$$10^7 = \text{ten million}$$
$$10^8 = \text{hundred million}$$
$$10^9 = \text{billion}$$

There are names for a few higher powers of ten, but most of these are relatively unfamiliar. It is best, therefore, to use the exponential notation on the left as often as possible. By this notation we write 627 in the form

$$627 = (6 \times 10^2) + (2 \times 10) + 7$$

In order to refer to these ideas in the future we need to define some terms:

DEFINITIONS

DECIMAL EXPANSION
1. A *decimal expansion* of a whole number is an expression of the form

$$(a \times 10^3) + (b \times 10^2) + (c \times 10) + d$$

where a, b, c, and d are whole numbers.

PROPER DECIMAL EXPANSION
2. A *proper decimal expansion* is an expansion of the above form where a, b, c, and d are fundamental symbols $(0, 1, 2, \ldots, 9)$.

DIGITS
3. In a proper decimal expansion the numbers a, b, c, and d are called its *digits*.

COMPACT FORM
4. The *compact form* of the proper decimal expansion

$$(5 \times 10^3) + (4 \times 10^3) + (8 \times 10) + 3$$

is 5483.

EXPANDED FORM
5. The *expanded form* of the whole number 2054 is

$$(2 \times 10^3) + (0 \times 10^2) + (5 \times 10) + 4$$

1. The place-value system can be thought of as a packaging problem. We have symbols for any number of objects up to nine (in the base ten system). When we deal with more than nine we group the objects together in sets of ten. If there are fewer than ten of these sets the numeral we write describes how many such sets and how many were not "packaged". Thus 73 means 7 groups of __ten__ and 3 left over.

> ten

2. If there are more than nine of these sets of ten we group the sets of ten in tens, and so on. Each digit of a numeral refers to a different-sized "package". For convenience we give some of the larger "packages" names. Thus a package of ten groups of ten units is called a __hundred__ and a package of ten groups of a hundred is called a __thousand__.

> hundred   thousand

3. The digit 8 in 8763 tells us that in "packaging" this many objects we needed 8 packages of the __1,000__ size. The 7 describes how many packages of the __100__ size were left over after the 8 larger-sized packages were filled.

> 1000   100

4. The number 8763 of frame 3 is equal to the __sum__ of all the numbers represented by the individual terms in the expansion in frame 3.

> sum

5. When a number such as 627 is written as the sum of its individual terms it is said to be in proper decimal expansion. Thus the expanded form of 627 is $(6 \times 10^2) + (2 \times 10) + 7$.

> $(6 \times 10^2) + (2 \times 10) + 7$

6. One of the important uses of the symbol for zero is to indicate the absence of some power of the base. Thus 504 in expanded form is $(5 \times 10^2) + (0 \times 10) + 4$.

> $504 = (5 \times 10^2) + (0 \times 10) + 4$

7. When the digits of which a numeral is composed are written adjacent to one another (in the proper order) the symbol is said to be in compact form. The compact form of $(3 \times 10^3) + (7 \times 10^2) + (2 \times 10) + 9$ is __3,729__.

3729

8. If one or more terms in the expanded form is missing, the symbol for zero must be inserted in the compact form to indicate this fact. Thus $(3 \times 10^4) + (4 \times 10^2) + 8$ should not be written as 348, but as $\underline{30,408}$.

30,408

9. If the digits of a number are 3 and 8, in this order, what is the number? $\underline{38}$

38.

10. If the digits of a number are a and b, in this order, what is the number? $\underline{10a + b}$

$10a + b$ (*not* ab; ab means $a \times b$; $3 \times 8 \neq 38$).

11. If the digits of a number are a, b, and c, in this order, what is the number? $\underline{100a + 10b + c}$

$100a + 10b + c$.

12. The Hindu–Arabic system uses powers of a base (ten) in the expanded form of a number. For this reason an understanding of the resulting arithmetic requires that we have a good grasp of the arithmetic of such powers. 10^4 means $\underline{10 \cdot 10 \cdot 10 \cdot 10 = 10,000}$.

10,000 (or $10 \times 10 \times 10 \times 10$)

13. Write $7 \times 7 \times 7 \times 7 \times 7$ in a more compact form. $\underline{7^5}$

7^5 is one.

14. If a is any whole number, $a^5 \cdot a^3$ means $(aaaaa)(aaa)$. It is thus the product of $\underline{8}$ factors each of which is a, so that $a^5 \cdot a^3 = \underline{a^8}$.

8   a^8

15. In general, if m and n are any natural numbers, $a^m \cdot a^n$ is the product of one number consisting of m factors, each of which is a and another number consisting of n factors each of which is a. The product then has $\underline{m+n}$ factors, each of which is a, so that $a^m \cdot a^n = \underline{a^{m+n}}$.

$m + n$ a^{m+n}

Anything to the zero power is 1.

16. If we wish this addition of exponents to be used when one of the exponents is zero, we must be guided by the fact that $a^0 \cdot a^m = a^{0+m} = a^m$. For this reason <u>we define a^0 to be 1 if $a \neq 0$. The symbol 0^0 is not defined.</u>

In this way, if a is any whole number and if m is any natural number, a^m is defined. In addition, a^0 is defined provided $a \neq 0$. What numbers are represented by the symbols $3^2, 3^0, 0^3, 0^0$? *9, 1, 0, undefined*

> 9, 1, 0, 0^0 is undefined.

17. Using the expanded form of 387 and the distributive law, multiply 387 by $100 = 10^2$. Leave the result in expanded form. *[(3×10²)+(8×10¹) +7]×10²=(3×10⁴)+(8×10³)+(7×10²)*

> $[(3 \times 10^2) + (8 \times 10^1) + 7] \times 10^2 = (3 \times 10^4) + (8 \times 10^3) + (7 \times 10^2)$

18. Before rewriting this numeral in compact form we note that two terms of the complete expanded form are missing. Which ones? *No 10's and no 1's*

> There is neither a tens term nor a units term.

19. We can supply these using zero multipliers, since $0 \cdot a = 0$ and $b + 0 = b$. Thus $387 \times 100 = (3 \times 10^4) + (8 \times 10^3) + (7 \times 10^2) + (0 \times 10) + 0$. In compact form this would be written *38,700* .

> 38,700

20. Frames 17 to 19 above provide the justification for the following rule. To multiply a number n by 100 affix *two* zeros on the right of the base 10 numeral for n.

> two

21. To multiply a whole number n by 10, affix *one zero* on the right of the base 10 numeral for n.

> one zero

Complete the chapter by reading Sections 13.3 and 13.4 and doing the relevant exercises.

13.3 Numerals with Other Bases

The common base ten system is so familiar that we have difficulty subjecting it to careful analysis and study. In order for you to appreciate its many useful properties, it is helpful for you to consider similar systems using other bases. These are less familiar, and in working with them you will have to think what you are doing! The benefits of the study of these systems are similar to those obtained from the study of Latin as an aid to the understanding of English. For by working with other bases you will really learn the structure of the common base ten system.

BASE FIVE   **BASE 5**

We can use any whole number except 0 or 1 as a base for a system of numeration, and for purposes of illustration we consider base 5. In this system

(1) The symbol for any number is a combination of the *fundamental symbols*

$$0, 1, 2, 3, 4$$

(2) The *fundamental group size* is 5. Other group sizes are $5^2, 5^3, 5^4, \ldots$.

(3) The meaning of a fundamental symbol depends upon its position just as in the base 10 system, but the meaning is different. For example, in the base 5 system consider the numeral 243. The 2 means 2×5^2, the 4 means 4×5, and the 3 means 3×1. In general, the positional scheme is

$$\cdots 5^5 \quad 5^4 \quad 5^3 \quad 5^2 \quad 5 \quad 1$$

(4) The symbol for a number is additive as in base ten. Thus in base 5

$$243 = (2 \times 5^2) + (4 \times 5) + 3$$

TABLE 2

Base	Numerals	Name	Use
2	0, 1	Binary	Internal arithmetic in high-speed computers.
8	0, 1, 2, 3, 4, 5, 6, 7	Octile	External communication with some binary computers.
12	0, 1, 2, 3, 4, 5, 6, 7, 8, 9, t, e	Duodecimal	Appears in one use of *dozen* and gross = 12×12. Also in old British monetary system, where 12 pence = 1 shilling. Proposal for general use has little support.
20	None common	Vigesimal	Vestigal system appearing in our use of *score* (= 20), and old British monetary system, where 20 shillings = 1 pound. Also in French, where 83 is "quatre-vingt trois" or $(4 \times 20) + 3$.
60	None common	Sexagesimal	One aspect of the Babylonian system. Currently appears in our measurement of time and angles: 60 min = 1 hr, 60 sec = 1 min, etc.

Since symbols like 243 have meaning as numerals to base ten as well as base five, we need a notation that identifies the base when it is not clear.

For base ten we write 243_{ten}.
For base five we write 243_{five}.

Thus

$$243_{\text{ten}} = (2 \times 10^2) + (4 \times 10) + 3$$
$$243_{\text{five}} = (2 \times 5^2) + (4 \times 5) + 3 \quad \text{base } 10.$$

There is nothing magic about the bases five and ten. Any whole number except 0 or 1 can be used as a base. Several of these were used historically and have traces in current systems of measurement. Others are used today for specialized purposes. Examples are listed in Table 2.

BASE b When we have a general base, b,

(1) The symbol for any number is a combination of the *fundamental symbols*:

$$0, 1, 2, \ldots, b - 1$$

(2) The *fundamental group size* is b; other group sizes are $b^2, b^3, b^4, \ldots$.
(3) A symbol such as xyz (where x, y, and z are fundamental symbols) means

$$xyz = (x \times b^2) + (y \times b) + z$$

Since bases larger than ten require the invention of fundamental symbols in addition to the familiar 0, 1, 2, 3, 4, 5, 6, 7, 8, 9, we shall hereafter in this book assume that the base b is between 2 and 10 inclusive. This restriction is purely for convenience and simplicity of exposition; there is no theoretical reason for not using larger numbers as bases.

---

1. Care should be used in reading numerals in bases other than ten. 23_{five}, for example, is not "twenty-three base five". It is usually read as "two-three base five". Read the symbol 54_{seven}. _Five-four base seven_

> Five-four base seven.

2. Read the symbol 300_{eight}. _Three-zero-zero base eight._

> Three-zero-zero base eight.

3. What is the meaning of the digit 6 in 637_{eight} in terms of the expansion $637_{\text{eight}} = (a \times 8^2) + (b \times 8) + c$? _$a = 6$_

> $a = 6$ (or 6 is the coefficient of 8^2).
> _(factor)_

4. Express the number $(6 \times 8^2)_{ten}$ in base eight notation: _600_8_

> 600_{eight}.

5. Thus, whether in base eight or base ten $637 = 600 + 30 + 7$. The symbols 600 and 30 have different meanings in each system but the forms are identical. What is the meaning of 600 as a base eight numeral? _____
6×8^2

> 6×8^2 (or 384_{ten}).

6. How is eight written in base eight? _10_

> 10.

7. How is b written in base b? _10_

> 10.

8. How many fundamental symbols are required in base seven? _7_ What are they? _$0,1,2,3,4,5,6$_

> Seven.   0, 1, 2, 3, 4, 5, and 6.

9. How many fundamental symbols are required in base two? _2_ What are they? _$0,1$_

> Two   0 and 1.

10. What are the fundamental symbols in base b? _$0,1,2 \ldots, b-1,$_

> $0, 1, 2, \ldots, b - 1$.

11. What is the fundamental group size in base b? _b_. What are three other group sizes in base b? _b^2, b^3, b^4_

> b. $b^2, b^3, b^4, \ldots$.

12. Why are the following expansions in base five notation not in *proper* form: (a) $(27 \times 5^2) + (4 \times 5) + 3$. _27 is not in base 5_
(b) $(7 \times 5^2) + (2 \times 5) + 5$. _7+5 are not in base 5._

> (a) 27 is not a fundamental symbol, base five.   (b) 7 and 5 are not fundamental symbols, base five.

13.4 Change of Base

As an aid to your understanding of unfamiliar bases, we shall now examine two related problems:

(1) Given a numeral in base b, what is the numeral in base ten for the same number?

(2) Given a numeral in base ten, what is the numeral in base b for the same number?

BASE b TO BASE 10

BASE b TO BASE TEN

Let us illustrate this process for base seven. Suppose that we have the numeral 524_{seven} and wish to find the corresponding base 10 numeral. We know that

$$524_{seven} = [(5 \times 7^2) + (2 \times 7) + 4]_{ten}$$
$$= [(5 \times 49) + (2 \times 7) + 4]_{ten}$$
$$= [245 + 14 + 4]_{ten}$$
$$= 263_{ten}$$

Notice that every numeral on the right is in base ten, and that we have used ordinary (base ten) arithmetic in our computation.

As a second example, consider 3012_{seven}. Then

$$3012_{seven} = [(3 \times 7^3) + (0 \times 7^2) + (1 \times 7) + 2]_{ten}$$
$$= [(3 \times 343) + (0 \times 49) + (1 \times 7) + 2]_{ten}$$
$$= [1029 + 7 + 2]_{ten}$$
$$= 1038_{ten}$$

BASE 10 TO BASE b

BASE TEN TO BASE b

Let us illustrate this process using base four. To begin with we need a table of powers of the base four.

$$4^1 = 4$$
$$4^2 = 16$$
$$4^3 = 64$$
$$4^4 = 256$$
$$4^5 = 1024$$

Suppose that the problem is to convert 766_{ten} to base four. Choose the largest power of 4 which is smaller than 766; this is $4^4 = 256$. Then divide 766 by 256 and obtain

$$766 = (2 \times 4^4) + 254$$

Note that the remainder, 254, must be less than 256. Next choose the largest power of 4 which is smaller than 254, $4^3 = 64$. Divide 254 by 64 and obtain

$$254 = (3 \times 4^3) + 62$$

Continuing we find that

$$62 = (3 \times 4^2) + 14$$
$$14 = (3 \times 4) + 2$$

Assembling all these results, we find that

$$766 = (2 \times 4^4) + (3 \times 4^3) + (3 \times 4^2) + (3 \times 4) + 2$$

Therefore,

$$766_{ten} = 23{,}332_{four}$$

In this process we must watch for missing powers of 4 and insert zeros in their places. As an example, here is the process of converting 147_{ten} to base four.

$$147 = (2 \times 4^3) + 19$$
$$= (2 \times 4^3) + (1 \times 4^2) + 3$$
$$= (2 \times 4^3) + (1 \times 4^2) + (0 \times 4) + 3$$
$$= 2103_{four}$$

1. If you have 25 objects and use them to fill boxes whose capacity is 7 objects each, how many full boxes will result? __3__

3.

2. How many objects will be left over? __4__

4.

3. This is the problem of converting 25_{ten} to a base seven numeral. $25_{ten} = $ __34__ $_{seven}$.

34

4. If you have 50 objects and use them to fill boxes whose capacity is 4 objects each, how many full boxes will result? __12__

12.

5. How many objects will be left over? __2__

2.

6. If you take the 12 full boxes (frame 4) and use them to fill the crates that hold four boxes each, how many full crates will result? __3__

> 3.

7. How many boxes will be left over? __0__

> 0.

8. Use the results of frames 4 to 7 to write 50_{ten} as a base four numeral.

__302_4__

> $50_{ten} = 302_{four}$.

9. Complete the partial table of powers of 3:

$$3^0 = 1$$
$$3^1 = 3$$
$$3^2 = \underline{9}$$
$$3^3 = \underline{27}$$
$$3^4 = \underline{81}$$

> 9   27   81

10. Use the table of frame 9 to convert 186_{ten} to a base three numeral.

__$20,220_3$__

> $186 = (2 \times 3^4) + 24$
> $\quad = (2 \times 3^4) + (0 \times 3^3) + (2 \times 3^2) + (2 \times 3) + 0$
> $\quad = 20,220_{three}$

11. Use the table of frame 9 to convert $12,021_{three}$ to a base ten numeral.

__142_{10}__

> $(1 \times 3^4) + (2 \times 3^3) + (0 \times 3^2) + (2 \times 3) + 1$
> $\quad = 81 + 54 + 0 + 6 + 1$
> $\quad = 142_{ten}$

12. Express as numerals in base ten:

(a) $652_{seven} \cdot$ __331_{10}__ (b) $223_{four} \cdot$ __43_{10}__
(c) $210_{three} \cdot$ __21_{10}__ (d) $10,101_{two} \cdot$ __21_{10}__
(e) $72,054_{eight} \cdot$ __$29,740_{10}$__

278

(a) 331_{ten}.   (b) 43_{ten}.   (c) 21_{ten}.   (d) 21_{ten}.
(e) $28,672 + 1024 + 0 + 40 + 3 = 29,739_{ten}$.

13. Express the following base ten numerals as numerals in the stated base:

(a) 13_{ten} in base 2. ____1101₂____   (b) 17_{ten} in base 3. ____122₃____
(c) 513_{ten} in base 5. ____4023₅____   (d) 49_{ten} in base 7. ____100₇____
(e) 368_{ten} in base 8. ____560₈____

(a) 1101_{two}.   (b) 122_{three}.   (c) 4023_{five}.   (d) 100_{seven}.
(e) 560_{eight}.

14. (*Discovery Exercise*) Professor Gawain Peter found the following inscriptions drawn on a wall of a cave once inhabited by the Indian Chief Thunder. From the archaeological researches of Jeremiah Datsun he knew that the first three sets of symbols refer to the numbers of braves killed in a series of famous battles. They stand for 796, 133, and 591, respectively. Knowing that Chief Thunder had six fingers on each hand, Professor Peter concluded that the fourth set of symbols stood for ____926____ braves killed in another battle.

First inscription   *Second inscription*

Ø   /
00   00Ø
/Ø   796   133

Third inscription   *Fourth inscription*

0   //
/   /Ø
Ø   591   00

1. base 6 or base 12
2. read symbols from bottom up, units place on top.
3. Bigger than any no. held.

You should now fully understand the decimal notation for numbers. In addition, you should be familiar with place-value notations that use other bases. Check your understanding by working the following Post Test. Do not *refer to the text while working this test*. Check your response against the key after you have completed the entire test.

POST TEST

1. In base 7 what are the fundamental symbols? __0,1,2,3,4,5,6__
2. In base 7 what is the fundamental group size? __7__ What are three other group sizes? __$7^2, 7^3, 7^4$__

3. Write 253_{six} in expanded form. $(2 \times 10^2) + (5 \times 10) + 3$

4. Write 4278_{ten} in expanded form. $(4 \times 10^3) + (2 \times 10^2) + (7 \times 10) + 8$

5. Write $[(5 \times 6^4) + (4 \times 6) + 3]_{ten}$ in compact form base six.
$50,043_6$

6. Why is the following expansion in base 8 not in proper form: $[(2 \times 8^2) + (9 \times 8) + 6]_{ten}$? 9 is not in base 9

7. What numbers base 10 are represented by the symbols 4^3, 4^2, 4^0, 0^4?
64 16, 1, 0

8. If $3^x \times 3^y = 3^z$, express z in terms of x and y. $z = x + y$

9. If the digits of a base ten numeral are 3 and 4, in this order, what is the number? 34_{10}

10. If the digits of a base five numeral are 3 and 4, in this order, what is the number? 34_5

11. If the digits of a base seven numeral are a and b, in this order, what is the number? $7a + b_{10}$ $10a + 0_7$

12. Express 227_{ten} as (a) a base eight numeral. 343_8
(b) a base four numeral. 3203_4

13. Express 203_{five} as a base ten numeral. 53_{10}

14. To multiply a whole number n by seven, affix one zero to the right of the base seven numeral for n.

1. 0, 1, 2, 3, 4, 5, 6.
2. 7; 7^2, 7^3, 7^4.
3. $[(2 \times 6^2) + (5 \times 6) + 3]_{ten}$.
4. $[(4 \times 10^3) + (2 \times 10^2) + (7 \times 10) + 8]_{ten}$.
5. $50,043_{six}$.
6. 9 is not a fundamental symbol in base 8.
7. 64, 16, 1, 0.
8. $z = x + y$.
9. 34_{ten}.
10. 34_{five} (or 19_{ten}).
11. $7a + b_{ten}$.
12. (a) 343_{eight}.   (b) 3203_{four}.
13. 53_{ten}.
14. one zero.

If you were successful in this test, go to Chapter 14 and work the Readiness Test.

Addition
Algorithms

Before beginning this chapter, you should have completed Chapter 9 (Addition), Chapter 12 (The Distributive Law), and Chapter 13 (Systems of Numeration). In Chapter 14 we shall discuss various practical means for carrying out the addition process. To be sure that you are ready for this chapter, complete the Readiness Test below.

READINESS TEST

1. Write the commutative law for the addition of whole numbers. For all a and b, $\underline{a+b=b+a}$.

$a + b = b + a.$

2. Write the associative law for the addition of whole numbers. For all a, b, and c, $\underline{(a+b)+c = a+(b+c)}$

$(a + b) + c = a + (b + c)$

3. Write the distributive property of multiplication over addition for whole numbers. For all a, b, and c, $\underline{a(b+c)=(ab)+(ac)}$.

$a(b + c) = (ab) + (ac).$

4. Write the associative law for the multiplication of whole numbers. For all a, b, and c, $\underline{a \cdot (b \cdot c)=(a \cdot b) \cdot c}$

$a \cdot (b \cdot c) = (a \cdot b) \cdot c$

5. The decimal expansion of 53 is $53 = (\underline{5 \times}\ 10) + \underline{3}$.

$5 \times \qquad 3$

6. The decimal expansion of 367 is $367 = (\underline{3} \times \underline{10^2}) + (\underline{6} \times \underline{10}) + \underline{7}$.

$3 \qquad 10^2 \qquad 6 \qquad 10 \qquad 7$

7. The fundamental symbols used in the base five system of numeration are $\underline{0,1,2,3,4}$.

$0, 1, 2, 3, 4$

8. In base 5 notation $24 = (\underline{2} \times \underline{5}) + \underline{4}$.

$2 \qquad 5 \qquad 4$

9. The decimal numeral that represents the same number as 24_{five} is ___.

14

10. In the base two system, 1110 represents the same number as the decimal numeral ___.

14

If your answers were almost all correct, read Sections 14.1 through 14.3 and work the program following Section 14.3.

14.1 Introduction

The definition of the addition of two numbers in Chapter 9 can be used as a simple method for carrying out the process of addition. We recall that to add $3 + 6$ we find disjoint sets A and B such that $n(A) = 3$ and $n(B) = 6$. Then by counting we find $n(A \cup B) = 9$. We can also use the number line to find this sum (Figure 14.1). Place the elements of a set with three elements

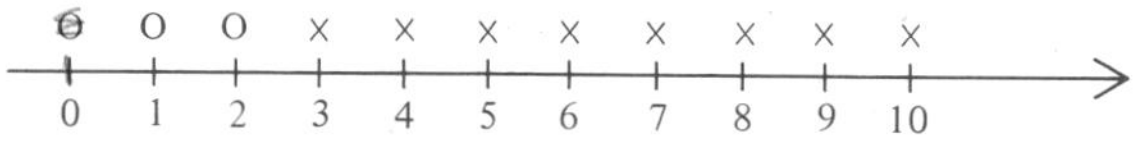

FIGURE 14.1. *Addition on the number line.*

along the number line beginning at 1. Immediately to the right place a set with six elements. The last numeral covered by an element of the second set is 9. Hence $3 + 6 = 9$.

This process works well for small numbers, but it gets very tedious if the numbers are large. We therefore need to develop more convenient methods for addition. We shall call these *algorithms* and show you several possibilities in this chapter. The word "algorithm", sometimes written "algorism", is derived from the name of Mohammed ben Musa al-Khwarizmi, an Arabian mathematician. About 820 A.D. he wrote a book on rules of arithmetic. The Arabic title included the word "al-jebr", from which "algebra" is derived. The Latin title was *Liber Algorism*, meaning "the book of al-Khwarizmi". You must note, however, that each algorithm must be justified through the use of the properties of the whole numbers. We shall, therefore, explain not only *how* the algorithms work, but *why* they give the correct result.

ADDITION TABLES ## 14.2 Basic Addition Table

All the algorithms using base 10 assume a knowledge of the basic addition table, Table 1. The entries in this table are computed by the method of

Chapter 9 and should be thoroughly memorized. In using a particular entry in this table in a later computation we may refer to this entry as an *addition fact*.

TABLE 1. Base Ten Addition Table

+	0	1	2	3	4	5	6	7	8	9
0	0	1	2	3	4	5	6	7	8	9
1	1	2	3	4	5	6	7	8	9	10
2	2	3	4	5	6	7	8	9	10	11
3	3	4	5	6	7	8	9	10	11	12
4	4	5	6	7	8	9	10	11	12	13
5	5	6	7	8	9	10	11	12	13	14
6	6	7	8	9	10	11	12	13	14	15
7	7	8	9	10	11	12	13	14	15	16
8	8	9	10	11	12	13	14	15	16	17
9	9	10	11	12	13	14	15	16	17	18

If the computations are to be done in some other base, the corresponding addition table for that base must be computed. For example, the tables for base two and base four are given in Tables 2 and 3. If we were using base

TABLE 2. Base Two Addition Table

+	0	1
0	0	1
1	1	10

TABLE 3. Base Four Addition Table

+	0	1	2	3
0	0	1	2	3
1	1	2	3	10
2	2	3	10	11
3	3	10	11	12

four (for example) systematically in our computations, we would memorize the base four addition table. For your work, however, it is unnecessary to memorize this. In doing such computations, you are free to refer to the table above.

14.3 Addition of a Column of Digits

The first step in the process of developing addition algorithms is to find a means for adding a single column of digits. Let us consider the sum

SINGLE-DIGIT ADDITION

$$
\begin{array}{r}
2 \\
5 \\
8 \\
6 \\
9 \\
+4 \\
\hline
\end{array}
\quad \text{(base ten)}
$$

Before we can proceed we must know what this sum means. In Chapter 9 we found that $a + b + c = (a + b) + c$. Given this knowledge, we can define the sum $a + b + c + d$ to be $(a + b + c) + d$; and using this idea step by step we can define the sum of any finite number of whole numbers. This process depends upon the following definition:

DEFINITION. Let $a_1, \ldots, a_n, a_{n+1}$ be any whole numbers. If the sum $a_1 + a_2 + \cdots + a_n$ has already been defined, then the sum $a_1 + a_2 + \cdots + a_n + a_{n+1}$ is defined to be $(a_1 + a_2 + \cdots + a_n) + a_{n+1}$.

The application of this definition to the multiple sum above gives the following result:

$$2 + 5 + 8 + 6 + 9 + 4 = (2 + 5 + 8 + 6 + 9) + 4$$
$$= ((2 + 5 + 8 + 6) + 9) + 4$$
$$= (((2 + 5 + 8) + 6) + 9) + 4$$
$$= ((((2 + 5) + 8) + 6) + 9) + 4$$

In its final form the sum is then expressed as a sequence of sums in each of which only two numbers are to be added.

As we have just analyzed this problem, we effectively added our column from the *top down* (or left to right as we wrote it above). From the generalized commutative law we know that we can rearrange the order of addition as we please and still obtain the same result. In particular, we can add from the *bottom up* (or right to left as written below). In doing so we have

$$2 + 5 + 8 + 6 + 9 + 4 = ((((4 + 9) + 6) + 8) + 5) + 2$$

A convenient check on the accuracy of addition is to add from the top down and from the bottom up and then to compare the answers. They must be equal.

To carry out the actual addition after we have inserted parentheses as above, we begin at the left and add the two digits in the inside parentheses. This sum is what we have called an *addition fact*. Using the addition of our column from the bottom up as our example, we first obtain

$$4 + 9 = 13$$

Next we must add $13 + 6$. Since this sum is not an addition fact, we need to use a slightly more complicated procedure. Write

$$13 = 10 + 3 \qquad \text{Decimal notation.}$$
$$13 + 6 = (10 + 3) + 6$$
$$= 10 + (6 + 3) \qquad \text{Associative law.}$$
$$= 10 + 9 \qquad \text{Addition fact.}$$
$$= 19 \qquad \text{Decimal notation.}$$

284

Then we add $19 + 8$. This is a bit more complicated. We write

$$19 = 10 + 9 \qquad \text{Decimal notation.}$$

$$
\begin{aligned}
19 + 8 &= (10 + 9) + 8 \\
&= 10 + (9 + 8) & \text{Associative law.} \\
&= 10 + 17 & \text{Addition fact.} \\
&= 10 + (10 + 7) & \text{Decimal notation.} \\
&= (10 + 10) + 7 & \text{Associative law.} \\
&= (1 + 1) \times 10 + 7 & \text{Distributive law.} \\
&= (2 \times 10) + 7 & \text{Addition fact.} \\
&= 27 & \text{Decimal notation.}
\end{aligned}
$$

Continuing this process step by step we have $27 + 5 = 32$ and finally $32 + 2 = 34$. Therefore,

$$2 + 5 + 8 + 6 + 9 + 4 = 34$$

If we had added our column from the top down, we would have performed the successive additions

$$2 + 5 = 7; 7 + 8 = 15; 15 + 6 = 21; 21 + 9 = 30; 30 + 4 = 34$$

The same method is employed if the digits are expressed in any other base. For example, consider the sum

$$
\begin{array}{r}
2 \\
1 \\
3 \quad \text{(base four)} \\
2 \\
+1 \\
\hline
\end{array}
$$

Adding from the bottom up and using base four notation exclusively we have the sequence of sums (base four)

$$1 + 2 = 3; 3 + 3 = 12; 12 + 1 = 13; 13 + 2 = 21$$

As an alternative method we can consider the digits as base ten digits, add base ten, and convert the answer to base four. If we do this, we write

$$1 + 2 + 3 + 1 + 2 = 9_{\text{ten}} = 21_{\text{four}}$$

In practice, the work of adding a single column is done mentally and only the answer is written down. In this section we have written every step so that you will understand the process. Children should probably follow our example and write each step until they understand what they are doing and gradually develop the ability of adding mentally.

285

1. Use the method of Chapter 9 to find the sum 5 + 7. Write your response on a separate piece of paper.

> Let $A = \{1, 2, 3, 4, 5\}$ so that $n(A) = 5$. $B = \{6, 7, 8, 9, 10, 11, 12\}$ so that $n(B) = 7$ and $A \cap B = \emptyset$. $A \cup B = \{1, 2, 3, 4, 5, 6, 7, 8, 9, 10, 11, 12\}$. $n(A \cup B) = 12$.
> Other sets A and B could be used.

2. By counting on the section of the number line find 36 + 7.

34 35 36 37 38 39 40 41 42 43 44

> Start   Count 7 to the right ⟶ End
>
> 34 35 36 37 38 39 40 41 42 43 44

3. Supposing that $a + b + c + d$ is defined, what is the sum $a + b + c + d + e$? $(a+b+c+d)+e$

> $(a + b + c + d) + e$.

4. Why is $2 + 7 + 6 + 4 + 8 = 8 + 4 + 6 + 7 + 2$? GENERALIZED COMMUTATIVE LAW.

> Generalized commutative law.

5. Insert parentheses in the sum $2 + 7 + 6 + 4 + 8$ to indicate the process of adding from left to right. $(((2+7)+6)+4)+8$

> $(((2 + 7) + 6) + 4) + 8$.

6. Insert parentheses in the sum in frame 5 to indicate the process of adding from right to left. $(((8+4)+6)+7)+2$

> $(((8 + 4) + 6) + 7) + 2$ [or $2 + (7 + (6 + (4 + 8)))$].

7. Give reasons for the following steps in the computation of 47 + 8.

(a)	$47 = 40 + 7$	Decimal notation
(b)	$47 + 8 = (40 + 7) + 8$	
(c)	$= 40 + (7 + 8)$	Associative Law
(d)	$= 40 + 15$	Addition fact
(e)	$= 40 + (10 + 5)$	Decimal notation
(f)	$= (40 + 10) + 5$	Associative law.
(g)	$= (4 + 1) \times 10 + 5$	Distributive

286

(h) $= (5 \times 10) + 5$ *Addition fact*
(i) $= 55$ *Decimal notation*

> (a) Decimal notation.   (c) Associative law.   (d) Addition fact.
> (e) Decimal notation.   (f) Associative law.   (g) Distributive
> law.   (h) Addition fact.   (i) Decimal notation.

8. On a separate piece of paper write the steps needed for the computation of $56 + 7$ in a form similar to that in frame 7. Give reasons as you go.

> $56 = 50 + 6$ Decimal notation.
>
> $56 + 7 = (50 + 6) + 7$
>
> $= 50 + (6 + 7)$ Associative law.
>
> $= 50 + 13$ Addition fact.
>
> $= 50 + (10 + 3)$ Decimal notation.
>
> $= (50 + 10) + 3$ Associative law.
>
> $= (5 + 1) \times 10 + 3$ Distributive law.
>
> $= (6 \times 10) + 3$ Addition fact.
>
> $= 63$ Decimal notation.

9. Write the sequence of sums needed to add $4 + 3 + 7 + 5 + 9 + 6$ (base ten) from left to right: $4 + 3 = \underline{7}$, $\underline{7} + 7 = \underline{14}$, $\underline{14 + 5 = 19, 9 + 9 = 28, 28 + 6 = 34}$.

> 7   7   14 $14 + 5 = 19, 19 + 9 = 28, 28 + 6 = 34$

10. Write the sequence of sums needed to add $4 + 3 + 7 + 5 + 9 + 6$ (base ten) from right to left. $6 + 9 = \underline{15}$, $\underline{15 + 5 = 20, 20 + 7 = 27,}$ $\underline{27 + 3 = 30, 30 + 4 = 34}$.

> 15 $15 + 5 = 20, 20 + 7 = 27, 27 + 3 = 30, 30 + 4 = 34$

11. Give reasons for the following steps in the computation of $22 + 3$ (base four). Use base four numerals exclusively.

(a) $22 = 20 + 2$ *Base four notation*
(b) $22 + 3 = (20 + 2) + 3$
(c) $= 20 + (2 + 3)$ *Associative*
(d) $= 20 + 11$ *Addition fact*
(e) $= 20 + (10 + 1)$ *Base four notation*
(f) $= (20 + 10) + 1$ *Associative law*
(g) $= (2 + 1) \times 10 + 1$ *Distributive law*

(h) $= (3 \times 10) + 1$
(i) $= 31$

Addition fact
Base four notation

(a) Base four notation.   (c) Associative law.   (d) Addition fact.   (e) Base four notation.   (f) Associative law.   (g) Distributive law.   (h) Addition fact.   (i) Base four notation.

---

12. On a separate piece of paper write the steps needed for the computation of $13 + 2$ (base four) in a form similar to that in frame 11. Use base four numerals exclusively and give reasons as you go.

(a) $13 = 10 + 3$ Base four notation.
(b) $13 + 2 = (10 + 3) + 2$
(c) $= 10 + (3 + 2)$ Associative law.
(d) $= 10 + 11$ Addition fact.
(e) $= 10 + (10 + 1)$ Base four notation.
(f) $= (10 + 10) + 1$ Associative law.
(g) $= (1 + 1) \times 10 + 1$ Distributive law.
(h) $= (2 \times 10) + 1$ Addition fact.
(i) $= 21$ Base four notation.

---

13. Using base four notation exclusively, find the following sums:

	(a)	(b)	(c)	
	2	3	1	
	3	1	2	
	3	2	3	(base four)
	1	2	3	
	+2	1	2	
	23	+3	+1	
		30	30	

(a) 23   (b) 30   (c) 30   (base four)

---

14. Write the basic addition table for base five.

+	0	1	2	3	4
0	0	1	2	3	4
1	1	2	3	4	10
2	2	3	4	10	11
3	3	4	10	11	12
4	4	10	11	12	13

+	0	1	2	3	4
0	0	1	2	3	4
1	1	2	3	4	10
2	2	3	4	10	11
3	3	4	10	11	12
4	4	10	11	12	13

15. Using the table in your answer to frame 14 and base five notation exclusively find the following sums:

	(a)	(b)	(c)	
	4	3	1	
	3	1	4	
	1	4	3	(base five)
	2	1	4	
	+3	4	+4	
	23	+2	31	
		30		

(a) 23   (b) 30   (c) 31   (base five)

14.4 Sums Involving Several Columns

We are now ready for our discussion of the general case. As an example, consider the problem (base ten)

MULTIDIGIT ADDITION

$$375$$
$$596$$
$$+487$$

Using decimal notation each of these is expanded as in Chapter 13:

$$375 = (3 \times 10^2) + (7 \times 10) + 5$$
$$596 = (5 \times 10^2) + (9 \times 10) + 6$$
$$487 = (4 \times 10^2) + (8 \times 10) + 7$$

When we take the sum of the given three numbers, we can use the generalized commutative law to write

$$375 + 596 + 487 = [(3 \times 10^2) + (5 \times 10^2) + (4 \times 10^2)]$$
$$+ [(7 \times 10) + (9 \times 10) + (8 \times 10)]$$
$$+ [5 + 6 + 7]$$

Then we use the extended distributive law to rewrite this in the form

$$375 + 596 + 487 = [(3 + 5 + 4) \times 10^2] + [(7 + 9 + 8) \times 10]$$
$$+ [5 + 6 + 7]$$

The problem is now reduced to that discussed in Section 14.3, for now we must compute three sums of single digits. Supposing that this is understood, we then write

$$375 + 596 + 487 = (12 \times 10^2) + (24 \times 10) + 18$$

This result is promising, but we are not yet finished; for the sum is not in proper decimal notation. In this notation the coefficients of the respective

289

powers of ten must be single-digit numbers, but here they are two-digit numbers. If we note that $(12 \times 10^2) = 1200$ and $24 \times 10 = 240$, we can write our sum in the form

$$
\begin{array}{r}
375 \\
596 = \\
+487 \\
\hline
\end{array}
\qquad
\begin{array}{r}
18 \\
240 \\
+1200 \\
\hline
\end{array}
\qquad
\text{or alternatively} =
\begin{array}{r}
1200 \\
240 \\
+18 \\
\hline
\end{array}
$$

This is now a new problem in addition, but it is simpler because of the presence of several zeros. So we repeat the above process:

$$18 = 10 + 8$$

$$240 = (2 \times 10^2) + (4 \times 10)$$

$$1200 = (1 \times 10^3) + (2 \times 10^2)$$

$$18 + 240 + 1200 = (1 \times 10^3) + [(2 + 2) \times 10^2] + [(1 + 4) \times 10] + 8$$

$$= (1 \times 10^3) + (4 \times 10^2) + (5 \times 10) + 8$$

This is now in proper decimal notation, so we finally have

$$375 + 596 + 487 = 18 + 240 + 1200 = 1458$$

BASIC METHOD

BASIC METHOD OF ADDITION

We can summarize all this in the following form, which we shall call the *basic method of addition*:

$$
\begin{array}{r}
375 \\
596 = \\
+487 \\
\hline
\end{array}
\qquad
\begin{array}{r}
18 \ \text{ones} \\
240 \ \text{tens} \\
+1200 \ \text{hundreds} \\
\hline
1458 \\
\end{array}
$$

Here we have added the right column first and proceeded from right to left. We could just as well have gone from left to right and written

$$
\begin{array}{r}
375 \\
596 = \\
+487 \\
\hline
\end{array}
\qquad
\begin{array}{r}
1200 \ \text{hundreds} \\
240 \ \text{tens} \\
+ \ \ 18 \ \text{ones} \\
\hline
1458 \\
\end{array}
$$

Sometimes we must repeat this cycle three or more times. Eventually we will arrive at a sum in proper decimal notation and have our result. For example,

$$
\begin{array}{r}
384 \\
892 \\
988 \\
+867 \\
\hline
\end{array}
=
\begin{array}{r}
21 \\
310 \\
+2800 \\
\hline
\end{array}
=
\begin{array}{r}
1 \\
30 \\
1100 \\
+2000 \\
\hline
3131 \\
\end{array}
$$

Although this process is still too long for a convenient algorithm, it is the basis for all the algorithms that follow. These algorithms are nothing but shortcuts that put the steps above into a more compact form.

14.4 Sums Involving Several Columns

The same procedure is just as effective when we use other bases. Consider this example in base four:

$$
\begin{array}{r}
22 \\
313 \\
201 \\
133 \\
+212 \\
\hline
2131
\end{array} \quad \text{(base four)}
$$

We have

$$
\begin{array}{r}
313 \\
201 \\
133 \\
+212
\end{array} =
\begin{array}{r}
21 \\
110 \\
+2000 \\
\hline
2131
\end{array} \quad \text{(base four)}
$$

---

1. Give reasons for each step in the following process for adding: $25 + 47 + 73 + 19$.

(a) $25 = (2 \times 10) + 5$ — *Decimal notation*
(b) $47 = (4 \times 10) + 7$ — *Decimal notation*
(c) $73 = (7 \times 10) + 3$ — *Decimal notation*
(d) $19 = (1 \times 10) + 9$ — *Decimal notation*
(e) $25 + 47 + 73 + 19$
$= [(2 \times 10) + (4 \times 10) + (7 \times 10) + (1 \times 10)]$
$+ [5 + 7 + 3 + 9]$ — *Gen. commutative prop.*
(f) $= [(2 + 4 + 7 + 1) \times 10] + [5 + 7 + 3 + 9]$ — *Distributive law*
(g) $= (14 \times 10) + 24$ — *Section 14.3*

This addition will be continued in frame 2.

> (a), (b), (c), (d) Decimal notation.   (e) Generalized commutative law.   (f) Distributive law.   (g) 14.3.

2. We should like to write $14 \times 10 = 140$ as step (h) in frame 1. Give reasons for the following justification of this result.

(a) $14 = 10 + 4$ — *Decimal notation*
(b) $14 \times 10 = (10 + 4) \times 10$
(c) $\qquad = (1 \times 10^2) + (4 \times 10)$ — *Distributive law*
(d) $\qquad = 140$ — *Decimal notation*

> (a) Decimal notation.   (c) Distributive law.   (d) Decimal notation.

3. Now complete the addition in frame 1 by writing all the steps needed to add $140 + 24$. Use a separate piece of paper, and justify each step.

291

You should have written something like this:

$140 = (1 \times 10^2) + (4 \times 10) + 0$	Decimal notation.
$24 = (2 \times 10) + 4$	Decimal notation.
$140 + 24$	Generalized
$\quad = (1 \times 10^2) + [(4 \times 10) + (2 \times 10)] + [0 + 4]$	commutative law.
$\quad = (1 \times 10^2) + [(4 + 2) \times 10] + [0 + 4]$	Distributive law.
$\quad = (1 \times 10^2) + (6 \times 10) + 4$	Addition fact.
$\quad = 164$	Decimal notation.

4. As in frame 2, write on a separate piece of paper the steps needed to show that $36 \times 10^2 = 3600$. Give reasons for each step.

You should have written something like this:

$36 = (3 \times 10) + 6$	Decimal notation.
$36 \times 10^2 = [(3 \times 10) + 6] \times 10^2$	
$\quad = [(3 \times 10^3) + (6 \times 10^2)]$	Distributive law.
$\quad = 3600$	Decimal notation.

5. Use the basic method of this section to find the sums below where base ten notation is employed. Work from right to left.

(a) $\begin{array}{r} 469 \\ 253 = \\ +718 \\ \hline \end{array}$ $\begin{array}{r} 20 \\ 120 \\ +1300 \\ \hline 1440 \end{array}$ (b) $\begin{array}{r} 536 \\ 895 = \\ +675 \\ \hline \end{array}$ $\begin{array}{r} 16 \\ 190 \\ 1900 \\ \hline 2106 \end{array} = \begin{array}{r} 6 \\ 100 \\ 1000 \\ 1000 \\ \hline 2106 \end{array}$

(a) $\begin{array}{r} 20 \\ 120 \\ +1300 \\ \hline 1440 \end{array}$ (b) $\begin{array}{r} 16 \\ 190 = \\ +1900 \\ \hline \end{array}$ $\begin{array}{r} 6 \\ 100 \\ 1000 \\ +1000 \\ \hline 2106 \end{array}$

6. Use the basic method to find the sums where base ten notation is employed. Work from left to right.

(a) $\begin{array}{r} 624 \\ 135 = \\ +278 \\ \hline \end{array}$ $\begin{array}{r} 900 \\ 120 \\ 17 \\ \hline 1037 \end{array}$ (b) $\begin{array}{r} 986 \\ 795 = \\ +689 \\ \hline \end{array}$ $\begin{array}{r} 2200 \\ 250 \\ 20 \\ \hline 2470 \end{array}$

(a) $\begin{array}{r} 900 \\ 120 \\ + \quad 17 \\ \hline 1037 \end{array}$ (b) $\begin{array}{r} 2200 \\ 250 \\ + \quad 20 \\ \hline 2470 \end{array}$

7. Use the basic method to find the sums where base four notation is employed. Work from right to left.

(a) 210
    332 =   *120* = *1000*   (base four)
 +221   *1300*   *1000*
                       2023

(b) 132   *12*
    211 = *100*   (base four)
 +303 *1200*
         1312

(a)			(b)	
	3	3		12
120 =	20			100
+1300	1000			+1200
		+1000		1312
		2023		

8. Use the basic method to find the sums below where base five notation is employed. Work from left to right.

(a) 324 *1300*   *1000*   *1000*
    131 = *140* = *400* = *1000* (base five)
 +442   *12*   *100*   *0*
                2   *2*
                      2002

(b) 413 *1200*
    230 = *110*   (base five)
 +124   *12*
       1322

(a)			(b)	
1300	1000	1000		1200
140	400	1000		110
+ 12	100	0		+ 12
	+ 2	+ 2		1322
		2002		

14.5 Algorithms

The common algorithms for addition are all relatively simple modifications of the basic method of Section 14.4. The idea is to condense the format so that the computation can be performed as compactly as possible.

CONDENSED BASIC METHOD   **(1) CONDENSED BASIC METHOD**

In this we use the basic method but arrange the work in one array, omitting all unnecessary zeros. In some versions of the method each number is written as close to the line as possible in the interest of saving space. Thus we can rewrite one of our previous examples as

```
    375            375
    596            596
    487            487
   ────           ────
     18           1218
     24            24
     12           ────
   ────           1458
   1458
```
            or

Another possibility is

```
    375            375
    596            596
    487            487
   ────    or     ────
     12           1248
     24            21
     18           ────
   ────           1458
   1458
```

Similarly, we write

```
    384            384            384
    892            892            892
    988            988            988
    867            867            867
   ────    or     ────    or     ────
     21            28            2811
     31            31             32
     28            21           ────
   ────          ────           2131
   1131             2              1
      2           1131          ────
   ────          ────           3131
   3131           3131
```

(2) CARRYING METHOD

CARRYING METHOD

In the algorithms discussed so far we can write the column sums in any order. We have exhibited two possibilities: left to right and right to left. Other orders are acceptable but are not commonly employed.

The "carrying method", which is the one usually taught in school, requires us to work from right to left. It is a very slight modification of the basic right to left method. Previously we wrote

```
    375
    596
    487
   ────
     18
     24
     12
   ────
   1458
```

In the carrying method, instead of writing the 18 below the line we write the 8 below the line and the 1 at the top of the middle column. Then we have

```
   1
 375
 596
 487
 ───
   8
```

The sum of the middle column is now $1 + 24 = 25$. We write the 5 below the line and "carry" the 2 to the top of the left column:

```
  21
 375
 596
 487
 ───
  58
```

Finally, we add the left column and obtain $2 + 12 = 14$, and then write the answer:

```
  21
 375
 596
 487
 ────
1458
```

Notice that in this method we perform exactly the same additions as in the basic method, but we arrange the work in a slightly different fashion. The justification is, therefore, the same as for the basic method.

---

1. Find the sums by (a) the right to left basic method and (b) the carrying method.

```
        (a)   462     (b)   462
              357           357
            + 683         + 683
                         ──────
                          1502
```

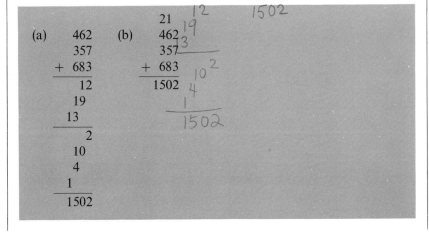

```
(a)    462     (b)    462
       357            357
     + 683          + 683
     ─────          ─────
        12           1502
        19
        13
     ─────
         2
        10
         4
         1
     ─────
      1502
```

2. Find the sums by the carrying method.

	(a) 258	(b) 2174	(c) 2503
	973	36	6798
	+1604	+ 526	+1376
	2835	2736	10677

	111	11	111
(a)	258	(b) 2174	(c) 2503
	973	36	6798
	+1604	+ 526	+ 1376
	2835	2736	10677

3. Find the following sums, where all numerals are expressed in base four notation. Use the carrying method.

	(a) 213	(b) 333	(c) 230	
	302	132	321	(base four)
	+231	+210	+211	
	2012	2001	2022	

	11	21	1	
(a)	213	(b) 333	(c) 230	
	302	132	321	(base four)
	+ 231	+ 210	+ 211	
	2012	2001	2022	

4. Find the following sums, where all numerals are expressed in base five notation. Use the carrying method.

	(a) 432	(b) 342	(c) 341	
	122	134	424	(base five)
	+244	+240	+131	
	1403	1321	2001	

	21	21	21	
(a)	432	(b) 342	(c) 341	
	122	134	424	(base five)
	+ 244	+ 240	+ 131	
	1403	1321	2001	

5. Why can the basic method be performed right to left or left to right? Generalized commutative law.

Generalized commutative law.

6. Why must addition by the carrying method go from right to left? The numbers that are carried are placed in the column to the _left_ of that which was summed.

left

7. In the sum

$$
\begin{array}{r}
654 \\
198 \\
362 \\
+\ 147 \\
\hline
21 \\
24 \\
11 \\
\hline
1361
\end{array}
\qquad \text{or} \qquad
\begin{array}{r}
22 \\
654 \\
198 \\
362 \\
+\ 147 \\
\hline
1361
\end{array}
$$

the sum of the right-hand column is 21. This is 21 = (2 × _10_) + _1_ . The digits in the middle column are coefficients of _10_ in the decimal expansions of the corresponding numbers. We carry the 2 to the top of the middle column and add. We therefore have $(2 + 5 + 9 + 6 + 4) \times$ _10_ .

| 10 | 1 | 10 | 10 |

8. In frame 7 we carry another 2 to the top of the left-hand column. This 2 represents 2 × _10^2_ . The sum of the left-hand column is then $(2 + 6 + 1 + 3 + 1) \times$ _10^2_ .

10^2 (or 100) 10^2 (or 100)

You should now be able to add numbers of any size which are written in any system of numeration and be able to explain why your steps are correct. To check your ability to do this, work the following Post Test. Do not refer to the text while working this test. Check your answers with the key after you have completed the test.

POST TEST

1. Make an addition table for numbers in base three notation.

+	0	1	2
0	0	1	2
1	1	2	10
2	2	10	11

In Problems 2 through 5 name the property of whole numbers which justifies the equality:

2. $78 = (7 \times 10) + 8$. *place-value system*

3. $[(7 \times 10) + 8] + [(5 \times 10) + 4] = [(7 \times 10) + (5 \times 10)] + [8 + 4]$. *Generalized commutative law of +.*

4. $[(7 \times 10) + (5 \times 10)] + [8 + 4] = [(7 + 5) \times 10] + [8 + 4]$. *Distr. law.*

5. $[(7 + 5) \times 10] + [8 + 4] = (12 \times 10) + 12$. *Addition facts*

6. Is there a single correct order for adding a column? *No.* Justify your answer (briefly). *Generalized comm. prop. law for + says can add in any order*

7. In base five write the steps needed to show that $12 + 3 = 20$ giving reasons for each step. Use base five numerals exclusively. Write your answer on a separate piece of paper.

8. Use the basic method of addition to find the following sum of numerals in base ten notation. Work from left to right.

$$
\begin{array}{r}
245 \\
37 \\
+192 \\
\end{array}
=
\begin{array}{r}
300 \\
160 \\
14 \\
\hline
474 \\
\end{array}
$$

9. Add by the condensed basic method (right to left). Base ten notation is used.

$$
\begin{array}{r}
762 \\
819 \\
+237 \\
\end{array}
\quad
\begin{array}{r}
18 \\
10 \\
17 \\
\hline
1818 \\
\end{array}
$$

10. Add by the carrying method (base ten):

$$
\begin{array}{r}
\overset{1\,1\,2}{1357} \\
864 \\
+\ 29 \\
\hline
2250 \\
\end{array}
$$

11. Add by the left-to-right basic method (base 5):

$$
\begin{array}{r}
431 \\
204 \\
+324 \\
\end{array}
=
\begin{array}{r}
1400 \\
100 \\
14 \\
\hline
2014 \\
\end{array}
=
\begin{array}{r}
1000 \\
1000 \\
10 \\
4 \\
\hline
2014 \\
\end{array}
$$

12. Add by the carrying method (base 4):

$$
\begin{array}{r}
\overset{1\ 1}{323} \\
102 \\
+231 \\
\hline
1322 \\
\end{array}
$$

13. Write in compact form: $(3 \times 10^3) + (12 \times 10^2) + (9 \times 10) + 16$.

4,306

14. Why can we use the basic method from right to left or from left to right? *Generalized Commutative property.*

1.

+	0	1	2
0	0	1	2
1	1	2	10
2	2	10	11

2. System of numeration or place-value system, decimal system of numeration.

3. Generalized commutative law of addition.

4. Distributive law.

5. Addition facts.

6. No. The generalized commutative law for addition permits adding in any order whatever.

7. (a) $12 = 10 + 2$ Base five notation.
   (b) $12 + 3 = (10 + 2) + 3$
   (c) $= 10 + (2 + 3)$ Associative law.
   (d) $= 10 + 10$ Addition fact.
   (e) $= 10 + (10 + 0)$ Base five notation.
   (f) $= (10 + 10) + 0$ Associative law.
   (g) $= (1 + 1) \times 10 + 0$ Distributive law.
   (h) $= (2 \times 10) + 0$ Addition fact.
   (i) $= 20$ Base five notation.

```
8.    300
      166
    +  14
      474

9.    762
      819
    + 237
       18
       10
    + 17
     1818

10.   112
     1357
      864
    +  29
     2250
```

```
11.    1400        1000
        100 =      1000
      +  14          10
      ——————      +    4
                   ——————
                     2014

        11
12.    323
       102
     + 231
     ——————
      1322
```

13. 4306.

14. Generalized commutative law.

If you are successful in this test, proceed to Chapter 15, Subtraction Algorithms, and complete its Readiness Test.

15

Subtraction Algorithms

Before beginning this chapter you should review Chapter 10, Subtraction. There are many algorithms for subtraction, and in this chapter we shall show you the usual methods as well as one unusual one.

You should recall that

$a - b$ *is defined if and only if* $a \geq b$
$a - b = c$ *if and only if* $a = b + c$

The following Readiness Test will review the ideas needed for the understanding of this chapter.

READINESS TEST

1. Which of the following differences is (are) defined on the set of whole numbers? (a) $6 - 9$. (b) $11 - 11$. (c) $12 - 7$.

(b) and (c).

2. Why is $7 - 9$ not defined on the set of whole numbers? ___$7 < 9$___

$7 < 9$.

3. Since $6 + 9 = 15$, what is $15 - 6$? ___9___

9.

4. Why are you sure that $8 - 3 = 5$? ___$8 = 3 + 5$___

$8 = 3 + 5$.

5. Since $9 - 4 = 5$, what is $(9 + 7) - (4 + 7)$? ___5___

5.

6. $(20 + 6) - (10 + 3) = (20 - 10) + ($___$6 - 3$___$)$.

$6 - 3$

7. Is subtraction commutative? ___No___
(yes, no)

No.

8. Is subtraction associative? _No_
(yes, no)

No.

9. What is the decimal expansion of 369? $(3 \times 10^2) + (6 \times 10) + 9$

$(3 \times 10^2) + (6 \times 10) + 9.$

10. What is the decimal expansion of 1002? $(1 \times 10^3) + 2$

$(1 \times 10^3) + 2.$

If you are now ready, read Sections 15.1 and 15.2 and work the corresponding programs.

15.1 Introduction

The difference of two whole numbers has been defined (Chapter 10) for any two whole numbers a and b with $b \leq a$. According to the definition, $a - b = c$, where c is the whole number such that $a = b + c$. This definition permits us to use the addition tables of Section 14.1 as subtraction tables.

   EXAMPLE. To find $12 - 3$ (base ten) enter the base ten table in the column headed 3 and read down until you reach 12. Then read to the left and find the number of the corresponding row: It is 9. So $3 + 9 = 12$ or $12 - 3 = 9$.

   EXAMPLE. To find $11 - 2$ (base four) enter the base four table in the column headed 2. Read down until you reach 11. The corresponding row is labeled 3, so $11 - 2 = 3$.

   This method applies only when a and b are in the corresponding addition table, and so we shall need other methods for most subtraction problems. When you compute a difference by this method, you may call the answer a "subtraction fact".

SUBTRACTION FACTS

1. Using the addition table base ten compute the differences:
(a) $14 - 6.$ ___8___ (b) $9 - 3.$ ___6___

(a) 8.   (b) 6.

2. Using the addition table base four compute the differences:
(a) 12 − 3 ___3___ (b) 10 − 2. ___2___ (c) 10 − 1.___3___

(a) 3.   (b) 2.   (c) 3.

3. What theorem justifies the method of subtraction described in this section? _x − y = z ∼ x = y + z_

$a − b = c$ is equivalent to $a = b + c$.

15.2 Basic Method of Subtraction

We assume that you are familiar with the basic subtraction facts and are ready to proceed with subtraction where the minuend and subtrahend contain more than one digit. Suppose we have the problem $58 − 32$. Probably you say to yourself immediately, the difference is 26. Let us justify this answer.

$$58 = (5 \times 10) + 8 \qquad \text{Decimal notation.}$$

$$32 = (3 \times 10) + 2 \qquad \text{Decimal notation.}$$

$$58 − 32 = [(5 \times 10) + 8] − [(3 \times 10) + 2]$$

In Theorem 11, Chapter 10, we showed that if $a \geq c$ and $b \geq d$, then $(a + b) − (c + d) = (a − c) + (b − d)$. We can apply this result here and write

$$58 − 32 = [(5 \times 10) − (3 \times 10)] + [8 − 2]$$

$$= [(5 − 3) \times 10] + [8 − 2] \qquad \text{Distributive law.}$$

$$= (2 \times 10) + 6 \qquad \text{Subtraction facts.}$$

$$= 26 \qquad \text{Decimal notation.}$$

This operation is relatively simple. Children seldom have difficulty with subtraction problems where every digit in the minuend is greater than or equal to the corresponding digit in the subtrahend.

The general theory behind the basic method is merely a formalization of the steps used in the above example. We need an obvious extension of Theorem 11, Chapter 10.

THEOREM 1. If $a_0, a_1, \ldots, a_n, b_0, b_1, \ldots, b_n$ are whole numbers and if for each i $(i = 0, \ldots, n)$ $a_i \geq b_i$, then

$$(a_n + a_{n-1} + \cdots + a_1 + a_0) − (b_n + b_{n-1} + \cdots + b_1 + b_0)$$

$$= (a_n − b_n) + (a_{n-1} − b_{n-1}) + \cdots + (a_1 − b_1) + (a_0 − b_0)$$

303

Subtraction Algorithms

Now suppose that we have two whole numbers c and d whose decimal expansions are, respectively,

$$c = (c_n \times 10^n) + (c_{n-1} \times 10^{n-1}) + \cdots + (c_1 \times 10) + c_0$$
$$d = (d_n \times 10^n) + (d_{n-1} \times 10^{n-1}) + \cdots + (d_1 \times 10) + d_0$$

where for each i ($i = 0, \ldots, n$) $c_i \geq d_i$. Then because of Theorem 1 and the distributive law,

BASIC METHOD

$$c - d = (c_n - d_n) \times 10^n + (c_{n-1} - d_{n-1}) \times 10^{n-1} + \cdots$$
$$+ (c_1 - d_1) \times 10 + (c_0 - d_0)$$

Since for each i, $c_i \geq d_i$, the subtractions indicated in the parentheses can be performed, and the result is the decimal expansion for the difference.

---

1. In the ordinary decimal expansion

$$c = (c_n \times 10^n) + (c_{n-1} \times 10^{n-1}) + \cdots + (c_1 \times 10) + c_0$$

how many digits are there in each of the coefficients, c_i? _____

One.

2. Answer the question in frame 1 for the decimal expansion of d.
_____

One.

3. Since c_i and d_i each are one digit numerals, and since $c_i \geq d_i$, the difference $c_i - d_i$ can be read from the _____ table. The result is a _____ fact.

addition   subtraction

4. How many digits are there in each of the differences $c_i - d_i$?
_____

One.

5. The expansion: $(c_n - d_n) \times 10^n + \cdots + (c_0 - d_0)$ is therefore the decimal expansion of _____.

$c - d$

6. Use this method to subtract:

(a)	7652	(b)	8526	(c)	6921
	− 5310		− 315		− 11

(a) 2342   (b) 8211   (c) 6910

7. Why does this method fail to work in the problem

$$\begin{array}{r} 3547 \\ -2185 \\ \hline \end{array}$$

_____

4 is less than 8.

8. Subtract the following numbers expressed as base four numerals:

(a) $\begin{array}{r} 2132 \\ -1121 \\ \hline \end{array}$ (b) $\begin{array}{r} 3102 \\ -2101 \\ \hline \end{array}$ (c) $\begin{array}{r} 1230 \\ -\ 120 \\ \hline \end{array}$ (base four)

(a) 1011   (b) 1001   (c) 1110   (base four)

9. We can check the result of a subtraction by recalling that $a - b = c$ if and only if $a = b + c$. Thus to check that $58 - 32 = 26$, we compute $58 = 26 + 32$. Apply this method to check the answers to frame 6.

(a)   (b)   (c)

(a) $\begin{array}{r} 5310 \\ +2342 \\ \hline 7652 \end{array}$ (b) $\begin{array}{r} 315 \\ +8211 \\ \hline 8526 \end{array}$ (c) $\begin{array}{r} 11 \\ +6910 \\ \hline 6921 \end{array}$

10. Similarly, check your answers to frame 8.

(a)   (b)   (c)   (base four)

(a) $\begin{array}{r} 1121 \\ +1011 \\ \hline 2132 \end{array}$ (b) $\begin{array}{r} 2101 \\ +1001 \\ \hline 3102 \end{array}$ (c) $\begin{array}{r} 120 \\ +1110 \\ \hline 1230 \end{array}$

11. Upon what theorem does this "basic method" of subtraction depend? _____

Theorem 1, or more simply: For any whole numbers a, b, c, and d where $c \leq a$ and $d \leq b$, $(a + b) - (c + d) = (a - c) + (b - d)$.

Now read Section 15.3 and complete the exercises at its end.

15.3 "Borrowing Method"

The basic method of Section 15.2 is effective only if each digit of the minuend is greater than or equal to the corresponding digit in the subtrahend. Since this is frequently not the case, we must modify this method to handle problems such as

$$42$$
$$-18$$

The idea of the modification is to rewrite the expansion of the minuend into an expansion that meets the conditions of Theorem 1. Let us see how this is done in the problem: $42 - 18$. In the ordinary decimal expansion of 42 we have

$$42 = (4 \times 10) + 2$$

This is of no use in the calculation of $42 - 18$, since $2 < 8$. We see, however, that $42 = 30 + 12$, or that

$$42 = (3 \times 10) + 12$$

Since

$$18 = (1 \times 10) + 8$$

the conditions of Theorem 1 are now met and we can subtract. So

$$42 - 18 = (3 - 1) \times 10 + (12 - 8)$$
$$= (2 \times 10) + 4$$
$$= 24$$

This method is called "borrowing". We have borrowed 1 from the 4 and used it to convert 2 into 12. Usually the process is written

$$\begin{array}{r} 3 \\ 4\,^{1}2 \\ -1\ 8 \\ \hline 2\ 4 \end{array}$$

The logic behind this is given by the following steps:

$42 = (4 \times 10) + 2$	Decimal notation.
$= (3 + 1) \times 10 + 2$	Addition fact.
$= [(3 \times 10) + (1 \times 10)] + 2$	Distributive law.
$= (3 \times 10) + [(1 \times 10) + 2]$	Associative law.
$= (3 \times 10) + 12$	Decimal notation.

In order to give a more general discussion let us suppose that in the expansion of the minuend the last two terms are $(c_1 \times 10) + c_0$ and the corresponding terms in the subtrahend are $(d_1 \times 10) + d_0$. The problem before us is that of handling the situation where $c_0 < d_0$.

If $c_1 \neq 0$, we can borrow and write

$$(c_1 \times 10) + c_0 = (c_1 - 1) \times 10 + (10 + c_0)$$

which is an immediate consequence of the distributive law. Then we can find the difference $(10 + c_0) - d_0$ from the addition table.

The same idea applies if a similar situation occurs in any column other than that on the extreme left. The expansions of c and d can be written as follows, where we assume that $i \neq n$.

$$c = (c_n \times 10^n) + \cdots + (c_{i+1} \times 10^{i+1}) + (c_i \times 10^i) + \cdots + c_0$$

$$d = (d_n \times 10^n) + \cdots + (d_{i+1} \times 10^{i+1}) + (d_i \times 10^i) + \cdots + d_0$$

We are in trouble in Theorem 1 if $c_i < d_i$. If $c_{i+1} \neq 0$, we can write

$$c_{i+1} = (c_{i+1} - 1) + 1$$

$$c_{i+1} \times 10^{i+1} = (c_{i+1} - 1) \times 10^{i+1} + (1 \times 10^{i+1})$$

$$= (c_{i+1} - 1) \times 10^{i+1} + (10 \times 10^i)$$

Finally,

$$(c_{i+1} \times 10^{i+1}) + (c_i \times 10^i)$$

$$= (c_{i+1} - 1) \times 10^{i+1} + (10 \times 10^i) + (c_i \times 10^i)$$

$$= (c_{i+1} - 1) \times 10^{i+1} + (10 + c_i) \times 10^i$$

Then the difference $(10 + c_i) - d_i$ is a subtraction fact.

The practical format for the "borrowing process" is the following:

$$
\begin{array}{r}
2\ 3\ 5\ 2 \\
-1\ 8\ 2\ 7 \\
\hline
\end{array}
$$

This proceeds by a series of steps:

$$
\begin{array}{r}
4 \\
2\ 3\ 5^{1}2 \\
-1\ 8\ 2\ 7 \\
\hline
2\ 5
\end{array}
\qquad
\begin{array}{r}
1\quad 4 \\
2^{1}3\ 5^{1}2 \\
-1\ 8\ 2\ 7 \\
\hline
5\ 2\ 5
\end{array}
$$

As a slightly harder problem consider the example

$$
\begin{array}{r}
3\ 2\ 3\ 4 \\
-1\ 4\ 7\ 8 \\
\hline
\end{array}
$$

The steps are

$$
\begin{array}{r}
2 \\
3\ 2\ 3^{1}4 \\
-1\ 4\ 7\ 8 \\
\hline
6
\end{array}
\qquad
\begin{array}{r}
1^{1}2 \\
3\ 2\ 3^{1}4 \\
-1\ 4\ 7\ 8 \\
\hline
5\ 6
\end{array}
\qquad
\begin{array}{r}
2^{1}1^{1}2 \\
3\ 2\ 3^{1}4 \\
-1\ 4\ 7\ 8 \\
\hline
1\ 7\ 5\ 6
\end{array}
$$

Finally, how do we handle the case where some $c_{i+1} = 0$ and we need to borrow 1 from it?

$$
\begin{array}{r}
3\ 5\ 0\ 2 \\
-1\ 2\ 3\ 5 \\
\hline
\end{array}
$$

Subtraction Algorithms

First, we move one column to the left and borrow 1 from the 5:

$$
\begin{array}{r}
4\\
3\ 5^1 0\ 2\\
-\ 1\ 2\ 3\ 5\\
\hline
\end{array}
$$

Now we can borrow 1 from the 10 and proceed as usual:

$$
\begin{array}{r}
4\ 9\\
3\ 5^\cancel{1} 0^1 2\\
-\ 1\ 2\ 3\ 5\\
\hline
2\ 2\ 6\ 7
\end{array}
$$

1. Give the reasons for the following steps:

(a) $75 = (7 \times 10) + 5$ _Decimal notation_
(b) $\quad = [(6 + 1) \times 10] + 5$ _Addition fact_
(c) $\quad = [(6 \times 10) + (1 \times 10)] + 5$ _Distributive_
(d) $\quad = (6 \times 10) + [(1 \times 10) + 5]$ _Associative_
(e) $\quad = (6 \times 10) + 15$ _Decimal notation_

(a) Decimal notation.
(b) Addition fact.
(c) Distributive law.
(d) Associative law.
(e) Decimal notation.

2. Give reasons for the following steps:

(a) $632 = (6 \times 10^2) + (3 \times 10) + 2$ _Decimal notation_
(b) $\quad = (5 + 1) \times 10^2 + (3 \times 10) + 2$ _Addition fact_
(c) $\quad = [(5 \times 10^2) + (1 \times 10^2)] + (3 \times 10) + 2$ _Distributive_
(d) $\quad = (5 \times 10^2) + [(1 \times 10^2) + (3 \times 10)] + 2$ _Associative_
(e) $\quad = (5 \times 10^2) + [(10 \times 10) + (3 \times 10)] + 2$ _Meaning of 10^2_
(f) $\quad = (5 \times 10^2) + [(10 + 3) \times 10] + 2$ _Distributive_
(g) $\quad = (5 \times 10^2) + (13 \times 10) + 2$ _Decimal notation_

(a) Decimal notation.   (d) Associative law.
(b) Addition fact.   (e) Meaning of 10^2.
(c) Distributive law.   (f) Distributive law.
                             (g) ~~Addition fact.~~ _Decimal notation_

3. Our formula

$$(c_{i+1} \times 10^{i+1}) + (c_i \times 10^i)$$

$$= (c_{i+1} - 1) \times 10^{i+1} + (10 + c_i) \times 10^i$$

does not hold when $i = n$, that is, when the ith column is the extreme left-hand column, for there is no column numbered $i + 1$ on its left. This does not bother us, since we are sure that $c_n \geq d_n$. Why is this the case?

we assume that $c \geq d$, this is not true if $c_n < d_n$

> We must assume that $c \geq d$ in order for the subtraction to be possible. This cannot be true if $c_n < d_n$.

4. Subtract and check.

(a) $\begin{array}{r} 5\ 4\ \overset{3}{3}\ 6 \\ -1\ 2\ 2\ 7 \\ \hline 4\ 2\ 0\ 9 \end{array}$ (b) $\begin{array}{r} \overset{2}{3}\ 4\ \overset{0}{1}\ 6 \\ -1\ 8\ 0\ 7 \\ \hline 1\ 6\ 0\ 9 \end{array}$ (c) $\begin{array}{r} \overset{3}{4}\ 2\ \overset{11}{1}\ \overset{10}{3} \\ -3\ 8\ 7\ 6 \\ \hline 3\ 3\ 7 \end{array}$

Check: (a) (b) (c)

(a)	4209	(b)	1609	(c)	337
	1227		1807		3876
	+4209		+1609		+ 337
	5436		3416		4213

5. Consider the subtraction problem

$$\begin{array}{r} 1000 \\ -\ 427 \end{array}$$

Borrowing is essential, and the only digit of the minuend from which we can borrow is the 1. As the first step we write

$1000 = (1 \times 10^3) = (\underline{0} \times 10^3) + (\underline{10} \times 10^2) + (0 \times 10) + 0$

> 0   10

6. One further borrowing gives us

$1000 = (0 \times 10^3) + (10 \times 10^2) + (0 \times 10) + 0$

$ = (0 \times 10^3) + (\underline{9} \times 10^2) + (\underline{10} \times 10) + 0$

> 9   10

7. The final borrowing gives

$1000 = (0 \times 10^3) + (9 \times 10^2) + (10 \times 10) + 0$

$ = (0 \times 10^3) + (9 \times 10^2) + (\underline{9} \times 10) + \underline{10}$

> 9   10

309

Subtraction Algorithms

8. Therefore, $1000 - 427 = [(9 \times 10^2) + (9 \times 10) + 10] - [(4 \times 10^2) + (2 \times 10) + 7] = (\underline{5} \times 10^2) + (\underline{7} \times 10) + \underline{3}$.

5	7	3

9. Finally, $1000 - 427 = \underline{573}$

573

10. Write the computation of frames 5 to 9 in compact form.

$$
\begin{array}{r}
\overset{9}{} \\
1\,0\,0\,0 \\
-\ \ 4\,2\,7 \\
\hline
573
\end{array}
$$

$\begin{array}{r} 9 \\ 9\,\cancel{1}0 \\ \cancel{1}\,0\,0^1 0 \\ -\ 4\,2\,7 \\ \hline 5\,7\,3 \end{array}$

11. What expansion for 1000 would be used in the computation of $1000 - 800$?

$1000 = (\underline{0} \times 10^3) + (\underline{10} \times 10^2) + (\underline{0} \times 10) + \underline{0}$

0	10	0	0

12. What expansion of 238 would be used in the computation of $238 - 43$?

$238 = (\underline{1} \times 10^2) + (\underline{13} \times 10) + \underline{8}$

1	13	8

13. What expansion of 238 would be used in the computation of $238 - 29$?

$238 = (\underline{2} \times 10^2) + (\underline{2} \times 10) + \underline{18}$

2	2	18

14. Subtract and check.

$$
\text{(a)}\quad
\begin{array}{r}
\overset{39}{2\,4\,\cancel{0}\,6} \\
-2\,3\,5\,9 \\
\hline
4\,7
\end{array}
\qquad
\text{(b)}\quad
\begin{array}{r}
\overset{299}{3\,0\,0\,1} \\
-1\,2\,3\,4 \\
\hline
1767
\end{array}
\qquad
\text{(c)}\quad
\begin{array}{r}
2\,3\,0\,1 \\
-2\,5\,4\,2 \\
\hline
\text{Impossible} \\
2301 < 2542
\end{array}
$$

Check: (a)   (b)   (c)

2359   1234   2301 < 2542
+ 47   1767
2406   3001

(a)   47.   (b)   1767.   (c) Impossible.

2359   1234   2301 < 2542
+ 47   +1767
2406   3001

15. The following numerals are in base four notation. Subtract and check.

(a)   2 1 3 1   (b)   3 2 0 1   (c)   2 1 0 1
    − 1 2 1 3   − 1 3 1 0   − 1 2 3 3   (base four)
        312   1231   202

Check: (a)   (b)   (c)

1213   1310   1233
 312   1231   202
2131   3201   2101

(a)   312.   (b)   1231.   (c)   202.

1213   1310   1233
+ 312   +1231   + 202   (base four)
2131   3201   2101

Another algorithm for subtraction is given in Section 15.4. Read this section and work the exercises.

15.4 Alternative to "Borrowing"

ALTERNATIVE TO
BORROWING

Instead of rewriting the expansion of the minuend as described in the borrowing process of Section 15.3, we can achieve the same result in another way by adding an appropriate power of 10 to both the minuend and the subtrahend. This is justified by Theorem 12, Chapter 10, which states that

$$a - b = (a + c) - (b + c)$$

We shall choose c to be 10, 10^2, 10^3, ..., according to our needs.

As an example, consider $42 - 18$ above. Then

$$42 = (4 \times 10) + 2$$
$$18 = (1 \times 10) + 8$$

We should like to add 10 to 42 so that we get

$$42 + 10 = (4 \times 10) + 12$$

To keep matters straight we must also add 10 to 18:

$$18 + 10 = (2 \times 10) + 8$$

You will observe that in $42 + 10$ we added 10 to the 2, but in $18 + 10$ we added 10 to (1×10). Then

$$42 - 18 = (42 + 10) - (18 + 10)$$
$$= [(4 \times 10) + 12] - [(2 \times 10) + 8]$$
$$= (4 - 2) \times 10 + (12 - 8)$$
$$= (2 \times 10) + 4$$
$$= 24$$

The computation may be expressed in the following form:

$$\begin{array}{r} 4^12 \\ 2 \\ -\cancel{1}\,8 \\ \hline 2\;4 \end{array}$$

This method will be illustrated further in the exercises below.

---

1. To subtract $45 - 27$ by this method we write

$$45 = (4 \times 10) + 5$$
$$27 = (2 \times 10) + 7$$

Now we add 10 to each of the numbers. In the addition of 10 to $45 = (4 \times 10) + 5$ we add the 10 to the __5__ and obtain __15__.

5	15

2. In the addition of 10 to $27 = (2 \times 10) + 7$ we write $27 + 10 = [(2 \times 10) + (1 \times 10)] + 7$. This is $(3 \times 10) + 7$. Why?__Distributive law__. Then

$$45 + 10 = (4 \times 10) + 15$$
$$27 + 10 = (3 \times 10) + 7$$

So

$$45 - 27 = \underline{18}$$

Distributive law. 18

3. In the subtraction by this method of

$$365$$
$$- 283$$

we add __100__ to the minuend and the subtrahend.

100

4. After the addition in frame 3, the problem   365 is rewritten
                                                  − 283

(handwritten:)
$$3^16\ 5$$
$$3$$
$$\cancel{2}\ 83$$
$$8\ 2$$

$$3^16\ 5$$
$$3$$
$$-2\ 8\ 3$$

5. The answer to the problem in frames 3 and 4 is __82__.

82

6. The check of the answer in frame 5 is

(handwritten:)
$$283$$
$$+\ \ 82$$
$$365$$

$$283$$
$$+\ \ 82$$
$$365$$

7. In applying this method to the following problems (see frame 4, Section 15.3), what do we add to the minuend and subtrahend? Complete the problems by this method.

(a) $\begin{array}{r} 5436 \\ -1227 \end{array}$ add __10__, rewrite as

(handwritten:)
$$543^16$$
$$-123\ 7$$
$$4209$$

(b) $\begin{array}{r} 3416 \\ -1807 \end{array}$ add __10__, __1000__, rewrite as

(handwritten:)
$$3^14^16$$
$$\cancel{2}\cancel{8}\ 8\ \cancel{0}7$$
$$1609$$

(c) $\begin{array}{r} 4213 \\ -3876 \end{array}$ add __10__, __100__, __1000__, rewrite as

(handwritten:)
$$4^12^13$$
$$-4986$$
$$337$$

313

(a) 10 $5\ 4\ 3^1 6$
            3
        $-1\ 2\ 2\ 7$
        $\overline{4\ 2\ 0\ 9}$

(b) 10   1000 $3^1 4\ 1^1 6$
                   $2\ \ \ \ 1$
              $-1\!\!\!/\ 8\ 0\ 7$
              $\overline{1\ 6\ 0\ 9}$

(c) 10   100   1000 $4^1 2^1 1^1 3$
                          $4\ 9\ 8$
                    $-3\ 8\ 7\!\!\!/\ 6$
                    $\overline{3\ 3\ 7}$

8. Subtract by this method (see frame 14, Section 15.3).

(a) $2\ 4^{|}0^{|}6$ (b) $3^{|}0^{|}0^{|}1$
         $4\ 6$ $2\ 3\ 4$
    $-2\ 3\!\!\!/5\ 9$ $-1\!\!\!/\ 2\ 3\!\!\!/\ 4$
    $\overline{4\!\!\!/7}$ $\overline{1\ 7\ 6\ 7}$

(a) $2\ 4^1 0^1 6$ (b) $3^1 0^1 0^1 1$
         $4\ 6\ 6$ $2\ 3\ 4$
    $-2\ 3\ 5\ 9$ $-1\ 2\ 3\ 4$
    $\overline{\ \ \ \ 4\ 7}$ $\overline{1\ 7.6\ 7}$

9. Subtract by this method the following numbers expressed in base four numerals (see frame 15, Section 15.3).

(a) $2^{|}1\ 3^{|}1$ (b) $3^{|}2^{|}0\ 1$ (c) $2^{|}1^{|}0^{|}1$
         $2\ \ \ 2$ $2\ 1\ 0$ $2\ 3\ 1\ 0$
    $-1\!\!\!/\ 2\ 1\!\!\!/\ 3$ $-1\!\!\!/\ 3\ 1\ 0$ $-1\!\!\!/\ 2\ 3\!\!\!/\ 3$ (base four)
    $\overline{3\ 1\ 2}$ $\overline{1\ 2\ 3\ 1}$ $\overline{2\ 0\ 2}$

(a) $2^1 1\ 3^1 1$ (b) $3^1 2^1 0\ 1$ (c) $2^1 1^1 0^1 1$
         $2\ \ \ 2$ $2\ 1\ 0$ $2\ 3\ 1\ 0$
    $-1\ 2\ 1\ 3$ $-1\ 3\ 1\ 0$ $-1\ 2\ 3\ 3$ (base four)
    $\overline{3\ 1\ 2}$ $\overline{1\ 2\ 3\ 1}$ $\overline{2\ 0\ 2}$

10. In frame 9 what did we add to each of the minuend and subtrahend?

(a) $10_4, 1000_4$ _____. (b) $100_4, 1000_4$ _____.
(c) $10_4, 100_4, 1000_4$ _____.

(a) $10_{four}, 1000_{four}$ (b) $100_{four}, 1000_{four}$
    [or $4_{ten}, (4^3)_{ten}$]   [or $(4^2)_{ten}, (4^3)_{ten}$]
(c) $10_{four}, 100_{four}, 1000_{four}$
    [or $4_{ten}, (4^2)_{ten}, (4^3)_{ten}$]

11. In this method we added a power of 10 to each of the minuend and subtrahend. Of course we could have added any other number to them and still had an equivalent problem. Why did we choose powers of 10? *They correspond to whatever base is being used.*

> Powers of 10 correspond to powers of the base used in the system of numeration.

12. Subtract 45 (base ten) by adding 6 to the minuend and subtrahend.

$$
\begin{array}{r}
45 \\
-37 \\
\end{array}
\quad
\begin{array}{r}
4\ 11 \\
-4\ \ 3 \\
\hline
8
\end{array}
$$

$$
\begin{array}{r}
4\ 5 \\
-3\ 7 \\
\hline
\end{array}
\ =\
\begin{array}{r}
4\ 11 \\
-4\ \ 3 \\
\hline
8
\end{array}
$$

13. Upon what theorem is the "alternative to borrowing" method based? *for whole no. a, b, c w/ b ≤ a, a − b = (a + c) − (b + c)*

> For all whole numbers a, b, and c with $b \le a$, $a - b = (a + c) - (b + c)$.

An unfamiliar but effective algorithm is described in Section 15.5. Read it through and apply it as indicated below. You will probably not teach this in school but will find the method amusing. Continue on through Section 15.6.

15.5 Method of Complements

If you are good at adding, but not so skillful in subtraction, here is a method of subtracting by adding.

COMPLEMENTS

DEFINITION. The *complement* of a digit a is $9 - a$.

The method consists of the following steps:

(1) Find the complement of each digit of the subtrahend. If the subtrahend is 5927 we thus write 4072.

(2) Add the result to the minuend. So if our problem is

$$
\begin{array}{r}
6205 \\
-5927 \\
\end{array}
$$

we add

$$\begin{array}{r} 6205 \\ +\ 4072 \\ \hline 10277 \end{array}$$

(3) Subtract 1 from the left-hand digit of the sum and add one to the right-hand digit. This is the answer! In the problem above we get the answer 278. Check it out!

---

1. When we wrote the complements of the digits in 5927 we obtained 4072. Actually we have $9999 - 5927 = $ _____.

> 4072

2. When we formed the sum $\quad 6205$ we really added:
$$+4072$$
$6205 + ($ _____ $-$ _____ $)$.

> 9999   5927

3. So our answer 10,277 is, in fact,
$$6205 + (9999 - 5927) = (6205 - 5927) + \underline{\hspace{2cm}}$$

> 9999

4. Now $9999 = 10,000 - $ _____.

> 1

5. So we have
$$10,277 = (6205 - 5927) + 10,000 - 1$$
Therefore,
$$6205 - 5927 = \underline{\hspace{3cm}}$$
$$= \underline{\hspace{2cm}}$$

> $10,277 - 10,000 + 1$ 278

6. Use the method of complements on the following problems (see frame 4, Section 15.3).

$$\begin{array}{lll}
\text{(a)} \quad 5436 & \text{(b)} \quad 3416 & \text{(c)} \quad 4213 \\
\quad\ \ -1227 & \quad\ \ -1807 & \quad\ \ -3876
\end{array}$$

(a)	5436	(b)	3416	(c)	4213
	+ 8772		+ 8192		+ 6123
	14208		11608		10336
	Ans. 4209		Ans. 1609		Ans. 337

7. In applying this method in base four, we take complements relative to $4 - 1 = 3$. Use the method for the following problems in base four notation (see frame 15, Section 15.3).

$$
\begin{array}{lll}
\text{(a)} \quad 2131 & \text{(b)} \quad 3201 & \text{(c)} \quad 2101 \\
\quad\; -1213 & \quad\; -1310 & \quad\; -1233
\end{array}
$$

(a)	2131	(b)	3201	(c)	2101
	+ 2120		+ 2023		+ 2100
	10311		11230		10201
	Ans. 312		Ans. 1231		Ans. 202

15.6 Additive Method

MAKING CHANGE   This procedure is most frequently met in making change. If a $5 bill is used to pay for an article costing $2.38 the clerk may say as he counts out the change, "2.38, 2.40, 2.50, 3.00, 4.00, 5.00". He has given the customer $0.02 + 0.10 + 0.50 + 1.00 + 1.00$, which equals $2.62. Notice that this is equivalent to the subtraction problem $500 - 238 = 262$. The difficulties of repeated borrowing in mental arithmetic are obvious.

The additive method of subtraction consists of answering the question: What must I add to the subtrahend in order to make a sum equaling the minuend? This device rests on the solid mathematical foundation, "$a - b = c$ if and only if $a = b + c$".

1. Use the additive method to find mentally the differences here:
(a) $60 - 48 = $ __12__.   (b) $91 - 48 = $ __43__.
(c) $1967 - 1890 = $ __77__.   (d) $1727 - 1642 = $ __85__.

> (a) 12 (48 + 2 = 50 and 50 + 10 = 60).
> (b) 43 (48 + 2 = 50, 50 + 40 = 90, and 90 + 1 = 91).
> (c) 77 (1890 + 10 = 1900 and 1900 + 67 = 1967).
> (d) 85 [1642 + 8 = 1650, 1650 + 50 = 1700, 1700 + 20 = 1720, 1720 + 7 = 1727 (8 + 50 + 20 + 7 = 85)].
>
> *Remark:* There is not just one correct way to use the additive method. Different paths to the same answer are quite possible. Always use the steps that seem most convenient to you.

Each of the algorithms of this chapter has certain advantages and difficulties. The important thing is that you understand why they are correct and that you have not merely memorized the steps.

Now test yourself on the following Post Test. Do not refer to the text while working this test. Check your answer against the key after you have completed the entire test.

POST TEST

Write the addition table base six.

+	0	1	2	3	4	5
0	0	1	2	3	4	5
1	1	2	3	4	5	10
2	2	3	4	5	10	11
3	3	4	5	10	11	12
4	4	5	10	11	12	13
5	5	10	11	12	13	14

2. Use the addition table base six to find the differences (base six): (a) 11 − 3. ___4___ (b) 14 − 5. ___5___

3. Under what circumstances can the basic method of subtraction be applied? _____

4. Give reasons for the following steps in finding 65 − 23 (base ten) by the basic method
 (a) 65 = (6 × 10) + 5
 23 = (2 × 10) + 3

 ___Decimal notation___
 (reason)

 (b) 65 − 23 = [(6 × 10) + 5] − [(2 × 10) + 3]

(c) $\qquad = [(6 \times 10) - (2 \times 10)] + [5 - 3]$ $\underline{(a+b)-(c+d)=(a-c)+}$

$(b-d)$

(relevant theorem)

(d) $\qquad = [(6 - 2) \times 10] + [5 - 3]$ $\underline{\text{Distributive prop.}}$

(reason)

(e) $\qquad = [4 \times 10] + 2$ $\underline{\text{Subtraction facts}}$

(reason)

(f) $\qquad = 42$ $\underline{\text{Decimal notation}}$

(reason)

5. Subtract using the borrowing method (base six):

$$\begin{array}{r} 5\ 2\ \overset{1}{1}\ 4 \\ -3\ 1\ 4\ 2 \\ \hline 2\ 0\ 3\ 2 \end{array}$$

6. What decimal expansion of 342 would be used in the borrowing method to compute $342 - 186$ (base ten)? $342 = \underline{(2 \times 10^2) + (13 \times 10) + 12}$.

7. Subtract using the "alternative to borrowing" method (base ten):

$$\begin{array}{r} 7\ 8\ \overset{1}{2}\ 4 \\ -6\ \overset{3}{2}\ 7\ 3 \\ \hline 1\ 5\ 5\ 1 \end{array}$$

What number have you added to minuend and subtrahend? $\underline{100}$

8. Upon what theorem is the "alternative to borrowing method" based? $\underline{\text{For all whole no. } a, b, c, \text{ when } b \le a, \ a-b =}$

$\underline{(a+c) - (b+c)}$

9. Subtract by the method of complements (base ten):

$$\begin{array}{r} 3614 \\ -2837 \\ \hline \end{array}$$

10. Subtract mentally by the additive method $85 - 42$. $\underline{43}$

6. $(2 \times 10^2) + (13 \times 10) + 12$

7. $\begin{array}{ccc} 7 & 8 & 12 & 4 \\ -6 & 3 & 7 & 3 \\ \hline 1 & 5 & 5 & 1 \end{array}$; 100.

8. For all whole numbers a, b, and c with $b \leq a$, $a - b = (a + c) - (b + c)$.

9. $\begin{array}{r} 3614 \\ +7162. \end{array}$ Ans. 777.

10. Many possible answers, for example, $3 + 5 + 30 + 5 = 43$.

If you were successful in this test, proceed to Chapter 16, Multiplication Algorithms, and work the Readiness Test.

16
Multiplication Algorithms

Before beginning this chapter you should have completed Chapter 14, Addition Algorithms. You should also review Chapter 11, Multiplication and Division. In this chapter we shall present several algorithms for the practical multiplication of whole numbers.

You should be familiar with the
 definition of the product of two whole numbers
 properties of multiplication
 distributive law
 decimal system of numeration
 addition algorithms

The following Readiness Test checks your knowledge of many of these topics.

R E A D I N E S S   T E S T

1. The distributive property of multiplication over addition states that
   $a(b+c) = (ab)+(ac)$

   $a(b + c) = (ab) + (ac)$

2. Two applications of the distributive property of multiplication over addition enable us to write $(a + b)(c + d)$ in the form $ac+ad+bc+bd$.

   $ac + ad + bc + bd$

3. If $10^2 \times 10^3 = 10^x$, what is x? 5

   5.

4. The product of any whole number n and 10^3 can be obtained by affixing $three$ zeros to the right of the base 10 numeral for n.

   three

5. Write 362 in expanded form, $362 = (3\times10^2)+(6\times10)+2$.

   $(3 \times 10^2) + (6 \times 10) + 2$

6. Find the sum   231 in base four. 1100
                 $+203$

   1100.

16.1　Introduction

As in the cases of addition and subtraction, you can multiply any two whole numbers by elementary methods (Chapter 11). For large numbers, this process is far too tiresome, so we must develop shortcuts called algorithms. All of these assume that we have available the basic multiplication table for the base used in the given system of numeration. The entries in this table are computed by the method of Chapter 11. Three such tables are given as Tables 1, 2, and 3.

TABLE 1. Basic Multiplication Table, Base Ten

×	0	1	2	3	4	5	6	7	8	9
0	0	0	0	0	0	0	0	0	0	0
1	0	1	2	3	4	5	6	7	8	9
2	0	2	4	6	8	10	12	14	16	18
3	0	3	6	9	12	15	18	21	24	27
4	0	4	8	12	16	20	24	28	32	36
5	0	5	10	15	20	25	30	35	40	45
6	0	6	12	18	24	30	36	42	48	54
7	0	7	14	21	28	35	42	49	56	63
8	0	8	16	24	32	40	48	56	64	72
9	0	9	18	27	36	45	54	63	72	81

TABLE 2. Basic Multiplication Table, Base Two

×	0	1
0	0	0
1	0	1

TABLE 3. Basic Multiplication Table, Base Four

×	0	1	2	3
0	0	0	0	0
1	0	1	2	3
2	0	2	10	12
3	0	3	12	21

The entries in these tables may be referred to as "multiplication facts". It is usual to memorize the base ten table, and the tables for other bases should be made available for reference as needed.

16.2　"Russian Peasant" Algorithm

**RUSSIAN PEASANT
ALGORITHM**

There are many algorithms for multiplication. As one example, consider the so-called "Russian peasant algorithm". We shall illustrate by using it to find 19×26.

INSTRUCTION		ILLUSTRATION	
(1) Write the numbers in adjacent columns.		19 $\times$	26
(2) Divide the number in column 1 by 2, ignoring any remainder. Record the result in column 1.		9	52
(3) Multiply the number in the second column by 2. Record the result in column 2 opposite the result of step 2.			
(4) Repeat steps 2 and 3 until the result in column 1 is a 1.		4	~~104~~
		2	~~208~~
		1	416

(5) Cross out any entries in column 2 that are opposite even numbers in column 1.

(6) The sum of the remaining numbers in column 2 is the desired product.

$$\underline{}$$
$$494$$

This algorithm is presented mainly because it is unfamiliar to most of you and thus consists of blindly following rules that someone guarantees will lead to the correct result (if the arithmetic is correctly done). There is sometimes a tendency to teach algorithms in this way without explanations. Such an approach makes the algorithm appear to be a form of magic, completely independent of the basic concepts of arithmetic. An explanation of the Russian peasant algorithm will be given in the exercises.

16.3 Multiplication by a Single Digit

Let us begin by considering the product in which one factor is a single digit. As an illustration we shall use 7×385. By our system of numeration any multidigit numeral represents a sum. Each term of that sum is the product of one of the digits and an appropriate power of ten. $385 = (3 \times 10^2) + (8 \times 10) + 5$. To multiply this by 7 we use the distributive law and write

$$7 \times 385 = 7 \times [(3 \times 10^2) + (8 \times 10) + 5]$$
$$= [7 \times (3 \times 10^2)] + [7 \times (8 \times 10)] + [7 \times 5]$$

The associative property of multiplication permits us to write this as

$$7 \times 385 = [(7 \times 3) \times 10^2] + [(7 \times 8) \times 10] + [7 \times 5]$$

At this point we use the multiplication facts and write

$$7 \times 385 = 2100 + 560 + 35$$

and the original multiplication problem becomes one of addition. Since addition is usually done in a vertical column we would probably have written the work thus:

$$
\begin{array}{r}
385 \\
7 \\
\hline
2100 \\
560 \\
35 \\
\hline
2695
\end{array}
$$

323

This can also be written in the following form, in which the multiplication is performed from right to left:

LONG FORM

$$
\begin{array}{r}
385 \\
7 \\
\hline
35 \\
560 \\
2100 \\
\hline
2695
\end{array}
$$

We shall call this method of multiplication "the long form".

A more compact form can be obtained by multiplying from right to left and recording only one digit at a time, remembering to add to the next column those numbers not yet recorded. Thus

COMPACT FORM

$$
\begin{array}{r}
385 \\
7 \\
\hline
2695
\end{array}
$$

Note how thoroughly the process hides what really happened. The expanded forms above are much more informative.

16.4 General Case

In general we must be able to multiply two multidigit numbers. The method depends upon a consequence of the distributive law which was proved in Chapter 12:

$$(a + b)(c + d) = ac + ad + bc + bd$$

This says that to find the product $(a + b)(c + d)$, multiply a by each of c and d, then multiply b by each of c and d, and add the four numbers so obtained. More generally, the following theorem is true:

FUNDAMENTAL THEOREM

THEOREM 1. If $a_0, a_1, \ldots, a_n$ and $b_0, b_1, \ldots, b_m$ are any whole numbers, then the product

$$(a_n + a_{n-1} + \cdots + a_1 + a_0) \times (b_m + b_{m-1} + \cdots + b_1 + b_0)$$

is equal to the sum of all terms of the form $a_i b_j$, where i takes all values from 0 to n and j takes all values from 0 to m.

When this is applied to two whole numbers, c and d, in expanded form we consider

$$c \times d = [(c_n \times 10^n) + \cdots + (c_1 \times 10) + c_0]$$

$$\times [(d_m \times 10^m) + \cdots + (d_1 \times 10) + d_0]$$

Then by Theorem 1, $c \times d$ is equal to the sum of all products of the form

$$(c_i \times 10^i) \times (d_j \times 10^j)$$

where i takes all values from 0 to n and j takes all values from 0 to m. Now

$$(c_i \times 10^i) \times (d_j \times 10^j) = (c_i \times d_j) \times 10^{i+j}$$

So we can obtain the product $c \times d$ as follows:

(1) Multiply each digit of c by each digit of d, thus forming products $c_i \times d_j$.

(2) Count the number of digits to the right of c_i (this is the number i) and the number of digits to the right of d_j (this is the number j).

(3) Multiply each $c_i \times d_j$ by 10^{i+j}.

(4) Form the sum of all the products in step 3.

Let us apply this procedure to find the product 385×287. We form the products

LONG METHOD

5×7	$=$	35
$(5 \times 8) \times 10$	$=$	400
$(5 \times 2) \times 10^2$	$=$	1,000
$(8 \times 7) \times 10$	$=$	560
$(8 \times 8) \times 10^2$	$=$	6,400
$(8 \times 2) \times 10^3$	$=$	16,000
$(3 \times 7) \times 10^2$	$=$	2,100
$(3 \times 8) \times 10^3$	$=$	24,000
$(3 \times 2) \times 10^4$	$=$	60,000
		110,495

and add the results. So $385 \times 287 = 110,495$. Notice that since 385 has 3 digits and since 287 also has 3 digits, there are $3 \times 3 = 9$ products to be added.

The usual algorithms are systematic ways for carrying out these steps in such a way that no products are omitted and so that the format is as compact as possible. We illustrate one of these by the example below:

$$\begin{array}{r} 385 \\ \times\, 287 \\ \hline \end{array}$$

(1) Multiply 385×7 as in Section 16.3. Record the result below the line.

$$\begin{array}{r} 385 \\ \times\, 287 \\ \hline 2695 \end{array}$$

(2) Multiply $385 \times 8 = 3080$. This result must be multiplied by 10, since the 8 really represents 80. So we can either write the result as 30,800 or we can omit the last zero and write the other digits in the columns where they would have appeared if the last zero had been present.

$$\begin{array}{r} 385 \\ \times\, 287 \\ \hline 2695 \\ 30800 \end{array} \quad \text{or} \quad \begin{array}{r} 385 \\ \times\, 287 \\ \hline 2695 \\ 3080 \end{array}$$

325

Multiplication Algorithms

(3) Multiply $385 \times 2 = 770$ and record the result in either of the ways described in step (2):

SHORT METHOD

$$
\begin{array}{r}
385 \\
\times\,287 \\
\hline
2695 \\
30800 \\
77000 \\
\end{array}
\quad\text{or}\quad
\begin{array}{r}
385 \\
\times\,287 \\
\hline
2695 \\
3080 \\
770 \\
\end{array}
$$

(4) Add the results of steps (1), (2), and (3):

$$
\begin{array}{r}
385 \\
\times\,287 \\
\hline
2695 \\
30800 \\
77000 \\
\hline
110495 \\
\end{array}
\quad\text{or}\quad
\begin{array}{r}
385 \\
\times\,287 \\
\hline
2695 \\
3080 \\
770 \\
\hline
110495 \\
\end{array}
$$

In this procedure we have multiplied by ordering the digits of 287 from right to left. We could equally well proceed in the opposite direction:

$$
\begin{array}{r}
385 \\
\times\,287 \\
\hline
77000 \\
30800 \\
2695 \\
\hline
110495 \\
\end{array}
\quad
\begin{array}{r}
385 \\
\times\,287 \\
\hline
770 \\
3080 \\
2695 \\
\hline
110495 \\
\end{array}
$$

Each of these shorter formats is nothing more than a condensation of the long method described earlier.

---

1. Let us examine the Russian peasant algorithm. For convenience the arithmetic used in multiplying 19×26 is reproduced in the adjacent table. To use the algorithm one needs to know only multiplication by two, division by two, and addition. In the illustration, 19×26, how many times did we multiply by two? _____ 4X _____

19	26
9	52
4	~~104~~
2	~~208~~
1	416
	494

Four times.

2. What is 2^4? _____ 16

16.

3. In the last line, then, 26 had been multiplied by 16. We crossed out the two preceding lines, in which 26 had been multiplied by _____ 4 and _____ 8 .

326

> 8   4   (in either order)

4. In lines 1 and 2, which we used in computing the sum, 26 had been multiplied by __1__ and __2__.

> 1   2

5. The numbers that we added to get the final result represented $26 \times$ __16__, $26 \times$ __2__, and $26 \times$ __1__.

> 16   2   1

6. What is the sum of 16, 2, and 1? __19__

> 19.

7. $19 \times 26 = (16 + 2 + 1) \times 26 = (16 \times 26) + (2 \times 26) + (1 \times 26)$. It is these numbers that we added to get 494. The Russian peasant algorithm consists fundamentally in using one of the numbers in base __2__ representation.

> two

8. Write 19 as a base two numeral. $19_{\text{ten}} =$ __10011_2__.

> 10011_{two}

9. In expanded form this base two numeral is $(1 \times 2^4) + (0 \times 2^3) + (0 \times 2^2) + (1 \times 2) + 1$

> $(1 \times 2^4) + (0 \times 2^3) + (0 \times 2^2) + (1 \times 2) + 1$

10. What is the reason for step 5? (Cross out any entries in column 2 that are opposite even numbers in column 1) _They are the same as the zeros in base 2._

> They correspond to the zeros in the base two representation of the multiplier.

11. Use this algorithm to multiply 28×29. Use a separate piece of paper.

28	29		29	28
14	~~58~~		14	~~56~~
7	116	or	7	112
3	232		3	224
1	464		1	448
	812			812

12. Express 28_{ten} as a base two numeral. _____ 11100 _____ $_2$

> 11100_{two}.

13. Use the "long form" of the usual algorithm to multiply 28×29. Use a separate piece of paper.

> 400
> 160
> 180
> 72
> ———
> 812

14. The usual algorithm provides for all possible products of a digit of one number and a digit of the other. Each such product is also multiplied by an appropriate power of 10. By what power of 10 is the product of the 2 (in 28) and the 2 (in 29) multiplied? _____ 10^2 _____

> The second power (or 10^2).

15. In our system of numeration what does the 2 in 28 represent? _____ 20 _____

> 20 (or 2×10).

16. Likewise, the 2 in 29 represents 2×10. $(2 \times 10) \times (2 \times 10) = (2 \times 2) \times (10 \times 10)$ by _generalized commutative_ _property of multiplication_ .

> the generalized commutative law for multiplication

17. In finding the product 635×248, by what power of 10 should we multiply 6×4? _____ $10^2 \times 10^1 = 10^3$ _____

> $10^2 \times 10^1 = 10^3$.

18. In finding the product 756×24 by the long form, how many terms must occur in the resulting sum? _____ $3 \times 2 = 6$ _____

> $2 \times 3 = 6$.

19. If

$$p = (a \times 10^3) + (b \times 10^2) + (c \times 10) + d$$
$$q = (r \times 10^2) + (s \times 10) + t$$

how many terms must be added to obtain the product $p \times q$? _____ $4 \times 3 = 12$ _____

> $4 \times 3 = 12$.

20. In the problem of frame 19, by what power of 10 should the term $a \times s$ be multiplied? $\underline{10^3 \times 10^1 = 10^4}$

> $10^3 \times 10^1 = 10^4$.

21. To multiply $a \times b$, where

$$a = (a_n \times 10^n) + (a_{n-1} \times 10^{n-1}) + \cdots + (a_i \times 10^i)$$
$$+ \cdots + (a_1 \times 10) + a_0$$
$$b = (b_m \times 10^m) + (b_{m-1} \times 10^{m-1}) + \cdots + (b_j \times 10^j)$$
$$+ \cdots + (b_1 \times 10) + b_0$$

(a) Find all possible products $a_i \times b_j$.
(b) Multiply $a_i \times b_j \times 10^x$, where $x = \underline{i + j}$.
(c) Find the $\underline{sum}$ of all products formed in step (b).

> $i + j$ sum

22. In finding 317×28 below, which term has not been recorded? $\underline{300 \times 8}$

$$6000$$
$$56$$
$$200$$
$$80$$
$$140$$

> 300×8 (or 2400).

23. Give reasons for the following steps in the proof that $(a + b)(c + d) = ac + bc + ad + bd$:
(a) $(a + b)(c + d) = a(c + d) + b(c + d)$ $\underline{Distributive\ law}$
(b) $\qquad\qquad\ = ac + ad + bc + bd$ $\underline{Distributive\ law}$

> (a) Distributive law.   (b) Distributive law.

24. If computation in any other base is to be performed, the rules of frame 21 can still be used; the only modification is that 10 (one zero) is now to be thought of as the particular base used, not necessarily ten. In base five how is the number five written? $\underline{10}$

> 10.

25. Write 423_{five} in expanded form, and use the distributive property to multiply 423_{five} by 5^2. Leave the result in expanded form.

$$423 = (\underline{4 \times 5^2}) + (\underline{2 \times 5}) + \underline{3}$$
$$5^2 \times 423 = (\underline{4 \times 5^4}) + (\underline{2 \times 5^3}) + (\underline{3 \times 5^2})$$

$(4 \times 5^2) \qquad (2 \times 5) \qquad 3$
$(4 \times 5^4) \qquad (2 \times 5^3) \qquad (3 \times 5^2)$

26. Before rewriting this in compact form we add two terms on the right. They are 0×5 and 0. Write $(4 \times 5^4) + (2 \times 5^3) + (3 \times 5^2) + (0 \times 5) + 0$ as a numeral in base five. _42,300_

42,300.

27. In base five notation how is the product of any whole number and 5^2 indicated? By affixing _two zero_ to the _right_ of the number.

two zeros   right   (just as the product of any number and 10^2 is indicated in base ten)

28. Use the basic multiplication table for base five shown together with the rules of frame 21 to multiply $322_{\text{five}} \times 43_{\text{five}}$. (Do not forget that the addition is also in base five.)

Base Five

×	0	1	2	3	4
0	0	0	0	0	0
1	0	1	2	3	4
2	0	2	4	11	13
3	0	3	11	14	22
4	0	4	13	22	31

```
  322
x  43
 2021
2443
31001
```

```
    11
   110
  1400
   130
  1300
 22000
 31001
```

29. Find
(a)   231
    × 322   (base four)

```
 1122
1122
2013
220302
```

(b)   121
    × 12   (base three)

```
1012
 121
2222
```

<table>
<tr><td>(a)</td><td>231</td><td>(b)</td><td>121</td></tr>
</table>

(a)   231   (b) 121
      322   12
    ————   ————
   1122   1012
   1122   121
   2013   ————
 ————   2222
220302

[handwritten:]
26
20
520
−26
494

30. A knowledge of fundamentals enables one to use shortcuts instead of blindly following rules. Use $19 = 20 - 1$ to compute 26×19. *[handwritten: $26 \times 19 = 26(20 - 26 \times 1 = 520 - 26 = 494$]*

> One way: $26 \times 19 = 26(20 - 1) = (26 \times 20) - (26 \times 1) = 520 - 26 = 494$.

31. Find a shortcut for multiplying 998×25. *[handwritten: $(1000 - 2)25 = 25,000 - 50 = 24,950$]*

> One way: $998 = 1000 - 2$, so $998 \times 25 = (1000 - 2)25 = 25,000 - 50 = 24,950$.

32. Find shortcuts for finding (a) 48×36. *[handwritten: $(50 - 2)36 = 1800 - 72 = 1728$]* (b) 32×28. *[handwritten: $(30 + 2)28 = 840 + 56 = 896$]*

[handwritten margin: 20, 28, 240]

> Possible answers: (a) $48 \times 36 = (50 - 2)36 = (50 \times 36) - (2 \times 36) = 1800 - 72 = 1728$. (b) $32 \times 28 = (30 + 2)(30 - 2) = 900 - 4 = 896$.

16.5 Other Algorithms (optional)

(1) A MATRIX ALGORITHM

MATRIX ALGORITHM   Another algorithm for multiplication is illustrated below for the product of 382×49. Each space is filled in with the basic multiplication facts for the digits opposite which the space is found.

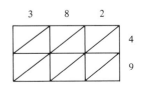

If a product has two digits the first is written above the diagonal and the second below it. If it has only one digit a zero is written above the diagonal. The device then looks like this:

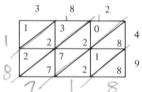

The product is then obtained by adding digits between adjacent diagonals starting at the lower right and "carrying" from right to left if required.

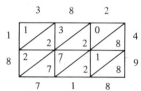

The product is read "around the corner" as 1 8 7 1 8.

1. On the diagonal in the lower right appears the units digit of 9 × 2. On the next diagonal appear the digits 2, 1, and 8. What does each represent? 2 represents _tens of 9×80_ ; 1 represents _the tens of 9×2_ ; 8 represents _the tens of 40×2_ .

> the tens digit of 9 × 80   the tens digit of 9 × 2   the tens digit of 40 × 2

2. What do the digits 7, 7, 2, 0 on the next diagonal represent?
7 represents _the hundreds of 300 × 9_ .
7 represents _the hundreds of 80 × 9_ .
2 represents _the hundreds of 40 × 80_ .
0 represents _the hundreds of 40 × 2_ .

> the hundreds digit of 300 × 9   the hundreds digit of 80 × 9
> the hundreds digit of 40 × 80   the hundreds digit of 40 × 2

3. Continuing in this way you should be able to explain how the algorithm works. Use this algorithm to multiply 432 by 357. _154 224_

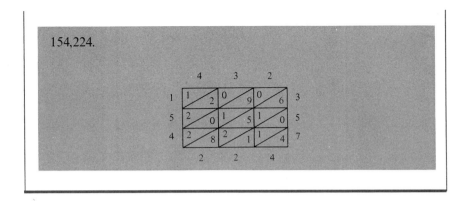

154,224.

(2) NAPIER'S BONES

A related device, known as *Napier's bones* (after the Scottish mathematician John Napier 1550–1617), consists of strips on which one column of the multiplication table is recorded in a similar way. By placing several such strips side by side, products of any number with a single digit can be read off. Napier's bones for 3, 8, and 2 are shown side by side.

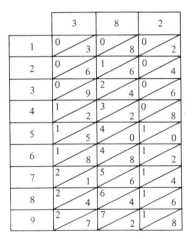

4. Using one row of this figure read off 9×382:

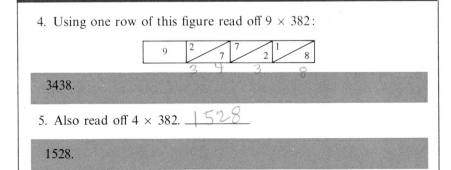

3438.

5. Also read off 4×382.   1528

1528.

6. Describe how you would use the results of frames 4 and 5 to find 49 × 382. 15,280 + 3438 = 18,718

Multiply 1528 by 10 and add to 3438: 49 × 382 = 15,230 + 3438 = 18,718.

This completes our discussion of various algorithms for multiplication. We have shown how they are justified by the known properties of addition and multiplication and by the distributive law.

Now check your comprehension of these methods by completing the following Post Test. Do not refer to the text while working this test. Check your answers with the key after you have completed the entire test.

POST TEST

1. Write the basic multiplication table for base six.

×	0	1	2	3	4	5
0	0	0	0	0	0	0
1	0	1	2	3	4	5
2	0	2	4	10	12	14
3	0	3	10	13	20	23
4	0	4	12	20	24	32
5	0	5	14	23	32	41

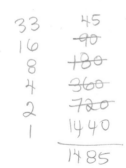

```
33      45
16      90
8      180
4      360
2      720
1     1440
      1485
```

2. Use the Russian peasant algorithm to multiply 33 × 45. Do your work on a separate piece of paper. _____

3. To find 7 × 524, we write

(a) $524 = (\underline{5} \times 10^2) + (\underline{2} \times 10) + \underline{4}$

(b) $7 \times 524 = [7 \times (5 \times 10^2)] + [7 \times (2 \times 10)] + [7 \times 4]$ Distributive
(reason)

(c) $= [(7 + 5) \times 10^2] + [(7 \times 2) \times 10] + [7 \times 4]$ Associative
(reason)

(d) $= 3500 + 140 + 28$ Multiplication
(reason) facts

(e) $= \underline{3668}$

4. Multiply 423 (base six), using the long form.

$$
\begin{array}{r}
\times 5 \\
\hline
23 \\
140 \\
3200 \\
\hline
3363 \\
\end{array}
$$

5. How many terms are there in the expansion of the product 3419 × 57 (base ten)? $\underline{4 \times 2 = 8}$

6. In the expansion of 3419 × 57, the product 4 × 5 is multiplied by 10^x. What is x? $\underline{x = 3}$

7. Find   423
   × 34 (base five).

$$
\begin{array}{r}
3302 \\
2324 \\
\hline
32042 \\
\end{array}
$$

8. Use a shortcut method to find 998 × 15. $\underline{15,000 - 30 = 14,970.}$

(1,000 - 2)15
15,000 - 30 = 14,970

9. If the matrix algorithm is used to find 273 × 46 we write

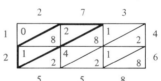

What do each of the digits 1, 8, 2 within diagonals indicated by heavy lines represent? 1 represents $\underline{1,000^{th}\ digit\ of\ 200 \times 6}$. 8 represents $\underline{1,000^{th}\ digit\ of\ 200 \times 40}$. 2 represents $\underline{1,000^{th}\ digit\ of\ 70 \times 40.}$.

1.

×	0	1	2	3	4	5
0	0	0	0	0	0	0
1	0	1	2	3	4	5
2	0	2	4	10	12	14
3	0	3	10	13	20	23
4	0	4	12	20	24	32
5	0	5	14	23	32	41

2. 33   45
   16   ~~90~~
    8   ~~100~~ 180
    4   ~~360~~
    2   ~~720~~
    1   1440
         ____
         1485

3. (a) 5; 2; 4. (b) Distributive law. (c) Associative law. (d) Multiplication facts. (e) 3668

4.
$$
\begin{array}{r}
435 \\
\times \quad 5 \\
\hline
41 \\
230 \\
3200 \\
\hline
3511 \\
\end{array}
$$

5. $4 \times 2 = 8$.

6. $2 + 1 = 3$.

7.
$$
\begin{array}{r}
423 \\
\times \quad 34 \\
\hline
3302 \\
2324 \\
\hline
32042 \\
\end{array}
$$

8. $998 \times 15 = (1000 - 2) \times 15 = 15,000 - 30 = 14,970$.

9. the thousands digit of 200×6; the thousands digit of 200×40; the thousands digit of 70×40

If you now understand multiplication proceed to the beginning of Chapter 17, Division Algorithms.

17

Division Algorithms

Before beginning this chapter you should review Sections 11.6 through 11.9 of Chapter 11 (Division), especially Theorem 18. The purpose of this chapter is to examine the practical algorithms by means of which you can find the quotient and remainder in a division problem. Before beginning this chapter, check yourself by working the following Readiness Test.

READINESS TEST

1. When a is divided by d so that $a = qd + r$, a is called the ___dividend___, d is called the ___divisor___, q is called the ___quotient___, r is called the ___remainder___.

> dividend   divisor   quotient   remainder

2. The remainder r must be ___less than___ d.

> less than

3. The divisor d cannot be equal to ___zero___.

> zero

4. If $a < d$, then $q =$ ___0___ and $r =$ ___a___.

> 0   a

5. If $a = 0$, then $q =$ ___0___ and $r =$ ___0___.

> 0   0

6. In order to check the result of a division problem we add the ___remainder___ to the product of the ___divisor___ and the ___quotient___. This sum must equal the ___dividend___.

> remainder   divisor   quotient   dividend

7. If 27 is divided by 5, the quotient is ___5___ and the remainder is ___2___.

> $q = 5$ $r = 2$

8. Division is *exact* if the remainder is ___zero___.

> zero

---

9. The statement "*d* divides *a*" means that the division is _exact_.

exact

10. 36 is a _multiple_ of 4.

multiple

If you are now ready, read Sections 17.1 through 17.3 and work the exercises following Section 17.3.

17.1 Introduction

In this chapter we shall be concerned with division with remainder, which we discussed in Chapter 11. The foundation of our work is Theorem 17 of that chapter:

THEOREM 1. If *a* and *d* are any whole numbers with $d \neq 0$, there exist whole numbers *q* and *r* with $r < d$ such that

$$a = qd + r$$

In this notation *a* is called the dividend, *d* the divisor, *q* the quotient, and *r* the remainder.

The practical problem before us is the following:

PROBLEM. Given the dividend *a* and the divisor *d*, find the quotient *q* and the remainder *r*.

USE OF MULTIPLICATION TABLE

The methods for doing this are called *division algorithms*. When the numbers *a* and *d* are small, we can use the multiplication table as a basis for division. For example, to find $18 \div 6$ enter the table in the column headed 6. Read down until you come to 18, then read to the left and find that this row is labeled 3. Therefore, $18 = 6 \times 3$, or $18 \div 6 = 3$.

As another example consider $18 \div 7$. Using the same idea, enter the table in the column headed 7. Read down to find 18; unfortunately it does not appear. So we look for the largest number in this column which is less than 18; it is 14. Since $14 = 2 \times 7$ and $18 - 14 = 4$, we conclude that

$$18 = (2 \times 7) + 4$$

The quotient is 2 and the remainder is 4.

This method does not apply to $77 \div 6$ or $96 \div 12$, for the numbers are beyond the range of the table. The development of methods for handling such problems is the purpose of this chapter.

17.2 Strategy of Division

There are many variations of division algorithms, but all of them are based upon a common strategy. We recall that we are given a and d and are to find q and r with $r < d$ such that

$$a = q \times d + r$$

BASIC STRATEGY   The fundamental idea is to examine the multiples of d:

$$0 \times d, 1 \times d, 2 \times d, \ldots$$

and to find the largest of these, say $q \times d$, which is less than or equal to a. Then $r = a - qd$. Of course, this becomes very tedious when a is large, and so we need to find more efficient methods called algorithms. There are many *correct* methods, some of which are *systematic* in the sense that every step is precisely stated so that an automaton who can follow directions accurately is sure to get the correct result. Others require guessing or estimation, followed by corrections for bad guesses; these methods require the intervention of human judgement, and their effectiveness depends on the skill and experience of the person doing the calculation. Both types of method are useful, for the novice can follow a systematic method and find the answer (although he may take a fairly long time to do the job), and the expert can cut corners and make informed guesses and thus finish the calculation in jig time.

We shall illustrate methods of both kinds. You may well encounter others in textbooks, for it seems that every author has his own pet tricks. We hope, however, that your experience with the methods explained here will enable you to understand other methods that you may need to deal with.

17.3 Division by Single-Digit Numbers (Systematic Method)

Before discussing the general case, let us illustrate the method with the following example: Divide 93,572 by 8. Write the dividend in the partially expanded form

$$93,572 = 90,000 + 3572$$

STEP-BY-STEP METHOD   Then divide 9 by 8 allowing for a remainder. The result is

$$9 = (1 \times 8) + 1$$

so

$$90,000 = (10,000 \times 8) + 10,000$$

and

(1) $$93,572 = (10,000 \times 8) + 13,572$$

This expression is of the required form with $q = 10,000$ and $r = 13,572$.

But it is not an acceptable answer since $13{,}572 > 8$. So repeat the process on the remainder 13,572:

$$13{,}572 = 13{,}000 + 572$$

$$13 = (1 \times 8) + 5$$

$$13{,}000 = (1000 \times 8) + 5000$$

(2) $$13{,}572 = (1000 \times 8) + 5572$$

Putting (1) and (2) together we obtain

(3) $$93{,}572 = [(10{,}000 + 1000) \times 8] + 5572$$

$$= (11{,}000 \times 8) + 5572$$

Since the remainder 5572 is still greater than 8, we run through the cycle again:

$$5572 = 5500 + 72$$

$$55 = (6 \times 8) + 7$$

$$5500 = (600 \times 8) + 700$$

$$5572 = (600 \times 8) + 772$$

(4) $$93{,}572 = (11{,}600 \times 8) + 772$$

The remainder is getting smaller, but it is still larger than 8; so we recycle again:

$$772 = 770 + 2$$

$$77 = (9 \times 8) + 5$$

$$770 = (90 \times 8) + 50$$

$$772 = (90 \times 8) + 52$$

(5) $$93{,}572 = (11{,}690 \times 8) + 52$$

Since $52 > 8$, another cycle is required.

$$52 = (6 \times 8) + 4$$

(6) $$93{,}572 = (11{,}696 \times 8) + 4$$

Since $4 < 8$, we are finished and have $q = 11{,}696$ and $r = 4$.

SHORT AND LONG DIVISION In practice the calculations are performed in one of two formats:

$$
\begin{array}{r}
1\ 1\ 6\ 9\ 6 \\
8\,\overline{)\,9^{1}3^{5}5^{7}7^{5}2}
\end{array}
\qquad \text{or} \qquad
\begin{array}{r}
11696 \\
8\,\overline{)\,93572} \\
8 \\
\overline{13}\ \checkmark \\
8 \\
\overline{55}\ \checkmark \\
48 \\
\overline{77}\ \checkmark \\
72 \\
\overline{52}\ \checkmark \\
48 \\
\overline{4}
\end{array}
$$

$$r = 4$$

340

17.3 Division by Single-Digit Numbers (Systematic Method)

In the first of these, called "short division", the quotients are written at the top and the remainders are "carried" to the next digit to the right. In the second, called "long division", the numbers which are checked (✓) are those which we divided by 8 in the various stages of the above discussion.

1. Divide and check.

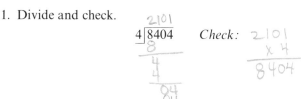

$$4\overline{)8404}$$

Check:

2101 × 4 = 8404

	2101
2101	× 4
	8404

2. Why was frame 1 so easy? Each digit of 8404 is _a multiple_ by 4, and so at each step there is no _remainder_ to carry forward to the next step.

divisible   remainder

3. In order to divide $7\overline{)28,714}$ the first step is to write $28,714 = \underline{28,000} + 714$. Then

$$28 = (\underline{4} \times 7) + \underline{0}$$
$$28,000 = (\underline{4,000} \times 7) + \underline{0}$$

so

$$28,714 = (\underline{4,000} \times 7) + \underline{714}$$

Why must we continue this process? $\underline{714 > 7}$

28,000   4;0   4000;0   4000;714   714 > 7

4. In the next step of the problem in frame 3 write

$$714 = \underline{700} + \underline{14}$$
$$7 = (\underline{1} \times 7) + \underline{0}$$
$$700 = (\underline{100} \times 7) + \underline{0}$$
$$714 = (\underline{100} \times 7) + \underline{14}$$
$$28,714 = (\underline{4,100} \times 7) + \underline{14}$$

Why must we continue this process? $\underline{14 > 7}$

700;14   1;0   100;0   100;14   4100;14   14 > 7

5. In the last step of the problem of frame 3, write

$$14 = (\underline{2} \times 7) + \underline{0}$$

$$28,714 = (\underline{4102} \times 7) + \underline{0}$$

Why are we finished with the problem? $\underline{0 < 7}$

> 2; 0   4102; 0   0 < 7

6. The answer to the problem of frame 3 is $q = \underline{4102}$ and $r = \underline{0}$.

> 4102   0

7. Write the division of frame 3 in short and long forms:

```
     4102              4102
   _____          _____
 7|2 8 7 1ᴵ4        7|2 8 7 1 4
                      28
                       7
                      ___
                      14
                      14
                      ___
                       0
```

> ```
>      4 1 0 2            4 1 0 2
>    _____        _____
>  7|2 8 7 1ᴵ4        7|2 8 7 1 4
>                       2 8
>                         7
>                       ___
>                         7
>                       ___
>                         1 4
>                         1 4
>                       _____
> ```

8. Divide and check. Use the long form.

```
     1207                      5
   _____         Check:   1207
 8|9 6 5 6                      8
   8                         _____
   ___                       9656
   16
   16
   ___
    56
```

17.3 Division by Single-Digit Numbers (Systematic Method)

$$
\begin{array}{r}
1\ 2\ 0\ 7 \\
8\overline{)9\ 6\ 5\ 6} \\
8 \\
\overline{1\ 6} \\
1\ 6 \\
\overline{5\ 6} \\
5\ 6
\end{array}
\qquad
\begin{array}{r}
1207 \\
\times\ \ 8 \\
\hline
9656
\end{array}
$$

9. In the problem of frame 8, let us do the division step by step. We write

$$9656 = 9000 + \underline{656}$$
$$9 = (\underline{1} \times \underline{8}) + \underline{1}$$
$$9000 = (\underline{1{,}000} \times \underline{8}) + \underline{1000}$$
$$9656 = (\underline{1{,}000} \times \underline{8}) + \underline{1656}$$

656	1; 8; 1	1000; 8; 1000	1000; 8; 1656

10. Do the next step in the process of frame 9 without any hints.

$$1656 = 1600 + 56$$
$$16 = (2 \times 8) + 0$$
$$1600 = (200 \times 8) + 0$$
$$1656 = (200 \times 8) + 56$$
$$9656 = (1{,}200 \times 8) + 56$$

$1656 = 1600 + 56$
$16 = (2 \times 8) + 0$
$1600 = (200 \times 8) + 0$
$1656 = (200 \times 8) + 56$
$9656 = (1200 \times 8) + 56$

11. Complete the division begun in frame 9.

$$56 = (7 \times 8) + 0$$
$$9656 = (1207 \times 8) + 0$$

Hence $q = \underline{1207}$, $r = \underline{0}$

$$56 = (7 \times 8) + 0$$
$$9656 = (1207 \times 8) + 0$$
$$1207 \qquad 0$$

12. Divide by "short division" $8\overline{)9\,6\,5\,6}$.

(handwritten above: 1207)

$$
\begin{array}{r}
1\ 2\ 0\ 7 \\
8\overline{)9^16\ 5^56}
\end{array}
$$

13. Divide by the short method and check:

$$4\overline{)2\ 1^{\,}6\ 9^{\,}2}$$

(handwritten above: 5423)

Check: 5423 × 4 = 21692

$$
\begin{array}{r}
5\ 4\ 2\ 3 \\
4\overline{)2\ 1^16\ 9^12}
\end{array}
\qquad
\begin{array}{r}
5423 \\
\times \qquad 4 \\
\hline
21692
\end{array}
$$

14. Divide by "long division" $4\overline{)2\ 1\ 6\ 9\ 2}$.

(handwritten long division showing 5423 with steps: 20, 16, 16, 9, 8, 12, 12, 0)

$$
\begin{array}{r}
5\ 4\ 2\ 3 \\
4\overline{)2\ 1\ 6\ 9\ 2} \\
2\ 0 \\
\hline
1\ 6 \\
1\ 6 \\
\hline
9 \\
8 \\
\hline
1\ 2 \\
1\ 2
\end{array}
$$

15. Divide by the long method and check.

$$
\begin{array}{r}
3513 \\
6\,|\,2\,1\,0\,8\,0 \\
\underline{18} \\
30 \\
\underline{30} \\
8 \\
6 \\
\underline{20} \\
\end{array}
$$

Check: 3513 · 6 = 21078 + 2 = 21080

r = 2

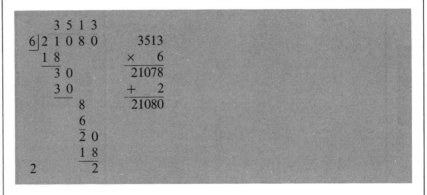

```
      3 5 1 3
6|2 1 0 8 0        3513
  1 8            ×    6
    3 0            21078
    3 0          +     2
        8          21080
        6
        2 0
        1 8
2         2
```

16. Divide by the short method and check.

$$
8\,|\,6\,0^{4}9^{1}0^{2}8
$$

r = 4   Check: 7613 × 8 = 60904 + 4 = 60908

```
      7 6 1 3
8|6 0⁴9¹0²8     4        7613
                       ×    8
                       60904
                     +      4
                       60908
```

17. If you are so familiar with division that these explanations seem to be beside the point, try the following division problem, base six. If you

BASES ≠ 10

can do it without help and can explain it to your roommate, proceed to Section 17.4. If you need help, work through frames 18 through 25. Then try frame 26 by yourself.

$$4\overline{)2\ 3\ 4\ 5}\quad\text{(base six)}$$

quotient = 354   remainder = 1

354	1

18. The multiplication table, base six, is

×	1	2	3	4	5
1	1	2	3	4	5
2	2	4	10	12	14
3	3	10	13	20	23
4	4	12	20	24	32
5	5	14	23	32	41

×	1	2	3	4	5
1	1	2	3	4	5
2	2	4	10	12	14
3	3	10	13	20	23
4	4	12	20	24	32
5	5	14	23	32	41

19. The largest multiple of 4 (base six) which is less than or equal to 23 is ___20___. So the first digit of the quotient is ___3___. The first step in long division is

$$4\overline{)2\ 3\ 4\ 5}$$

20	3	$4\overline{)2\ 3\ 4\ 5}$
		2 0
		⎯⎯⎯
		3 4

20. The largest multiple of 4 (base six) which is less than or equal to 34 is _32_. So the second digit in the quotient is _5_. The long division now is of the form

```
          3
    4⟌2 3 4 5
      2 0
      ───
        3 4
```

```
                 3 5
  32    5    4⟌2 3 4 5
               2 0
               ───
                 3 4
                 3 2
                 ───
                   2 5
```

21. The largest multiple of 4 (base six) which is less than or equal to 25 is _24_. So the third digit of the quotient is _4_. The long division now is written as

```
              3 5
        4⟌2 3 4 5
          2 0
          ───
            3 4
            3 2
            ───
              2 5
```

```
                   3 5 4
  24    4     4⟌2 3 4 5
                2 0
                ───
                  3 4
                  3 2
                  ───
                    2 5
                    2 4
                    ───
                      1
```

22. The quotient is _354_, the remainder is _1_.

```
  354    1
```

Check: 32
354
4
———
2344
1
———
2345

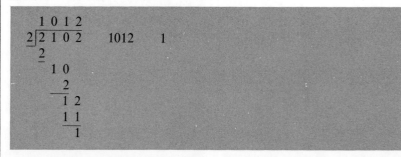

```
  354
×   4
———
 2344
+   1
———
 2345
```

23. In frames 19 through 21 what part of the multiplication table, base six, was used? ___the 4's column___

The column headed 4.

24. To divide in base six by 3, we need what part of the multiplication table? the 3's column .

The column headed 3.

25. To divide in base six by 24, what abbreviated multiplication table would be useful? ___multiples of 24___

A table of multiples of 24.

26. Divide 2$\overline{)2\ 1\ 0\ 2}$ (base three). Use the long form.

```
    1012
 2)2 1 0 2
   2
   ——
    1 0
     2
    ——
    1 2
    1 1
    ——
      1
```

Quotient = 1012. remainder = 1 .

```
   1 0 1 2
 2)2 1 0 2      1012      1
   2
   —
    1 0
     2
    ——
     1 2
     1 1
     ——
       1
```

Now read Sections 17.4 through 17.6 and work the corresponding exercises.

17.4 Division by Multidigit Numbers (Systematic Method)

The principles here are the same as in the last section, but the practice is more difficult, for we do not have a multiplication table at hand for products of multidigit numbers. Let us illustrate the situation by an example:

$$39\overline{)1\ 8\ 9\ 9\ 3}$$

Since the quotients in $1 \div 39$ and $18 \div 39$ are zero, the first serious step is $189 \div 39$. We are seeking numbers q and r such that

$$189 = (q \times 39) + r \qquad \text{and} \qquad r < 39$$

To find these numbers in a systematic fashion, we construct a table of the products of 39 by $1, 2, \ldots, 9$. The result is

TABLE OF MULTIPLES OF THE DIVISOR

×	39
1	39
2	78
3	117
4	156
5	195
6	234
7	273
8	312
9	351

The largest entry in this table which is less than or equal to 189 is 156. Hence

$$189 = (4 \times 39) + (189 - 156)$$
$$= (4 \times 39) + 33$$

so

$$18{,}993 = 18900 + 93$$
$$= (400 \times 39) + 3300 + 93$$
$$= (400 \times 39) + 3393$$

Proceeding as in Section 17.3, we write

$$3393 = 3390 + 3$$

Our table of multiples of 39 tells us that

$$339 = (8 \times 39) + (339 - 312)$$
$$= (8 \times 39) + 27$$

349

Division Algorithms

So

$$3390 = (80 \times 39) + 270$$

$$3393 = (80 \times 39) + 273$$

$$18,993 = (480 \times 39) + 273$$

Since the remainder 273 is greater than 39, another cycle is required:

$$273 = (7 \times 39) + 0$$

$$18,993 = (487 \times 39) + 0$$

Therefore, the quotient is 487 and the remainder is zero.

These computations are usually expressed in the more compact (long) form:

```
          4 8 7
39 | 1 8 9 9 3
     1 5 6
       3 3 9
       3 1 2
         2 7 3
         2 7 3
```

---

1. To divide $83\overline{)3\ 9\ 6\ 9}$ by this method, we form the table of multiples of 83:

×	1	2	3	4	5	6	7	8	9
83	83	166	249	332	415	498	581	664	747

×	1	2	3	4	5	6	7	8	9
83	83	166	249	332	415	498	581	664	747

2. Using the table in frame 1, we find that

$$396 = (\underline{4} \times 83) + \underline{64}$$

4   64

3. Hence

$$3960 = (\underline{40} \times 83) + \underline{640}$$

$$3969 = (\underline{40} \times 83) + \underline{649}$$

40; 640   40; 649

350

4. Also

$$649 = \underline{640} + 9$$
$$640 = (\underline{7} \times 83) + \underline{59}$$
$$649 = (\underline{7} \times 83) + \underline{68}$$
$$3969 = (\underline{47} \times 83) + \underline{68}$$

640	7; 59	7; 68	47; 68

5. Why does the process of frames 1 to 4 end with frame 4? $\underline{68 < 83}$
$q = \underline{47}, r = \underline{68}$.

68 < 83	47	68

6. Write the division of frame 1 in the usual long form, and check.

$$83 \overline{)3969} \quad \frac{47}{332}$$

Check:

```
        47
83 3 9 6 9          83        649      83
   3 3 2          ×  47       581      47
   ─────          ─────        68     ───
     6 4 9           581              581
       5 8 1         332              332
       ─────       ─────            ─────
         6 8        3901             3901
                  +   68               68
                  ─────             ─────
                    3969             3969
```

7. When the divisor is 57, what is the largest possible remainder? $\underline{56}$

56.

8. Make a table of multiples of 57.

×	1	2	3	4	5	6	7	8	9
57	57	114	171	228	285	342	399	456	513

×	1	2	3	4	5	6	7	8	9
57	57	114	171	228	285	342	399	456	513

351

9. Divide $57 \overline{)1\ 1\ 3\ 9}$ and check.

$$
\begin{array}{r}
19 \\
57\,\overline{)1139} \\
57 \\
\hline
569 \\
513 \\
\hline
56
\end{array}
\qquad
\begin{array}{r}
57 \\
\times\ 19 \\
\hline
513 \\
57 \\
\hline
1083 \\
+\ \ 56 \\
\hline
1139
\end{array}
$$

10. Make a table of multiples of 13 (base 4).

×	1	2	3
13	13	32	111

Then divide $13 \overline{)2\ 3\ 1\ 3}$ (base four) and check.

$$
\begin{array}{r}
122 \\
13\,\overline{)2313} \\
13 \\
\hline
101 \\
32 \\
\hline
33 \\
32 \\
\hline
1
\end{array}
\qquad
\begin{array}{r}
122 \\
\times\ 13 \\
\hline
1032 \\
122 \\
\hline
2312 \\
+\ \ \ 1 \\
\hline
2313
\end{array}
$$

352

$$101\overline{)1101011}\ \ \ \frac{10101}{}$$
101
110
101
111
101
10

10101
101
10101
10101
110101
+10
1101011

11. On a separate piece of paper make a table of multiples of 101 (base two). Then divide $101\overline{)1101011}$ (base two) and check.

$q = \underline{10101}$ and $r = \underline{10}$.

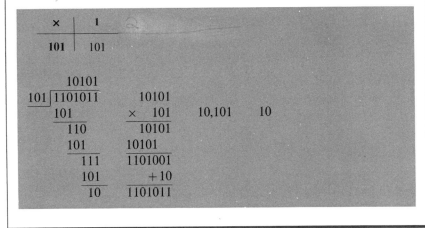

×	1
101	101

$$101\overline{)1101011}\ \ \ \frac{10101}{}$$

$$\begin{array}{r} 10101 \\ \times\ 101 \\ \hline 10101 \\ 10101\ \ \ \\ \hline 1101001 \\ +\ \ 10 \\ \hline 1101011 \end{array}$$

10,101   10

17.5 Other Methods of Division

Although the systematic method of Section 17.4 will always solve the problem, it has an awkward feature in its requirement that we write a table of multiples of the divisor. Novices find such a table very helpful, just as you will undoubtedly need such a table if your numbers are expressed in a base other than ten. Experts, however, save time by processes of estimation and intelligent guessing.

GUESSING

To illustrate some of these alternatives let us return to the worked example of Section 17.4:

$$39\overline{)18993}$$

The first step is to divide 189 by 39. Since 39 is almost 40, and since in $18 \div 4$ the quotient is 4, we guess that the quotient in $189 \div 39$ is about 4. Possibly it is 5, but no other choices are reasonable.

So we try 4 and obtain as the first step

$$\begin{array}{r} 4\ \ \ \ \ \\ 39\overline{)18993} \\ 156\ \ \ \ \\ \hline 33\ \ \ \ \end{array}$$

The product 156 is less than 189, so subtraction is possible, and the remainder, 33, is less than 39. Thus we were right the first shot.

353

Division Algorithms

Suppose, however, that we were not such experienced estimators. We might have guessed 3. Then we would have

$$
\begin{array}{r}
3 \\
39\overline{)1\ 8\ 9\ 9\ 3} \\
1\ 1\ 7 \\
\hline
7\ 2
\end{array}
$$

Subtraction is still possible, but $72 > 39$, so the requirements are not met. Our guess, 3, was too small. What shall we do next? We can erase and try again, but this is a bit frustrating. Another possibility is to divide 72 by 39. We are now practically sure to get the quotient 1 and write

$$
\begin{array}{r}
1 \\
39\overline{)7\ 2} \\
3\ 9 \\
\hline
3\ 3
\end{array}
$$

The trouble is that there is no room in the usual algorithm for this calculation.

If we wish to follow these ideas, another format for division is helpful. As the first step, we write

$$
\begin{array}{r}
39\overline{)1\ 8\ 9\ 9\ 3} \\
1\ 1\ 7\quad 300 \\
\hline
7\ 2
\end{array}
$$

where instead of the digit 3 we write 300, since in the final quotient 3 appears as the coefficient of 10^2.

We then divide 72 by 39 and write

$$
\begin{array}{r}
39\overline{)1\ 8\ 9\ 9\ 3} \\
1\ 1\ 7\quad\ 300 \\
\hline
7\ 2 \\
3\ 9\quad\ 100 \\
\hline
3\ 3
\end{array}
$$

As we proceed and make our various guesses, we may well obtain

$$
\begin{array}{r}
39\overline{)1\ 8\ 9\ 9\ 3} \\
1\ 1\ 7\quad\ 300 \\
\hline
7\ 2 \\
3\ 9\quad\ 100 \\
\hline
3\ 3\ 9 \\
2\ 3\ 4\quad\ 60 \\
\hline
1\ 0\ 5 \\
7\ 8\quad\ 20 \\
\hline
2\ 7\ 3 \\
2\ 3\ 4\quad\ 6 \\
\hline
3\ 9 \\
3\ 9\quad\ 1 \\
\hline
487
\end{array}
$$

The final quotient is the sum of the numbers in the right-hand column.

In a variation of this process the numbers in the right-hand column are written above the line as in the illustration:

$$
\begin{array}{r}
4\ 8\ 7 \\
\hline
1\ 2\ 1 \\
3\ 6\ 6 \\
\end{array}
\qquad q = 487, r = 0
$$

$$
\begin{array}{r}
39\,\overline{)\,1\ 8\ 9\ 9\ 3} \\
1\ 1\ 7 \\
\hline
7\ 2 \\
3\ 9 \\
\hline
3\ 3\ 9 \\
2\ 3\ 4 \\
\hline
1\ 0\ 5 \\
7\ 8 \\
\hline
2\ 7\ 3 \\
2\ 3\ 4 \\
\hline
3\ 9 \\
3\ 9 \\
\hline
\end{array}
$$

Another variation of this process is obtained if we consider division to be repeated subtraction. Thus to divide 189 by 39, we can subtract 39 successively from 189 until subtraction is no longer possible:

$$
\begin{array}{r}
189 \\
-\ 39 \\
\hline
150 \\
-\ 39 \\
\hline
111 \\
-\ 39 \\
\hline
72 \\
-\ 39 \\
\hline
33 \\
\end{array}
$$

Since 39 was subtracted 4 times, the quotient is 4.

This process can be speeded up by subtracting multiples of the divisor in the early stages, for example

$$
\begin{array}{rl}
189 & \\
-\ 78 & \quad 2 \\
\hline
111 & \\
-\ 39 & \quad 1 \\
\hline
72 & \\
-\ 39 & \quad 1 \\
\hline
33 & \quad \overline{4} \\
\end{array}
$$

REPEATED SUBTRACTION

Although methods like these are favored by some recent textbooks, they are clumsy and should only be used as interim measures while the children are gaining experience with the process of division. Notice that they are effective only if the successive guesses are either correct or too small. They are of no help when the guesses are too large.

355

Let us now look at the situation where our guess is too large. Suppose that we guessed 5 as the quotient in the first step of the division

$$39\overline{)1\ 8\ 9\ 9\ 3}$$

Then we would write

$$\begin{array}{r} 5 \\ 39\overline{)1,8\ 9\ 9\ 3} \\ 1\ 9\ 5 \end{array}$$

We seem to be stopped, since subtraction is not possible. We can recover, however, if we subtract 39 from 195 enough times to bring the difference below 189. In this case one subtraction is enough:

$$\begin{array}{r} 195 \\ -39 \\ \hline 156 \end{array}$$

Hence the correct quotient is $5 - 1 = 4$.

---

1. Divide by the usual method of long division:

$$\begin{array}{r} 37 \\ 26\overline{)9\ 6\ 2} \\ 78 \\ \hline 1\ 82 \\ 182 \\ \hline 0 \end{array}$$

$$\begin{array}{r} 37 \\ 26\overline{)962} \\ 78 \\ \hline 182 \\ 182 \\ \hline \end{array}$$

2. If our first guess in frame 1 was too small, say 2, we could write:

$$\begin{array}{r} 26\overline{)9\ 6\ 2} \\ 5\ 2 \\ \hline 4\ 4 \\ 2\ 6 \\ \hline 1\ 8\ 2 \\ 1\ 8\ 2 \end{array} \qquad \begin{array}{r} 20 \\ 10 \\ 7 \\ \hline \end{array}$$

Sum = 37

| 20 | 10 | 7 | 37 |

3. If our first guess in frame 1 had been 4, we would have had

$$
\begin{array}{r}
4 \\
26\overline{\smash{\big)}\ 9\ 6\ 2} \\
1\ 0\ 4 \\
\end{array}
$$

Since 104 > 96, subtraction is ___not defined___ and we must try again with a ___smaller___ guess.
(smaller, larger)

impossible (or not defined)	smaller

4. To proceed from frame 3, we compute 104 − 26 = 78. Since 78 < ___96___, the correct quotient is 4 − ___1___ = ___3___.

96	1	3

5. In the computation of 2382 ÷ 6, a possible expression for 2382 is 2382 = 2400 − 18. Hence 2382 ÷ 6 = ___2400___ ÷ 6 − ___18___ ÷ 6 = 400 − ___3___ = ___397___.

2400	18	3	397

6. In "Continental division" most of the intermediate calculations are done mentally or on scratch paper. A typical division is written

$$
\begin{array}{r|l}
412.005 & 79 \\
170 & \overline{5215} \\
1\ 20 & \\
415 & \\
20 & r = 20 \\
\end{array}
$$

The dividend is 412.005, where the dot takes the place of a comma in U.S. notation. We would have written: 412,005. In Continental notation decimal points are written in the center of the line, as in 32·48. The divisor is 79 and the quotient is 5215.

What is the role of 170? ___79 × 5 + 17___
Of 120? ___Remainder next digit down___
Of 415? ___Remainer next digit down___
Of 20? ___Final Remainder___

> For 170: 412 = 79 × 5 + 17. So 170 = 10 × the remainder in the first division plus the next digit, 0, of the dividend.
> For 120: 120 = 10 × the remainder 12 (= 170 − 158) of the second division plus the next digit, 0, of the dividend.
> For 415: 415 = 10 × the remainder 41 (= 120 − 79) of the third division plus the next digit, 5, of the dividend.
> For 20: 20 (= 415 − 395) is the remainder of the fourth division.

357

17.6 Rounding Off

One who does not make good guesses for quotients can do division problems quite adequately but will probably not work as fast as one who guesses more accurately. For this reason (and others, also) practice in guessing is helpful. An elementary device that is useful in guessing is "rounding off" or approximating. The simplest rounding-off maneuver is accomplished as follows:

(1) If the second digit of a number is smaller than 5, retain the first digit and replace each succeeding digit by a zero.

(2) Otherwise, increase the first digit by one and replace each succeeding digit by a zero.

This type of rounding off is generally used for the divisor. By considering multiples of the rounded-off divisor, one can then find one digit of the quotient. Occasionally the digit obtained in this way is too large or too small, but it provides a starting point for further guesses.

Another principle involved in successful guessing is cancellation for multiplication. If both divisor and dividend are rounded off as described above, common powers of ten can be canceled in seeking the next guess. For example, if we wish to find $58,616 \div 1724$, we seek a number x (if it exists) for which $1724x = 58,616$. If, for guessing purposes, we replace 1724 by 2000 and 58,616 by 60,000, the equation becomes $2000x = 60,000$. By the associative and commutative properties of multiplication this can be written as $(2x) \times 1000 = 60 \times 1000$ and (by cancellation for multiplication) as $2x = 60$. This kind of maneuver—usually carried out mentally—makes guessing easier.

---

1. Using the process described in the above section, round off:
(a) 3976. __4000__   (b) 8. __10 (8)__   (c) 65. __70__   (d) 800. __800__
(e) 96,963. __100,000__

(a) 4000.   (b) 8.   (c) 70.   (d) 800.   (e) 100,000.

2. If you follow the procedures in the above section what is your first guess for $58,616 \div 1724$? __30__

30.

3. Successive steps in the division process are repetitions of this process. After this first guess for $58,616 \div 1724$, we have

$$
\begin{array}{r}
3 \\
1724\overline{)58616} \\
51720 \\
\hline
6896
\end{array}
$$

What is the division problem required to obtain the next digit of the answer? $6896 \div 1724$

> 6896   1724.

4. To perform this division we wish to solve what equation for x and y? $6896 = 1724x + y$.

> 6896   1724x   y

5. Using approximations for 1724 and 6896, about how big is x (in the answer to frame 4)? x is about _3 or 4_

> Either $x = 3$ or $x = 4$ would be reasonable.

6. By trial we find $x = 4$ and $y = 0$, so $58,616 \div 1724 = $ _34_.

> 34

7. An approximation even more simple than that indicated in Section 17.6 can be obtained by successively multiplying the divisor by 0, 1, 10, 100, $\cdots$, and observing between which two multiples the dividend lies. By this process you can determine how many digits there will be in the quotient. As an illustration to find $58,616 \div 1724$, we have

$$0 \times 1724 = 0 \qquad 10 \times 1724 = 17,240$$
$$1 \times 1724 = 1724 \qquad 100 \times 1724 = 172,400$$

And 58,616 lies between 17,240 and 172,400. Thus $58,616 \div 1724$ lies between _10_ and _100_ and thus has _two_ digits.

> 10   100   two

8. How many digits are in the quotient for $2,392,806 \div 26$? _5_

> 5.

9. In studying the division algorithm we have used two forms of the distributive law: For each triple of whole numbers a, b, and c for which each expression has meaning:

$$(a + b) \div c = (a \div c) + (b \div c)$$
$$(a - b) \div c = (a \div c) - (b \div c)$$

Many students are tempted to invent another:

$$a \div (b + c) = (a \div b) + (a \div c)$$

359

Find a counterexample to disprove this equation: $a =$ _____, $b =$ _____, $c =$ _____.

> Any triple of numbers a ($\neq 0$), b, and c for which each expression is defined will do. This "equation" is not true for any whole numbers, unless $a = 0$. For example, $(12 \div 2) + (12 \div 4) = 6 + 3 = 9 \neq (12 \div 6)$.

17.7 Divisibility Tests

It is often desirable to have an easy way of telling when a whole number in decimal notation is divisible (remainder zero) by another whole number. In this section we present tests for divisibility by 2, 3, 4, 5, 6, 8, 9, and 10.

2, 5, OR 10

(1) DIVISIBILITY BY 2, 5, AND 10

The decimal expansion of a whole number a is

$$a = (a_n \times 10^n) + (a_{n-1} \times 10^{n-1}) + \cdots + (a_1 \times 10) + a_0$$

Using the right-distributive property of division, we conclude that

$$a \div d = [(a_n \times 10^n) \div d] + \cdots + [(a_1 \times 10) \div d] + [a_0 \div d]$$

Since 2 divides every power of ten, the divisions $[(a_n \times 10^n) \div 2], \cdots,$ $[(a_1 \times 10) \div 2]$ are exact. So the divisibility of a by d depends only on whether a_0 is divisible by 2. We know that a_0 is divisible by 2 if and only if a_0 is even (i.e., if $a_0 = 0, 2, 4, 6,$ or 8). Therefore,

A whole number is divisible by 2 if and only if its last digit is even.

Similarly, 5 divides every power of ten, and so 5 divides a if 5 divides a_0. For this to be true a_0 must be 0 or 5. Therefore,

A whole number is divisible by 5 if and only if its last digit is 0 or 5.

Since 10 divides every power of ten, a is divisible by 10 if a_0 is divisible by 10. But since a_0 is a single-digit number this means that a_0 must be zero. Therefore,

A whole number is divisible by 10 if and only if its last digit is 0.

4 AND 8

(2) DIVISIBILITY BY 4 AND 8

Clearly the last digit of a whole number must be even if it is divisible by 4 or 8, but this is not enough. To examine divisibility by 4, let us write

$$a = [(a_n \times 10^n) + \cdots + (a_2 \times 10^2)] + [(a_1 \times 10) + a_0]$$

Since 4 divides $10^2, 10^3, \ldots, 10^n$, the question is whether 4 divides $(a_1 \times 10) + a_0$. It will if and only if $(a_1 \times 10) + a_0$ is divisible by 4. Therefore,

A whole number is divisible by 4 if and only if the number formed from its last two digits is divisible by 4.

To test divisibility by 8, let us write

$$a = [(a_n \times 10^n) + \cdots + (a_3 \times 10^3)] + [(a_2 \times 10^2) + (a_1 \times 10) + a_0]$$

Since 8 divides $10^3, 10^4, \ldots, 10^n$, the question is whether $(a_2 \times 10^2) + (a_1 \times 10) + a_0$ is divisible by 8. Therefore,

A whole number is divisible by 8 if and only if the number formed from its last three digits is divisible by 8.

3 AND 9   **(3) DIVISIBILITY BY 3 AND 9**

To handle this question we need to be a bit clever. We write a in the form

$$a = [a_n + a_n \times (10^n - 1)] + \cdots + [a_1 + a_1 \times (10 - 1)] + a_0$$

$$= [a_n + a_{n-1} + \cdots + a_1 + a_0] + [a_n \times (10^n - 1) + \cdots + a_1 \times (10 - 1)]$$

The expressions $(10^n - 1), \ldots, (10 - 1)$ on the right are all of the form $\ldots, 9999, 999, 99, 9$, so the second term above is divisible by both 3 and 9. This puts the burden on $(a_n + a_{n-1} + \cdots + a_1 + a_0)$, which is the sum of the digits of a. Therefore,

A whole number is divisible by 3 or 9 if the sum of its digits is divisible by 3 or 9 (respectively).

6   **(4) DIVISIBILITY BY 6**

If a whole number a is divisible by 6, then $a = 6k$, where k is a whole number. Thus if a is divisible by 6, it is also divisible by 2 and by 3. We need to prove the converse: *If a is divisible by 2 and by 3, then it is divisible by 6.*

Proof
1. Since a is divisible by 2, $a = 2k_1$
2. Since a is divisible by 3, $a = 3k_2$.
3. Therefore, $2k_1 = 3k_2$, and so $3k_2$ is even.
4. k_2 cannot be odd, for the product of two odd numbers is odd. But $3k_2$ is even. Then k_2 is even.
5. So $k_2 = 2k_3$ and $a = 3(2k_3) = 6k_3$; that is, b is divisible by 6.

A whole number is divisible by 6 if and only if it is divisible by 2 and by 3.

SUMMARY
A whole number

$$a = (a_n \times 10^n) + (a_{n-1} \times 10^{n-1}) + \cdots + (a_2 \times 10^2) + (a_1 \times 10) + a_0$$

361

is divisible by

> 2 if a_0 is divisible by 2; that is, a_0 is even
> 3 if the sum of the digits is divisible by 3
> 4 if $(a_1 \times 10) + a_0$ is divisible by 4
> 5 if a_0 is divisible by 5; that is, $a_0 = 0$ or 5
> 6 if a is divisible by 2 and by 3
> 8 if $(a_2 \times 10^2) + (a_1 \times 10) + a_0$ is divisible by 8
> 9 if the sum of the digits is divisible by 9
> 10 if $a_0 = 0$

---

1. By which of 2, 3, 4, 5, 6, 8, 9, and 10 is each of the following numbers divisible?
(a) 872. _2, 4, 8_   (b) 695. _5_
(c) 9330. _2 3 5 6 10_   (d) 3748. _2, 4_
(e) 95112. _2 3 4 6 8 9_

> (a) 2.   (b) 5.   (c) 2, 3, 5, 6, 10.   (d) 2, 4.   (e) 2, 3, 4, 6, 8, 9.

2. 654,129 is divisible by 9 since _6+5+4+1+2+9_ = _27_ is divisible by 9. Is there an easy way to show that 27 is divisible by 9? _2+7_ = _9_.

> $6 + 5 + 4 + 1 + 2 + 9$ 27 $2 + 7$ 9

3. Is 1,035,056 divisible by 8? _yes_ Why? _056 = 8×7_

> Yes $056 = 8 \times 7$.

4. Is 2142 divisible by 6? _yes_ Why? _Is divisible by 2+3_

> Yes.   It is divisible by both 2 and 3.

5. The whole number $a = (a_3 \times 10^3) + (a_2 \times 10^2) + (a_1 \times 10) + a_0$ is divisible by 7 if and only if $6a_3 + 2a_2 + 3a_1 + a_0$ is divisible by 7. Apply this test to 2415. _(6×2)+(2×4)×(3×1)+5 = 12+8+ 3+5 =28, yes is divisible by 7_

> $(6 \times 2) + (2 \times 4) + (3 \times 1) + 5 = 12 + 8 + 3 + 5 = 28$. Hence 2415 is divisible by 7.

6. (Discovery Exercise) Why does the test of frame 5 succeed? Can you extend it to test the divisibility of $a = (a_4 \times 10^4) + (a_3 \times 10^3) + (a_2 \times 10^2) + (a_1 \times 10) + a_0$ by 7?

7. (Discovery Exercise) Find a test for the divisibility of a whole number by 11.

In this chapter we have presented a systematic algorithm for division which anyone should be able to follow. It can be shortened by skillful guessing, and so we have suggested ways of improving your ability as a guesser.

Novices should begin with the systematic method, then use various interim methods while learning to guess, and then as experts be able to carry out long division in the usual way.

In addition, we have discussed rapid tests for divisibility of whole numbers by 2, 3, 4, 5, 6, 8, 9, and 10.

As a test of your comprehension of these methods, work the Post Test that follows. Do not *refer to the text while working this test. Check your answers with the key after you have completed the entire test.*

POST TEST

1. The statement that $a \div d$ gives a quotient q and a remainder r means that $a = \underline{qd+r}$, where $r \underline{\ <\ } d$.

2. Use the basic multiplication table base six (frame 18, Section 17.3), to divide 30_{six} by 4_{six}. $q = \underline{4}$, $r = \underline{2}$.

3. The quotient q is that multiple of the divisor d such that qd is the _____ multiple of d which is _____ than or _____ to a. The remainder $r = $ _____.

4. To divide 763 by 4 showing all details we first write

$$763 = 700 + \underline{63}$$

Then

$$7 = (\underline{1} \times 4) + \underline{3}$$
$$700 = (\underline{100} \times 4) + \underline{3}$$
$$763 = (\underline{100} \times 4) + \underline{363}$$

[handwritten right side]
$363 = 360 + 3$
$360 = 90 \times 4$
$763 = (190 \times 4) + 3$
$q = 190 \quad r = 3$

On the lines on the right above complete the division by this process.
$q = \underline{190}$, $r = \underline{3}$.

5. Divide $3\overline{)3122}$ (base four). $q = \underline{1020}$, $r = \underline{2}$.

6. On a separate piece of paper make a table of multiples of 34 base five. Using this table divide $34\overline{)4312}$ (base five). $q = \underline{110}$, $r = \underline{22}$.

[handwritten left margin:]

102

$$\begin{array}{r} 4\ \dot0\ 2 \\ \overline{25\,)} \\ 25\ \ 5's\ or\ ... \end{array}$$

×	1	2	3
34	34	123	212

1020 r 2
$3\overline{)3122}$
3
12
12
2

363

Division Algorithms

7. In the division $52\overline{)23179}$ (base ten) suppose that we guess the first digit of the quotient to be 3. Then we obtain

$$
\begin{array}{r}
3 \\
52\overline{)23179} \\
156 \\
\hline
75
\end{array}
$$

Does this guess meet our requirements? <u>No</u> Why? <u>75 > 52</u>

8. In dividing $52\overline{)23179}$ by an alternative method we write the first step using 3 as the first guess:

$$52\overline{)23179} \qquad 300$$

Complete the division by this method. $q =$ <u>445</u>, $r =$ <u>39</u>.

9. On a separate piece of paper, divide 724 by 125 by repeated subtraction. $q =$ <u>5</u>, $r =$ <u>99</u>.

10. To aid in guessing we may round the divisor. If the divisor is 347, it is rounded to <u>300</u>.

11. In the division of 36,249 by 1423 (base ten)

$1 \times 1423 =$ <u>1423</u>
$10 \times 1423 =$ <u>14,230</u>
$100 \times 1423 =$ <u>142,300</u>

So 36,249 lies between <u>14,230</u> and <u>142,300</u>. Therefore, the quotient has <u>2</u> digits.

12. Using the tests of this chapter show that 7200 is divisible by 2, 3, 4, 5, 6, 8, 9, and 10. Give reasons.

2. <u>last digit even</u>
3. <u>7+2=9, 9 is divisible by 3</u>
4. <u>00 is divisible by 4</u>
5. <u>the last digit is 0</u>
6. <u>it's divisible by 2 and 3</u>
8. <u>200 is divisible by 8</u>
9. <u>7+2=9, 9 is divisible by 9.</u>
10. <u>the last digit is 0.</u>

---

1. $qd + r$; $<$
2. 4; 2
3. largest; less; equal; $a - qd$
4. $763 = 700 + 63$ $\qquad$ $363 = 360 + 3$

$\qquad 7 = (1 \times 4) + 3$ $\qquad$ $360 = 90 \times 4$

$\qquad 700 = (100 \times 4) + 300$ $\qquad$ $363 = (90 \times 4) + 3$

$\qquad 763 = (100 \times 4) + 363$ $\qquad$ $763 = (190 \times 4) + 3$

$\qquad\qquad\qquad\qquad q = 190, r = 3$

5.
```
      1020
   3 )3122     q = 1020, r = 2
     3
     ‾‾
     12
     12
     ‾‾
      2
```

6.

×	1	2	3	4
34	34	73	212	301

```
       110
   34 )4312     q — 110, r = 22
      34
      ‾‾
      41
      34
      ‾‾
      22
```

7. No.   75 > 52.

8.
```
   52 )23179
      156       300     q = 445, r = 39
      ‾‾‾                (other possibilities are
       75       100     also correct)
       52
       ‾‾
      237
      156        30
      ‾‾‾
       81
       52        10
       ‾‾
      299
      260         5
      ‾‾‾       ‾‾‾
       39       445
```

9.
```
   724    4
   500          q = 5, r = 99
   ‾‾‾
   224
   125    1
   ‾‾     ‾
    99    5
```

10. 300

11. 1423 ; 14,230 ; 142,300 ; 14,230 ; 142,300 ; two

12. 2. The last digit is even.

   3. 7 + 2 = 9, and 9 is divisible by 3.

   4. 00 is divisible by 4.

   5. The last digit is 0.

   6. It is divisible by 2 and by 3.

   8. 200 is divisible by 8.

   9. 7 + 2 = 9, and 9 is divisible by 9.

   10. The last digit is 0.

Epilogue

In the last four chapters we have discussed the algorithms for the four operations of arithmetic. The question now is: How should these be treated in an elementary school?

The purpose of an algorithm is to give a procedure that one can apply rapidly without thinking. Speed and accuracy in computing are very important, and these require automatic behavior—for thinking will only get in the way and slow down the arithmetic. Therefore, there must be enough drill on the algorithms to ingrain them in the minds of the students.

Why, then, have we spent so much time on the reasoning behind the algorithms? The reason is that we should treat our students as intelligent human beings and explain to them *why* a particular procedure will do the required job. Once they are convinced that the algorithm is a sensible way to attack their problem, they are more likely to show interest in it and to be able to follow its rules.

Although we have emphasized the *why* in these chapters (on the assumption that *you* already knew the *how*), you will undoubtedly put more emphasis on the *how* in your own teaching. The object of arithmetic is to get the *right* answer; no amount of theoretical knowledge will make up for an inability to compute accurately and rapidly!

This concludes Part III. Before beginning Part IV use the following Summary Test to help you review this material.

Summary
Test for
Part III

Circle the number of every true statement in this section.

1. In the decimal system (base ten) the fundamental symbols are 1, 2, 3, 4, 5, 6, 7, 8, 9, 10.
2. In the decimal system (base ten) the fundamental group size is 10.
3. In base b, the fundamental symbols are $0, 1, 2, \ldots, b - 1$.
4. In base b, the possible group sizes are $b, 2b, 3b, \ldots$.
5. 25_{ten} and 25_{five} are names for the same number.
6. 25_{ten} and 200_{five} are names for the same number.
7. There is only one correct algorithm for subtraction.
8. 57,651 is divisible by 3.
9. 24,580 is divisible by 4.
10. 36,251 is divisible by 9.

B

11. Write 5372 in expanded decimal notation. _____

12. In adding $233 + 514 + 397$, what properties justify writing

$$
\begin{array}{r}
233 \\
514 \\
397
\end{array}
$$

and then adding each column? _____

13. In adding the right-hand column of the sum indicated in question 12, what property justifies the use of $(7 + 3) + 4$ instead of $(7 + 4) + 3$ or $(3 + 4) + 7$? _____

14. The numbers in the left-hand column of the sum indicated in question 12 are actually 2×10^2, 5×10^2, and 3×10^2. What property justifies writing the sum of these as $(2 + 5 + 3) \times 10^2$? _____

15. In finding the difference $403 - 28$, by the "borrowing" algorithm we use 403 as _____ $\times 10^2 +$ _____ $\times 10 +$ _____ instead of $(4 \times 10^2) + (0 \times 10) + 3$.

16. In finding 423×5691 by the usual multiplication algorithm, what power of 10 multiplies 4×5? _____ 2×9? _____

367

17. Complete the base six addition and multiplication tables.

+	0	1	2	3	4	5
0						
1						
2						
3						
4						
5						

×	1	2	3	4	5
1					
2					
3					
4					
5					

18. Use these base six tables (question 17) to find $312_{six} \times 54_{six}$.

$$\begin{array}{r} 312 \\ \times 54 \\ \hline \\ \hline \end{array}$$

19. Use these base six tables (question 17) to find $312_{six} - 54_{six}$.

$$\begin{array}{r} 3\ 1\ 2 \\ -\ 5\ 4 \\ \hline \end{array}$$

20. Use these base six tables (question 17) to find $3300_{six} \div 4_{six}$.

$$4\overline{)3\ 3\ 0\ 0}$$

21. Without dividing, how can you show that a whole number in decimal notation is divisible by 6? _____
_____

22. If each of the following numerals are in base six, find $10 - 1 =$
_____, $100 - 1 =$ _____, $1000 - 1 =$ _____

23. Based on the results of question 22 and its extension to other powers of 10_{six}, find a criterion for the divisibility of a whole number in base six notation by 5_{six}. _____

24. Apply your answer to question 23 to determine whether $24{,}234_{six}$ is divisible by 5_{six}. _____
(yes, no)

25. 110_{six} is divisible by what numbers in base six notation? _____

When you have completed this test, you may proceed to Chapter 18, Modular Arithmetic.

PART IV

Extensions of the Whole Number System

Chapters 18 through 27

18

Modular Arithmetic

As the beginning of our study of number systems other than the whole numbers, we introduce you to modular arithmetic. *Before beginning the chapter you should have finished Chapter 17, Division Algorithms, and should review the definitions of an equivalence relation (Section 4.8) and of equivalence classes (Section 5.6). You should also remind yourself of the meaning of the term* uniquely defined *as it applies to operations of arithmetic (Sections 9.3, 9.8, 11.3, and 11.10). The following Readiness Test will help you review these ideas.*

READINESS TEST

1. Find whole numbers q and r so that $a = qd + r$ and $r < d$ when (a) $a = 27$, $d = 5$; (b) $a = 6$, $d = 8$. $27 =$ _____ ; $6 =$ _____ .

> $27 = \underline{5} \times 5 + \underline{2}$ $6 = \underline{0} \times 8 + \underline{6}$

2. Write in compact decimal notation: $(3 \times 10^3) + (5 \times 10^2) + (0 \times 10) + 7.$ _____

> 3507.

3. Write 284 in the expanded form used in frame 2. _____ _____

> $(2 \times 10^2) + (8 \times 10) + 4.$

4. A whole number is even if it is divisible by _____ .

> 2

5. A relation $a \approx b$ is an equivalence relation if it is (1) _____ , (2) _____ , and (3) _____ .

> reflexive   symmetric   transitive.

6. Which of the following relations are equivalence relations? (a) $a = b$ for whole numbers. (b) $a \leq b$ for whole numbers. (c) $A \sim B$ for sets. _____

> (a) and (c).

7. An equivalence class of sets is a collection of sets such that every two sets in the collection are _____.

> mutually equivalent

8. In Section 5.6 we used the symbol _____ as a name for the equivalence class of sets

$$\{\{a\}, \{x\}, \{\varnothing\}, \{0\}, \ldots\}$$

> $\langle\{x\}\rangle$

9. Since the equivalence class in frame 8 is determined by any of its elements, another name for this class could be _____.

> Many answers, such as $\langle\{a\}\rangle$ or $\langle\{\varnothing\}\rangle$.

10. The statement that the sum of two whole numbers is *uniquely defined* means that this sum does not depend upon our _____ of the sets A and B used to define $a + b$ provided that $n(A) =$ _____, $n(B) =$ _____, and A and B are _____.

> choices a b disjoint

11. Write the basic addition and multiplication tables for the whole numbers base two.

+	0	1
0		
1		

×	0	1
0		
1		

+	0	1
0	0	1
1	0	10

×	0	1
0	0	0
1	0	1

If necessary, review these ideas until you understand them. Then read Sections 18.1 and 18.2 and work the exercises following Section 18.2.

18.1 Introduction

In Parts II and III we have dealt exclusively with the whole numbers. Now in Part IV we shall consider the arithmetic of other systems of numbers in common use. As an introduction to this topic, this chapter is devoted to a number system that looks remarkably like the whole numbers but whose arithmetic is quite different. It is called *modular arithmetic*.

18.2 Even and Odd Numbers

EVEN AND ODD   It has already been pointed out that an *even* number is a whole number that is divisible by 2. That is, an even number a can be written in the form $a = 2q$, where q is a whole number. Similarly, an *odd* number is a whole number whose remainder is 1 when it is divided by 2. Hence an odd number a can be written in the form $a = 2q + 1$, where q is a whole number. We summarize these definitions in Table 1.

TABLE 1. **Number with Given Remainder when Divided by 2**

Remainder	General Form	Subset of the Whole Numbers	Name
0	$2q$	$\{0, 2, 4, 6, 8, 10, \ldots\}$	even
1	$2q + 1$	$\{1, 3, 5, 7, 9, 11, \ldots\}$	odd

Let us prove a few facts about even and odd numbers.

(1) *The sum of two even numbers, a and b, is even.* For we can write $a = 2q_1$ and $b = 2q_2$. So $a + b = 2q_1 + 2q_2 = 2(q_1 + q_2)$. Thus $a + b$ is even.

(2) *The sum of two odd numbers, a and b, is even.* For we can write $a = 2q_1 + 1$ and $b = 2q_2 + 1$. So $a + b = (2q_1 + 1) + (2q_2 + 1) = 2(q_1 + q_2) + 2 = 2(q_1 + q_2 + 1)$. Thus $a + b$ is even.

(3) *The sum of an even number a and an odd number b is odd.* For we can write $a = 2q_1$ and $b = 2q_2 + 1$. Thus $a + b = 2q_1 + (2q_2 + 1) = 2(q_1 + q_2) + 1$. Thus $a + b$ is odd.

In view of (1), (2), and (3) we can write an addition table for even and odd numbers, Table 2.

TABLE 2. **Addition Table for Even and Odd Numbers**

+	even	odd
even	even	odd
odd	odd	even

Much more may be said about the sums of even and odd numbers, and we leave this for you to work out in the following exercises.

SUMS

1. First, the sum of any number of even numbers. Since for each even number to be added there exists a whole number n such that the even number equals $2n$, we can express the sum as $2n_1 + 2n_2 + 2n_3 + \cdots + 2n_r$,

where r represents the number of numbers to be added. But we know $2n_1 + 2n_2 + 2n_3 + \cdots + 2n_r = 2(n_1 + n_2 + n_3 + \cdots + n_r)$. Why is this?

The extended distributive law.

2. Why, then, is $2n_1 + \cdots + 2n_r$ even? _____

It is equal to a multiple of 2, and hence is even.

3. Now consider a sum of odd numbers. For two odd numbers the sum is _____ .
   (even, odd)

even

4. If to the sum of two odd numbers we add a third odd number, the result will be _____ .
   (even, odd)

odd

5. If to the sum of three odd numbers we add a fourth odd number, the result will be _____ .
   (even, odd)

even

6. You might guess from these few examples that the sum of a list of odd numbers will be even if the number of odd numbers to be added is _____ .
   (even, odd)

even

7. The easiest way to prove this is to notice that if an even number of odd numbers is to be added then the numbers can be paired with each other. The sum of each pair will be even; and since the sum of any number of even numbers is even, the sum of all the pairs will be _____ .
   (even, odd)

even

8. But the sum of all the pairs is the sum of an even number of odd numbers and hence the sum of an even number of odd numbers is _____.
(even, odd)

> even

9. On the other hand, the sum of an odd number of odd numbers is odd. For we see that if we add all but one of the numbers, we will be adding an even number of odd numbers and the result is sure to be _____.
(even, odd)

> even

10. Now to that even sum we add the one remaining odd number and the sum will be _____.
(even, odd)

> odd

11. Hence the sum of an odd number of odd numbers is _____.
(even, odd)

> odd

Now let us consider the following proposition: The number of people everywhere in the world who shook hands an odd number of times yesterday was even. Perhaps this does not seem like the sort of thing that can be proved mathematically, but let's see what we can do. Let us enlist the help of a giant computer. We shall ask the computer to record every handshake that was shaken yesterday by listing the name of each person who shook hands and putting an × after the name every time the person shook hands. We shall have to insist that a handshake involves two and only two people, no dogs allowed, no matter how cute and clever.

Now notice first of all that our giant machine records 2 ×'s everytime a handshake occurs. Therefore, the total number of ×'s is even, a fact we shall refer to again. After the records are complete we set the machine to counting the ×'s after each name and recording the number of handshakes for each person. Then we finally call upon the computer to sort the names into two lists, the "even list" for those who have shaken hands an even number of times and the "odd list" for those who have shaken hands an odd number of times. The proposition we are discussing says that the "odd list" will contain an even number of names.

375

In fact, we can now prove the proposition. In the first place the total number of ×'s is even and in the second place the number of ×'s belonging to the people on the "even list" is even. Now only

12. even + _____ = even.

even

So we see that the total number of ×'s belonging to people on the "odd list" is even. Then we have a sum of odd numbers which is even and according to the facts we proved earlier a sum of a list of odd numbers will be even only if there is an even number of odd numbers in the list.

13. Let us summarize the facts we have stated about sums of even and odd numbers.
 (a) The sum of any number of even numbers is _____.
 (b) The sum of an even number of odd numbers is _____.
 (c) The sum of an odd number of odd numbers is _____.

(a) even   (b) even   (c) odd

14. Can you portion out 10 lumps of sugar among 3 cups of tea so that every cup will contain an odd number of lumps? _____

No. The sum of three odd numbers must be odd and therefore not equal to 10.

15. At a certain prom there were 125 people who danced. Of these 80 danced an even number of dances and 45 danced an odd number of dances. Circle your comment: (a) Sounds reasonable. (b) Impossible! (c) So what?

The situation would be possible if someone danced one solo dance (or if any odd number of dancers performed solo an odd number of times).

PRODUCTS Next let us consider products of even and odd numbers.

16. Prove that the product of two even numbers, *a* and *b*, is even.

> **Proof.** $a = 2q_1$ and $b = 2q_2$. So $ab = (2q_1) \times (2q_2) = 4q_1q_2$. Thus ab is divisible by 2 and so is even.

17. Prove that the product of two odd numbers, a and b, is odd.

> **Proof.** $a = 2q_1 + 1$ and $b = 2q_2 + 1$. So $ab = (2q_1 + 1) \times (2q_2 + 1) = 4q_1q_2 + 2q_1 + 2q_2 + 1 = 2(2q_1q_2 + q_1 + q_2) + 1$. Therefore, ab is odd.

18. Prove that the product of an even number a and an odd number b is even. _____

> **Proof.** $a = 2q_1$ and $b = 2q_2 + 1$. So $ab = (2q_1)(2q_2 + 1) = 2(2q_1q_2 + q_7)$. Thus ab is even.

19. Make a multiplication table for even and odd numbers.

×	even	odd
even		
odd		

×	even	odd
even	even	even
odd	even	odd

18.3 Congruences

We have seen that by a special case of the division algorithm every whole number can be classified as even or odd, according as the remainder is zero or one when the number is divided by two. We can classify whole numbers similarly when they are divided by whole numbers other than two. For example, the division algorithm assures us that when any whole number is divided by three there will be a remainder of 0, 1, or 2. Thus the set of whole numbers can be divided into three subsets as indicated in Table 3.

377

TABLE 3. **Numbers with Given Remainder when Divided by 3**

Remainder	General Form	Subset of the Whole Numbers
0	$3q$	$\{0, 3, 6, 9, 12, \ldots\}$
1	$3q + 1$	$\{1, 4, 7, 10, 13, \ldots\}$
2	$3q + 2$	$\{2, 5, 8, 11, 14, \ldots\}$

If the divisor is four, the same process results in Table 4.

TABLE 4. **Numbers with Given Remainder when Divided by 4**

Remainder	General Form	Subset of the Whole Numbers
0	$4q$	$\{0, 4, 8, 12, 16, \ldots\}$
1	$4q + 1$	$\{1, 5, 9, 13, 17, \ldots\}$
3	$4q + 2$	$\{2, 6, 10, 14, 18, \ldots\}$
3	$4q + 3$	$\{3, 7, 11, 15, 19, \ldots\}$

In the same way tables like Tables 1, 3, and 4 can be prepared for any divisor ($\neq 0$). Instead of inventing names like *even* and *odd* for the subsets in these tables (as we did when the divisor was 2), we shall introduce the new concept of a *congruence*.

CONGRUENCE MODULO *m*   **DEFINITION.** Let m be any whole number $\neq 0$. Then two whole numbers are *congruent modulo m* if and only if they have the same remainder when they are divided by m.

NOTATION. The statement that a and b are congruent modulo m is written

$$a \equiv b \bmod m$$

The whole number m ($\neq 0$) is called the *modulus*.

EXAMPLES
1. From Table 1, $12 \equiv 6 \bmod 2$ and $15 \equiv 7 \bmod 2$.
2. From Table 3, $13 \equiv 4 \bmod 3$ and $14 \equiv 5 \bmod 3$.
3. From Table 4, $17 \equiv 9 \bmod 4$ and $15 \equiv 3 \bmod 4$.

If the modulus m is given, congruence is a relation between pairs of whole numbers of the type discussed in Section 4.8. Recall that such a relation is an *equivalence relation* if and only if it is reflexive, symmetric, and transitive. Let us show that congruence is an equivalence relation.

EQUIVALENCE RELATION   **THEOREM 1.** For any fixed modulus m, congruence modulo m is an equivalence relation.

Proof
(a) *Reflexive:* $a \equiv a \bmod m$. For the two remainders are obviously the same.

378

(b) *Symmetric:* If $a \equiv b \bmod m$, then $b \equiv a \bmod m$. The hypothesis states that when a and b are divided by m, their remainders are equal. So they continue to be equal in the conclusion of the above statement.

(c) *Transitive:* If $a_1 \equiv a_2 \bmod m$ and $a_2 \equiv a_3 \bmod m$, then $a_1 \equiv a_3 \bmod m$. Write $a_1 = q_1 m + r_1$; $a_2 = q_2 m + r_2$ and $a_3 = q_3 m + r_3$. We are required to show that if $r_1 = r_2$ and $r_2 = r_3$, then $r_1 = r_3$. But this is true because of the transitive property of equality.

CONGRUENCE CLASSES

Since congruence modulo m is an equivalence relation, it determines a collection of equivalence classes called *congruence classes* (sometimes called *residue classes*).

DEFINITION. A *congruence class modulo m* is a subset of the whole numbers each of whose elements is congruent modulo m to every other element of the class and such that every whole number congruent modulo m to some member of the class is itself a member of the class.

You should compare this definition with that of an *equivalence class of sets* given in Section 5.6.

EXAMPLES

1. In Table 1 the sets of even and odd numbers are congruence classes modulo 2.
2. In Table 3 the three sets listed are congruence classes modulo 3.
3. In Table 4 the four sets listed are congruence classes modulo 4.

PARTITION

The congruence classes modulo m form a *partition* of the whole numbers in the sense described in Section 5.6. This partition has the following properties:

(1) Every whole number belongs to one and only one congruence class.

(2) The elements of a congruence class are all mutually congruent.

(3) No element of one congruence class is congruent to any element of a different congruence class.

It would be convenient to have an easier way than doing two divisions and checking the remainders to find out if two numbers are congruent modulo some m. There is such a way, and we will prove here that it is reliable.

THEOREM 2. If a, b, and m are whole numbers with $m \neq 0$ and if $a \equiv b \bmod m$, then either $a - b$ or $b - a$, whichever is a whole number, is a multiple of m.

Proof. First, let us take care of the possibility that $a = b$ by observing that in that case $a - b = b - a = 0$, and that for all whole numbers m, 0 is a multiple of m since there exists a whole number, 0, such that $0 = 0 \times m$. If $a - b \neq 0$, then either $a > b$ or $b > a$. Let us call the greater of the two a and then the difference $a - b$ is a whole number. If $a = q_1 m + r$ with $r < m$, by hypothesis $b = q_2 m + r$. Hence $a - b = q_1 m - q_2 m = (q_1 - q_2)m$, and so $a - b$ is a multiple of m.

EXAMPLES

1. $50 \equiv 22 \bmod 7$ (both yield remainder 1) and so their difference, 28, is a multiple of 7.

2. $238 \equiv 13 \bmod 9$ (verify this) and so their difference, 225, must be a multiple of 9. (It is 9×25.)

The converse of Theorem 2 is also true. It is stated as Theorem 3.

THEOREM 3. If $a - b$ is a multiple of m, then $a \equiv b \bmod m$.

Proof. According to the hypothesis there is a whole number k such that $a - b = km$, or, $a = b + km$. Now there exist whole numbers q and r, $r < m$, such that $b = qm + r$ and accordingly $a = qm + r + km = m(q + k) + r$. Clearly, r is the remainder when either a or b is divided by m. Hence $a \equiv b \bmod m$ and the theorem is proved.

Let us combine Theorems 2 and 3 as follows:

THEOREM 4. For all whole numbers a and b, $a \equiv b \bmod m$ if and only if the difference ($a - b$ or $b - a$, whichever is a whole number) is a multiple of m.

---

1. If there is a remainder of 1 when we divide a number by 3, we say the number is _____ to 1, modulo 3.

> congruent

2. If there is a remainder of 2 when a is divided by 3, then a is _____ to _____ modulo _____.

> congruent   2   3

3. Which of the following numbers is not congruent to the other numbers in the list, modulo 3? 7, 10, 19, 29, 301, 1000. _____

> 29.

4. Write down five numbers that are of the form $5k + 2$. _____

> Any of these numbers will do: 2, 7, 12, 17, 22, 27, ...

5. List five numbers that are congruent to 3 mod 8. _____

> Any of these will do: 3, 11, 19, 27, 35, 43, 51, 59, 67, 75, 83, ...

---

6. If a number is congruent to 1 mod 4 we may say it is of the form
_____$k +$ _____ .

> 4   1

7. Fill in the blanks in these congruences. In each case use the smallest whole number that fits.
   (a) $5 \equiv$ _____ mod 2.   (b) $24 \equiv$ _____ mod 4.
   (c) $91 \equiv$ _____ mod 10.   (d) $49 \equiv$ _____ mod 9.
   (e) $247 \equiv$ _____ mod 3.   (f) $50 \equiv$ _____ mod 8.

> (a) 1   (b) 0   (c) 1   (d) 4   (e) 1   (f) 2

8. Since 10 and 7 are both congruent to 1 mod 3, we know that $10 \equiv 7 \bmod 3$. Similarly, try to verify the congruences below and label them true or false.
   (a) $42 \equiv 52 \bmod 10$. _____ (b) $17 \equiv 36 \bmod 5$. _____ (c) $13 \equiv 17 \bmod 2$.
   _____

> (a) T.   (b) F.   (c) T.

9. Even numbers are congruent to _____ mod 2 and odd numbers are congruent to _____ mod 2.

> 0 and 1 are the commonest correct answers, but your answer is correct if you put any even number in the first blank and any odd number in the second blank.

10. Use Theorem 4 to test these congruences. Mark them true or false according to the result.
    (a) $31 \equiv 0 \bmod 1$. _____   (b) $31 \equiv 1 \bmod 2$. _____
    (c) $31 \equiv 1 \bmod 3$. _____   (d) $31 \equiv 1 \bmod 4$. _____
    (e) $31 \equiv 1 \bmod 5$. _____   (f) $31 \equiv 1 \bmod 6$. _____
    (g) $31 \equiv 1 \bmod 7$. _____ .   (h) $187 \equiv 205 \bmod 9$. _____
    (i) $1967 \equiv 67 \bmod 4$. _____   (j) $3386 \equiv 6 \bmod 10$. _____

> (a) T.   (b) T.   (c) T.   (d) F.   (e) T.   (f) T.   (g) F.
> (h) T.   (i) T.   (j) T.

11. In Theorem 1 we have seen that the congruence relation is reflexive, symmetric, and transitive. Any relation that has these properties is called an *equivalence relation*. Find (a) another equivalence relation between whole numbers. _____ (b) an equivalence relation between sets. _____

> (a) Equality of numbers.   (b) Equivalence of sets.

12. Given a modulus m, we can partition the set of whole numbers into a collection of disjoint sets such that every two whole numbers in a given set are mutually congruent.

   (a) If $m = 5$, how many sets must we write down? _____

   (b) List five members of each of the sets of the partition corresponding to $m = 5$. { _____ } { _____ }

   { _____ }   { _____ }

   { _____ }

The sets in this partition are called _____ classes.

> (a) 5
> (b) {0, 5, 10, 15, 20, ...}
>   {1, 6, 11, 16, 21, ...}
>   {2, 7, 12, 17, 22, ...}
>   {3, 8, 13, 18, 23, ...}
>   {4, 9, 14, 19, 24, ...}
>   congruence

18.4 Theorems about Congruences

There are two theorems about congruences that will be needed in our study of modular arithmetic. The first is Theorem 5.

SUMS

THEOREM 5. If $a \equiv b \bmod m$ and $c \equiv d \bmod m$, then $a + c \equiv b + d \bmod m$.

Proof

1. By hypothesis $a - b = k_1 m$ or $a = b + k_1 m$.
2. Similarly, $c - d = k_2 m$ or $c = d + k_2 m$.
3. Therefore, $a + c = (b + d) + (k_1 + k_2)m$.
4. Hence $(a + c) - (b + d) = (k_1 + k_2)m$.
5. From Theorem 4: $a + c \equiv b + d \bmod m$.

Theorem 6 is a parallel theorem about products.

PRODUCTS

THEOREM 6. If $a \equiv b \bmod m$ and $c \equiv d \bmod m$, then $ac \equiv bd \bmod m$.

Proof

1. As in Theorem 5, $a = b + k_1 m$ and $c = d + k_2 m$.
2. Hence

$$ac = (b + k_1 m)(d + k_2 m)$$

$$= bd + (k_1 d + k_2 b)m + (k_1 k_2)m^2$$

$$= bd + (k_1 d + k_2 b + k_1 k_2 m)m.$$

3. From Theorem 4, $ac \equiv bd \bmod m$.

18.5 Modular Arithmetic

In the case of even and odd numbers it was possible to form addition and multiplication tables like Table 2. In modular arithmetic we do the same thing for congruence classes with an arbitrary modulus.

First, we must give names to the congruence classes modulo m. As an example, let $m = 3$. Then we can extend Table 3 to include names for the congruence classes as shown in Table 5. Thus we name each congruence

TABLE 5. **Names for Congruence Classes Modulo 3**

CONGRUENCE CLASSES
MOD 3

Remainder	General Form	Congruence Classes	Names
0	$3q$	$\{0, 3, 6, 9, \ldots\}$	$\langle 0 \rangle$
1	$3q + 1$	$\{1, 4, 7, 10, \ldots\}$	$\langle 1 \rangle$
2	$3q + 2$	$\{2, 5, 8, 11, \ldots\}$	$\langle 2 \rangle$

class by writing its smallest element between pointed brackets, $\langle\ \rangle$. Other names are also possible, for any element of a congruence class determines it. So when $m = 3$, we can write

$$\langle 0 \rangle = \langle 3 \rangle = \langle 6 \rangle = \langle 9 \rangle = \cdots$$

$$\langle 1 \rangle = \langle 4 \rangle = \langle 7 \rangle = \langle 10 \rangle = \cdots$$

$$\langle 2 \rangle = \langle 5 \rangle = \langle 8 \rangle = \langle 11 \rangle = \cdots$$

If we are working with a fixed modulus, these names are satisfactory, but if several different moduli are involved we must distinguish among the names by writing

$$\langle 0 \rangle_2 = \{0, 2, 4, 6, 8, \ldots\} \qquad \text{(modulo 2)}$$

$$\langle 0 \rangle_3 = \{0, 3, 6, 9, 12, \ldots\} \qquad \text{(modulo 3)}$$

and so forth.

Since modulo 2 $\langle 0 \rangle$ represents the even numbers and $\langle 1 \rangle$ the odd numbers, the addition and multiplication tables for even and odd numbers can be

TABLE 6. **Addition and Multiplication Tables for Congruence Classes Modulo 2**

+	$\langle 0 \rangle$	$\langle 1 \rangle$
$\langle 0 \rangle$	$\langle 0 \rangle$	$\langle 1 \rangle$
$\langle 1 \rangle$	$\langle 1 \rangle$	$\langle 0 \rangle$

×	$\langle 0 \rangle$	$\langle 1 \rangle$
$\langle 0 \rangle$	$\langle 0 \rangle$	$\langle 0 \rangle$
$\langle 1 \rangle$	$\langle 0 \rangle$	$\langle 1 \rangle$

written as in Table 6. These tables look remarkably like the tables in Chapters 14 and 15 for arithmetic base 2, but they are *different*. Compare them closely!

Our task now is to devise similar addition and multiplication tables for the congruence classes modulo m. Again suppose $m = 3$ as an illustration. How shall we define $\langle 1 \rangle + \langle 2 \rangle$? Choose any element, say 7, in $\langle 1 \rangle$ and any element, say 11, in $\langle 2 \rangle$. Then $7 + 11 = 18$. Since $18 = 6 \times 3 + 0$, 18 is an element of $\langle 0 \rangle$. So a reasonable guess is that we want

$$\langle 1 \rangle + \langle 2 \rangle = \langle 0 \rangle$$

You should be a bit suspicious, however, for in the above calculation we chose elements 7 and 11 at *random*. What if we had made other choices; would the result have been the same? Try 13, an element of $\langle 1 \rangle$, and 14, an element of $\langle 2 \rangle$. Then $13 + 14 = 27$, and 27 is an element of $\langle 0 \rangle$. Perhaps you are beginning to be convinced that our choices make no difference in the result. So we might as well choose 1 from $\langle 1 \rangle$ and 2 from $\langle 2 \rangle$. Then $1 + 2 = 3$ and 3 is an element of $\langle 0 \rangle$, and $\langle 1 \rangle + \langle 2 \rangle = \langle 0 \rangle$. The general situation is as follows:

ADDITION OF CLASSES

DEFINITION. Let $\langle a \rangle$ and $\langle b \rangle$ be congruence classes modulo m. Choose **any** element a of $\langle a \rangle$ and any element b of $\langle b \rangle$. Then

$$\langle a \rangle + \langle b \rangle = \langle c \rangle$$

where $\langle c \rangle$ is the congruence class to which $a + b$ belongs. Thus

$$\langle a \rangle + \langle b \rangle = \langle a + b \rangle$$

For this definition to make good sense, we must show that $\langle c \rangle$ does not depend upon our choices of a and b. That is, we must show that addition of congruence classes is *uniquely defined* (compare Sections 9.3 and 9.8, and 11.3 and 11.10).

THEOREM 7. The addition of congruence classes is uniquely defined.

Proof. We must show that if a_1 and a_2 are elements of $\langle a \rangle$ and b_1 and b_2 are elements of $\langle b \rangle$, then $b_1 + a_2 \equiv b_1 + a_2 \bmod m$. This is an immediate consequence of Theorem 5.

These arguments permit us to write Table 7.

TABLE 7. Addition Table for Congruence Classes Modulo 3

+	$\langle 0 \rangle$	$\langle 1 \rangle$	$\langle 2 \rangle$
$\langle 0 \rangle$	$\langle 0 \rangle$	$\langle 1 \rangle$	$\langle 2 \rangle$
$\langle 1 \rangle$	$\langle 1 \rangle$	$\langle 2 \rangle$	$\langle 0 \rangle$
$\langle 2 \rangle$	$\langle 2 \rangle$	$\langle 0 \rangle$	$\langle 1 \rangle$

REMARK

Here we have been guilty of a minor sin called "abuse of notation". In the equation

$$\langle a \rangle + \langle b \rangle = \langle a + b \rangle$$

384

the addition on the left is addition of congruence classes (which is being defined) and the addition on the right is that of whole numbers (which has already been defined). If we wish to be especially careful, we should use two different symbols for these two types of addition, say $\oplus$ and $+$, respectively. Then the above equation becomes

$$\langle a \rangle \oplus \langle b \rangle = \langle a + b \rangle$$

This notation becomes clumsy in general use, and so we shall not adopt it. Nevertheless, you should be aware of the distinction between these two types of addition, both of which we shall represent by the single symbol $+$.

As for multiplication of congruence classes, we have the following definition and theorem.

MULTIPLICATION OF CLASSES   **DEFINITION.** Let $\langle a \rangle$ and $\langle b \rangle$ be congruence classes modulo m. Choose any element a of $\langle a \rangle$ and any element b of $\langle b \rangle$. Then

$$\langle a \rangle \times \langle b \rangle = \langle c \rangle$$

where $\langle c \rangle$ is the congruence class to which $a \times b$ belongs. Thus

$$\langle a \rangle \times \langle b \rangle = \langle a \times b \rangle$$

THEOREM 8. The multiplication of congruence classes is uniquely defined.

Proof. This is an immediate consequence of Theorem 6.

The multiplication table of congruence classes modulo 3 is given in Table 8.

TABLE 8. Multiplication Table for Congruence Classes Modulo 3

$\times$	$\langle 0 \rangle$	$\langle 1 \rangle$	$\langle 2 \rangle$
$\langle 0 \rangle$	$\langle 0 \rangle$	$\langle 0 \rangle$	$\langle 0 \rangle$
$\langle 1 \rangle$	$\langle 0 \rangle$	$\langle 1 \rangle$	$\langle 2 \rangle$
$\langle 2 \rangle$	$\langle 0 \rangle$	$\langle 2 \rangle$	$\langle 1 \rangle$

REMARK

Again we are guilty of "abuse of notation". The equation

$$\langle a \rangle \times \langle b \rangle = \langle a \times b \rangle$$

is more properly written

$$\langle a \rangle \otimes \langle b \rangle = \langle a \times b \rangle$$

where $\otimes$ represents multiplication of congruence classes and $\times$ represents multiplication of whole numbers. For the reasons discussed in the similar situation for addition, we shall not use this notation.

Modular arithmetic is the subject that deals with the arithmetic of congruence classes. You should observe the following difference between it and the arithmetic of whole numbers:

In the arithmetic of congruence classes modulo m there are exactly m "numbers" involved instead of infinitely many as in the case of whole numbers.

The "numbers" modulo m are

$$\langle 0 \rangle, \langle 1 \rangle, \ldots, \langle m - 1 \rangle$$

and they are added and multiplied according to the definitions in this section. Thus modular arithmetic is sometimes called *finite arithmetic*.

1. When the modulus m is 4, how many congruence classes are there? _____ What are their names? _____

   4. $\langle 0 \rangle, \langle 1 \rangle, \langle 2 \rangle, \langle 3 \rangle.$

2. If $m = 4$, what are the sets named as follows:
   $\langle 0 \rangle =$ _____
   $\langle 1 \rangle =$ _____
   $\langle 2 \rangle =$ _____
   $\langle 3 \rangle =$ _____

   $\{0, 4, 8, 12, 16, \ldots\}$
   $\{1, 5, 9, 13, 17, \ldots\}$
   $\{2, 6, 10, 14, 18, \ldots\}$
   $\{3, 7, 11, 15, 19, \ldots\}$

3. Write the addition table for the congruence classes modulo 4.

+	$\langle 0 \rangle$	$\langle 1 \rangle$	$\langle 2 \rangle$	$\langle 3 \rangle$
$\langle 0 \rangle$				
$\langle 1 \rangle$				
$\langle 2 \rangle$				
$\langle 3 \rangle$				

+	$\langle 0 \rangle$	$\langle 1 \rangle$	$\langle 2 \rangle$	$\langle 3 \rangle$
$\langle 0 \rangle$	$\langle 0 \rangle$	$\langle 1 \rangle$	$\langle 2 \rangle$	$\langle 3 \rangle$
$\langle 1 \rangle$	$\langle 1 \rangle$	$\langle 2 \rangle$	$\langle 3 \rangle$	$\langle 0 \rangle$
$\langle 2 \rangle$	$\langle 2 \rangle$	$\langle 3 \rangle$	$\langle 0 \rangle$	$\langle 1 \rangle$
$\langle 3 \rangle$	$\langle 3 \rangle$	$\langle 0 \rangle$	$\langle 1 \rangle$	$\langle 2 \rangle$

4. Is addition a binary operation on the set of congruence classes modulo 4? _____

> Yes.

5. Is addition modulo 4 commutative? _____ Why? _____
_____

> Yes.   The table in frame 3 is symmetric about its diagonal.

6. From frame 3 are $(\langle 2 \rangle + \langle 1 \rangle) + \langle 1 \rangle$ and $\langle 2 \rangle + (\langle 1 \rangle + \langle 1 \rangle)$ equal? _____ Why? _____ This suggests that addition of this type is _____.

> Yes.   Both equal $\langle 0 \rangle$.   Associative

7. Using the table in frame 3 as a subtraction table as in Chapter 15, answer the following questions: (a) What is the value of $\langle 3 \rangle - \langle 1 \rangle$? _____ (b) What is the value of $\langle 1 \rangle - \langle 2 \rangle$? _____

> $\langle 2 \rangle$, since $\langle 1 \rangle + \langle 2 \rangle = \langle 3 \rangle$. $\langle 3 \rangle$, since $\langle 2 \rangle + \langle 3 \rangle = \langle 1 \rangle$.

8. Is the difference of every two sets of this type defined? _____. If not, find a difference that is not defined. _____

> Yes.   All differences are defined.

9. How does the result of frame 8 differ from the situation in the set of whole numbers? _____
_____

> In the present situation $\langle a \rangle - \langle b \rangle$ is defined for all a and b, but in the whole numbers $a - b$ is defined only if $a \geq b$.

10. Using Table 8 as a division table for modulo 3 answer the following questions: (a) What is the value of $\langle 2 \rangle \div \langle 1 \rangle$? _____
(b) What is the value of $\langle 1 \rangle \div \langle 2 \rangle$? _____

> $\langle 2 \rangle$, since $\langle 1 \rangle \times \langle 2 \rangle = \langle 2 \rangle$. $\langle 2 \rangle$, since $\langle 2 \rangle \times \langle 2 \rangle = \langle 1 \rangle$.

11. In the arithmetic modulo 3 is the quotient $\langle a \rangle \div \langle b \rangle$ defined for all a and b? _____

> Yes.

12. Write the multiplication table for the congruence classes modulo 4.

×	⟨0⟩	⟨1⟩	⟨2⟩	⟨3⟩
⟨0⟩				
⟨1⟩				
⟨2⟩				
⟨3⟩				

×	⟨0⟩	⟨1⟩	⟨2⟩	⟨3⟩
⟨0⟩	⟨0⟩	⟨0⟩	⟨0⟩	⟨0⟩
⟨1⟩	⟨0⟩	⟨1⟩	⟨2⟩	⟨3⟩
⟨2⟩	⟨0⟩	⟨2⟩	⟨0⟩	⟨2⟩
⟨3⟩	⟨0⟩	⟨3⟩	⟨2⟩	⟨1⟩

13. Using the answer to frame 12 as a division table answer the following questions modulo 4: (a) ⟨3⟩ ÷ ⟨1⟩ = _____. (b) ⟨1⟩ ÷ ⟨3⟩ = _____. (c) ⟨3⟩ ÷ ⟨2⟩ = _____.

(a) ⟨3⟩ (b) ⟨3⟩ (c) not defined, for no multiple of ⟨2⟩ is equal to ⟨3⟩.

14. In the arithmetic modulo 4 is the quotient ⟨a⟩ ÷ ⟨b⟩ defined for all a and b? _____

No (see frame 13c).

15. (*Discovery Exercise*) In frame 11 it was observed that in arithmetic modulo 3 all quotients ⟨a⟩ ÷ ⟨b⟩ are defined. But in frame 14 it developed that in arithmetic modulo 4 some quotients are not defined. In general, for what moduli are all quotients defined and for what moduli are some quotients not defined?

16. (*Discovery Exercise*) In Chapter 10 we developed the law of trichotomy for the whole numbers: For any two whole numbers a and b exactly one of the following relations is true: $a < b, a = b, a > b$. We also had the transitive law, and the fact that if $a < b$, then $a + c < b + c$. Can you define the concepts of *less than* and *greater than* for the congruence classes modulo 3 in a fashion that satisfies all the above properties? Suppose you try $0 < 1, 1 < 2, 0 < 2$. What goes wrong? Perhaps some other arrangement will work? You find out.

18.6 Clock Arithmetic

CLOCK ARITHMETIC

An application of modular arithmetic in daily life is clock arithmetic. As an introduction to this subject, consider the following question: It is now 9 o'clock. What time will it be 7 hours from now?

The correct answer is 4 o'clock, but the important question is, How did you do the problem? Did you think $(9 + 7) - 12 = 4$? Try this method to answer the question: It is now 5 o'clock. What time will it be 30 hours from now?

To answer this question we compute $5 + 30 - 2(12) = 11$ o'clock.

What have we been doing? We are really doing arithmetic modulo 12. For modulo 12, 5 is an element of $\langle 5 \rangle$ and 30 is an element of $\langle 6 \rangle$. So $\langle 5 \rangle + \langle 6 \rangle = \langle 11 \rangle$.

---

1. It is now 6 o'clock. What time will it be 10 hours from now?
_____

4 o'clock.

2. It is now 8 o'clock. What time will it be 73 hours from now?
_____

9 o'clock.

3. Let us number the days of the week:

Sunday	Monday	Tuesday	Wednesday	Thursday	Friday	Saturday
1	2	3	4	5	6	7

Today is Tuesday. What day will it be 24 days from now?_____

Friday.

4. Your answer to frame 3 is an application of modular arithmetic with what modulus? _____

Seven.

18.7 Casting Out Nines

Another application of congruences is a process for checking the accuracy of ordinary arithmetic calculations. This method depends on the following result:

THEOREM 9.   Let the whole number a be written in the form

$$a = (a_n \times 10^n) + (a_{n-1} \times 10^{n-1}) + \cdots + (a_1 \times 10) + a_0$$

389

Then $a \equiv (a_n + a_{n-1} + \cdots + a_1 + a_0) \bmod 9$. That is, a whole number is congruent modulo 9 to the sum of its digits.

Proof. In Section 17.7 it was shown that $a = [a_n + \cdots + a_0] + [a_n \times (10^n - 1) + \cdots + a_1(10 - 1)]$, where the right-hand term is divisible by 9. If we write this right-hand term as $9b$, it follows that $a - [a_n + \cdots + a_0] = 9b$ and hence that $a \equiv [a_n + \cdots + a_0] \bmod 9$.

CHECKS BY CASTING OUT NINES

EXAMPLE. $764 \equiv 17 \bmod 9$ and $17 \equiv 8 \bmod 9$. So $764 \equiv 8 \bmod 9$.

Let us illustrate casting out nines by the following example.

EXAMPLE. Check the multiplication

$$
\begin{array}{r}
3\ 2\ 8 \\
\times 1\ 4\ 3 \\
\hline
9\ 8\ 4 \\
1\ 3\ 1\ 2 \\
3\ 2\ 8 \\
\hline
4\ 6\ 9\ 0\ 4 \\
\end{array}
$$

First, $328 \equiv 4 \bmod 9$, $143 \equiv 8 \bmod 9$, and $46{,}904 \equiv 5 \bmod 9$. From Theorem 6 it should be true that $4 \times 8 \equiv 5 \bmod 9$. Since this is true, we have a check on our computation.

An important fact is the limitation of this theorem. Notice in the example the thought behind the check was

$$328 \equiv 4 \bmod 9$$

$$143 \equiv 8 \bmod 9$$

$328 \times 143 \equiv 4 \times 8 \bmod 9$ and so $328 \times 143 \equiv 5 \bmod 9$. Then we looked at the product to see if our answer was, in fact, congruent to $5 \bmod 9$. Since it was, in this case, we said the problem checks and we stopped. But notice that there are lots of numbers congruent to $5 \bmod 9$ and we may by chance have made a mistake which causes us to write down as the product some wrong number which is congruent to $5 \bmod 9$. So this check is not perfectly reliable. We might say that if the answer is incorrect, it is equally likely to be congruent to any of the 9 whole numbers less than 9. So there is about one chance in nine that a wrong answer will go undetected by the check of casting out nines.

1. Perform these multiplications and check your work by casting out the nines.

$$
\begin{array}{cccc}
\text{(a)} & 4537 & \text{(b)} & 3184 \\
& \times\ \ \ 26 & & \times\ \ 703 \\
\end{array}
$$

```
(a)    4537          (b)    3184
     ×   26               ×  703
     -------             --------
      27222                9552
      9074               222880
     -------             --------
     117962             2238352
```

4537 ≡ 1 mod 9	3184 ≡ 7 mod 9
26 ≡ 8 mod 9	703 ≡ 1 mod 9
product must be	product must be
≡ 8 mod 9	≡ 7 mod 9
117962 ≡ 8 mod 9	2238352 ≡ 7 mod 9

2. Some people have difficulty remembering multiplication combinations. A common confusion is "9 × 6 = 56". Every multiple of 9, however, is congruent to _____ mod 9, while 56, as shown by casting out nines, is congruent to _____ mod 9.

0	2

3. Since casting out the nines is not a perfect check, one should know other ways to check multiplication. One of them depends on the commutative property of multiplication. Check this multiplication by using the commutative property:

```
         749
       × 428
       ------
        5992
        1498
        2996
       ------
      310572
```

```
     428
   × 749
   ------
    3852
    1712
    2996
   ------
  320572
```

The multiplication was incorrect. Notice that this is not a perfect check either. One is just about as likely to go wrong in checking as in the original working of the problem.

4. Casting out nines can be used to check addition by using Theorem 5. Check the addition problems below in the same pattern as the first one which we have done for you.

326	2	428		207
471	3	793		313
28	1	314		448
+ 240	6	+ 92		+671
1065	3			
	3			

428	5	207	0
793	1	313	7
314	8	448	7
+ 92	2	+671	5
1627	7	1639	1
	7		1

5. Can division be checked by casting out nines? _____

Yes.

6. What multiplication–addition problem is equivalent to this division problem?

$$\begin{array}{r} 22 \\ 234\overline{\smash)5280} \\ 468 \\ \hline 600 \\ 468 \\ \hline 132 \end{array}$$

$22 \times 234 + 132 = 5280.$

7. Check the problem of frame 6 by casting out nines in your answer. (All congruences here understood to be mod 9.)

$$22 \equiv \underline{\hspace{1cm}}$$

$$234 \equiv \underline{\hspace{1cm}}$$

$$22 \times 234 \equiv \underline{\hspace{1cm}}$$

$$22 \times 234 + 132 \equiv \underline{\hspace{1cm}}$$

$$5280 \equiv \underline{\hspace{1cm}}$$

4	0	0	6	6

8. Could you check multiplication by congruences mod 2? _____
If so, what are the chances that a wrong answer will escape detection?
_____

> Yes.   About 1 in 2 (*not* a very good check).

In this chapter we have discussed the concept of the congruence of two whole numbers, which is written

$$a \equiv b, \bmod m$$

We can show that $a \equiv b$, mod m, is true in either of two ways:

(1) Show that a and b have the same remainder when they are divided by m.

(2) Show that $a - b$ (or $b - a$, whichever is a whole number) is divisible by m.

It was proved that congruence is an equivalence relation, and congruence classes modulo m were defined as the corresponding equivalence classes. The notation $\langle a \rangle_m$ was used for a congruence class modulo m.

The concept of congruence was applied to

(1) modular arithmetic and clock arithmetic

(2) the check on ordinary arithmetic called "casting out nines".

If you think you are ready, you can verify your mastery of this material by working the following Post Test.

POST TEST

1. Every even number a can be written in the form _____q, where q is a _____ number.

2. Every odd number a can be written in the form _____, where q is a _____ number.

3. Fill in the blanks in the following tables with "even" or "odd".

+	even	odd
even		
odd		

×	even	odd
even		
odd		

4. Which of the following numbers is *not* congruent to the others mod 6? 11, 17, 25, 53, 65, 605. _____

5. List 5 values of x such that $x \equiv 16 \bmod 7$. _____

6. List 5 values of x such that $4 \equiv x$, mod 3. _____

7. $17 \equiv 9$, mod 4 because $17 - 9$ is _____ by 4.

8. The statement that congruence modulo m is transitive means that
_____

9. $a \equiv b \bmod m$ if and only if $a - b$ (or $b - a$, whichever is a whole number) is a _____ of m.

10. The congruence classes modulo 3 are
$$\{ \qquad\qquad\qquad \}$$
$$\{ \qquad\qquad\qquad \}$$
$$\{ \qquad\qquad\qquad \}$$

11. If $x \equiv 4 \bmod 5$ and $y \equiv 3 \bmod 5$, then $xy \equiv$ _____ mod 5.

12. The symbol $\langle 4 \rangle$ represents what congruence class mod 5?
$$\{ \qquad\qquad \}$$

13. Define the sum $\langle a \rangle + \langle b \rangle$ modulo m. _____

14. What do we mean by saying that the product of congruence classes is *uniquely defined*? _____

15. For congruence classes modulo 5, find $\langle 1 \rangle \div \langle 4 \rangle$. _____

16. Today is Friday; what day will it be 83 days from now?
_____

17. Check by casting out nines: $348 \times 253 = 87{,}564.$ _____

1. 2; whole
2. $2q + 1$; whole
3.

+	even	odd
even	even	odd
odd	odd	even

×	even	odd
even	even	even
odd	even	odd

4. 25.
5. Any of 2, 9, 16, 23, 30, 37, 44, 51, ...
6. Any of 1, 4, 7, 10, 13, 16, 19, ...
7. divisible
8. if $a \equiv b$, mod m and $b \equiv c$, mod m, then $a \equiv c$, mod m.
9. multiple
10. $\{0, 3, 6, 9, 12, \ldots\}$; $\{1, 4, 7, 10, 13\}$; $\{2, 5, 8, 11, 14, \ldots\}$
11. 12 (or 2)
12. $\{4, 9, 14, 19, 24, \ldots\}$.
13. Choose any element a of $\langle a \rangle$ and any element b of $\langle b \rangle$. Then $\langle a \rangle + \langle b \rangle = \langle c \rangle$ where $\langle c \rangle$ is the class to which $a + b$ belongs.

14. The product $\langle a \rangle \times \langle b \rangle$ does not depend upon the choices of elements a of $\langle a \rangle$ and b of $\langle b \rangle$ used to compute $\langle a \rangle \times \langle b \rangle$.

15. $\langle 4 \rangle$, since $\langle 4 \rangle \times \langle 4 \rangle = \langle 1 \rangle$.

16. Thursday.

17. $348 \equiv 6$, mod 9; $253 \equiv 1$, mod 9; so the product is congruent to 6, mod 9; but $87564 \equiv 3$, mod 9, therefore, the multiplication is incorrect.

If you were successful in this Post Test proceed to Chapter 19. Otherwise, review Chapter 18 until you have mastered it.

19

The Integers —Addition and Subtraction

Before beginning this chapter you should review Chapter 9 (Addition) and Chapter 10 (Subtraction). To be sure that you are ready for this chapter, complete the Readiness Test below.

1. Addition of whole numbers on the number line can be accomplished as in the example $2 + 3 = 5$ by drawing an arrow of length _____ to the

right of 0 and then an arrow of length _____ to the right of the end point of the first arrow. The second arrow ends at _____.

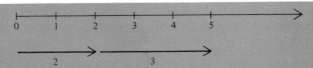

First arrow of length 2, second of length 3, together they reach 5.

2. Since addition is a binary operation on the set of whole numbers, the sum of any two whole numbers a and b, $a + b$, is a _____ number.

whole

3. The commutative property of the addition of whole numbers states that for any two whole numbers a and b, the sum $a + b =$ _____.

$b + a$

4. The associative property of the addition of whole numbers states that: For all whole numbers a, b, and c: _____ —.

$(a + b) + c = a + (b + c)$

5. For any whole number a, $a + 0 =$ _____.

a

6. The cancellation law for the addition of whole numbers states that: For all whole numbers a, b, and c: If $a + c = b + c$, then _____.

$a = b$

7. For all whole numbers a, b, and c, the subtraction statement $a - b = c$ is equivalent to what addition statement? _____

$a = b + c.$

8. The difference $a - b$ is defined in the set of whole numbers if and only if what relation between a and b is true? _____

$b \leq a$ (or $a \geq b$).

9. Subtraction _____ a binary operation on the set of whole
                (is, is not)
numbers.

is not

10. Subtraction on the set of whole numbers fails to have the following properties which are true of addition: (1) _____ and (2) _____ .

commutative property   associative property

11. For all whole numbers a and b, with $a \geq b : (a - b) + b =$ _____ .

a

You should now be ready to read this chapter and to work the problems included in it.

19.1 Introduction

The natural numbers, as we have seen, arose from man's need to count and were developed very early in the history of civilization. The addition of zero to the system of natural numbers (thus providing the whole numbers) is usually attributed to the Hindus, but possibly the Babylonians had it earlier. Quite independently zero appeared in the arithmetic of the Mayas of Central America in the period 200–600 A.D. The whole numbers, however, are insufficient for the purposes of contemporary civilization, and new types of numbers such as negative integers, fractions, and rational numbers have been introduced to serve these needs.

Although fractions were used by the Babylonians and Egyptians, the system of rational numbers is a contemporary development. Negative numbers were rejected by the Greeks and the mathematicians of the Middle

Ages, and no free use of the negative numbers was made until the seventeenth century. The systematic development of their arithmetic, which is discussed in this and later chapters, is of modern origin.

Although the whole numbers, as we have introduced them, are abstractions, they do seem to be something quite natural. On the other hand, the negative and rational numbers appear to be artificial constructions of a higher order of abstraction. Since they do not arise naturally from set theory, they are harder for the novice and great care must be used in their introduction. The German mathematician L. Kronecker (1823–1891) described this situation in his famous assertion: "God made the natural numbers; all the rest is the work of man".

In this chapter we shall introduce the negative integers and develop their properties, and in later chapters we shall discuss the positive and negative rational numbers. These will merge into the number system called "the rational numbers". Even when this is accomplished, however, we are not finished with our contemporary number system, for the system of real numbers remains to be discussed. Since this plays only a minor role in the arithmetic taught in the elementary school, it appears only in an informal fashion in Chapter 25.

19.2 Need for Directed Numbers

In Chapter 5 we introduced the number line as a means for representing the whole numbers (Figure 19.1). We may think of this as a measuring

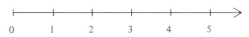

FIGURE 19.1. *Number line.*

device (like a yardstick) which can be used to measure (approximate) distances to the right of zero. It is not well adapted, however, to the measurement of distances to the left of zero. We can imagine a two-way ruler that measures in both directions, such as that in Figure 19.2. Here 1*R*, 2*R*, 3*R*, ...

DIRECTED NUMBERS

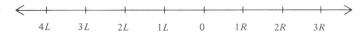

FIGURE 19.2. *Distances to left and right.*

represent distances of 1, 2, and 3 units to the right, and 1*L*, 2*L*, 3*L*, ... distances of 1, 2, and 3 units to the left. These are then illustrations of directed distances.

We can interpret the number line in other ways. If we think of zero as the present, 1, 2, 3, ... may represent units of time (say years) into the future. If the number line is also to represent the past, we might write it as in Figure 19.3. Here 1*F*, 2*F*, 3*F*, ... represent times in the future and 1*P*, 2*P*, 3*P*, ... times in the past.

FIGURE 19.3. *Past, present, and future.*

Since many other interpretations of the number line are possible, it is desirable to have a notation that can be applied to any of these. The notation

The Integers—Addition and Subtraction

TWO-WAY NUMBER LINE

usually adopted is shown in Figure 19.4. Here we read $^+1$, $^+2$, $^+3$, ... as "positive one, positive two, positive three, ..." and $^-1$, $^-2$, $^-3$, ... as "negative one, negative two, negative three, ...".

FIGURE 19.4. *Two-way number line.*

Our use of $+$ and $-$ here may be confusing, for we have already used these symbols to indicate addition and subtraction. So that this possible ambiguity will be avoided, we write these symbols in a raised position when we wish to use them to indicate positive and negative numbers respectively.

DEFINITIONS

1. The set $\{^+1, ^+2, ^+3, \ldots\}$ is called the set of *positive integers*.
2. The set $\{^-1, ^-2, ^-3, \ldots\}$ is called the set of *negative integers*.
3. The union of the three sets $\{0\}$, $\{^+1, ^+2, ^+3, \ldots\}$, and $\{^-1, ^-2, ^-3, \ldots\}$

THE INTEGERS

is called the set of *integers*.

---

1. What symbol is used to represent the point on the number line 15 units to the left of 0? _____ 12 units to the right of 0? _____

> $^-15$. $^+12$.

2. What is the name of the set $\{\ldots, ^-3, ^-2, ^-1, 0, ^+1, ^+2, ^+3, \ldots\}$?

_____

> The integers.

3. If we compare Figures 19.2 and 19.4, distances to the right are represented in Figure 19.4 by _____ integers and distances to the left by _____ integers.

> positive   negative

4. If we compare Figures 19.3 and 19.4, the past is represented in Figure 19.4 by _____ integers and the future by _____ integers.

> negative   positive

5. Let the number line be placed in a vertical position with the positive integers uppermost. If 0 represents sea level, the positive integers represent distances _____ and the negative integers represent distances _____.

> above sea level   below sea level

400

6. In the notation of frame 5, what symbol should be used to represent the height of a mountain whose summit is 14,000 feet above sea level? _____ The depth of an oceanic trench 6000 feet below sea level? _____.

> $^+$14,000. $^-$6000.

7. Here are some examples of numbers used in situations where directed numbers are useful. What integer can be used to describe:
(a) 40 degrees below zero? _____
(b) 90 degrees above zero? _____
(c) 250 dollars in debt? _____
(d) A profit of 100 dollars? _____
(e) An angle of 25° measured counterclockwise? _____
(f) An angle of 45° measured clockwise? _____

> (a) $^-$40°.   (b) $^+$90°.   (c) $^-$250.   (d) $^+$100.   (e) $^+$25°.
> (f) $^-$45°.

8. If the following quantities are represented by positive integers, what quantities are represented by the corresponding negative integers?
(a) Income. _____
(b) Profit. _____
(c) Surplus. _____
(d) Distance north. _____
(e) Speed forward. _____

> (a) Outgo (or expenditures).   (b) Loss.   (c) Deficit.
> (d) Distance south.   (e) Speed backward.

9. In bookkeeping how are colors of ink used to distinguish between positive and negative integers? Positive. _____ Negative. _____

> Black.   Red.

10. In our calendar, years A.D. are theoretically numbered after the birth of Christ and years B.C. are numbered before the birth of Christ. How could the set of integers be used as a notation alternative to this? Years A.D., _____ integers. Years B.C., _____ integers.

> positive   negative

OPPOSITES

OPPOSITES   Since $^+$3 and $^-$3 are at equal distances from 0, but in opposite directions, it is reasonable to call them *opposites*. More generally we have the following definition:

DEFINITION. If n is a natural number, then ^+n and ^-n are a pair of *opposites*.

The opposite of ^+n is ^-n; the opposite of ^-n is ^+n. So that every integer will have an opposite, we arbitrarily say that zero is its own opposite.

NOTATION. If we let a stand for an arbitrary integer, we need a notation for the opposite of a. Here we encounter an awkward situation in the literature. The notation used in standard mathematics at the college level and beyond is

$$\text{opposite of } a = -a$$

But this is possibly confusing since the minus sign $(-)$ is also used for subtraction.

In the past decade it has become popular at the elementary and secondary levels to write

$$\text{opposite of } a = {}^-a$$

This is also confusing, for the raised minus sign $(^-)$ indicates a negative integer, whereas the opposite of each negative integer such as $(^-3)$ is positive $(^+3)$.

Thus we need an unambiguous notation for opposite, and will write

opp a

$$\text{opposite of } a = \text{opp } a$$

This will be a temporary notation, and when the situation has become completely clear we shall revert to the usual notation of standard mathematics and write

$$\text{opposite of } a = -a$$

The concept of opposite is illustrated in Figure 19.5.

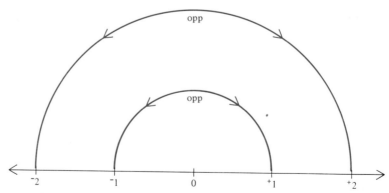

FIGURE 19.5. *Opposites of integers.*

Associated with each integer is a whole number called its *absolute value.*

ABSOLUTE VALUE

DEFINITION. The undirected distance of an integer from 0 is called its *absolute value.* The absolute value of an integer a is written $|a|$. Thus when n is a natural number,

$$|^+n| = n \qquad |^-n| = n \qquad |0| = 0$$

The concept of the absolute value of an integer is illustrated in Figure 19.6.

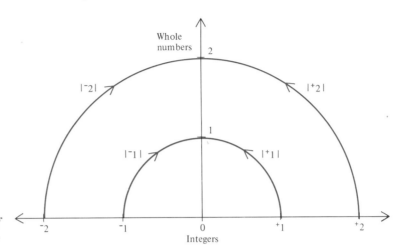

FIGURE 19.6. *Absolute values of integers.*

In this figure the two-way number line of the integers is drawn horizontally and the one-way number line of whole numbers is drawn vertically. The arrows show how to find the absolute value of an integer.

EXAMPLES
1. $|^+5| = 5$.
2. $|^-6| = |^+6| = 6$.
3. $|0| = 0$.

11. Find the opposites of the following integers: (a) $^+4$. _____
(b) $^-5$. _____ (c) 0. _____ (d) $^-102$. _____ (e) $^+36$. _____

(a) $^-4$. (b) $^+5$. (c) 0. (d) $^+102$. (e) $^-36$.

12. What are the values of the following? (a) opp $^-6$. _____
(b) opp $^+7$. _____ (c) opp $^+21$. _____ (d) opp $^-12$. _____
(e) opp 0. _____

(a) $^+6$. (b) $^-7$. (c) $^-21$. (d) $^+12$. (e) 0.

13. Find the absolute value $|a|$ of the integer a when a is (a) $^+4$.
_____ (b) $^-10$. _____ (c) $^-12$. _____ (d) $^+13$. _____
(e) 0. _____

(a) 4. (b) 10. (c) 12. (d) 13. (e) 0.

14. The absolute value of a deficit of $200 is _____.

> $200

15. The absolute value of a temperature of 20 degrees below zero is _____ degrees.

> 20

16. Find the values of the following expressions: (a) |opp $^+3$|. _____ (b) |opp $^-6$|. _____ (c) |opp 0|. _____

> (a) 3.   (b) 6.   (c) 0.

17. Let the opposite of the opposite of a be written opp(opp a). Then opp(opp $^+4$) = opp _____ = _____.

> $^-4$ $^+4$

18. Similarly, opp(opp $^-5$) = _____, and in general opp(opp a) = _____.

> $^-5$ a

19. If a is positive, then opp a is _____; if a is negative, then opp a is _____.

> negative   positive

20. What are the values of the following? (a) |opp(opp $^-3$)|. _____ (b) |opp(opp ^+n)|. _____ (c) |opp(opp ^-n)|. _____ (d) |opp(opp 0)|. _____ (e) |opp(opp a)|. _____ (Remember that n is a natural number and that a is any integer.)

> (a) 3.   (b) n.   (c) n.   (d) 0.   (e) |a|.

19.3 Addition of Integers (Intuitive Treatment)

Since the integers are a new system of numbers, we must define what we mean by the sum of two integers: $a + b$. Although we have complete freedom in deciding upon this definition, we should like it to be as useful as possible and to agree with our intuition. In particular, it is important that the addition of integers obey the laws that we have already developed for the addition of the whole numbers. So let us recall how we added whole numbers on the number line (Section 10.5). To find the sum 2 + 4, we first drew an arrow two units long starting at 0 and pointing to the right (Figure 19.7). Then from its head (at 2) we drew another arrow four units long and pointing to the right. The head of this arrow is at 6, so 2 + 4 = 6.

FIGURE 19.7. *Method for finding* *2 + 4.*

GRAPHICAL ADDITION   To add integers we proceed in the same way, drawing arrows pointing to the right for positive integers and to the left for negative integers.

EXAMPLES
1. $^+2 + {}^+3 = {}^+5$.

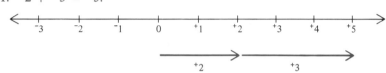

2. $^-3 + {}^-4 = {}^-7$.

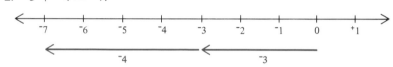

3. $^+6 + {}^-2 = {}^+4$.

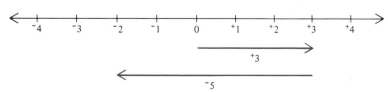

4. $^-2 + {}^+6 = {}^+4$.

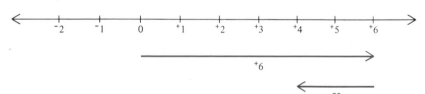

5. $^+3 + {}^-5 = {}^-2$.

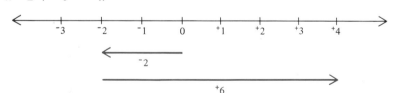

405

6. $^-5 + {}^+3 = {}^-2$.

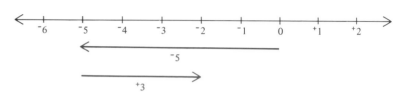

7. $^+4 + {}^-4 = 0$.

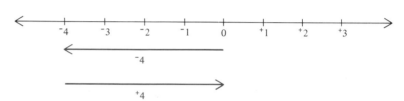

8. $^-4 + {}^+4 = 0$.

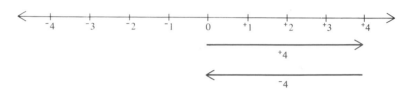

1. Draw arrows on the number line and thus find the sum $^-3 + {}^-5 =$ _____.

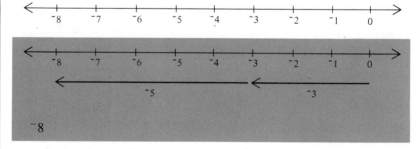

2. As in frame 1 find $^-5 + {}^-3 =$ _____.

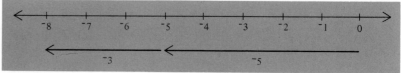

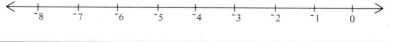

$^-8$

3. Comparison of frames 1 and 2 suggests what property of the addition of negative integers? _____

Commutative property.

4. Using arrows on the number line show that
$$(^-2 + {}^-3) + {}^-4 = {}^-2 + (^-3 + {}^-4)$$
What property of the addition of negative integers does this suggest?
_____

Associative property.

5. Using arrows on the number line find $^-5 + {}^+3 =$ _____ and $^+3 + {}^-5 =$ _____.

$^-2$ $^-2$

6. Using arrows on the number line find $^-2 + {}^+5 =$ _____ and $^+5 + {}^-2 =$ _____.

$^+3$ $^+3$

7. What property of addition is suggested by frames 5 and 6?
_____

Commutative property.

8. Use arrows on the number line to compute the following sums. If you can visualize the arrows instead of actually drawing them, so much the better.
(a) $^+3 + {}^+6 =$ _____.   (b) $^-5 + {}^-4 =$ _____.
(c) $^+3 + 0 =$ _____.   (d) $^-4 + 0 =$ _____.
(e) $^-3 + {}^+6 =$ _____.   (f) $^+7 + {}^-9 =$ _____.
(g) $^-56 + {}^+42 =$ _____.   (h) $^-15 + {}^+31 =$ _____.

(a) $^+9$ (b) $^-9$ (c) $^+3$ (d) $^-4$ (e) $^+3$ (f) $^-2$
(g) $^-14$ (h) $^+16$

9. Compute (in any fashion) $^+2 + (^-3 + {}^-5)$ and $(^+2 + {}^-3) + {}^-5$. The results are _____ and _____. What property of addition is suggested by these computations? _____

$^-6$ $^-6$ Associative property.

10. We may write the sum $^+6 + {}^-2 = (^+4 + {}^+2) + {}^-2 = {}^+4 +$ (_____ + _____) = $^+4 +$ (_____) = _____.

$^+2$ $^-2$ 0 $^+4$

11. Use arrows on the number line to compute $^+6 + {}^-2$ as the sum $(^+4 + {}^+2) + {}^-2$.

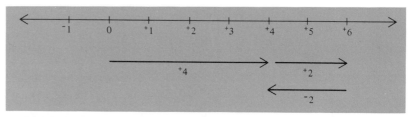

12. Use arrows on the number line to compute $^-7 + {}^+3$ as the sum $(^-4 + {}^-3) + {}^+3$.

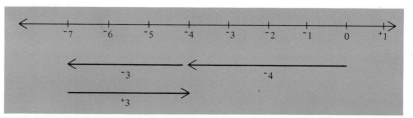

13. The use of arrows on the number line suggests that the sum of every ordered pair of integers is an integer. This can be expressed by statement: Addition is a _____ operation on the set of _____.

binary   integers

14. Frames 3 and 7 suggest that for any two integers a and b, $a + b = b + a$. This can be expressed by the statement: addition of integers is _____.

commutative

15. The observation that for any three integers a, b, and c, $a + (b + c) = (a + b) + c$ is expressed by the statement: Addition of integers is _____.

associative

16. For any integer a, what are the values of $a + 0 =$ _____ and $0 + a =$ _____? We call this the *additive property of zero*.

a a

17. If n is a natural number, $^{+}n + {}^{-}n =$ _____? And $^{-}n + {}^{+}n =$ _____?

zero   zero

18. If a is any integer, $a + (\text{opp } a) =$ _____? Also $(\text{opp } a) + a =$ _____? We call this the *additive property of opposites*.

zero   zero

19.4 Addition of Integers (Formal Treatment)

The use of arrows on the number line has suggested that the addition of integers has the following properties:

PROPERTIES OF ADDITION

PROPERTIES OF ADDITION OF INTEGERS

(1) *Binary operation.* Addition is a binary operation on the set of integers.
(2) *Commutative property.* For all integers a and b, $a + b = b + a$.
(3) *Associative property.* For all integers a, b, and c, $(a + b) + c = a + (b + c)$.
(4) *Additive property of zero.* For any integer a, $a + 0 = 0 + a = a$.
(5) *Additive property of opposites.* For any integer a,

$$a + (\text{opp } a) = (\text{opp } a) + a = 0.$$

Our tasks now are to define the sum $a + b$ for any pair of integers and to prove that the above properties are true. In formulating this definition we shall be guided by the intuitive results obtained above by adding on the number line.

(1) ADDITION OF ZERO

The simplest situation is the addition of zero. We shall obtain property 4 if we agree upon the following definition:

DEFINITION OF ADDITION

DEFINITION. If n is a natural number, $^{+}n + 0 = 0 + {}^{+}n = {}^{+}n$; $^{-}n + 0 = 0 + {}^{-}n = {}^{-}n$; $0 + 0 = 0$.

409

(2) ADDITION OF POSITIVE INTEGERS

Since we wish the positive integers to behave like the natural numbers, we define $^+n + {}^+m$ as follows:

DEFINITION. If n and m are natural numbers,

$$^+n + {}^+m = {}^+(n + m)$$

REMARK

Since $^+m + {}^+n = {}^+(m + n) = {}^+(n + m)$, it follows that $^+n + {}^+m = {}^+m + {}^+n$ and the addition of positive integers is commutative. Similarly, the addition of positive integers is associative.

(3) ADDITION OF NEGATIVE INTEGERS

From the examples discussed in the frames above, we are led to the following definition:

DEFINITION. If n and m are natural numbers, $^-n + {}^-m = {}^-(n + m)$.

REMARK

From this definition it follows at once from the properties of the natural numbers that the addition of negative integers is commutative and associative.

(4) ADDITION OF OPPOSITES

As a simple case of the addition of a positive integer and a negative integer, let us consider the sums $^+n + {}^-n$ and $^-n + {}^+n$. From frames 17 and 18 of Section 19.3 we are led to the following definition:

DEFINITION. If n is any natural number, $^+n + {}^-n = 0$; $^-n + {}^+n = 0$.

REMARK

Since we have seen that $0 + 0 = 0$ and opp $0 = 0$ we can write the following more general statement:

If a is any integer, $a + (\text{opp } a) = 0$; $(\text{opp } a) + a = 0$.

(5) ADDITION OF A POSITIVE AND A NEGATIVE INTEGER

This is the only case that needs special care. In frame 10 of Section 19.3 we found the value of $^+6 + {}^-2$ by first writing $^+6 = {}^+4 + {}^+2$. Then we wrote

$$^+6 + {}^-2 = ({}^+4 + {}^+2) + {}^-2 = {}^+4 + ({}^-2 + {}^+2) = {}^+4 + 0 = {}^+4$$

In frame 12 we found $^-7 + {}^+3$ in a similar fashion by writing $^-7 = {}^-4 + {}^-3$. In each case we rewrote one of our numbers as a sum in such a way that the solution of the problem became self-evident. How shall we do this in general?

410

Suppose that we wish to define $^+n + {}^-m$, and that $n > m$. Then we can write

$$n = (n - m) + m \qquad \text{or} \qquad {}^+n = {}^+(n - m) + {}^+m$$

where the minus sign indicates subtraction. Then

$$
\begin{aligned}
{}^+n + {}^-m &= {}^+(n - m) + {}^+m + {}^-m \\
&= {}^+(n - m) + 0 \\
&= {}^+(n - m)
\end{aligned}
$$

Similarly, $^-m + {}^+n = {}^+(n - m)$.

On the other hand, suppose we wish to define $^+n + {}^-m$, where $m > n$. Then we can write

$$m = n + (m - n) \qquad \text{or} \qquad {}^-m = {}^-n + {}^-(m - n)$$

Hence

$$
\begin{aligned}
{}^+n + {}^-m &= {}^+n + {}^-n + {}^-(m - n) \\
&= 0 + {}^-(m - n) \\
&= {}^-(m - n)
\end{aligned}
$$

And similarly, $^-m + {}^+n = {}^-(m - n)$.

We can summarize these observations in the following definitions:

DEFINITIONS. Let n and m be any natural numbers.
1. If $n > m$, then $^+n + {}^-m = {}^-m + {}^+n = {}^+(n - m)$.
2. If $m > n$, then $^+n + {}^-m = {}^-m + {}^+n = {}^-(m - n)$.

EXAMPLES
1. $^+5 + {}^-3 = {}^+(5 - 3) = {}^+2$.
2. $^+4 + {}^-8 = {}^-(8 - 4) = {}^-4$.

This completes the definition of addition for integers in all possible cases. From these definitions we see at once that all the desired properties (except the associative law) are verified. The proof that the associative law is true requires us to consider a large number of special cases, and to do so would be very tedious. Hence we omit this proof and merely verify this law in numerical cases in the exercises below.

SUMMARY

We may summarize and rephrase these definitions by using the absolute-value notation as follows:

DEFINITION OF ADDITION OF INTEGERS
(1) For all integers a, $a + 0 = 0 + a = a$.
(2) For positive a and b, $a + b = {}^+(|a| + |b|)$.

(3) For negative a and b, $a + b = {}^-(|a| + |b|)$.

(4) For a positive, b negative,

$$\text{If } |a| \geq |b|, a + b = {}^+(|a| - |b|).$$
$$\text{If } |a| \leq |b|, a + b = {}^-(|b| - |a|).$$

(5) For a negative, b positive,

$$\text{If } |a| \geq |b|, a + b = {}^-(|a| - |b|).$$
$$\text{If } |a| \leq |b|, a + b = {}^+(|b| - |a|).$$

Addition, so defined, is a commutative and associative binary operation on the set of integers.

REMARK

In the above discussion we have been guilty of an "abuse of notation" which should be pointed out. When we write, for instance,

$${}^+n + {}^+m = {}^+(n + m)$$

the addition on the left is addition of integers (which is being defined) and the addition on the right is the addition of natural numbers (which was defined in Chapter 9). If we wish to be fussy, we should use a new symbol, say $\oplus$, for the addition of integers and keep $+$ for the addition of natural numbers. In this notation the above equation becomes

$${}^+n \oplus {}^+m = {}^+(n + m)$$

Similar changes should be made throughout the whole discussion.

We have not done so, however, in order to keep our notation simple. It is hoped that you can make this distinction if it ever seems to be important to you.

---

1. If n and m are natural numbers with $n > m$, then ${}^+n + {}^-m =$ _____.

${}^+(n - m)$

2. If n and m are natural numbers with $n < m$, then ${}^+n + {}^-m =$ _____.

${}^-(m - n)$

3. Use the above definitions of addition to verify the associative law in the special case ${}^+4 + ({}^-3 + {}^+5) = ({}^+4 + {}^-3) + {}^+5$.

$${}^+4 + ({}^-3 + {}^+5) = {}^+4 + \underline{\hspace{1cm}} = \underline{\hspace{1cm}}$$

$$({}^+4 + {}^-3) + {}^+5 = \underline{\hspace{1cm}} + {}^+5 = \underline{\hspace{1cm}}$$

$^+2$ $^+6$ $^+1$ $^+6$

4. As in frame 3 verify that $^-3 + (^-8 + ^+2) = (^-3 + ^-8) + ^+2$.

$$^-3 + (^-8 + ^+2) = ^-3 + \underline{\hspace{1cm}} = \underline{\hspace{1cm}}$$

$$(^-3 + ^-8) + ^+2 = \underline{\hspace{1cm}} + ^+2 = \underline{\hspace{1cm}}$$

$^-6$ $^-9$ $^-11$ $^-9$

5. Since the addition of integers is both commutative and associative, the generalized commutative property is true. This states that the sum of any finite set of integers is independent of the _____ in which these integers appear in the sum.

order

6. Using the generalized commutative property we may group the positive and negative terms below and write

$$^+3 + ^-6 + ^+8 + ^-5 = ^+3 + ^+8 + ^-6 + ^-5$$

$$= (^+3 + ^+8) + (^-6 + ^-5)$$

$$= \underline{\hspace{1cm}} + \underline{\hspace{1cm}}$$

$$= \underline{\hspace{1cm}}$$

$^+11$ $^-11$ 0

7. Use the method of frame 6 to compute the sums:
(a) $^-4 + ^-6 + ^+10 + ^-3 + ^+9 = \underline{\hspace{1cm}}$.
(b) $^+5 + ^-3 + ^+7 + ^+6 + ^-10 = \underline{\hspace{1cm}}$.
(c) $^+12 + ^-3 + ^+10 + ^-5 + ^-6 = \underline{\hspace{1cm}}$.

(a) $^+6$ (b) $^+5$ (c) $^+8$

On separate pieces of paper prove the following theorems.

8.
THEOREM 1. If a, b, and c are integers and if $a = b$, then $a + c = b + c$.

Proof. The same as for Theorem 8, Section 9.6.

9.
COROLLARY. If a, b, c, and d are any integers and if $a = b$ and $c = d$, then $a + c = \underline{\hspace{2cm}}$.

Many answers, such as $b + d$.

10.

THEOREM 2. CANCELLATION LAW. If a, b, and c are any integers and if $a + c = b + c$, then $a = b$.

Proof

1. $a + c = b + c$
   _____ (reason)

2. $(a + c) + (\text{opp } c) = (b + c) + $ _____
   _____ (reason)

3. $a + (c + \text{opp } c) = b + ($_____$)$
   _____ (reason)

4. $a + $ _____ $ = b + $ _____
   _____ (reason)

5. $a = b$
   _____ (reason)

1. Given.   2. opp c; Theorem 1.   3. $c + \text{opp } c$; Associative property.   4. 0; 0; Addition of opposites.   5. Additive property of zero.

11.

THEOREM 3. If a and b are any integers and $a = b$, then opp $a = $ opp b.

Proof

1. $a + \text{opp } a = 0$ Addition of opposites.
2. $b + \text{opp } b = 0$ Addition of opposites.
3. $a + \text{opp } a = b + \text{opp } b$ Property of equality.
4. Since $a = b$, we have from 3:
5. $a + \text{opp } a = a + \text{opp } b$ Substitution.
6. opp $a = $ opp b Cancellation law.

12.

COROLLARY. If a and b are integers and if opp $a = $ opp b, then $a = $ _____.

b

19.5 Subtraction of Integers

When we discussed subtraction for whole numbers, we observed that $a - b$ was defined if and only if $a \geq b$. According to this definition we said that $a - b = c$ if and only if $a = b + c$.

Here we extend this definition of subtraction to arbitrary pairs of integers as follows.

DEFINITION OF SUBTRACTION

DEFINITION. Let a and b be any two integers. Then their difference $a - b$ is defined to be the integer c such that $a = b + c$.

For this definition to make sense, it is necessary for us to prove that a suitable integer c exists and is unique.

THEOREM 4. For any two integers a and b there is a unique integer c such that $a = b + c$.

Proof.
1. $c = a + (\text{opp } b)$ has the required property. For then $b + c = b + (a + \text{opp } b) = a + [b + (\text{opp } b)] = a + 0 = a$.
2. Suppose that some other integer, say c', satisfies $a = b + c'$. Then

$$b + c = b + c'$$

and, from the cancellation law, $c = c'$. Hence c is unique.

Because of Theorem 4, we can rephrase the definition of subtraction as follows:

DEFINITION OF SUBTRACTION

DEFINITION. Let a and b be any two integers. Then, by definition,

$$a - b = a + (\text{opp } b)$$

Note that in contrast to the situation for whole numbers $a - b$ is defined for *every* pair of integers.
For example,

$$^+4 - {}^+7 = {}^+4 + {}^-7 = {}^-3$$

$$^+6 - {}^-5 = {}^+6 + {}^+5 = {}^+11$$

$$^-8 - {}^-3 = {}^-8 + {}^+3 = {}^-5$$

Therefore, subtraction is a binary operation on the set of integers.

---

1. Find the values of
(a) $^+6 - {}^+10 =$ _____.   (b) $^+6 - {}^-3 =$ _____.
(c) $^-7 - {}^+5 =$ _____.   (d) $^-9 - {}^-4 =$ _____.
(e) $^-11 - {}^-11 =$ _____.

(a) $^-4$ (b) $^+9$ (c) $^-12$ (d) $^-5$ (e) 0

2. Subtraction is not a binary operation on the set of whole numbers. Why *is* it a binary operation on the set of integers? _____
_____

It is defined for every pair of integers.

3. Show that subtraction in the set of integers is not commutative. A counterexample is ———————.

> For example, $^+5 - {}^+3 = {}^+2$, but $^+3 - {}^+5 = {}^-2$.

4. Show that subtraction in the set of integers is not associative. A counterexample is ———————.

> For example, $^+8 - ({}^+5 - {}^+3) = {}^+8 - {}^+2 = {}^+6$, but $({}^+8 - {}^+5) - {}^+3 = 0$.

Write the proofs of the following theorems on separate pieces of paper.

5.

THEOREM 5. If a, b, and c are integers and $a = b$, then $a - c = b - c$.

> ***Proof.*** Similar to that of Theorem 8, Section 10.5.

6.

THEOREM 6. If a, b, and c are integers and $a - c = b - c$, then $a = b$.

> ***Proof***
> 1. $a - c = b - c$ — Given.
> 2. $a + \operatorname{opp} c = b + \operatorname{opp} c$ — Definition of subtraction.
> 3. $a = b$ — Cancellation law.

7.

THEOREM 7. If $a + b = 0$, then $b = \operatorname{opp} a$. (Also $a = \operatorname{opp} b$).

> ***Proof***
> 1. $a + \operatorname{opp} a = 0$ — Addition of opposites.
> 2. $a + b = 0$ — Given.
> 3. Hence $a + b = a + \operatorname{opp} a$ — Property of equality.
> 4. Thus $b = \operatorname{opp} a$ — Cancellation law.

8.

THEOREM 8. If a and b are any two integers, $\operatorname{opp}(a + b) = \operatorname{opp} a + \operatorname{opp} b$.

> ***Proof***
> 1. $(a + b) + (\operatorname{opp} a + \operatorname{opp} b) = (a + \operatorname{opp} a) + (b + \operatorname{opp} b)$ — Generalized commutative law.
> 2. $= 0 + 0$ — Addition of opposites.
> 3. $= 0$ — Additive property of zero.
> 4. $\operatorname{opp} a + \operatorname{opp} b = \operatorname{opp}(a + b)$ — Theorem 7.

9.

THEOREM 9. For any integer a, $a - a = 0$.

Proof. $a - a = a + (\text{opp } a) = 0$.

10.

THEOREM 10. For any integers a, b, c, and d,

$$(a + c) - (b + d) = (a - b) + (c - d)$$

Proof
1. $(a + c) - (b + d)$
   $= a + c + \text{opp}(b + d)$ Definition.
2. $= a + c + (\text{opp } b) + (\text{opp } d)$ Theorem 8.
3. $= (a + \text{opp } b) + (c + \text{opp } d)$ Generalized commutative law.
4. $= (a - b) + (c - d)$ Definition.

11.

THEOREM 11. For any integers a, b, and c, $a - b = (a + c) - (b + c)$.

Proof
1. $(a + c) - (b + c)$
   $= a + c + \text{opp}(b + c)$ Definition.
2. $= a + c + (\text{opp } b) + (\text{opp } c)$ Theorem 8.
3. $= a + (\text{opp } b) + (c + \text{opp } c)$ Generalized commutative law.
4. $= a + (\text{opp } b) + 0$ Addition of opposites.
5. $= a + (\text{opp } b)$ Additive property of zero.
6. $= a - b$ Definition.

12.

THEOREM 12. For any integers a, b, and c, $a - (b + c) = (a - b) - c$.

Proof
1. $a - (b + c) = a + \text{opp}(b + c)$ Definition.
2. $= a + [(\text{opp } b) + (\text{opp } c)]$ Theorem 8.
3. $= [a + \text{opp } b] + \text{opp } c$ Associative law.
4. $= (a - b) - c$ Definition.

13.

THEOREM 13. For any integers a and b, $(a + b) - b = a$.

Proof
1. $(a + b) - b = (a + b) + \text{opp } b$ Definition.
2. $= a + (b + \text{opp } b)$ Associative law.
3. $= a + 0$ Addition of opposites.
4. $= a$ Additive property of zero.

14.

THEOREM 14. For any integers a, b, and c, $(a + b) - c = a + (b - c)$.

> *Proof*
> 1. $(a + b) - c = (a + b) + \text{opp } c$ Definition.
> 2. $\qquad\qquad = a + (b + \text{opp } c)$ Associative law.
> 3. $\qquad\qquad = a + (b - c)$ Definition.

SOLUTION OF EQUATIONS

15. To find the integer x that satisfies the equation $^+4 + x = {}^+2$, add $^-4$ to both sides of the equation. The result is _____ $+ (^+4 + x) =$ _____. The left-hand side equals _____, and the right-hand side equals _____. Hence $x =$ _____.

> $^-4 \qquad {}^-4 + {}^+2 \qquad x \qquad {}^-2 \qquad {}^-2$

16. Use the method of frame 15 to find values of x that satisfy the following equations:
  (a) $^+3 + x = {}^+7$; $x =$ _____.   (b) $^+6 + x = {}^-4$; $x =$ _____.
  (c) $^-4 + x = {}^+8$; $x =$ _____.   (d) $^-5 + x = {}^-10$; $x =$ _____.
  (e) $x + {}^+3 = {}^-2$; $x =$ _____.   (f) $^+4 + {}^-5 = x$; $x =$ _____.

> (a) $^+4$ (b) $^-10$ (c) $^+12$ (d) $^-5$ (e) $^-5$ (f) $^-1$

17.

THEOREM 15. If a and b are any integers, there is an integer x that satisfies the equation $a + x = b$.

> **Proof.** $x = b - a$ or $x = b + \text{opp } a$ has the required property.

18.

THEOREM 16. If a and b are any integers, and if x_1 and x_2 are integers such that $a + x_1 = b$ and $a + x_2 = b$, then $x_1 = x_2$.

> **Proof.** $a + x_1 = a + x_2$. Hence $x_1 = x_2$ by the cancellation law.

19. Theorems 15 and 16 can be combined into the following theorem:

THEOREM 17. If a and b are any integers, there is a _____ integer x which satisfies the equation _____.

> unique $a + x = b$

418

In this chapter we have discussed the need for directed numbers and so have introduced the set of *integers*. If a is an integer we have defined the opposite of a, opp a, and its absolute value $|a|$.

We have learned how to add integers graphically on the number line and saw that addition, so defined, is commutative and associative. We then gave a formal definition of addition and developed its properties.

Subtraction was then defined by the equation $a - b = a + $ opp b, and we learned that subtraction is neither commutative nor associative.

Proofs of theorems involving addition and subtraction were given, and now you should be able to use these methods to prove other theorems.

Finally, we showed that every equation of the form $a + x = b$, where a and b are integers, has a unique integer as its solution.

To test your mastery of this material, you should now work the following Post Test.

POST TEST

1. opp $^+15 = $ _____, opp $^-7 = $ _____, opp $0 = $ _____.
2. $|^+6| = $ _____, $|^-5| = $ _____, $|0| = $ _____.
3. $|$opp $^+32| = $ _____, $|$opp(opp $^-6)| = $ _____, opp(opp $^+|5|) = $ _____.
4. Using arrows on the number line find the value of the sum $(^-4 + {}^-2) + {}^+2 = $ _____.

5. What property of the addition of integers is illustrated by the equality: $^+2 + (^+7 + {}^-3) = {}^+2 + (^-3 + {}^+7)$? _____

6. What property of the addition of integers is illustrated by the equality $^+2 + (^+7 + {}^-3) = (^+2 + {}^+7) + {}^-3$? _____

7. What property of the addition of integers is illustrated by the equality (opp $^+4) + {}^+4 = 0$? _____

8. Group the positive and negative terms in the following sum and add: $^+2 + {}^-12 + {}^+16 + {}^-5 = $ _____.

9. Fill in the reason for each step in the following proof:

THEOREM. $(a + b) + (^-a + {}^-b) = 0$.
Proof
1. $(a + b) + (^-a + {}^-b) = a + [b + (^-a + {}^-b)]$ _____
2. $\phantom{(a + b) + (^-a + {}^-b)} = a + [b + (^-b + {}^-a)]$ _____
3. $\phantom{(a + b) + (^-a + {}^-b)} = a + [(b + {}^-b) + {}^-a]$ _____
4. $\phantom{(a + b) + (^-a + {}^-b)} = a + [0 + {}^-a]$ _____
5. $\phantom{(a + b) + (^-a + {}^-b)} = a + {}^-a$ _____
6. $\phantom{(a + b) + (^-a + {}^-b)} = 0$ _____

10. Prove: If a and b are integers and if opp a = opp b, then $a = b$. Use a separate piece of paper.

11. State what theorem on addition is used in the following statement: If $x + {}^-6 = {}^-2 + {}^-6$, then $x = {}^-2$. _____

12. By definition $a - b =$ _____.

13. For each of the following statements, state whether true or false and name the law used or violated.

(a) $({}^-4) + {}^+4 = {}^+4 + ({}^-4)$.

_____   _____
(T, F)   (law)

(b) $({}^-7) - {}^+5 = {}^+5 - ({}^-7)$.   _____   _____

(c) $({}^+2 + {}^+5) + ({}^-6) = {}^+2 + [{}^+5 + ({}^-6)]$.   _____   _____

(d) $({}^+2 - {}^+3) + {}^+7 = {}^+2 - ({}^+3 + {}^+7)$.   _____   _____

14. Find the first error in the "proof" of the following false theorem: For all integers a, b, and c, $(a + b) - c = c + (a - b)$.

1. $(a + b) - c = a + (b - c)$
2. $\qquad\qquad = a + (c - b)$
3. $\qquad\qquad = (a + c) - b$
4. $\qquad\qquad = (c + a) - b$
5. $\qquad\qquad = c + (a - b)$

15. Prove: For all integers a and b, $(a + b) - b = a$. Use a separate piece of paper.

16. Find the value of the expression $[{}^+2 - ({}^-3 + {}^+7)] - [({}^+4 - {}^-5) + {}^+6] =$ _____.

17. Solve for x: ${}^-5 + x = {}^+4$; $x =$ _____.

1. ${}^-15$; ${}^+7$; 0
2. 6; 5; 0
3. 32; 6; ${}^+5$
4.

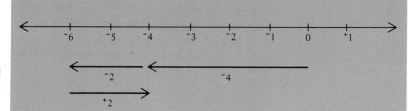

5. Commutative.
6. Associative.
7. (opp a) + $a = 0$, or additive property of opposites.
8. $({}^+2 + {}^+16) + ({}^-12 + {}^-5) = {}^+18 + {}^-17 = {}^+1$.
9. Associative. 2. Commutative. 3. Associative. 4. Addition of opposites. 5. Additive property of zero. 6. Addition of opposites.
10. 1. $a + $ opp $a = 0$. 2. $b + $ opp $b = 0$. 3. $a + $ opp $a = b + $ opp b. 4. But opp $a = $ opp b. 5. So $a + $ opp $a = b + $ opp a. 6. $a = b$.

11. Cancellation law.
12. $a + \text{opp } b$
13. (a) T, Commutative. (b) F, Commutative. (c) T, Associative. (d) F, Associative.
14. Line 2, $b - c \neq c - b$.
15. 1. $(a + b) - b) = (a + b) + \text{opp } b$
    2. $\qquad\qquad = a + (b + \text{opp } b)$
    3. $\qquad\qquad = a + 0$
    4. $\qquad\qquad = a$
16. $^-17$
17. $^+9$

You are now ready to begin Chapter 20 on the multiplication and division of the integers.

20

The Integers —Multiplication and Division

Before starting this chapter you should have completed the Post Test for Chapter 19 and should be familiar with Chapter 11 (Multiplication and Division) and Chapter 12 (The Distributive Law). The following Readiness Test will determine whether you are prepared to proceed.

READINESS TEST

1. Let a, b, and c be any whole numbers.
(a) The commutative law of multiplication states that $a \cdot b =$ _____.
(b) The associative law of multiplication states that _____ _____.
(c) The distributive law of multiplication over addition states that $a \cdot (b + c) =$ _____.
(d) $a \cdot 0 =$ _____.
(e) $a \cdot 1 =$ _____.
(f) If $a = b$, then $ac =$ _____.
(g) If $ac = bc$ and $c \neq 0$, then $a =$ _____.

> (a) $b \cdot a$ (b) $a \cdot (b \cdot c) = (a \cdot b) \cdot c$ (c) $(a \cdot b) + (a \cdot c)$ (d) 0
> (e) a (f) bc (g) b

2. Let a and q be whole numbers and d be a whole number not equal to zero.
(a) The statement $a \div d = q$ is equivalent to the multiplication statement _____.
(b) Is division a binary operation on the set of whole numbers? _____
(c) Is division of whole numbers commutative? _____
(d) Is division of whole numbers associative? _____
(e) $0 \div d =$ _____.
(f) $a \div 0$ is said to be _____.
(g) $0 \div 0$ is said to be _____.

> (a) $a = q \cdot d$ (b) No. (c) No. (d) No. (e) 0
> (f) undefined (g) undefined

If you believe that you are ready, proceed with Sections 20.1 through 20.3.

20.1 Introduction

The purposes of this chapter are to arrive at a suitable definition for the product of two integers, to derive the properties of these products, and to discuss division as an operation closely related to multiplication.

As in the case of the addition of integers, we cannot base the definition of multiplication on set theory and must proceed in a different fashion. Our idea is to extend to the integers the definition of multiplication that we have discussed in Chapter 11. To do so we need to define the products $a \cdot 0$ (where a is any integer) and $^+n \cdot {}^+m$, $^+n \cdot {}^-m$, $^-n \cdot {}^+m$, and $^-n \cdot {}^-m$ (where n and m are natural numbers). There are many conceivable ways of doing this, so how shall we choose? Our procedure will be to choose definitions for these products in such a way that the commutative, associative, and distributive properties of the whole numbers remain true for the integers.

ASSUMED PROPERTIES
OF MULTIPLICATION

20.2 Multiplication of Integers— Motivation

Although as yet we do not know how to multiply integers, let us suppose that this can be done and that it has all the properties of the multiplication of whole numbers: commutative, associative, and distributive over addition.

Let us also suppose that the product of two positive integers is the same as the product of the corresponding natural numbers. That is,

$$^+n \cdot {}^+m = {}^+(n \cdot m)$$

 Now let us find consequences of these properties which will motivate our definition of the product of the integers a and b.

THEOREM 1. For every integer a, $a \cdot 0 = 0$.

Proof

1. $0 + 0 = 0$ Additive property of 0.
2. $a \cdot (0 + 0) = a \cdot 0$
3. $(a \cdot 0) + (a \cdot 0) = a \cdot 0$ Distributive property.
4. $(a \cdot 0) + (a \cdot 0) = (a \cdot 0) + 0$ Additive property of 0.
5. $a \cdot 0 = 0$ Cancellation law.

THEOREM 2. For all integers a and b, $a \cdot \operatorname{opp} b = \operatorname{opp}(a \cdot b)$ and $(\operatorname{opp} b) \cdot a = \operatorname{opp}(a \cdot b)$.

Proof

1. $b + \operatorname{opp} b = 0$ Addition of opposites.
2. $a \cdot (b + \operatorname{opp} b) = a \cdot 0 = 0$ Theorem 1.
3. $(a \cdot b) + (a \cdot \operatorname{opp} b) = 0$ Distributive property.
4. $a \cdot \operatorname{opp} b = \operatorname{opp}(a \cdot b)$ Theorem 7, Chapter 19.
5. Also: $(\operatorname{opp} b) \cdot a = \operatorname{opp}(a \cdot b)$ Commutative property.

In particular, if $a = {}^+n$ and $b = {}^+m$, Theorem 2 states that

$$^+n \cdot {}^-m = {}^-({}^+n \cdot {}^+m) = {}^-(n \cdot m),$$

where *n* and *n* are natural numbers. Thus

$$^+3 \cdot {}^-5 = {}^-(3 \cdot 5) = {}^-15$$

$$^+3 \cdot ({}^-1) = {}^-(3 \cdot 1) = {}^-3$$

$$^-4 \cdot {}^+5 = {}^-(4 \cdot 5) = {}^-20$$

THEOREM 3.   For all integers *a* and *b*, (opp *a*) · (opp *b*) = *a* · *b*.

Proof
1. For *a* in Theorem 2 substitute opp *a*. Then we obtain
2. (opp *a*) · (opp *b*) = opp[(opp *a*) · *b*]
3.   = opp[opp(*a* · *b*)]   Theorem 2.
4.   = *a* · *b*   Section 19.2.

In particular, if $a = {}^+n$ and $b = {}^+m$, where *n* and *m* are natural numbers, Theorem 3 states that

$$({}^-n) \cdot ({}^-m) = ({}^+n \cdot {}^+m) = {}^+(n \cdot m)$$

Thus

$$({}^-5) \cdot ({}^-6) = ({}^+5) \cdot ({}^+6) = {}^+(5 \cdot 6) = {}^+30$$

20.3   Multiplication of Integers—Formal Definition

Theorems 1, 2, and 3 are proved only on the assumption that the product of two integers is defined so that it has the usual commutative, associative, and distributive properties. (As a matter of fact, only the distributive and commutative properties were used in these proofs.) Nevertheless, they must be true if our definition of multiplication is a reasonable one, and so they serve as motivation for the definitions which follow.

DEFINITION OF MULTIPLICATION

DEFINITION.   The product *a* · *b* of any two integers is defined by the following equations (where *n* and *m* are natural numbers):
(1) For any *a*, $a \cdot 0 = 0 \cdot a = 0$.
(2) For $a = {}^+n$, $b = {}^+m$, $a \cdot b = {}^+(n \cdot m)$.
(3) For $a = {}^+n$, $b = {}^-m$, or $a = {}^-n$, $b = {}^+m$, $a \cdot b = {}^-(n \cdot m)$.
(4) For $a = {}^-n$, $b = {}^-m$, $a \cdot b = {}^+(n \cdot m)$.

From this definition it follows that the multiplication of integers has the following properties:

PROPERTIES OF THE MULTIPLICATION OF INTEGERS
(1) Multiplication is a binary operation on the set of integers.
(2) *Commutative property.* For all integers *a* and *b*, $a \cdot b = b \cdot a$.
(3) *Associative property.* For all integers *a*, *b*, and *c*, $(a \cdot b) \cdot c = a \cdot (b \cdot c)$.
(4) *Multiplicative property of* $^+1$: For every integer *a*, $a \cdot {}^+1 = {}^+1 \cdot a = a$.

The Integers—Multiplication and Division

(5) *Cancellation law.* For all integers a, b, and c with $c \neq 0$, if $ac = bc$, then $a = b$.

(6) *Distributive property of multiplication over addition.* For all integers a, b, and c, $a \cdot (b + c) = (a \cdot b) + (a \cdot c)$.

Property (1) is true because the product is defined for *every* ordered pair (a, b) of integers. Property (2) follows from the definition of multiplication and the commutative property of the multiplication of whole numbers. The proofs of the associative and distributive properties require us to examine a large number of special cases. This is not difficult, but is very tedious.

The proof of property (4) is proposed in the exercises. The proof of property (5) (cancellation law) is the same as that for whole numbers (Theorem 6, Chapter 11).

REMARK

Again we have been guilty of an "abuse of notation". For instance, in

$$^+n \cdot {}^+m = {}^+(n \cdot m)$$

the product on the left is that of integers (which is being defined) and that on the right is that of natural numbers (which has already been defined). So more properly we should write the above equation as

$$^+n \odot {}^+m = {}^+(n \cdot m)$$

to distinguish between these two types of multiplication.

As in the case of the similar situation regarding addition, we shall not adopt this fancy notation but hope that, even so, you can make the necessary distinction.

---

1. Using the definition of the product of two integers, find the values of the following:

(a) $^+3 \cdot {}^+6 =$ _____.   (b) $^+3 \cdot {}^-4 =$ _____.

(c) $^-5 \cdot {}^+3 =$ _____.   (d) $^-7 \cdot {}^-4 =$ _____.

(e) $^+5 \cdot 0 =$ _____.   (f) $^-6 \cdot 0 =$ _____.

(g) $0 \cdot 0 =$ _____.

(a) $^+18$ (b) $^-12$ (c) $^-15$ (d) $^+28$ (e) 0   (f) 0
(g) 0

2. Verify the associative law by showing the truth of the equality $^+3 \cdot ({}^-2 \cdot {}^+4) = ({}^+3 \cdot {}^-2) \cdot {}^+4$.

$^+3 \cdot ({}^-2 \cdot {}^+4) =$ _____ ; $({}^+3 \cdot {}^-2) \cdot {}^+4 =$ _____.

$^+3 \cdot ({}^-8) = {}^-24$ $^-6 \cdot {}^+4 = {}^-24$

426

3. As in frame 2 verify the associative law for the following special case:
$^-5 \cdot (^-6 \cdot {}^+3) = (^-5 \cdot {}^-6) \cdot {}^+3$.
$^-5 \cdot (^-6 \cdot {}^+3) =$ _____; $(^-5 \cdot {}^-6) \cdot {}^+3 =$ _____.

> $^+90$ $^+90$

4. Verify the distributive law for the following special case:
$^+3 \cdot (^-2 + {}^+4) = (^+3 \cdot {}^-2) + (^+3 \cdot {}^+4)$.
$^+3 \cdot (^-2 + {}^+4) = {}^+3 \cdot$ _____ = _____
$(^+3 \cdot {}^-2) + (^+3 \cdot {}^+4) =$ _____ + _____ = _____

> $^+2$ $^+6$ $^-6$ $^+12$ $^+6$

5. Verify the distributive law for the following special case:
$^-5 \cdot (^-4 + {}^-6) = (^-5 \cdot {}^-4) + (^-5 \cdot {}^-6)$
$^-5 \cdot (^-4 + {}^-6) = {}^-5 \cdot$ _____ = _____
$(^-5 \cdot {}^-4) + (^-5 \cdot {}^-6) =$ _____ + _____ = _____

> $^-10$ $^+50$ $^+20$ $^+30$ $^+50$

Write proofs of the following theorems on separate pieces of paper.

6.
THEOREM 4. If a, b, and c are integers and if $a = b$, then $a \cdot c = b \cdot c$.

> (Similar to Theorem 8, Section 9.6.)

7.
THEOREM 5. MULTIPLICATIVE PROPERTY OF $^+1$. For all integers a, $a \cdot {}^+1 = {}^+1 \cdot a = a$.

> *Proof*
> 1. If a is positive, then $a = {}^+n$ and $a \cdot {}^+1 = {}^+n \cdot {}^+1 = {}^+n = a$.
> 2. If a is negative, then $a = {}^-n$ and $a \cdot {}^+1 = {}^-(n \cdot 1) = {}^-n = a$.
> 3. If a is 0, $0 \cdot {}^+1 = 0$ by definition.

8. The cancellation law for multiplication of integers states that: For all integers a, b, and c with c _____, if $ac = bc$, then _____.

> $\neq 0$ $a = b$

9. Give a counterexample to show that if $a \cdot c = b \cdot c$ and $c = 0$, it is not necessarily true that $a = b$. _____

> For example, $^+2 \cdot 0 = 0$, $^-3 \cdot 0 = 0$, but $^+2 \neq {}^-3$.

10.

THEOREM 6. DISTRIBUTIVE PROPERTY OF MULTIPLICATION OVER SUBTRACTION. For all integers a, b, and c, $a \cdot (b - c) = (a \cdot b) - (a \cdot c)$.

> ***Proof.*** $a \cdot (b - c) = a \cdot (b + \text{opp } c) = (a \cdot b) + (a \cdot \text{opp } c) = a \cdot b + \text{opp}(a \cdot c) = (a \cdot b) - (a \cdot c)$.

11. Verify Theorem 6 in the following special case: $^-3 \cdot (^+5 - {}^-8) = (^-3 \cdot {}^+5) - (^-3 \cdot {}^-8)$.

$$^-3 \cdot (^+5 - {}^-8) = {}^-3 \cdot \underline{\qquad} = \underline{\qquad}$$
$$(^-3 \cdot {}^+5) - (^-3 \cdot {}^-8) = \underline{\qquad} - \underline{\qquad} = \underline{\qquad}$$

> $^+13$ $^-39$ $^-15$ $^+24$ $^-39$

12. Give the name or statement of the theorem that justifies each of the following statements:

(a) If $^-3 \cdot {}^+4 = x \cdot {}^+4$, then $x = {}^-3$.   _____

(b) $^-6 \cdot (\text{opp } {}^+5) = \text{opp}(^-6 \cdot {}^+5)$.   _____

(c) $(\text{opp } {}^+3) \cdot (\text{opp } {}^-4) = ({}^+3 \cdot {}^-4)$.   _____

(d) $^+3 \cdot (^-2 \cdot {}^+7) = ({}^+3 \cdot {}^-2) \cdot {}^+7$.   _____

(e) $^+6 \cdot (^+4 \cdot {}^-5) = {}^+6 \cdot (^-5 \cdot {}^+4)$.   _____

> (a) Cancellation law.   (b) $a \cdot \text{opp } b = \text{opp}(a \cdot b)$.   (c) $(\text{opp } a) \cdot (\text{opp } b) = a \cdot b$.   (d) Associative property.   (e) Commutative property.

13. Evaluate the following expressions. Remember that expressions inside ( ) or [ ] should be evaluated first. Also recall (Section 12.8) that in a string of operations where parentheses are not inserted, multiplications and divisions are to be done *before* additions and subtractions.

(a) $^-2 \cdot [^+3 \cdot (^+4 - {}^+2) + {}^+6] + {}^+5 \cdot [^-2 \cdot (^-3 + {}^+8) + {}^+9)] = $ _____.

(b) $^+5 \cdot [^-9 \cdot (^+5 - {}^+2) + {}^+4] - {}^+4 \cdot [^+3 \cdot (^+4 + {}^+8) - {}^+45] = $ _____.

(c) $^+3 \cdot [^+8 \cdot (^-2 + {}^+4) + {}^-5 \cdot (^+7 + {}^-9)] + {}^+5[(^+4 - {}^+8) \cdot {}^+6 - (^+9 - {}^+4) \cdot {}^+3] = $ _____.

(d) $^-6 \cdot [^+3 \cdot (^+7 - {}^-6) - {}^+4 \cdot (^+3 - {}^+8)] + {}^-4 \cdot [(^+7 - {}^+3) \cdot {}^+9 + {}^-16] = $ _____.

(e) $^+4 \cdot \{[^-6 \cdot (^+3 - {}^+7) + {}^+5 \cdot (^+6 - {}^-3)] - {}^+16 \cdot (^+2 + {}^-3)\} + {}^-11 = $ _____.

(f) $^-3 \cdot \{[^+7 \cdot (^+9 - {}^+4) - {}^+6 \cdot (^+3 + {}^+7)] + {}^+5 \cdot (^-4 + {}^+8)\} + {}^+9 = $ _____.

> (a) $^-29$ (b) $^-79$ (c) $^-117$ (d) $^-434$ (e) $^+329$ (f) $^+24$

If you feel secure in your knowledge of how to multiply integers, you may proceed with Section 20.4 on division.

20.4 Division in the Set of Integers

The operation of division is defined as the reverse of multiplication, just as was done for the whole numbers.

DEFINITION OF DIVISION

DEFINITION. Let a, d, and q be integers with $d \neq 0$. Then the division statement $a \div d = q$ is defined to be equivalent to the multiplication statement $a = qd$.

Since this is merely an extension of the definition of division for the whole numbers, there is relatively little to add to what you have already learned in Chapter 11. The properties of division carry over to the present case and are as follows:

PROPERTIES OF DIVISION IN THE SET OF INTEGERS
For all integers a, d, and q, with $d \neq 0$:
(1) $a \div d = q$ if and only if $a = q \cdot d$. Thus the quotient $a \div d$ is defined if and only if d is a factor of a. Therefore, division is *not* a binary operation on the set of integers.
(2) When division is defined, the quotient is unique.
(3) Division is not commutative.
(4) Division is not associative.
(5) Division by zero is not defined.
(6) If $a \div d = b \div d$ and $d \neq 0$, then $a = b$ (cancellation law).
(7) Division is right-distributive over addition and over subtraction.

The only additional matter to consider is that of the sign of the quotient. Suppose that a is positive and d is negative; what is the sign of $q = a \div d$? Since $a = q \cdot d$, it follows that q must be negative. Similar discussion of the other cases gives a proof of Theorem 7.

SIGNS OF QUOTIENTS

THEOREM 7. If a and d are integers and the quotient $q = a \div d$ is defined, then
(1) if a and d are positive, q is positive.
(2) if a is positive and d is negative, q is negative.
(3) if a is negative and d is positive, q is negative.
(4) if a and d are negative, q is positive.
(5) if $a = 0$ (and d necessarily $\neq 0$), $q = 0$.

1. Find the values of the quotients:
(a) $^+8 \div {}^+4 = $ _____.　　　　　　(b) $^+12 \div {}^-2 = $ _____.
(c) $^-15 \div {}^+3 = $ _____.　　　　　　(d) $^-20 \div {}^-4 = $ _____.
(e) $0 \div {}^+6 = $ _____.　　　　　　(f) $0 \div {}^-3 = $ _____.

(a) $^+2$ (b) $^-6$ (c) $^-5$ (d) $^+5$ (e) 0   (f) 0

2. Which of the following statements are true and which are false for all integers a, b, and c (assuming that all quotients are defined):

(a) $a \div b = b \div a$. _____   (b) $0 \div a = 0$. _____   (c) $a \div 1 = a$. _____

(d) $a \div (b + c) = (a \div b) \div c$. _____

(e) If $a \div c = b \div c$, then $a = b$. _____

(f) $a \div (b + c) = (a \div b) + (b \div c)$. _____

(g) $(a + b) \div c = (a \div c) + (b \div c)$. _____

(h) $(a - b) \div c = (a \div c) - (b \div c)$. _____

(i) $a \div (b - c) = (a \div b) - (a \div c)$. _____

(j) If $a = b$, then $a \div c = b \div c$. _____

(a) F.   (b) T.   (c) T.   (d) F.   (e) T.   (f) F.   (g) T.
(h) T.   (i) F.   (j) T.

3. Find the values of the following expressions:

(a) $^+2 \cdot (^-3 + {}^+5) + (^+6 - {}^-4) \div (^-2) = $ _____.

(b) $[(^+9 + {}^+3) \div (^+3)] \cdot (^-4) = $ _____.

(c) $\{[(^-5) \cdot (^+6)] \div (^-10)\} + {}^+12 = $ _____.

(d) $^+12 \div [^-8 + {}^+5] - [(^+16 - {}^-12) \div (^-4)] = $ _____.

(e) $[(^+15 \div {}^+3) + {}^+10] \div (^-5) = $ _____.

(a) $^-1$ (b) $^-16$ (c) $^+15$ (d) $^+3$ (e) $^-3$

In this chapter we have defined the product $a \cdot b$ for any pair of integers and shown that multiplication so defined is closed, commutative, and associative. Moreover, multiplication is distributive over addition and subtraction.

Finally, we defined division in terms of multiplication and showed that it has the same properties that we discussed earlier in the case of the whole numbers.

You should test your mastery of this material by working the following Post Test.

POST TEST

1. Find the following products: (a) $^-2 \cdot {}^+5$. _____   (b) $^+4 \cdot {}^-3$. _____
(c) $^-6 \cdot {}^-7$. _____

2. In each of the following, identify the property of multiplication which is used and verify the equality by completing the indicated operations.

(a) $^+7 \cdot (^-2 \cdot {}^+4) = (^+7 \cdot {}^-2) \cdot {}^+4.$ _____

(b) $^+16 \cdot {}^-3 = {}^-3 \cdot {}^+16.$ _____

(c) $^-27 \cdot {}^+1 = {}^-27.$ _____

(d) $^-2 \cdot (^+3 + {}^-4) = (^-2 \cdot {}^+3) + (^-2 \cdot {}^-4).$ _____

3. Fill in the reason for each step in the proof of the theorem:

THEOREM. $(a + b)(a + b) = a^2 + 2ab + b^2.$

Proof

1. $(a + b)(a + b) = (a + b)a + (a + b)b$ _____
2. $ = [a^2 + ab] + [ab + b^2]$ _____
3. $ = a^2 + ab + ab + b^2$ _____
4. $ = a^2 + (1 + 1)ab + b^2$ _____
5. $ = a^2 + 2ab + b^2$ _____

4. Find the first error in the following "proof" of the false theorem:

THEOREM. $1 = 2.$

1. Let $a = b$. Then $ab = b^2$.
2. $ab - a^2 = b^2 - a^2$.
3. $a(b - a) = (b + a)(b - a)$.
4. $a = b + a = 2a$.
5. $1 = 2$.

5. *Prove*: For any integers a and b, $a(\text{opp } b) = \text{opp}(ab)$. Use a separate piece of paper.

6. Find the values of (a) $[(^-2) \cdot (^+5 + {}^-15) + {}^+3] \cdot (^-6) = $ _____.
(b) $^+5 \cdot [^-2 + (\text{opp}|17| - {}^+12) \cdot (^-2)] = $ _____.

7. Find the following quotients: (a) $^+4 \div {}^-2.$ _____ (b) $^-15 \div {}^+5.$ _____ (c) $^-20 \div {}^-4.$ _____

8. State whether true or false for all a, b, and c (assuming that all quotients are defined):

(a) $a \div (b + c) = (a \div b) + (a \div c).$ _____

(b) $(a - b) \div c = (a \div c) - (b \div c).$ _____

(c) $^+1 \div a = a.$ _____

(d) $a \div b = b \div a.$ _____

9. Prove that if multiplication of integers is defined so that it is commutative, associative, and distributive over addition, then for every integer a, $a \cdot 0 = 0$. Do not look at the proof of this theorem in the text. Use a separate piece of paper.

10. Find the value: $[^-7 + {}^+6 - {}^-1] \div [^+5 \cdot (^+3 - {}^-2) - (^+4 \cdot {}^-5) + {}^-17] = $ _____.

1. (a) $^-10.$ (b) $^-12.$ (c) $^+42.$

2. (a) Associative, both sides $= {}^-56.$ (b) Commutative, both sides $= {}^-48.$ (c) Multiplicative property of $^+1.$ (d) Distributive, both sides $= {}^+2.$

3. (a) Distributive. (b) Distributive. (c) Generalized commutative property of addition. (d) Distributive. (e) Addition fact.
4. Line 4; since $a = b$, $b - a = 0$ and cannot be canceled.
5. (See Theorem 2.)
6. (a) $^-138$. (b) $^+280$.
7. (a) $^-2$. (b) $^-3$. (c) $^+5$
8. (a) F. (b) T. (c) F. (d) F.
9. (See Theorem 1.)
10. 0

Now proceed to Chapter 21.

21

The Integers
—Additional
Topics and
Summary

Before beginning this chapter you should have completed the Post Test for Chapter 20. In addition, you should review the material on inequalities for whole numbers in Section 10.2 and the concept of an equivalence relation in Chapters 5 and 18. To be sure that your review has been adequate work the following Readiness Test.

READINESS TEST

1. If a and b are whole numbers, we say that $b < a$ if and only if $S(b)$ _____ $S(a)$.

$\subset$

2. The symbol $a \geq b$ is read _____.

a is greater than or equal to b

3. The law of trichotomy for inequalities involving whole numbers states that given a and b, one and only one of the following statements is true : (1) _____, (2) _____, and (3) _____.

$a < b \qquad a = b \qquad a > b$

4. If $a < b$ and a and b are represented on the number line, then a is to the _____ of b.

left

5. If $a < b$ and $b < c$, then what relation holds between a and c? _____ _____ This is called the _____ law of inequality.

$a < c$.   transitive

6. If $a < b$, then what relation holds between $a + c$ and $b + c$? _____ _____

$a + c < b + c$.

7. If $a < b$ and $c \neq 0$ (where a, b, and c are whole numbers), then ac _____ bc.

$<$

8. For two whole numbers a and b: $b < a$ if and only if there is a natural number c such that $a =$ _____.

$b + c$

9. An equivalence relation is required to have what three properties: (1) _____, (2) _____, and (3) _____.

reflexive   symmetric   transitive

10. An equivalence class is a set whose members are all _____ to each other.

equivalent

11. Equivalence classes of sets were used in Chapter 5 to define _____ _____.

whole numbers

12. The equivalence classes of whole numbers used in modular arithmetic (Chapter 18) are called _____.

congruence classes

Now proceed to our treatment of inequalities in the set of integers, Section 21.1.

21.1 Inequality in the Set of Integers

In Chapter 10 it was shown that for whole numbers: $b < a$ if and only if there is a natural number c such that $a = b + c$. In other words, $b < a$ if and only if the difference $a - b$ is defined and is not zero. We shall use this fact to motivate our definition of inequality in the set of integers.

DEFINITION OF $b < a$ **DEFINITION.**   For any pair of integers a and b, b is less than a (written $b < a$) if and only if $a - b$ is positive.

Similarly, b is greater than a (written $b > a$) if and only if $a - b$ is negative.

REMARKS
1. It follows that $b < a$ if and only if $a > b$.
2. If $b < a$, then on the number line b is to the left of a. If $b > a$, then on the number line b is to the right of a.

The essential theorems on inequalities are as follows:

434

21.1 Inequality in the Set of Integers

LAW OF TRICHOTOMY

THEOREM 1. LAW OF TRICHOTOMY. For any pair of integers precisely one of the following is true:

$$b < a \qquad b = a \qquad b > a$$

Proof. This follows from the fact that $a - b$ is positive, zero, or negative.

TRANSITIVE LAW

THEOREM 2. TRANSITIVE LAW. For any three integers: if $a < b$ and $b < c$, then $a < c$.

Proof
1. Since $a < b$, $b - a$ is positive.
2. Since $b < c$, $c - b$ is positive.
3. $c - a = (c - b) + (b - a)$
4. Hence $c - a$ is positive and $a < c$.

ADDITIVE LAW

THEOREM 3. ADDITIVE LAW. For any three integers, if $a < b$, then $a + c < b + c$. Proof deferred to the exercises.

MULTIPLICATIVE LAWS

THEOREM 4. For any three integers, if $a < b$ and c is positive, then $a \cdot c < b \cdot c$. Proof deferred to the exercises.

THEOREM 5. For any three integers, if $a < b$ and c is negative, then $a \cdot c > b \cdot c$. Proof deferred to the exercises.

---

1. Write the correct symbol $(<, >)$ between each pair of the following integers: (a) $^+3$ _____ $^-1$. (b) $^-2$ _____ $^+4$. (c) $^-3$ _____ $^-5$. (d) $^-6$ _____ $^-2$. (e) 0 _____ $^+3$. (f) 0 _____ $^-4$.

    (a) >   (b) <   (c) >   (d) <   (e) <   (f) >

2. If a is positive, then a _____ opp a.
   $(<, >)$

    >

3. If a is negative, then a _____ opp a.
   $(<, >)$

    <

4. $^-8 < ^-5$ and $a > 0$ implies ^-8a _____ ^-5a and $^-8 + a$ _____ $^-5 + a$.
   $(<, >)$ $(<, >)$

    <   <

435

5. $^-3 < {}^+6$ and $a < 0$ implies $^-3a \underline{\quad}_{(<, >)} {}^+6a$ and $^-3 + a \underline{\quad}_{(<, >)}$
$^+6 + a$.

> <

On separate pieces of paper prove the following theorems.

6.
THEOREM 3. For any three integers, if $a < b$, then $a + c < b + c$.

Proof. $(b + c) - (a + c) = b - a$. But since $a < b$, $b - a$ is positive. Therefore, $(b + c) - (a + c)$ is positive.

7.
THEOREM 4. For any three integers, if $a < b$ and c is positive, then $a \cdot c < b \cdot c$.

Proof. $(b \cdot c) - (a \cdot c) = (b - a) \cdot c$. But since $a < b$, $b - a$ is positive; and c is positive by hypothesis. Hence $(b - a) \cdot c$ is positive.

8.
THEOREM 5. For any three integers, if $a < b$ and c is negative, then $a \cdot c > b \cdot c$.

Proof. $(b \cdot c) - (a \cdot c) = (b - a) \cdot c$. By hypothesis $b - a$ is positive and c is negative. Hence $(b - a) \cdot c$ is negative.

21.2 Standard Mathematical Notation

To prevent any possible ambiguities we have introduced the relatively nonstandard notations ^+n, ^-n, and opp a. It is now time to convert to the notations commonly used in standard mathematics.

(1) We shall drop the $+$ in ^+n and write the positive integers as natural numbers. Thus we write 3 for $^+3$, and so on, and use $+$ only to represent addition.

(2) We shall lower the $-$ in ^-n and write the negative integers in the notation $-n$. Thus we write -3 for $^-3$. Since the minus sign $(-)$ has already been used for subtraction, this seemingly introduces an ambiguity in an expression such as $5 - 3$. Does this mean the difference "5 minus 3" or the sum "5 + (negative 3)"? Fortunately, in the previous notation $^+5 - {}^+3 = {}^+5 + {}^-3$, so the result is the same in either interpretation.

(3) Instead of opp a, we write $-a$. This suggests that $-a$ is negative, but such an interpretation is incorrect. If a is positive, $-a$ is negative; but if a

is negative, $-a$ is positive. Thus the symbol -3 means either "negative 3" or "opp 3"; but opp 3 = negative 3, so there is no confusion. Similarly, $-(-3)$ can mean opp(negative 3) = 3 or opp(opp 3) = 3. Again either interpretation gives the same result.

In summary, the minus sign has three meanings: (1) subtraction, as in $5 - 2$; (2) a negative integer, as in -3; and (3) the opposite, as in $-a$. Usually the meaning will be clear, but sometimes there is ambiguity. This ambiguity is unimportant, however, for all interpretations give the same result. The important thing to remember is that two adjacent minus signs may be replaced by a plus sign. Thus

$$5 - (-3) = 5 + 3 \qquad -(-4) = +4 = 4 \qquad \text{etc.}$$

In standard mathematics several other terms are introduced, as follows:

(4) Zero is called the *additive identity*. This comes from the fact that $a + 0 = a$ and $0 + a = a$; and so the addition of zero leaves a *identically* alone.

IDENTITIES AND INVERSES

(5) Given an integer a, the integer $-a$ (previously called opp a) is called the *additive inverse* of a. This follows from the fact that $a + (-a) = 0$ and $(-a) + a = 0$.

(6) The integer 1 is called the *multiplicative identity*. This represents the fact that $a \cdot 1 = a$ and $1 \cdot a = a$.

It might seem reasonable to define a *multiplicative inverse* at this time, but we cannot do so in the set of integers. One of the chief reasons for introducing the rational numbers (Chapter 23) is to construct a number system in which multiplicative inverses do exist.

21.3 Another Approach

In Chapters 19 and 20 we have defined the set of integers as the set $\{\ldots, -3, -2, -1, 0, 1, 2, 3, \ldots\}$ and have also defined the sum $a + b$ and the product $a \cdot b$ of any pair of integers. In view of these definitions we found that the integers have the collection of properties that is summarized in Section 21.4. This approach to the integers is treated in somewhat greater detail in Henkin, Smith, Varineau, and Walsh, *Retracing Elementary Mathematics*, Chapter XI.

Although this approach is strictly rigorous, it leaves us somewhat uneasy in one way. We have used the symbols $-1, -2, -3, \ldots,$ to represent negative integers, but just what is a negative integer? According to the treatment above, it is a symbol that marks a particular point on the two-way number line and behaves in a specified fashion with respect to addition and multiplication. But are there any such numbers? The mathematicians of the Middle Ages thought not and refused to consider them. Have we any reason to think differently.

A positive answer to these questions is given by another approach to the integers, which we merely sketch in this section. For a full discussion you may consult Garstens and Jackson, *Mathematics for Elementary School Teachers*, Chapter 6. The basic idea in this approach is to define the integers in terms of ordered pairs of natural numbers (which are supposed to have been developed earlier). The scheme is to define an integer a as being an ordered pair of natural numbers (n, m) such that in our previous notation $a = n - m$. The following table gives examples of this scheme:

Standard Notation	Corresponding Ordered Pair
4	(5, 1) or (6, 2) or (7, 3) or $\cdots$
0	(1, 1) or (2, 2) or (3, 3) or $\cdots$
-2	(1, 3) or (2, 4) or (3, 5) or $\cdots$

Thus a positive integer is represented by any of a set of ordered pairs of natural numbers $\{(n_1, m_1), (n_2, m_2), (n_3, m_3), \ldots\}$ such that $n_1 > m_1$, $n_2 > m_2, n_3 > m_3, \ldots$ and $n_1 - m_1 = n_2 - m_2 = n_3 - m_3 = \cdots$.

Zero is represented by any of a set of ordered pairs of natural numbers $\{(n_1, m_1), (n_2, m_2), (n_3, m_3), \ldots\}$ such that $n_1 = m_1$, $n_2 = m_2$, $n_3 = m_3, \ldots$.

A negative integer is represented by any of a set of ordered pairs of natural numbers $\{(n_1, m_1), (n_2, m_2), (n_3, m_3), \ldots\}$ such that $n_1 < m_1$, $n_2 < m_2$, $n_2 < m_3, \ldots$ and $m_1 - n_1 = m_2 - n_2 = m_3 - n_3 \cdots$.

Thus two ordered pairs (n_1, m_1) and (n_2, m_2) represent the same integer if and only if

$$n_1 - m_1 = n_2 - m_2 \qquad \text{when } n_1 \geq m_1 \text{ and } n_2 \geq m_2$$

or

$$m_1 - n_1 = m_2 - n_2 \qquad \text{when } m_1 \geq n_1 \text{ and } m_2 \geq n_2$$

We may write this more compactly by stating that *two ordered pairs of natural numbers* (n_1, m_1) *and* (n_2, m_2) *represent the same integer if and only if*

$$n_1 + m_2 = n_2 + m_1$$

This leads us to the concept of *equivalent* ordered pairs of natural numbers:

EQUIVALENT ORDERED PAIRS   **DEFINITION.** Two ordered pairs of natural numbers (n_1, m_1) and (n_2, m_2) are *equivalent* (written $\sim$) if and only if

$$n_1 + m_2 = n_2 + m_1$$

Here *equivalent* means that they represent the same integer.

EXAMPLES

1. $(4, 2) \sim (8, 6)$, since $4 + 6 = 8 + 2$.
2. $(2, 7) \sim (5, 10)$, since $2 + 10 = 5 + 7$.

THEOREM 6. The relation just defined for the equivalence of two ordered pairs of natural numbers is an equivalence relation.

Proof
(a) *Reflexive*: $(n, m) \sim (n, m)$ for $n + m = m + n$.

(b) *Symmetric*: If $(n_1, m_1) \sim (n_2, m_2)$, then $n_1 + m_2 = n_2 + m_1$. But $(n_2, m_2) \sim (n_1, m_1)$ if $n_2 + m_1 = n_1 + m_2$. Since the two right-hand equations are the same, it follows that if $(n_1, m_1) \sim (n_2, m_2)$ then $(n_2, m_2) \sim (n_1, m_1)$.

(c) *Transitive*: We must prove that if $(n_1, m_1) \sim (n_2, m_2)$ and $(n_2, m_2) \sim (n_3, m_3)$, then $(n_1, m_1) \sim (n_3, m_3)$.

By hypothesis,

$$n_1 + m_2 = n_2 + m_1$$

$$n_2 + m_3 = n_3 + m_2$$

Adding we have

$$n_1 + n_2 + m_2 + m_3 = n_2 + n_3 + m_1 + m_2$$

or

$$n_1 + m_3 = n_3 + m_1$$

Hence $(n_1, m_1) \sim (n_3, m_3)$.

Using this equivalence relation we can partition the set of *all* ordered pairs of natural numbers into a collection of disjoint equivalence classes. Each equivalence class is a set of ordered pairs each pair of which is equivalent to every other ordered pair in that class. Examples are

$$\{(3, 1), (4, 2), (5, 3), \ldots\}$$

$$\{(1, 1), (2, 2), (3, 3), \ldots\}$$

$$\{(1, 4), (2, 5), (3, 6), \ldots\}$$

From this point of view we shall define an integer as follows:

EQUIVALENCE CLASS
DEFINITION OF INTEGERS

D E F I N I T I O N. An *integer* is an equivalence class of ordered pairs of natural numbers, where $(n_1, m_1) \sim (n_2, m_2)$ if and only if $n_1 + m_2 = n_2 + m_1$.

As names for these integers, we can use the notations

$$2 = \langle 3, 1 \rangle = \langle 4, 2 \rangle = \langle 5, 3 \rangle = \cdots = \{(3, 1), (4, 2), (5, 3), \ldots\}$$

$$0 = \langle 1, 1 \rangle = \langle 2, 2 \rangle = \langle 3, 3 \rangle = \cdots = \{(1, 1), (2, 2), (3, 3), \cdots\}$$

$$-3 = \langle 1, 4 \rangle = \langle 2, 5 \rangle = \langle 3, 6 \rangle = \cdots = \{(1, 4), (2, 5), (3, 6), \ldots\}$$

These equivalence classes can be shown graphically as in Figure 21.1. If we plot the ordered pairs (n, m) as shown, with n measured to the right and m upward, we obtain a graphical interpretation of the Cartesian product of the set of integers with itself. As suggested by the figure, the points corresponding to the ordered pairs of a fixed equivalence class lie on a line making a 45° angle with the horizontal. These lines intersect the horizontal number line in the integers represented by the corresponding equivalence classes.

Next we must define the sum and product of any two integers. The motivation for these definitions is that we wish to have the ordered pairs (n, m) behave like differences $n - m$.

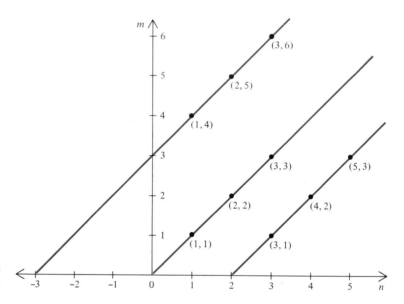

FIGURE 21.1 *The equivalence classes are represented by the colored lines.*

SUM OF INTEGERS

(1) SUM

Since $(n - m) + (r - s) = (n + r) - (m + s)$, the sum of two integers is defined as follows:

DEFINITION. The sum of two integers $\langle n, m \rangle$ and $\langle r, s \rangle$ is defined to be

$$\langle n, m \rangle + \langle r, s \rangle = \langle n + r, m + s \rangle$$

PRODUCT OF INTEGERS

(2) PRODUCT

Since $(n - m) \cdot (r - s) = (nr + ms) - (ns + mr)$, the product of two integers is defined as follows:

DEFINITION. The product of two integers $\langle n, m \rangle$ and $\langle r, s \rangle$ is defined to be

$$\langle n, m \rangle \cdot \langle r, s \rangle = \langle nr + ms, ns + mr \rangle$$

Finally, it is necessary to show that in view of these definitions the integers have all the standard properties. We will not give these proofs and refer you to Garstens and Jackson if you are interested in the full details.

---

1. The integer 5 is the equivalence class $\langle$_____$, 1 \rangle$, which is equal to the set of ordered pairs $\{$_____$\ldots\}$.

(list 3 members)

> 6   {(6, 1), (7, 2), (8, 3), ...}

2. The integer 0 is the equivalence class ⟨_____,1⟩ which is equal to the set of ordered pairs {_____...}.

> 1   {(1, 1), (2, 2), (3, 3), ...}

3. The integer −4 is the equivalence class ⟨1, _____⟩, which is equal to the set of ordered pairs {_____...}.

> 5   {(1, 5), (2, 6), (3, 7), ...}

4. What is the standard notation for the integers ⟨6, 3⟩ _____, ⟨2, 8⟩ _____, ⟨5, 5⟩ _____?

> 3   −6   0

5. According to our definition, ⟨5, 2⟩ + ⟨3, 4⟩ = ⟨8, 6⟩. Write this equality in standard notation. _____

> 3 + (−1) = 2.

6. According to our definition, ⟨2, 4⟩ · ⟨6, 2⟩ = ⟨12 + 8, 24 + 4⟩ = ⟨20, 28⟩. Write this equality in standard notation. _____

> (−2) · (4) = −8.

7. According to our definition, ⟨3, 8⟩ · ⟨2, 5⟩ = ⟨6 + 40, 16 + 15⟩ = ⟨46, 31⟩. Write this equality in standard notation _____.

> (−5) · (−3) = 15.

8. This idea can be explained to children by devices such as the following. Consider a set of black beads (represented by x's) and a set of colored beads (represented by o's)

$$\{x\ x\ x\ x\ x\ o\ o\ o\}$$

An integer is the difference of the numbers of beads of different colors, positive if there are more black beads than colored beads, and negative if there are more colored beads than black beads. Hence the diagram above represents 5 − 3 = 2.

To add two integers

$$\{x\ x\ x\ o\ o\ o\ o\} \quad \text{and} \quad \{x\ x\ o\}$$

take the union of the set of black beads and the union of the set of colored beads and get {x x x x x o o o o o}. Thus −1 + 1 = 0.

Using this device find the sum $2 + (-1)$:

$\{x\,x\,x\,x\,o\,o\} + \{x\,x\,o\,o\,o\} = \{$_____$\} = $ _____

$\{x\,x\,x\,x\,x\,x\,x\,o\,o\,o\,o\,o\}$ 1

The following frames are optional.

9. To add $6 + (-3)$ in this notation, we may write $6 = \langle 8, 2 \rangle$ and $-3 = \langle 4, 7 \rangle$. Then $6 + (-3) = \langle 8, 2 \rangle + \langle 4, 7 \rangle = \langle$_____ , _____$\rangle = $ _____.

12   9   3

10. In frame 9 we might have chosen other ways of writing 6 and -3 such as $6 = \langle 10, 4 \rangle$ and $-3 = \langle 7, 10 \rangle$. Then $6 + (-3) = \langle 17, 14 \rangle = 3$. Since the value of $6 + (-3)$ does not depend upon our *choice* of ways of writing 6 and (-3), we are led to believe that the addition of integers is _____.

uniquely defined

11. If $a = \langle p_1, q_1 \rangle = \langle p_2, q_2 \rangle$, then by definition, $p_1 + q_2 = $ _____ _____. Similarly, if $b = \langle r_1, s_1 \rangle = \langle r_2, s_2 \rangle$, then $r_1 + s_2 = $ _____.

$p_2 + q_1$ $r_2 + s_1$

12. Using the notations of frame 11, we might write

$$a + b = \langle p_1, q_1 \rangle + \langle r_1, s_1 \rangle = \langle p_1 + r_1, q_1 + s_1 \rangle$$

or

$$a + b = \langle p_2, q_2 \rangle + \langle r_2, s_2 \rangle = \langle p_2 + r_2, q_2 + s_2 \rangle$$

Why is it true that $\langle p_1 + r_1, q_1 + s_1 \rangle = \langle p_2 + r_2, q_2 + s_2 \rangle$? We must examine the truth of the equality $p_1 + r_1 + q_2 + s_2 = $ _____ _____. From frame 11, $p_1 + q_2 = $ _____ and $r_1 + s_2 = $ _____, so the equality is true. Thus we have proved that _____ _____.

$p_2 + r_2 + q_1 + s_1$ $p_2 + q_1$ $r_2 + s_1$ the addition of integers is uniquely defined.

13. (Discovery Exercise) As in frame 12, prove that the product of two integers is uniquely defined.

21.4 Summary of the Properties of Integers

The statements given below are the most important properties of the integers. All other properties of the integers (except mathematical induction, which is not discussed in this book) can be derived from these. It is understood that each of these statements is to be prefixed by the phrase "For all integers a, b, c, and d". Special exceptions are noted where necessary. When the symbol $a \div b$ is written, it is understood that a and b are such that this symbol is defined.

EQUALITY

1. If $a = b$, then $a + c = b + c$.
2. If $a = b$, then $a - c = b - c$.
3. If $a = b$, then $a \cdot c = b \cdot c$.
4. If $a = b$ and $c \neq 0$, then $a \div c = b \div c$.

ADDITION

1. Addition is a binary operation.
2. $a + b = b + a$ Commutative property.
3. $a + (b + c) = (a + b) + c$ Associative property.
4. $a + 0 = a$ Additive identity.
5. $a + (-a) = 0$ Additive inverse.

SUBTRACTION

1. Subtraction is a binary operation.
2. $a - b = a + (-b)$ Definition.
3. If $a - c = b - c$, then $a = b$ Cancellation law.

MULTIPLICATION

1. Multiplication is a binary operation.
2. $ab = ba$ Commutative property.
3. $(ab)c = a(bc)$ Associative property.
4. $a \cdot 1 = a$ Multiplicative identity
5. If $ac = bc$ and $c \neq 0$, then $a = b$ Cancellation law.

DIVISION

1. Division is *not* a binary operation, and is neither commutative nor associative.
2. $a \div d = q$ if and only if $a = qd$ Definition
3. If $a \div c = b \div c$, then $a = b$ Cancellation law.

DISTRIBUTIVE PROPERTIES

1. $a \cdot (b + c) = a \cdot b + a \cdot c$.
2. $a \cdot (b -- c) = a \cdot b - a \cdot c$.
3. $(a + b) \div c = (a \div c) + (b \div c)$.

INEQUALITY

1. Exactly one of the following is true:

    $a < b \qquad a = b \qquad a > b$ Trichotomy law.

2. If $a < b$ and $b < c$, then $a < c$ Transitive law.
3. If $a < b$, then $a + c < b + c$ Additive law.
4. If $a < b$ and $c > 0$, then $a \cdot c < b \cdot c$

    If $a < b$ and $c < 0$, then $a \cdot c > b \cdot c$ Multiplicative laws.

REFERENCES

Henkin, Leon, W. N. Smith, V. J. Varineau, and M. J. Walsh, *Retracing Elementary Mathematics*, Macmillan, New York, 1962.

Garstens, H. L., and S. B. Jackson, *Mathematics for Elementary School Teachers*, Macmillan, New York, 1967.

In this chapter we have defined inequality for integers and discussed its properties. We have introduced the standard mathematical notation for the integers, and also have written them as equivalence classes of ordered pairs of natural numbers.

Now review Chapters 19, 20, and 21 to be sure that you are fully familiar with the integers and their properties. Complete your review by working the following Post Test.

POST TEST

1. Order the following pairs of integers: (a) $^+3$, $^+5$. _____
(b) $^+1$, $^-5$. _____ (c) $^-6$, $^+7$. _____ (d) $^-1$, $^-7$. _____

2. Prove that if $a > b$ and $b > c$, then $a > c$. _____

---

3. Prove that if $a < b$ and $c < 0$, then $ac > bc$. _____

---

4. What does the transitive law for inequality tell us if we know that $a > b$ and $c > d$? _____

5. If $a < b$, order $a + c$ and $b + c$. _____

6. What is the additive identity? _____ What property does it have?
_____

7. What is the additive inverse of a? _____ What property does it have?
_____

8. What is the multiplicative identity? _____ What property does it have? _____

9. Why is there in general no multiplicative inverse of an integer a?

---

10. Prove that the cancellation law of addition is true for the integers.

_____

_____

11. What difference is there between the concepts of subtraction in the whole numbers and in the integers? _____

_____

12. Compare the multiplicative law for inequalities in the whole numbers (page 260) with the multiplicative law for inequalities in the integers. Why must there be two such laws in the integers? _____

_____

13. $^-4 < {}^+7$ and $a < 0$ implies that ^-4a _____ ^+7a.
$$(<, >)$$

14. The equivalence classes $\langle 4, 10 \rangle$, $\langle 12, 2 \rangle$, and $\langle 6, 6 \rangle$ represent what integers in ordinary notation? _____

15. Write $-2 + 8 = 6$ in the equivalence-class $\langle \ \rangle$ notation. _____

_____

16. Write $(-5) \cdot (-7)$ in the equivalence-class $\langle \ \rangle$ notation. _____

_____

17. $\langle 2, 7 \rangle \cdot \langle 3, 1 \rangle = \langle$ _____, _____ $\rangle$. Write this result in ordinary notation. _____

1. (a) $^+3 < {}^+5$. (b) $^-5 < {}^+1$. (c) $^-6 < {}^+7$. (d) $^-7 < {}^-1$.

2. Since $a > b$, $a - b$ is positive. Since $b > c$, $b - c$ is positive. Therefore, $a - c = (a - b) + (b - c)$ is positive. Hence $a > c$.

3. Since $a < b$, $b - a$ is positive. Then $(b - a)c$ is negative since c is negative. Therefore, $bc - ac$ is negative and $ac > bc$.

4. Nothing.

5. $a + c < b + c$.

6. 0; For all a, $a + 0 = 0 + a$.

7. $-a$; $a + (-a) = (-a) + a = 0$.

8. 1; For all a, $a \cdot 1 = 1 \cdot a = a$.

9. There is no integer x such that $0 \cdot x = 1$, or $2 \cdot x = 1$, for example.

10. CANCELLATION LAW: If $a + c = b + c$, then $a = b$.

Proof. If $a + c = b + c$, then $a + c + (-c) = b + c + (-c)$. Hence $a + [c + (-c)] = b + [c + (-c)]$, or $a + 0 = b + 0$ or $a = b$.

11. In the whole numbers $a - b$ is defined only when $a \geq b$; in the integers $a - b$ is defined for all a and b.

12. In the whole numbers c is positive or zero. In the integers we must also discuss the case where c is negative.

13. $>$
14. $-6, 10, 0.$
15. Many answers, such as $\langle 2, 4 \rangle + \langle 10, 2 \rangle = \langle 12, 6 \rangle$.
16. Many answers, such as $\langle 2, 7 \rangle \cdot \langle 3, 10 \rangle = \langle 76, 41 \rangle$.
17. $13, 23; (-5) \cdot 2 = -10.$

Now continue to Chapter 22, Fractions.

22

Fractions

In this chapter we begin the discussion of fractions and rational numbers. You should be familiar with a number of concepts from earlier chapters, which are reviewed in the following Readiness Test.

READINESS TEST

1. If a, b, and c are natural numbers and if $a = bc$, then b is a _____ of a, and a is a _____ of b.

> factor (or divisor)   multiple

2. If $a = qd$, where $d \neq 0$, then $a \div d =$ _____.

> q

3. The integers a and $-a$ are _____. On the number line they have the same _____ from 0, but are in _____ directions from 0.

> opposites   distance   opposite

4. A relation $a \approx b$ is an equivalence relation if it is (1)_____, (2)_____, and (3)_____.

> reflexive   symmetric   transitive

5. A relation $a \approx b$ is reflexive if _____.

> $a \approx a$

6. A relation $a \approx b$ is symmetric if _____.

> when $a \approx b$ it follows that $b \approx a$

7. A relation $a \approx b$ is transitive if _____.

> given $a \approx b$ and $b \approx c$, it follows that $a \approx c$

8. Let (a, b) and (c, d) be two ordered pairs of natural numbers. Then $(a, b) = (c, d)$ if and only if _____.

> $a = c$ and $b = d$

9. What equivalence relation between ordered pairs (a, b) and (c, d) of natural numbers was used to define the integers in Section 21.3?

_____

_____

$(a, b) \sim (c, d)$ if and only if $a + d = b + c$.

If your review of these concepts is complete, proceed with Section 22.1.

22.1 Introduction

Before beginning our study of the rational numbers, we shall devote this chapter to a review of your previous knowledge of fractions.

The simplest approach to fractions is their use to represent portions of objects. Let us consider some examples.

FIGURE 22.1. *The colored area represents 2/3.*

EXAMPLES

1. In the rectangle in Figure 22.1 the colored area represents $\frac{2}{3}$ of the total area.
2. If each circle in Figure 22.2 has area one, the colored area has area $\frac{5}{4}$.
3. If a pie is divided into six equal portions, each piece is $\frac{1}{6}$ of the pie. If each of 4 people is served one piece, the amount distributed is $\frac{4}{6}$ of the pie.
4. 90 minutes is $\frac{3}{2}$ of an hour.

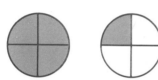

FIGURE 22.2. *The colored area represents 5/4.*

1. How many quarters are needed to equal a dollar? _____

4.

2. Seventy-five cents is what fractional part of a dollar? _____

$\frac{3}{4}$.

3. A penny is what fractional part of a dollar? _____

$\frac{1}{100}$.

4. Seventy-five cents can be represented by the fraction _____/100 as well as by $\frac{3}{4}$.

75

5. Six quarters can be represented as _____ of a dollar.

$\frac{6}{4}$ (or $\frac{3}{2}$ or $\frac{150}{100}$)

6. What fraction is suggested by the following figure? _____

$\frac{5}{2}$ is the most obvious, since the drawing shows five half-squares.

7. Frame 6 reminds you that the numerator of a fraction may be _____ than the denominator.

greater (or larger)

8. The regular hexagon below has area 1. Complete the drawing to represent the fraction $\frac{11}{6}$.

Many solutions possible. For example,

9. What fraction is suggested by each of the following figures?

(a) (b)

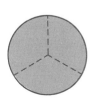 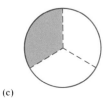

(c)

(a) $\frac{3}{4}$; (b) $\frac{2}{6}$ or $\frac{1}{3}$; (c) $\frac{4}{3}$

10. Can the numerator of a fraction be zero? _____ Can the denominator of a fraction be zero? _____

Yes.   No.

11. If 37 identical leaves together weight 1 ounce, how much does 1 leaf weigh? _____

$\frac{1}{37}$ ounce

12. Strands of wool are wound on a card until a total width of 1 inch is obtained. If 24 strands fill up 1 inch, how thick is one strand?
_____

$\frac{1}{24}$ inch.

13. If 500 sheets of paper make a stack 2 inches high, what is the thickness of one sheet? _____

$\frac{2}{500}$ (or $\frac{1}{250}$) inch.

Fractions can also be used to label points on the one-way number line (Figure 22.3). If the segment of this line between 0 and 1 is divided into two

FIGURE 22.3. *Position of 1/2 on the number line.*

equal parts, each of these can be said to be of length $\frac{1}{2}$. Hence the midpoint of this segment can be labeled $\frac{1}{2}$. We can extend this process and subdivide the entire line into divisions of length $\frac{1}{2}$ and label the points of subdivision as in Figure 22.4. In the same way we can divide the interval between 0 and 1 into n equal parts (where n is a natural number) and locate the points m/n on the number line for every natural number m. Thus each fraction of the form m/n represents a point on the one-way number line.

FIGURE 22.4. *Subdivision of the number line into halves.*

14. To locate the point on the number line which is represented by $\frac{5}{8}$, we divide the interval between 0 and 1 into _____ equal parts and lay off _____ of these to the right of 0.

8   5

15. If the interval between 0 and 1 is divided into 5 equal parts as in the figure, label the indicated points with fractions that represent them.

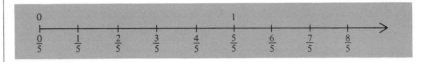

16. If 7 segments each of length $\frac{1}{7}$ are laid off consecutively, the total segment so obtained has length _____.

1

17. In view of frame 16 it is reasonable to define $7 \cdot \frac{1}{7} =$ _____.

1

18. As a generalization of frame 17 it is reasonable to define $n \cdot (1/n) =$ _____, where n is a natural number.

1

19. We have seen that $\frac{3}{5}$ represents a point on the number line obtained by laying off 3 segments each of length $\frac{1}{5}$ to the right of 0. Where is the point obtained by dividing a segment of length 3 into 5 parts and laying off one of these to the right of 0? _____

At the point labeled $\frac{3}{5}$.

20. From the result of frame 19, how shall we define $5 \cdot (\frac{3}{5})$? _____

3.

21. As a generalization of frame 20, what is the definition of $n \cdot (m/n)$? _____

m.

22. As a generalization of frame 21, what is $2n(m/n)$? _____ $kn(m/n)$? _____

$2m$ km.

451

You will note that we have *not* said what a fraction *is*. We have merely written symbols like *m/n* and 0/*n*, where *m* and *n* are natural numbers, and we have interpreted these as names for points on the number line. Although we have used the traditional notation for fractions, we observe that *m/n* denotes nothing more than an ordered pair of natural numbers and that we could just as well have written (*m*, *n*) instead of *m/n*. The use of the slash (/) in the traditional notation may suggest division to you, but we do not wish to give any suggestion that *m/n* represents a quotient; it is just another notation for an ordered pair! Another notation for the fraction *m/n* is $\dfrac{m}{n}$.

We shall use whichever of these is more convenient for the printer.

In this section, however, we have developed a small portion of the arithmetic of fractions by examining their properties as names for points on the number line. Let us summarize these in the following definitions:

DEFINITIONS

EQUALITY OF FRACTIONS

1. *Equality of fractions.* The fractions *m/n* and *p/q* are equal if and only if $m = p$ and $n = q$.

MULTIPLICATION BY NATURAL NUMBER

2. *Multiplication of a fraction by a natural number.* If *m*, *n*, and *k* are any natural numbers:

$$n \cdot (1/n) = 1 \qquad n \cdot (m/n) = m \qquad n \cdot (0/n) = 0 \qquad kn(m/n) = km$$

REMARK

This definition of the equality of fractions no doubt surprises you, for you are used to writing $\frac{1}{2} = \frac{2}{4} = \frac{3}{6} = \cdots$. To explain this situation let us anticipate ourselves and outline how we shall proceed. At the moment fractions are nothing but ordered pairs of whole numbers (*a*, *b*) with $b \neq 0$ which have physical and geometrical interpretations. As ordered pairs $a/b = c/d$ if and only if $a = c$ and $b = d$.

Later in this chapter we shall define *equivalent* fractions so that $\frac{1}{2}$, $\frac{2}{4}$, and $\frac{3}{6}$ are all equivalent. In Chapter 23 we shall define rational numbers to be equivalence classes of fractions. As explained there, the symbols $\frac{1}{2}$ and $\frac{2}{4}$ may be used as names for the equivalence class to which both belong. With this interpretation it will be correct to write $\frac{1}{2} = \frac{2}{4}$. But as fractions, rather than as rational numbers, $\frac{1}{2}$ and $\frac{2}{4}$ are not equal.

22.2 Additional Properties of Natural Numbers

Before we can do much more with fractions, we must introduce you to some additional properties of natural numbers. First let us consider their factorization.

A natural number *b* is a factor of a natural number *a* if and only if there is a natural number *c* such that $a = bc$. Every natural number *n* ($\neq 1$) has two factors, 1 and *n*, but many natural numbers have additional factors.

For example, the factors of 12 are 1, 2, 3, 4, 6, and 12. From the point of view of factorization we shall distinguish three types of numbers, as follows:

DEFINITIONS

UNIT
1. The number 1 is called the *unit*. It is its only factor.

PRIME
2. A natural number other than 1 whose only factors are itself and 1 is called a *prime*.

COMPOSITE
3. A natural number that is neither 1 nor a prime is called *composite*. A composite number has itself and 1 as factors but has other factors as well.

EXAMPLES. The first 10 primes are 2, 3, 5, 7, 11, 13, 17, 19, 23, and 29. On the other hand, 4, 6, 8, 9, 10, 12, 14, 15, 16, 18, ..., are composite.

A composite number, such as 60, can often be factored in several different ways; for example,

$$60 = 4 \cdot 15 \quad \text{and} \quad 60 = 3 \cdot 20$$

But frequently these factors themselves can be written as the products of other factors, such as

$$60 = 4(3 \cdot 5) \quad \text{and} \quad 60 = 3(4 \cdot 5)$$

In general, this process can be continued until all the factors are primes, and then it must stop. In the above example we have $60 = 2 \cdot 2 \cdot 3 \cdot 5$ and $60 = 3 \cdot 2 \cdot 2 \cdot 5$. Since this factorization into primes can be accomplished in many different ways, it is reasonable to ask whether the result is the same no matter how the process is carried out. The answer to this question is given in Theorem 1.

UNIQUE FACTORIZATION
THEOREM
THEOREM 1. UNIQUE FACTORIZATION THEOREM. The factorization of any natural number into primes is unique, apart from the order of the factors.

The proof of this theorem is too complicated for us to include in this book.

Two natural numbers may have one or more prime factors in common. For example, 3 and 5 are factors of both 45 and 60. The product of all these common, prime factors of the two numbers is called their *highest common factor* (HCF) or *greatest common divisor* (GCD). In general, we have the definition:

GREATEST COMMON DIVISOR
DEFINITION. The *greatest common divisor* (GCD) of two natural numbers n and m is the largest natural number that is a factor of both m and n.

Let us determine how to find the GCD of two natural numbers. For example, what is the GCD of 12 and 20? As a first step we write each of these as a product of its prime factors (Theorem 1):

$$12 = 2 \cdot 2 \cdot 3 \quad 20 = 2 \cdot 2 \cdot 5$$

Then we examine these products for common factors and find that 2 is the only common factor but that in each case it occurs twice. Therefore, the GCD is $2 \cdot 2 = 4$.

As another example let us find the GCD of 120 and 96. First,

$$120 = 2 \cdot 2 \cdot 2 \cdot 3 \cdot 5 \qquad 96 = 2 \cdot 2 \cdot 2 \cdot 2 \cdot 2 \cdot 3$$

Hence the GCD is $2 \cdot 2 \cdot 2 \cdot 3 = 24$. Note that 2 occurs three times as a factor of 120 and five times as a factor of 96. It therefore occurs three times in their GCD.

It is possible that a pair of natural numbers have no common factor except 1. In this case they are called relatively prime.

RELATIVELY PRIME   **D E F I N I T I O N .**   Two natural numbers n and m are *relatively prime* if and only if 1 is their only common factor; that is, 1 is the GCD of n and m.

The proof of the following theorem is immediate.

T H E O R E M 2 .   If k is the GCD of n and m, then $n \div k$ and $m \div k$ are relatively prime.

Proof.   In dividing by k, we have removed all the common factors of n and m except 1.

Another important theorem is the following:

T H E O R E M 3 .   If a, b, and c are natural numbers, where a and b are relatively prime and a is a factor of bc, then a is a factor of c.

Proof.   Since a is a factor of bc, all the prime factors of a must be factors of bc. But since a and b are relatively prime, none of these are factors of b. Hence they must be factors of c, and so a is a factor of c.

We now turn to a related problem. If we have two natural numbers a and b, can we find a natural number c such that each of a and b is a factor of c? Of course we can, for $c = ab$ is such a number. A number c of this kind is called a *common multiple* of a and b. The problem is to find the *least common multiple*, which is defined as follows:

LEAST COMMON MULTIPLE   **D E F I N I T I O N .**   The *least common multiple* (LCM) of two natural numbers a and b is the smallest natural number c such that each of a and b is a factor of c.

If we are given two natural numbers such as 12 and 20, how can we find this LCM? First we write their prime factorizations:

$$12 = 2 \cdot 2 \cdot 3 \qquad 20 = 2 \cdot 2 \cdot 5$$

The prime factors of the LCM must be just those primes which are factors of either 12 or 20 or both, and hence the LCM is the product of $2 \cdot 2 \cdot 3 \cdot 5 = 60$.

22.2 Additional Properties of Natural Numbers

As another example, let us find the LCM of 120 and 96. First,

$$120 = 2 \cdot 2 \cdot 2 \cdot 3 \cdot 5 \qquad 96 = 2 \cdot 2 \cdot 2 \cdot 2 \cdot 2 \cdot 3$$

The LCM is $2 \cdot 2 \cdot 2 \cdot 2 \cdot 2 \cdot 3 \cdot 5$. Note that 2 occurs three times as a factor of 120 and five times as a factor of 96. It therefore occurs five times in the LCM.

---

1. State whether each of the following natural numbers is the unit, a prime, or a composite number:

(a) 5. _____   (b) 24. _____

(c) 1. _____   (d) 30. _____

(e) 67. _____

> (a) Prime.   (b) Composite.   (c) Unit.   (d) Composite.
> (e) Prime.

2. A natural number $\neq 1$ is a prime if its only factors are _____ and _____.

> itself   one

3. A natural number that is neither the unit nor a prime is called _____.

> composite

4. List the first five primes larger than 29. _____

> 31, 37, 41, 43, 47.

5. True or false: (a) Every odd number is a prime. _____ (b) Every prime greater than 2 is an odd number. _____

> (a) F.   (b) T.

6. The factorization of 45 into primes is 45 = _____.

> $3 \cdot 3 \cdot 5$

7. The factorization of 90 into primes is 90 = _____.

> $2 \cdot 3 \cdot 3 \cdot 5$

8. The unique factorization theorem states that the factorization of a natural number into primes is _____

_____

unique apart from the order of the factors

9. Since 9 is a factor of 45 and since 3 is a factor of 9, it follows that 3 is a factor of _____.

45

10. Since $12 = 2 \cdot 2 \cdot 3$ and $15 = 3 \cdot 5$, the GCD of 12 and 15 is _____.

3

11. Since $36 = 2 \cdot 2 \cdot 3 \cdot 3$ and $27 = 3 \cdot 3 \cdot 3$, the GCD of 36 and 27 is _____.

$3 \cdot 3 = 9$

12. Find the GCD of 72 and 54. _____.

18. For $72 = 2 \cdot 2 \cdot 2 \cdot 3 \cdot 3$ and $54 = 2 \cdot 3 \cdot 3 \cdot 3$. So the GCD = $2 \cdot 3 \cdot 3 = 18$.

13. Since the GCD of 72 and 54 is 18, the quotients $72 \div 18 = 4$ and $54 \div 18 = 3$ have no factor in common. Hence they are called _____

_____.

relatively prime

14. When are two natural numbers relatively prime? _____

When 1 is their only common factor.

15. Which of the following pairs of numbers are relatively prime? (a) 25, 12. (b) 13, 6. (c) 30, 12. (d) 75, 15. (e) 21, 100. _____

(a), (b), and (e).

16. Since 3 and 5 are relatively prime, and since 3 is a factor of 105, and since $105 = 21 \cdot 5$, it follows that 3 is a factor of _____.

21

17. Since $12 = 2 \cdot 2 \cdot 3$ and $15 = 3 \cdot 5$, the LCM of 12 and 15 is _____.

$2 \cdot 2 \cdot 3 \cdot 5 = 60$

18. Since $36 = 2 \cdot 2 \cdot 3 \cdot 3$ and $27 = 3 \cdot 3 \cdot 3$, the LCM of 36 and 27 is _____.

$2 \cdot 2 \cdot 3 \cdot 3 \cdot 3 = 108$

19. Find the LCM of 72 and 54. _____

$72 = 2 \cdot 2 \cdot 2 \cdot 3 \cdot 3$, $54 = 2 \cdot 3 \cdot 3 \cdot 3$. So the LCM $= 2 \cdot 2 \cdot 2 \cdot 3 \cdot 3 \cdot 3 = 216$.

20. The product $72 \cdot 54 =$ _____. Hence $(72 \cdot 54) \div 216 =$ _____. Using the results of frames 12 and 19, it follows that $(72 \cdot 54) \div$ (LCM of 72 and 54) $=$ _____ of 72 and 54.

3888   18   GCD

21. Can you state the theorem that is illustrated in frame 20? If a and b are whole numbers, x is their LCM, and y is their GCD, then _____.

$(a \cdot b) \div x = y$

22.3 Equivalent Fractions

The use of fractions to represent points on the number line is complicated by the fact that two or more fractions may represent the same point on the number line. For example, $\frac{1}{2}, \frac{2}{4}, \frac{3}{6}, \ldots$ all correspond to the same point. A more general case of this complication is illustrated in Figure 22.5.

You may be accustomed to writing $\frac{1}{2} = \frac{2}{4} = \frac{3}{6} = \cdots$ to indicate the fact that all these fractions do represent the same point on the number line. We prefer not to do so, however; for, as discussed earlier, $\frac{1}{2}$ and $\frac{2}{4}$ are not equal. Instead, we shall use the concept of equivalent fractions:

EQUIVALENT FRACTIONS   **DEFINITION.** Two fractions a/b and c/d (where a, b, c, and d are whole numbers with $b \neq 0$ and $d \neq 0$) are *equivalent* if and only if they represent the same point on the number line.

This naturally raises the question: Without using the number line, how can we tell whether or not a/b and c/d are equivalent? Clearly $0/b$ and $0/d$

457

Fractions

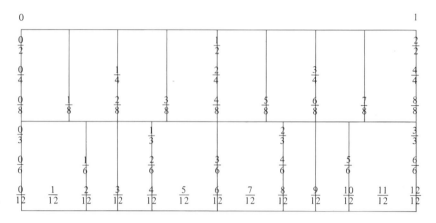

FIGURE 22.5. *Equivalent fractions.*

are equivalent, so let us further assume that $a \neq 0$ and $c \neq 0$. The answer to this question is given by Theorem 4.

THEOREM 4. Two fractions a/b and c/d (where a, b, c, and d are whole numbers none of which are zero) are equivalent if and only if $ad = bc$.

Proof. First suppose that a/b and c/d are equivalent; that is, they represent the same point on the number line. Then, from Section 22.1,

$$b(a/b) = a$$
$$bd(a/b) = ad$$

Also, $d(c/d) = c$ and $bd(c/d) = bc$. But since a/b and c/d represent the same point on the number line, it must be true that

$$bd(a/b) = bd(c/d)$$

Therefore, $ad = bc$.

On the other hand, if $ad = bc$, it follows that $bd(a/b) = ad = bc = bd(c/d)$. Now if we take a segment whose length is ad (or its equal, bc) and divide it into bd equal parts, the first point of subdivision can be labeled either a/b or c/d. Hence a/b and c/d are equivalent.

There is a certain fraction which is equivalent to a/b and which in a sense is the "simplest" such fraction. We say that this simplest fraction is in "lowest terms".

LOWEST TERMS
DEFINITION. A fraction a/b is in *lowest terms* if and only if a and b are relatively prime.

If we are given a fraction a/b, there is an easy way to find the fraction equivalent to a/b which is in lowest terms. This is given by Theorem 5.

THEOREM 5. Let k be the GCD of a and b. Then $(a \div k)/(b \div k)$ is in lowest terms and is equivalent to a/b.

Proof
1. $a \div k$ and $b \div k$ are relatively prime (Theorem 2).
2. $(a \div k)/(b \div k)$ and a/b are equivalent, for $a(b \div k) = (ab) \div k$; and $b(a \div k) = (ab) \div k$. Hence $a(b \div k) = b(a \div k)$.

Finally, if a/b is in lowest terms, we can find all the fractions equivalent to it by the following procedure:

THEOREM 6. If a/b is in lowest terms, then every fraction equivalent to a/b has the form an/bn, where n is some natural number.

Proof
1. Let c/d be equivalent to a/b. Then $ad = bc$.   Theorem 4.
2. a and b are relatively prime.   Definition of lowest terms.
3. a is a factor of bc.   From 1, by definition of a factor.
4. a is a factor of c.   Theorem 3.
5. $c = an$ for some natural number n.   Definition of factor.
6. $ad = ban = a(bn)$.   Substitution in 1.
7. $d = bn$.   Cancellation law.
8. Hence $c/d = an/bn$.   Substitution.

---

1. Show that $\frac{27}{90}$ and $\frac{36}{120}$ represent the same point on the number line. _____

> $27 \cdot 120 = 90 \cdot 36 = 3240.$

2. Which pairs of the following fractions represent the same point on the number line? $\frac{2}{4}, \frac{6}{40}, \frac{5}{10}, \frac{6}{8}, \frac{13}{65}, \frac{15}{100}, \frac{20}{100}, \frac{9}{12}$. _____
_____

> $\frac{2}{4}$ and $\frac{5}{10}$, $\frac{6}{40}$ and $\frac{15}{100}$, $\frac{6}{8}$ and $\frac{9}{12}$, $\frac{13}{65}$ and $\frac{20}{100}$.

3. Find fractions in lowest terms equivalent to the following fractions:
(a) $\frac{6}{8}$. _____
(b) $\frac{10}{20}$. _____
(c) $\frac{63}{27}$. _____
(d) $\frac{125}{30}$. _____
(e) $\frac{36}{36}$. _____

> (a) $\frac{3}{4}$.   (b) $\frac{1}{2}$.   (c) $\frac{7}{3}$.   (d) $\frac{25}{6}$.   (e) $\frac{1}{1}$

4. The fraction $\frac{5}{7}$ is in lowest terms. Find three fractions equivalent to it. _____, _____, _____.

> Many answers, such as $\frac{10}{14}, \frac{15}{21}, \frac{30}{42}$.

5. On a separate piece of paper prove that equivalence of fractions as defined in this section is an equivalence relation.

> **Proof**
>   1. It is *reflexive*, since a/b and a/b represent the same point on the number line.
>   2. It is *symmetric*, for if a/b and c/d represent the same point, then c/d and a/b represent the same point.
>   3. It is *transitive*, for if a/b and c/d represent the same point and if c/d and e/f represent the same point, then a/b and e/f represent this same point.

22.4 Generalized Fractions

So far we have restricted ourselves to fractions of the form a/b, where a and b are whole numbers and $b \neq 0$. What meaning shall we assign to fractions such as $\dfrac{-3}{5}$, $\dfrac{4}{-7}$, and $\dfrac{-6}{-13}$, where either the numerator or the denominator or both may be negative?

We can interpret fractions with negative numerators and positive denominators such as $\dfrac{-3}{5}$ by considering the two-way number line. For Figure 22.4 can be extended to the left of 0 as in Figure 22.6.

FIGURE 22.6.

The general definition is as follows:

$(-n)/m$ **DEFINITION.** Let n and m be natural numbers. Then the fraction $(-n)/m$ represents the point on the number line opposite to that represented by n/m.

Of course, two fractions of this form, such as $\dfrac{-4}{8}$ and $\dfrac{-3}{6}$, may represent the same point on the number line. If a, b, c, and d are positive integers, how can we determine in general when $\dfrac{-a}{b}$ and $\dfrac{-c}{d}$ represent the same point?

First, $\dfrac{-a}{b}$ and $\dfrac{a}{b}$ are at the same distance from 0 but in opposite directions. The same is true of $\dfrac{-c}{d}$ and $\dfrac{c}{d}$. Second, $\dfrac{a}{b}$ and $\dfrac{c}{d}$ represent the same point if and only if $ad = bc$. In such a case $\dfrac{-a}{b}$ and $\dfrac{-c}{d}$ also represent the same point. Therefore, $\dfrac{-a}{b}$ and $\dfrac{-c}{d}$ represent the same point if and only if $ad = bc$. Since $ad = bc$ if and only if $(-a)d = b(-c)$, we may state the result:

> **THEOREM 7.** Let a, b, c, and d be positive integers. Then the fractions $\dfrac{-a}{b}$ and $\dfrac{-c}{d}$ represent the same point on the number line if and only if $(-a)d = b(-c)$.

Fractions with negative denominators do not have such a natural interpretation, for we cannot divide a segment into a negative number of parts. Since fractions like $\dfrac{3}{-5}$ will turn up in our later work, however, we must find a way of giving meaning to them.

The clue to their interpretation is Theorem 4, which shows that for the case of whole numbers a, b, c, and d, with $b \neq 0$ and $d \neq 0$, two fractions a/b and c/d represent the same point on the number line if and only if $ad = bc$.

This suggests that $\dfrac{-3}{5}$ and $\dfrac{3}{-5}$ should represent the same point on the number line since $(-3) \cdot (-5) = 3 \cdot 5$. In general, then, we have the following interpretation for fractions with positive numerator and negative denominator:

n/(−m)   **INTERPRETATION.** The fraction $\dfrac{a}{-b}$ where a and b are whole numbers with $a \geq 0$ and $b > 0$ represents the same point on the number line as the fraction $\dfrac{-a}{b}$.

In the same way $\dfrac{a}{b}$ and $\dfrac{-a}{-b}$ represent the same point, for $a(-b) = (-a)(b)$. Hence we have the following interpretation:

(−n)/(−m)   **INTERPRETATION.** The fraction $\dfrac{-a}{-b}$, where a and b are whole numbers with $a \geq 0$ and $b > 0$, represents the same point on the number line as the fraction $\dfrac{a}{b}$.

If we put these interpretations together with Theorems 4 and 8 we have the following result:

> **THEOREM 8.** Let a, b, c, and d be integers with $b \neq 0$ and $d \neq 0$. Then the fractions a/b and c/d represent the same point on the number line if and only if $ad = bc$.

1. Which pairs of the following fractions represent the same point on the number line? $\dfrac{3}{6}, \dfrac{-12}{80}, \dfrac{-5}{10}, \dfrac{6}{-8}, \dfrac{15}{-100}, \dfrac{9}{-12}, \dfrac{2}{10}, \dfrac{-5}{-25}.$

$\dfrac{3}{6}$ and $\dfrac{-5}{-10}$, $\dfrac{-12}{80}$ and $\dfrac{15}{-100}$, $\dfrac{6}{-8}$ and $\dfrac{9}{-12}$, $\dfrac{2}{10}$ and $\dfrac{-5}{-25}$.

2. How shall we define $n[(-1)/n]$? ___

$-1.$

3. How shall we define $n[(-m)/n]$, where n and m are positive? __$-m$__

$-m.$

4. In general, if a is any integer and n is positive, what is $n[a/n]$? __a__

$a.$

5. If a and b are any integers with $b \neq 0$, how shall we define $b \cdot (a/b)$?
__a__

$a.$

6. If a, b, and c are any integers with $b \neq 0$, what is $bc(a/b)$? __ac__

$ac.$

SOLUTION OF EQUATIONS

22.5 Fractions as Solutions of an Equation

If we are dealing solely with integers, we find difficulty in solving equations of the form

$$bx = a$$

where a and b are integers and $b \neq 0$. There is no trouble in solving

$$2x = 6$$

for $x = 3$ has the required property. But there is no integer which is a solution of

$$4x = 7$$

In this section we shall learn how to use fractions to solve any equations of the form

$$bx = a$$

where a and b are integers and $b \neq 0$.

22.5 Fractions as Solutions of an Equation

EXAMPLE. If we wish to solve

$$4x = 7$$

we find that $x = \frac{7}{4}$ is a solution, since

$$4 \cdot \left(\tfrac{7}{4}\right) = 7$$

Similarly, $x = \frac{21}{12}$ is another solution.

You can learn the other important aspects of this process by answering the questions in the following frames.

---

1. Find a fraction that represents the solution of the equation $4x = 11$.

    [handwritten: $x = 11/4$]

> $x = \frac{11}{4}$, since $4 \cdot \frac{11}{4} = 11$.

2. Find fractions that represent the solution of the following equations:
    (a) $7x = 15$. *[handwritten: 15/7]*
    (b) $-19x = 8$. *[handwritten: 8/-19]*
    (c) $6x = -42$. *[handwritten: -42/6]*
    (d) $-32x = -16$. *[handwritten: -16/-32]*

> (a) $15/7$.   (b) $8/(-19)$.   (c) $(-42)/6$.   (d) $(-16)/(-32)$.

3. Find a fraction that represents the solution of $bx = a$, where a and b are integers and $b \neq 0$. *[handwritten: a/b]*

> a/b.

4. By considering a subdivision of the number line, how should we define $3 \cdot \left(\frac{4}{5}\right)$? *[handwritten: 12/5]* $4 \cdot \left(\frac{3}{5}\right)$? *[handwritten: 12/5]*.

> $\frac{12}{5}$ $\frac{12}{5}$

5. In general, if a, b, and c are integers and $b \neq 0$, how should we define $c \cdot (a/b)$? *[handwritten: ac/b]* $a \cdot (c/b)$? *[handwritten: ac/b]*

> $(ac)/b$ $(ac)/b$

6. Suppose that $x = c/d$ is a solution of $bx = a$; that is, $b(c/d) = a$. Prove that $ad = bc$. *[handwritten: $db(c/d) = ad; db(c/d) = bc.$ So $ad = bc$]*

> From the hypothesis $db(c/d) = ad$. But $db(c/d) = bc$. Hence $ad = bc$.

463

7. If $x = c/d$ is a solution of $bx = a$, a/b and c/d are __equal__.

equivalent (frame 6 and Theorem 8)

8. The fractions that satisfy $bx = a$, where a and b are integers and $b \neq 0$, are all __equal__.

equivalent

9. Let a, b, c, and d be integers such that $b \neq 0$ and $d \neq 0$. Prove that if $ad = bc$, then $x = c/d$ satisfies the equation $bx = a$. __$b(c/d) = (bc)/d$ $= (ad)/d = d \cdot (a/d) = a$__

$b(c/d) = (bc)/d = (ad)/d = d \cdot (a/d) = a$

10. Write three solutions of the equation $5x = 9$. __$9/5, {}^-9/5, \frac{18}{10}$__

$9/5$, $18/10$, $(-9)/(-5)$, and many others.

11. How many fractions represent the same point on the number line? __many__ How many fractions are solutions of the equation $bx = a$, where $b \neq 0$? __many__

Infinitely many.   Infinitely many.

In this chapter we have defined a fraction as the symbol a/b, where a and b are integers and $b \neq 0$. The rules for handling fractions may be summarized as follows (these rules are, in fact, definitions):

EQUALITY. $a/b = c/d$ if and only if $a = c$ and $b = d$.

EQUIVALENCE. a/b and c/d are equivalent if and only if $ad = bc$. Two equivalent fractions represent the same point on the number line.

MULTIPLICATION BY AN INTEGER. $b \cdot (a/b) = a$; $c \cdot (a/b) = (ac)/b$.

We have interpreted fractions as names for points on the two-way number line, such that two equivalent fractions are names for the same point.

We have also shown how to use fractions to solve equations of the form $bx = a$, where a and b are integers and $b \neq 0$. Moreover, two fractions are solutions of the same equation of this type if and only if they are equivalent.

Now test your mastery of these ideas by working the following Post Test.

POST TEST

1. Today is my twentieth birthday and I have lived in this town since my third birthday. What fraction of my life have I spent here? __17/20__

2. We can locate the point corresponding to $\frac{3}{5}$ on the number line by (a) dividing the segment between 0 and 1 into __5__ parts, and laying off __3__ of these to the __right__ of 0. (b) dividing the segment between 0 and 3 into __5__ parts, and laying off __1__ of these to the __right__ of 0.

3. What are the values of the following expressions where k, n, and m are natural numbers and $m \neq 0$? (a) $m(1/m)$. __1__ (b) $m(n/m)$. __n__ (c) $km(n/m)$. __kn__

4. The fractions a/b and c/d are equivalent if and only if __ad__ = __bc__.

5. On the number line two equivalent fractions represent the __same pt.__

6. Find a fraction in lowest terms equivalent to each of the following: (a) $\frac{5}{15}$. __1/3__ (b) $\frac{55}{100}$. __11/20__

7. Which pairs of fractions in this list represent the same point on the number line? (a) $\dfrac{-3}{24}$. (b) $\dfrac{4}{64}$. (c) $\dfrac{-7}{-112}$. (d) $\dfrac{-6}{-10}$. (e) $\dfrac{7}{-56}$. (f) $\dfrac{15}{25}$. __a+e__, __d+f__, __b+c__.

8. What fraction with a positive denominator is equivalent to the fraction $\dfrac{5}{-9}$? __-5/9__

9. Write a fraction which is a solution of each of the following equations: (a) $19x = 3$. __3/19__ (b) $15x = -6$. __-6/15__ (c) $-7x = 22$. __22/-7__

10. Is there a unique fraction which is a solution of $bx = a$? __No__

---

11. If $x = c/d$ and $x = e/f$ are both solutions of the equation $bx = a$, what can be said about the relation of c/d to e/f? __equivalent__

12. Find the factorization of 80 into primes. $80 =$ __2·2·2·2·5__.

13. Find the GCD of 15 and 72. __3__

14. Find the LCM of 16 and 30. __2·2·2·2·3·5__

15. The statement that a and b are relatively prime means that __have no factor in common except 1__.

---

1. $\frac{17}{20}$.
2. (a) 5; 3; right.   (b) 5; 1; right.
3. (a) 1. (b) n. (c) kn.
4. ad; bc

5. same point
6. (a) $\frac{1}{3}$. (b) $\frac{11}{20}$.
7. (a) and (e); (b) and (c); (d) and (f)
8. $(-5)/9$.
9. (a) 3/19. (b) $(-6)/15$ [or $(-2)/5$]. (c) $22/(-7)$ [or $(-22)/7$].
10. No. If $x = a/b$ is a solution, ka/kb is another solution.
11. They are equivalent, or represent the same point on the number line.
12. $2 \cdot 2 \cdot 2 \cdot 2 \cdot 5$
13. 3.
14. $2 \cdot 2 \cdot 2 \cdot 2 \cdot 3 \cdot 5 = 240$.
15. they have no factors in common except 1

If you were successful in this test proceed to Chapter 23.

23
Rational Numbers

Before beginning this chapter you should have completed Chapter 22, Fractions. As a review of topics needed for this chapter, work the following Readiness Test.

READINESS TEST

1. The fractions a/b and c/d are equivalent if and only if (a) they represent the <u>same point</u> on the number line (b) $ad = $ <u>bc</u> .

> (a) same point (b) bc

2. The relation "a/b is equivalent to c/d" is an equivalence relation because it is (1) <u>reflexive</u>, (2) <u>symmetric</u>, and (3) <u>transitive</u>

> reflexive symmetric transitive

3. In an equivalence class of fractions all the members of the class are mutually <u>equivalent</u>.

> equivalent

4. A binary operation $*$ on a set S must be defined for <u>every</u> ordered pair (a, b), where a and b are elements of S.

> every

5. Why is division not a binary operation on the set of integers? <u>It is not defined for all ordered pairs.</u>

> It is not defined for every ordered pair of integers. For example, $2 \div 3$ is not defined in the set of integers.

When you have completed the test proceed to Section 23.1 and work the program following it.

23.1 Introduction

The set of fractions of the form a/b, where a and b are integers and $b \neq 0$, constitutes a system of numbers which has a great deal of practical utility. It has the major disadvantages, however, that infinitely many fractions represent the same point on the number line and that there are an infinite number of solutions of the equation $bx = a$, where $b \neq 0$. To avoid these complications we shall introduce a new set of numbers, called the *rational numbers.*

The intuitive idea of a rational number is that it is the entire set of fractions which represent the same point on the number line, or which satisfy a particular equation of the form $bx = a$. An example of a rational number is the set of fractions $\left\{ \cdots, \dfrac{-6}{-9}, \dfrac{-4}{-6}, \dfrac{-2}{-3}, \dfrac{2}{3}, \dfrac{4}{6}, \dfrac{6}{9}, \dfrac{8}{12}, \cdots \right\}$.

To discuss rational numbers systematically we must define a new term:

EQUIVALENCE CLASS OF FRACTIONS

DEFINITION. An *equivalence class of fractions* is a set of fractions all of whose members are mutually equivalent, and such that every fraction which is equivalent to any member of the class is itself a member of the class.

The equivalence classes of fractions partition the set of all fractions into a collection of disjoint sets such that all members of any one of these are mutually equivalent.

RATIONAL NUMBER

DEFINITION. A *rational number* is an equivalence class of fractions.

These equivalence classes can be shown graphically as in Figure 23.1. In this figure a fraction a/b is plotted by measuring the numerator a vertically

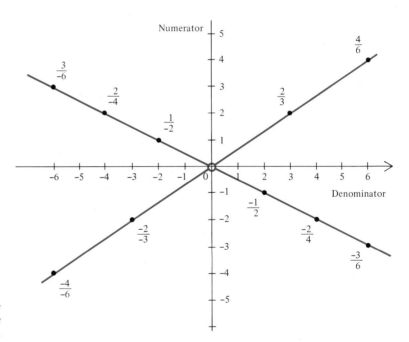

FIGURE 23.1. *The equivalence classes are represented by the colored lines through O.*

and the denominator b horizontally. It is evident from the figure that the fractions belonging to a particular equivalence class lie on a line through O. Thus the rational numbers are represented by lines through O. It should be

468

noted that the point O does not lie on any of these lines, for O should represent the fraction $0/0$, which is undefined. Moreover no fractions are represented by points on the vertical axis, for points on this axis should represent fractions of the form $a/0$, which are also undefined.

When we wish to designate a particular rational number, we can, of course, write down the symbol for the appropriate set, such as

$$\left\{ \ldots, \frac{-3}{6}, \frac{-2}{4}, \frac{-1}{2}, \frac{1}{-2}, \frac{2}{-4}, \frac{3}{-6}, \ldots \right\}$$

but this is very clumsy. Since this set is determined by the knowledge of any one of its elements, it is much simpler to name a rational number by any one of the fractions belonging to its equivalence class. Thus we can write

NAMES FOR RATIONAL NUMBERS

$$\left\langle \frac{2}{3} \right\rangle = \left\{ \ldots, \frac{-6}{-9}, \frac{-4,}{-6}, \frac{-2}{-3}, \frac{2}{3}, \frac{4}{6}, \frac{6}{9}, \frac{8}{12}, \ldots \right\}$$

$$\left\langle \frac{-6}{-9} \right\rangle = \left\{ \ldots, \frac{-6}{-9}, \frac{-4}{-6}, \frac{-2}{-3}, \frac{2}{3}, \frac{4}{6}, \frac{6}{9}, \frac{8}{12}, \ldots \right\}$$

In this notation we have placed the fractions $\frac{2}{3}$ and $\frac{-6}{-9}$ in brackets to indicate that $\left\langle \frac{2}{3} \right\rangle$ and $\left\langle \frac{-6}{-9} \right\rangle$ are names for the equivalence class and hence are not the same as the fractions $\frac{2}{3}$ and $\frac{-6}{-9}$. Earlier we used the term *numeral* to mean the name of a number, and so $\left\langle \frac{2}{3} \right\rangle$ and $\left\langle \frac{-6}{-9} \right\rangle$ are numerals that are names for the same rational number $\left\{ \ldots, \frac{-6}{-9}, \frac{-4}{-6}, \frac{-2}{-3}, \right.$ $\left. \frac{2}{3}, \frac{4}{6}, \frac{6}{9}, \ldots \right\}$. We also stated that two numerals are equal if and only if they are names for the same number. Hence we may properly write

$$\left\langle \frac{2}{3} \right\rangle = \left\langle \frac{-6}{-9} \right\rangle$$

In general, we have

$$\langle a/b \rangle = \langle c/d \rangle$$

if and only if a/b and c/d are equivalent.

REMARKS

1. There is a "simplest" name for any particular rational number, the numeral $\langle a/b \rangle$, where b is positive and $|a|/|b|$ is in *lowest terms*. For example, $\langle 1/2 \rangle$ and $\langle 2/3 \rangle$ are the names in lowest terms of the rational numbers

$$\left\{ \ldots, \frac{-2}{-4}, \frac{-1}{-2}, \frac{1}{2}, \frac{2}{4}, \frac{3}{6}, \ldots \right\} \text{ and } \left\{ \ldots, \frac{-6}{-9}, \frac{-4}{-6}, \frac{-2}{-3}, \frac{2}{3}, \frac{4}{6}, \frac{6}{9}, \ldots \right\}, \text{respectively.}$$

Rational Numbers

Similarly, $\left\langle\dfrac{-5}{3}\right\rangle$ is the name in lowest terms of the rational number
$$\left\{\dots,\dfrac{10}{-6},\dfrac{5}{-3},\dfrac{-5}{3},\dfrac{-10}{6},-\dfrac{15}{9},\dots\right\}.$$

2. The rational number $\left\langle\dfrac{a}{1}\right\rangle=\left\{\dots,\dfrac{-3a}{-3},\dfrac{-2a}{-2},\dfrac{-a}{-1},\dfrac{a}{1},\dfrac{2a}{2},\dfrac{3a}{3},\dots\right\}$
represents the same point on the number line as the integer a. Hence it is reasonable to write $\langle a\rangle$ as a name for this rational number. That is, we write $\langle a\rangle=\langle a/1\rangle$ for every integer a.

3. It has been desirable so far to distinguish between the *fraction* $\dfrac{7}{5}$ and the symbol $\left\langle\dfrac{7}{5}\right\rangle$, which is a name for the *rational number* $\left\{\dots,\dfrac{-21}{-15},\dfrac{-14}{-10},\dfrac{-7}{-5},\dfrac{7}{5},\dfrac{14}{10},\dfrac{21}{15},\dots\right\}$. The use of the brackets in $\left\langle\dfrac{7}{5}\right\rangle$, however, becomes very clumsy in our later work. Consequently, hereafter, we shall omit the brackets and write simply $\frac{7}{5}$ as a name of this rational number. This practice introduces ambiguity, since $\frac{7}{5}$ now has two meanings, but this will not bother you, since the context will tell you which interpretation is intended.

1. The fractions a/b and c/d, where a, b, c, and d are integers with $b\neq 0$ and $d\neq 0$, are equivalent if and only if $ad=\underline{bc}$.

bc

2. Which pairs of fractions in the following list are equivalent? 4/7, 6/9, $(-50)/100$, 8/12, $(-8)/(-14)$, $4/(-8)$. _4/7 + -8/-14, -50/100 + 4/-8, 8/12 + 6/9,_

$4/7$ and $(-8)/(-14)$, 6/9 and 8/12, $(-50)/100$ and $4/(-8)$.

3. If k is a nonzero integer, prove that a/b and $(ka)/(kb)$ are equivalent. _a(kb)=b(ka)_

$a(kb)=b(ka)$.

4. Using the result of frame 3 write three fractions equivalent to 4/5. _8/10, 12/15, -8/-10_

Many answers, such as 8/10, 12/15, and $(-8)/(-10)$.

5. According to the definition, a rational number is an _equivalence class_ of fractions.

equivalence class

6. Every pair of fractions in an equivalence class of fractions is _____

equivalent (handwritten)

equivalent

7. A name for the rational number $\left\{\cdots, \dfrac{-6}{-8}, \dfrac{-3}{-4}, \dfrac{3}{4}, \dfrac{6}{8}, \dfrac{9}{16}, \cdots\right\}$ is

_____. *3/4* (handwritten)

Many names, such as $\dfrac{3}{4}, \dfrac{6}{8}$, and $\dfrac{-3}{-4}$. It is not necessary to write these

as $\left\langle \dfrac{3}{4} \right\rangle, \left\langle \dfrac{6}{8} \right\rangle$, etc.

8. The "simplest" name for the rational number in frame 7 is _____. *3/4* (handwritten)

$\dfrac{3}{4}$

9. For what rational number is $\dfrac{10}{12}$ a suitable name? _____ *(handwritten: $\frac{-10}{-12}, \frac{-5}{-6}, \frac{5}{6}, \frac{10}{12}$)*

_____

$$\left\{\cdots, \dfrac{-10}{-12}, \dfrac{-5}{-6}, \dfrac{5}{6}, \dfrac{10}{12}, \dfrac{15}{18}, \cdots\right\}.$$

10. What is the "simplest" name for the rational number

$\left\{\cdots, \dfrac{-2}{-2}, \dfrac{-1}{-1}, \dfrac{1}{1}, \dfrac{2}{2}, \dfrac{3}{3}, \cdots\right\}$? _____ *1* (handwritten)

$\dfrac{1}{1}$ (or 1) (see frame 12 below).

11. The fraction 1/1 represents the same point on the number line as the integer _____. *1* (handwritten)

1

12. Since the fraction $a/1$ represents the same point on the number line as the integer _____, *a* (handwritten) we may use a as another name for the rational number whose name is _____. *a/1* (handwritten)

a $a/1$

13. Write five members of the equivalence class for which 0 is a suitable name. _0/1, 0/2, 0/3, 0/4, 0/5_

> 0/1, 0/2, 0/3, 0/4, 0/5, ...

14. Write five members of the equivalence class for which -3 is a suitable name. _$-3/1$, $-6/2$, $-9/3$, $3/-1$, $6/-2$_

> $(-3)/1$, $(-6)/2$, $(-9)/3$, $3/(-1)$, $6/(-2)$, ...

15. The equation $\langle 3/6 \rangle = \langle 6/12 \rangle$ means that $\langle 3/6 \rangle$ and $\langle 6/12 \rangle$ are names for _the same_ rational number.

> the same

16. If we drop the $\langle \rangle$ in frame 15, as is usually done, the equality $3/6 = 6/12$ means that $3/6$ and $6/12$ are _names for same rational no._

> names for the same rational number

THE SYMBOL $-\frac{a}{b}$

17. You have undoubtedly seen the symbol $-\frac{2}{3}$, which is so far undefined. A reasonable interpretation for this symbol is that it represents a point on the number line to the _left_ of O whose distance from O
(right, left)
is 2/3. Thus $-\frac{2}{3}$ can be defined to be a name for the rational number _$-2/3$ or $2/-3$_.

> left $(-2)/3$ [or $2/(-3)$]

18. In general, the symbol $-\frac{a}{b}$ is defined to be a name for the rational number _$-a/b$ or $a/-b$_. Hence we can write $-\frac{a}{b} =$ _$-a/b$ or $a/-b$_.

> $(-a)/b$ [or $a/(-b)$] $(-a)/b$ [or $a/(-b)$]

19. What is the value of $3\left(-\frac{4}{3}\right)$? _$3((-4/3)) = -4$_

> $3[(-4)/3] = -4$.

20. What is the value of $b\left(-\frac{a}{b}\right)$, where $b \neq 0$? _$-a$_

> $-a$.

23.2 Addition and Subtraction of Rational Numbers

Our next objective is to define the sum, difference, product, and quotient of pairs of rational numbers and then to develop the properties of these operations. As in Chapter 20, we wish to define these in a sensible fashion, and so we shall first operate in an intuitive fashion to see what definitions are likely to make sense.

Let us assume that the rational numbers behave in a fashion such that any reasonable commutative, associative, or distributive property is true. If $x = a/b$ and $y = c/d$ are two rational numbers, we know that the following equations are satisfied:

$$bx = a \quad \text{and} \quad dy = c$$

If we multiply both sides of the first equation by d and both sides of the second equation by b, we obtain

$$bdx = ad \quad \text{and} \quad bdy = bc$$

Hence by adding the two left sides and the two right sides, we have that

$$bdx + bdy = ad + bc$$

Therefore,

$$bd(x + y) = ad + bc$$

and so

$$x + y = (ad + bc)/bd$$

That is,

$$a/b + c/d = (ad + bc)/bd$$

We emphasize that this derivation has proved nothing; it merely suggests that if rational numbers are to behave in a reasonable fashion, their sum should be given by the last equation above. These considerations motivate the following definition:

ADDITION **DEFINITION.** If a/b and c/d are rational numbers, then by definition

$$a/b + c/d = (ad + bc)/bd$$

In similar fashion we can define subtraction:

SUBTRACTION **DEFINITION.** If a/b and c/d are rational numbers, then by definition

$$a/b - c/d = (ad - bc)/bd$$

The properties of these operations are exactly the same as those of addition and subtraction on the set of integers.

473

REMARKS

1. If we wish to be completely rigorous we should prove that these operations are *uniquely defined*. We have defined

$$\frac{1}{2} + \frac{5}{6} = \frac{6 + 10}{12} = \frac{16}{12}$$

Will we get the same result if we add the equivalent fractions: $\frac{2}{4} + \frac{10}{12}$? Let us see:

$$\frac{2}{4} + \frac{10}{12} = \frac{24 + 40}{48} = \frac{64}{48}$$

The sums are the same rational number if $\frac{16}{12}$ and $\frac{64}{48}$ are equivalent fractions.

Since both are equivalent to $\frac{4}{3}$, they are equivalent and all is well.

A general proof that the addition and subtraction of rational numbers are *uniquely defined* can be constructed in a similar fashion, but we shall not do so here.

2. Again we are guilty of "abuse of notation". In the formula

$$a/b + c/d = (ad + bc)/bd$$

the $+$ on the left indicates addition of rational numbers (which is being defined) and the $+$ on the right indicates addition of integers. So, to be precise we should write

$$a/b \oplus c/d = (ad + bc)/bd$$

As usual, we shall not introduce this complication in the hope that you understand what is involved. Similar remarks apply to subtraction.

---

1. From the definition of the sum of two rational numbers find the values of
   (a) $2/3 + 4/5 = $ _____ .
   (b) $7/3 + 2/9 = $ _____ .
   (c) $2/5 + 3/(-8) = $ _____ .
   (d) $(-5)/2 + 4/7 = $ _____ .
   (e) $(-9)/4 + (-11)/5 = $ _____ .

   (a) $22/15$ (b) $69/27$ (c) $(-1)/(-40)$ (d) $(-27)/14$
   (e) $(-89)/20$

2. If we apply the definition of addition to $a/b + c/b$ the sum is $\frac{ab + cb}{b^2}$.

If we apply the distributive law to the numerator, we derive that

$$\frac{a}{b} + \frac{c}{b} = \frac{(a + c)b}{b^2} = \underline{\qquad} .$$

$$\frac{a + c}{b}$$

3. The result of frame 2 can be expressed as follows: The sum of two rational numbers with the same denominator is equal to a rational number with this same denominator and whose numerator is *the sum of a given numerators* _____

the sum of the two given numerators

4. The sum of 5/6 and 7/6 is *12/6 or 2*.

12/6 = 2

5. The sum of $\frac{-8}{5}$ and $\frac{9}{5}$ is *1/5*.

1/5

6. We can apply frames 2 and 3 to add any two rational numbers as follows. Find $7/12 + 5/8$. We rewrite these using other names for 7/12 and 5/8 which have the same denominator. One choice is $56/96 + 60/96$. Hence the sum is $7/12 + 5/8 = 56/96 + 60/96 =$ *116/96*, or in lowest terms = *29/24*.

116/96   29/24

7. In frame 6 we could have reduced the size of the numbers involved by using the LCM as a common denominator. The LCM of 12 and 8 is *24*. Hence $7/12 + 5/8 = 14/24 + 15/24 =$ *29/24*. *Lowest Common Multiple*

24   29/24

8. The use of the LCM as a denominator is frequently helpful but is by no means compulsory. It is good practice, however, to reduce all answers to lowest terms. For the purposes of this frame, however, we ask you to use the LCM to find the sums:

(a) $\frac{-7}{9} + \frac{5}{12}$ LCM = *36*; sum = *-13/36*.

(b) $\frac{5}{16} + \frac{-3}{20}$ LCM = *80*; sum = *13/80*.

(c) $\frac{-7}{10} + \frac{-5}{4}$ LCM = *20*; sum = *-39/20*.

Rational Numbers

(d) $\dfrac{6}{7} + \dfrac{-11}{14}$ LCM = 14 ; sum = $1/14$.

(e) $\dfrac{23}{24} + \dfrac{-7}{36}$ LCM = 22 ; sum = $55/72$.

(handwritten in margin: 69 14 35)

(a) 36; (−13)/36   (b) 80; 13/80   (c) 20; (−39)/20   (d) 14; 1/14   (e) 72; 55/72

9. Is addition a binary operation on the set of rational numbers? __Yes__ Why? *the sum of the set of rational number is on the set of rational nos*

Yes.   It has two inputs and the sum of every pair of rational numbers is a rational number.

10. Is the addition of rational numbers commutative? __Yes__ . Why? $a/b + c/d = \dfrac{ad+bc}{bd}, c/d + a/b = \dfrac{bc+da}{bd},$ *(handwritten)* $\dfrac{ad+bc}{bd} = \dfrac{bc}{b}$

Yes. $a/b + c/d = \dfrac{ad+bc}{bd}, c/d + a/b = \dfrac{bc+da}{bd},$

$\dfrac{ad+bc}{bd} = \dfrac{bc+da}{bd}.$

11. Using the following example, verify that the addition of rational numbers is associative.

$$4/5 + [3/2 + (-7)/6] = 4/5 + \underline{1/3} = \underline{17/15}$$
$$[4/5 + 3/2] + (-7)/6 = \underline{23/10} + (-7)/6 = \underline{17/15}$$

1/3   17/15   23/10   17/15

12. What rational number c/d is the additive identity? That is, for all a/b, $a/b + c/d = a/b$ for what c/d? __0__

$c/d = 0/d = 0.$

13. What rational number c/d is the additive inverse of a/b; that is, $a/b + c/d = 0$? __−a/b__

$c/d = (-a)/b = a/(-b) = -(a/b).$

14. What is the additive inverse of 2/3? __$-\frac{2}{3}$__

$-\dfrac{2}{3}\left[\text{ or } \dfrac{(-2)}{3} \text{ or } \dfrac{2}{(-3)} \right].$

15. The difference of two rational numbers is defined as in the case integers by the formula

$$a/b - c/d = a/b + [-(c/d)]$$

$$= \frac{a}{b} + \frac{-c}{d}$$

$$= \frac{ad - bc}{bd}$$

Find the values of

(a) $5/4 - 7/15 =$ __47/60__. (b) $2/3 - 16/5 =$ __-38/15__.
(c) $2/3 - (-11)/36 =$ __35/36__. (d) $5/8 - 2/8 =$ __3/8__.
(e) $3/14 - 8/14 =$ __-5/14__.

(a) 47/60 (b) (−38)/15 (c) 35/36 (d) 3/8 (e) (−5)/14

23.3 Multiplication and Division of Rational Numbers

To motivate our definition of the product of two rational numbers, we let $x = a/b$ and $y = c/d$; then we know that

$$bx = a \qquad \text{and} \qquad dy = c$$

Now multiply the two left sides and the two right sides. The result is

$$bd(xy) = ac$$

Therefore, $xy = (ac)/(bd)$ or

$$\frac{a}{b} \cdot \frac{c}{d} = \frac{ac}{bd}$$

This suggests to us that the following definition is appropriate:

MULTIPLICATION   **DEFINITION.** If a/b and c/d are rational numbers, then by definition

$$\frac{a}{b} \cdot \frac{c}{d} = \frac{ac}{bd}$$

REMARKS

1. Again to be precise, we need to prove that multiplication is *uniquely defined*. If you like this sort of thing, you might try to construct a proof for yourself.

2. Once more, we are guilty of "abuse of notation". For instead of

$$\frac{a}{b} \cdot \frac{c}{d} = \frac{ac}{bd}$$

we properly should write

$$\frac{a}{b} \odot \frac{c}{d} = \frac{a}{b} \cdot \frac{c}{d}$$

to distinguish between the two types of multiplication involved.
Division is defined in the usual fashion:

DIVISION   **DEFINITION.**   If a/b, c/d, and r/s are rational numbers with $c \neq 0$,

$$(a/b) \div (c/d) = r/s$$

if and only if $a/b = (r/s)(c/d)$.

Multiplication has all the properties of multiplication on the set of integers.
But in division we have something new.

THEOREM 1.   Division is a binary operation on the set of nonzero
rational numbers.

Proof.   We must show that division is defined for every pair of nonzero
rational numbers. That is, given a/b and c/d nonzero, we must find a nonzero
rational number r/s such that

$$a/b = (r/s)(c/d)$$

In fact, $r/s = (a/b)(d/c)$ is such a number. For in this case

$$(r/s)(c/d) = (a/b \cdot d/c)(c/d)$$
$$= (a/b)(d/c \cdot c/d)$$
$$= (a/b) \cdot 1$$
$$= a/b$$

Moreover, since $a \neq 0$ and $d \neq 0$, $r/s = (a/b)(d/c) \neq 0$. As usual, division is
neither commutative nor associative.

---

1. Find the values of the products:
(a) $(4/5)(2/3) =$ __8/15__ .   (b) $(8/9)(3/2) =$ __4/3__ .
(c) $(-4/7)(2/5) =$ __-8/35__ .   (d) $(3/-2)(-5/8) =$ __15/16__ .

(a) 8/15   (b) 4/3   (c) --8/35   (d) 15/16

2. Is multiplication a binary operation on the set of rational numbers?
__Yes__

Yes.

3. Is multiplication of rational numbers commutative? __Yes__.
Why? $\dfrac{a}{b} \cdot \dfrac{c}{d} = \dfrac{ac}{bd} = \dfrac{ca}{db} = \dfrac{c}{d} \cdot \dfrac{a}{b}$

> Yes. $\dfrac{a}{b} \cdot \dfrac{c}{d} = \dfrac{ac}{bd} = \dfrac{ca}{db} = \dfrac{c}{d} \cdot \dfrac{a}{b}.$

4. Is multiplication of rational numbers associative? __Yes__.
Why? __Multiplication of integers is associative__

> Yes. Multiplication of integers is associative.

5. Is there a multiplicative identity for rational numbers, that is, a rational number c/d such that for all a/b $(a/b)(c/d) = (a/b)$? __Yes__.
If so, what is it? $c/d = 1/1 = 1$

> Yes $c/d = 1/1 = 1.$

6. If a/b is a rational number, does it have a multiplicative inverse, that is, a rational number c/d such that $(a/b)(c/d) = 1$? __Yes__. If so, what is it? __If $a \neq 0$, $c/d = b/a$__

> Yes. Provided $a \neq 0$, $c/d = b/a$.

7. The multiplicative inverse of a/b is sometimes called its reciprocal. Then the reciprocal of a/b $(a \neq 0)$ is __b/a__.

> b/a

8. The reciprocal of 2/3 is __3/2__.

> 3/2

9. The reciprocal of 2 is the reciprocal of 2/1, or __1/2__.

> 1/2

10. Show that the quotient $a/b \div c/d$ is equal to the product of a/b and the reciprocal of c/d. This justifies the common saying "To divide two fractions invert the divisor and multiply". $a/b \div c/d = (a/b)(d/c)$

> $a/b \div c/d = (a/b) \cdot (d/c)$. But d/c is the reciprocal of c/d, and hence the statement in the frame is true.

11. As in the case of whole numbers $(a/b) \div (0/d)$ and $(0/b) \div (0/d)$ are
_____ *not defined*

> not defined

12. Why is division a binary operation on the set of nonzero rational numbers? *the quotient of nonzero rationals is defined and is a nonzero rational no.*

> The quotient of every pair of nonzero rationals is defined and is a nonzero rational number

13. Find the values of the following quotients:
(a) $2/3 \div 7/9 =$ _____ *6/7*
(b) $1/8 \div 11/3 =$ _____ *3/88*.
(c) $[(-4)/9] \div [(-3)/7] =$ _____ *28/27*.
(d) $-\frac{9}{5} \div \frac{2}{5} =$ _____ *$-\frac{9}{2}$*.

> (a) 6/7   (b) 3/88   (c) 28/27   (d) $-\frac{9}{2}$

14. Another method of finding quotients is the following. Write $a/b \div c/d$ as the quotient of two rational numbers with equal denominators. For example, $\dfrac{a}{b} \div \dfrac{c}{d} = \dfrac{ad}{bd} \div \dfrac{bc}{bd}$. Then $\dfrac{a}{b} \div \dfrac{c}{d} = \dfrac{ad}{bd} \cdot \dfrac{bd}{bc} = ad/bc$. Apply this method to find the value of:
(a) $3/4 \div 7/5 = 15/20 \div 28/20 =$ _____ *15/28*.
(b) $[7/9] \div [(-5)/11] =$ _____ *$-77/45$*.
(c) $-\dfrac{15}{4} \div \dfrac{3}{7} =$ _____ *$-105/12$*.
(d) $25/3 \div 10/6 =$ _____ *5*.
(e) $[(-7)/(-4)] \div [5/3] =$ _____ *21/20*.

> (a) 15/28   (b) $(-77)/45$ (c) $(-105)/12$ (d) 5   (e) 21/20

15. We recall that $a/1 = a$ and $b/1 = b$. The quotient $(a/1) \div (b/1) = (a/1) \cdot (1/b) = a/b$. Therefore, the rational number a/b is the quotient of the rational numbers *a/1* and *b/1*.

> $a/1$ $b/1$ (or a and b)

16. Solve for x:
(a) $(3/2)x = 7/8$, $x = 7/8 \div 3/2 =$ _____ *7/12*.
(b) $(4/5)x = 5/6$, $x =$ _____ *25/24*.
(c) $[(-1)/3]x = 7/9$, $x =$ _____ *$-7/3$*.
(d) $5x = 2/11$, $x =$ _____ *2/55*.

> (a) 7/12   (b) 25/24   (c) $(-7)/3$ (d) 2/55

480

17. Show that the equation $(a/b)x = c/d$ with $a \neq 0$ has a rational number as its solution and find the solution. $X = \frac{c}{d} \cdot \frac{b}{a}$

$$x = \left(\frac{c}{d}\right)\left(\frac{b}{a}\right).$$

18. Show that the solution of the equation in frame 17 is unique. If x_1 and x_2 are two solutions, then $(a/b)x_1 = (a/b)x_2$. Since $a \neq 0$, b/a is defined. Then

$$b/a[(a/b)x_1] = X_1$$
$$b/a[(a/b)x_2] = X_2$$

Hence $X_1 = X_2$.

$x_1 \qquad x_2 \qquad x_1 = x_2$

19. How many rational numbers correspond to a point on the number line? __One__ How many rational numbers are solutions of the equation $(a/b)x = c/d$, where $a/b \neq 0$? __One__

One. One.

20. On a separate piece of paper prove that for rational numbers multiplication is distributive over addition.

$$\frac{a}{b}\left[\frac{c}{d} + \frac{r}{s}\right] = \frac{a}{b}\left[\frac{cs + rd}{ds}\right] = \frac{acs + ard}{bds}$$

$$\frac{a}{b} \cdot \frac{c}{d} + \frac{a}{b} \cdot \frac{r}{s} = \frac{ac}{bd} + \frac{ar}{bs} = \frac{acs + ard}{bds}$$

21. Is multiplication of rational numbers distributive over subtraction? __Yes__

Yes.

22. Is division of rational numbers left and/or right distributive over addition and subtraction? __Right__

Right only.

p. 248 - 49

23.4 Inequality in the Set of Rational Numbers

It is natural to call a rational number *positive* if it represents a point on the number line to the right of 0 and *negative* if it is to the left of 0. The formal definitions are:

Rational Numbers

DEFINITIONS

1. A rational number a/b is positive if and only if a and b have the same sign.

2. A rational number a/b is negative if and only if a and b have opposite signs.

3. A rational number a/b is zero if and only if $a = 0$.

In view of these definitions we can define the concept of less than ($<$) between two rational numbers as follows:

INEQUALITY   **DEFINITION.** For any two rational numbers $\dfrac{c}{d} < \dfrac{a}{b}$ if and only if $\dfrac{a}{b} - \dfrac{c}{d}$ is positive. Similarly, $\dfrac{c}{d} > \dfrac{a}{b}$ if and only if $\dfrac{a}{b} - \dfrac{c}{d}$ is negative.

The properties of these inequalities are precisely the same as those of the integers (Chapter 21), so it is unnecessary to restate them here.

---

1. Use the above definitions to insert the correct symbol in the inequality $4/9 \underline{\quad <\quad} 7/8$.
$(<, >)$

> $<$ $7/8 - 4/9 = (63 - 32)/72 = 31/72$, which is positive.

2. Using the above definition write the correct symbol between each pair of the following rational numbers. (a) $7/8 \underline{\quad >\quad} 2/3$. (b) $15/16 \underline{\quad <\quad} 31/32$. (c) $(-5)/7 \underline{\quad <\quad} 6/11$. (d) $11/3 \underline{\quad >\quad} (-12)/(-5)$. (e) $41/61 \underline{\quad >\quad} 39/64$.

> (a) $>$ (b) $<$ (c) $<$ (d) $>$ (e) $>$

3. If two rational numbers are expressed so that they have the same positive denominator, such as a/b and c/b, where $b > 0$, then $a/b - c/b = \underline{\quad \frac{a-c}{b}\quad}$. Hence $a/b - c/b$ with $b > 0$ is positive if and only if $a - c$ is positive or $a \underline{\quad >\quad} c$.
$(<, >)$

> $\dfrac{a-c}{b}$ $>$

4. The result of frame 3 states that when $b > 0$, $a/b > c/b$ if and only if $\underline{\quad a > c\quad}$.

> $a > c$

5. Use the method of frame 4 to write the correct symbol between the pair 8/5 _____ 3/2.
$(<, >)$

> $8/5 = 16/10$ and $3/2 = 15/10$. Since $16 > 15$, $8/5 > 3/2$.

6. Use the method of frame 4 to determine the correct ordering of the following pairs of rational numbers: (a) $3/4$ _____ $11/16$. (b) $(-3)/5$ _____ $-4/7$. (c) $17/18$ _____ $(-18)/(-19)$. (d) $7/(-3)$ _____ $13/(-6)$. (e) $(-5)/7$ _____ $7/(-5)$.

(a) $>$ (b) $<$ (c) $<$ (d) $<$ (e) $>$

23.5 Rational Numbers and Division

When we discussed division for whole numbers in Section 11.9, we proved the following theorem:

THEOREM 2. If a and d are any whole numbers with $d \neq 0$, there exist whole numbers q and r with $r < d$ such that

$$a = dq + r$$

The whole number q is called the *quotient* and r is called the remainder.

Now that rational numbers are available to us, this division process can be treated in another fashion. Let us write a as the rational number $a/1$ and b as $b/1$. Then we can form the quotient of these two rational numbers:

$$a/1 \div b/1 = (a/1)(1/b)$$
$$= a/b$$

Thus we can interpret a/b as the result of dividing a by b.

In order to relate these two approaches to division of whole numbers, let us prove the following theorem:

THEOREM 3. If a and d are any whole numbers with $d \neq 0$, and if $a = dq + r$, then $a/d = q/1 + r/d$.

Proof
1. $a = dq + r$.
2. $\dfrac{a}{d} = \dfrac{dq + r}{d}$.
3. $\dfrac{a}{d} = \dfrac{q}{1} + \dfrac{r}{d}$.

483

ILLUSTRATION. In Section 11.9 we wrote "$17 \div 6 = 2$ with a remainder of 5". That is, $17 = 2 \cdot 6 + 5$.

In view of Theorem 2 we can now write

$$17 \div 6 = \frac{2}{1} + \frac{5}{6}$$

which we can write as the "mixed number" $2\frac{5}{6}$ (see Section 23.6).

REMARKS

DIVISION

In view of Theorem 3, we often read the symbol a/d as "a divided by d".

2. We now have three interpretations of rational numbers:
   (a) Numbers that represent points on the number line.
   (b) Numbers that represent the solution of equations of the form $dx = a$, where a and d are integers and $d \neq 0$.
   (c) Numbers that represent the result of dividing one integer by another.

NOTATION. It is no longer necessary to distinguish between the symbols $a \div d$ and a/d, and so we shall adopt the common notation of representing division by the slash (/). We shall also extend this notation to apply the quotients of rational numbers and write

$$(a/b) \div (c/d) = (a/b)/(c/d)$$

In particular, the reciprocal of a/b (where $a \neq 0$ and $b \neq 0$) is $1/(a/b)$.

---

1. In terms of quotient and remainder $25 \div 7 = $ _3_ with a remainder of _4_.

> 3   4

2. As a rational number $25 \div 7 = $ _25/7_.

> 25/7

3. The reciprocal of $4/5 = 1/($ _4/5_ $) = $ _5/4_

> 4/5   5/4

4. If k is any nonzero rational number, $k(1/k) = $ _1_ ?

> 1

5. Let k represent any nonzero rational number. The multiplicative inverse of k is its reciprocal, _1/k_.

1/k

6. The multiplicative inverse of 2/3 is ___3/2___ .

3/2

7. Why does 0 not have a multiplicative inverse? __(a & b)/0 = 0,__

If a/b were the multiplicative inverse of 0, then $0(a/b) = 0 \neq 1$.

8. Compare the multiplicative properties of the rational numbers in the summary at the end of this chapter with the multiplicative properties of the integers in the summary at the end of Chapter 21. What essential difference is there __Nonzero rational no's have multiplicative inverses, integers don't__

The nonzero rationals have multiplicative inverses, the integers do not.

23.6 Mixed Numbers

MIXED NUMBERS According to the usual practice, certain rational numbers are often expressed as "mixed numbers". For example, $3\frac{2}{5}$ is a symbol that means $3 + \frac{2}{5}$. This can be expressed as a rational number in the usual notation by the following method:

$$3\tfrac{2}{5} = 3 + \tfrac{2}{5} = \tfrac{15}{5} + \tfrac{2}{5} = \tfrac{17}{5}$$

In the same fashion $-4\frac{1}{3}$ is defined to be $-(4 + \frac{1}{3}) = -\frac{13}{3}$. In a mixed number the numerator of the fractional part is to be less than the denominator.

Going in the opposite direction, we can express any rational number a/b with $|a| > |b|$ as mixed number. To express 25/9 as a mixed number, divide 25 by 9 showing the remainder

$$25 = 9 \cdot 2 + 7$$

Then

$$\tfrac{25}{9} = 2 + \tfrac{7}{9} = 2\tfrac{7}{9}$$

One way to add, subtract, multiply, or divide mixed numbers is to convert them to rational numbers in standard notation and then to apply the usual procedures.

EXAMPLE

$$2\tfrac{3}{5} + 4\tfrac{4}{5} = \tfrac{13}{5} + \tfrac{24}{5} = \tfrac{37}{5} = 7\tfrac{2}{5}$$

485

Rational Numbers

1. Write the following mixed numbers as rational numbers in standard notation: (a) $2\frac{5}{8} = $ _____. (b) $7\frac{3}{11}$ _____. (c) $-4\frac{2}{3}$ _____.
(d) $6\frac{1}{2} = $ _____. (e) $15\frac{11}{13} = $ _____.

> (a) 21/8   (b) 80/11   (c) (−14)/3   (d) 13/2   (e) 206/13

2. Express the following rational numbers as mixed numbers: (a) $36/5 = $ _____. (b) $17/4 = $ _____. (c) $\dfrac{-12}{5} = $ _____.
(d) $19/4 = $ _____. (e) $-\dfrac{36}{11} = $ _____.

> (a) $7\frac{1}{5}$ (b) $4\frac{1}{4}$ (c) $-2\frac{2}{5}$ (d) $4\frac{3}{4}$ (c) $-3\frac{3}{11}$

3. Express the results of the following divisions as mixed numbers: (a) $16 \div 3 = $ _____. (b) $22 \div 5 = $ _____. (c) $7 \div 12 = $ _____. (d) $(-19) \div 7 = $ _____. (e) $(-17) \div (-6) = $ _____.

> (a) $5\frac{1}{3}$ (b) $4\frac{2}{5}$ (c) $0 + \frac{7}{12} = \frac{7}{12}$ (d) $-2\frac{5}{7}$ (e) $2\frac{5}{6}$

4. Perform the indicated operations: (a) $6\frac{1}{8} - 2\frac{3}{4} = $ _____. (b) $5\frac{4}{7} + 3\frac{2}{3} = $ _____. (c) $4\frac{2}{3} - 2\frac{3}{4} = $ _____. (d) $7\frac{3}{8} + 5\frac{1}{9} = $ _____. (e) $(3\frac{1}{2})(4\frac{3}{4}) = $ _____. (f) $(4\frac{1}{3}) \div (3\frac{1}{4}) = $ _____.

> (a) $3\frac{3}{8}$ (b) $9\frac{5}{21}$ (c) $1\frac{11}{12}$ (d) $12\frac{35}{72}$ (e) $16\frac{5}{8}$ (f) $1\frac{1}{3}$

We have defined rational numbers as equivalence classes of fractions, and hereafter use the notation a/b with $b \neq 0$ for a rational number. Since $a = a/1$, the integers are special cases of rational numbers. We have interpreted rational numbers as:

(1) Names for points on the number line.

(2) Solutions of equations of the form $bx = a$, with $b \neq 0$.

(3) An extension of the concept of the division of whole numbers, so that a/b is equal to $a \div b$ for any pair of integers where $b \neq 0$.

We defined

$$a/b + c/d \text{ to be } \frac{ad + bc}{bd}$$

$(a/b)(c/d)$ to be $(ac)/bd$

$(a/b)/(c/d)$ to be $(a/b)(d/c) = (ad)/(bc)$ provided $c \neq 0$

The properties of rational numbers are summarized below.

Summary of the Properties of the Rational Numbers

The statements given below are the most important properties of the rational numbers. All other properties of the rational numbers can be derived from these. It is understood that each of these statements is to be prefixed by the phrase: "For all rational numbers a, b, c, and d". Special exceptions are noted as necessary.

EQUALITY

1. If $a = b$, then $a + c = b + c$.
2. If $a = b$, then $a - c = b - c$.
3. If $a = b$, then $ac = bc$.
4. If $a = b$ and $c \neq 0$, then $a/c = b/c$.

ADDITION

1. Addition is a binary operation.
2. $a + b = b + a$ Commutative property.
3. $(a + b) + c = a + (b + c)$ Associative property.
4. $a + 0 = a$ Existence of additive identity.
5. For each a there is a rational number $(-a)$ such that $a + (-a) = 0$ Existence of additive inverse.

SUBTRACTION

1. Subtraction is a binary operation that is neither commutative nor associative.
2. $a - b = c$ if and only if $a = b + c$ Definition.
3. If $a + c = b + c$, then $a = b$ Cancellation law.

MULTIPLICATION

1. Multiplication is a binary operation.
2. $ab = ba$ Commutative property.
3. $(ab)c = a(bc)$ Associative property.
4. $a \cdot 1 = a$ Existence of multiplicative identity.
5. For each $a \neq 0$, there is a rational number $1/a$ such that $a(1/a) = 1$ Existence of multiplicative inverse.

DIVISION

1. Division is a binary operation on the set of nonzero rationals.
2. $a/b = c$ if and only if $a = bc$ Definition.
3. If $ac = bc$ and $c \neq 0$, then $a = b$ Cancellation law.

DISTRIBUTIVE LAWS

1. $a(b + c) = ab + ac$; $(b + c)a = (ba + ca)$.
2. $a(b - c) = ab - ac$; $(b - c)a = (ba - ca)$.
3. $(a + b)/c = (a/c) + (b/c)$.

487

Rational Numbers

INEQUALITY

1. Exactly one of the following is true: Trichotomy law.

$$a < b \qquad a = b \qquad a > b$$

2. If $a < b$ and $b < c$, then $a < c$ — Transitive law.
3. If $a < b$, then $a + c < b + c$ — Additive law.
4. If $a < b$ and $c > 0$, then $ac < bc$ — Multiplicative laws.
5. If $a < b$ and $c < 0$, then $ac > bc$

Now test your mastery of this chapter by working the following Post Test.

POST TEST

1. A rational number is an _equivalence class_ of fractions.
2. For what rational number (expressed as an equivalence class of fractions) is the fraction $(-2)/9$ an appropriate name? $\frac{-4}{18}, \frac{-6}{27}, \frac{4}{-18}, \frac{6}{-2}$ _____
3. What is the "simplest name" for the rational number: $\left\{ \ldots, \dfrac{-10}{-8}, \dfrac{-5}{-4}, \dfrac{5}{4}, \dfrac{10}{8}, \dfrac{15}{12}, \ldots \right\}$? $\quad 5/4$
4. Express the rational number -3 as an equivalence class of fractions. $-2, \frac{3}{4}, \frac{-3}{4}, \frac{-9}{2}$
5. The symbol $-\dfrac{a}{b}$ is a name for the rational number ____ $-a/b \text{ or } a/-b$.
6. $16\left(-\dfrac{3}{8}\right) = -6$.
7. Find the following sum expressing your answer in lowest terms: $6/4 + 7/3 = 23/6$.
8. What is the additive identity for rational numbers? 0
9. What is the additive inverse of the rational number a/b? $-a/b$
10. Find $5/4 - 9/13$. $29/52$
11. Write $4\frac{2}{9}$ as a rational number. $38/9$
12. Write $36/11$ as a mixed number. $3\,3/11$
13. Find the sum $6\frac{11}{12} + 1\frac{2}{3}$. $8\,7/12$
14. Find the product $3/4 \cdot 8/23$. $6/23$
15. What is the multiplicative identity for rational numbers? 1
16. What is the multiplicative inverse of a/b, where $a \neq 0$? b/a
17. The reciprocal of $5/4$ is $4/5$.
18. Find the quotient $18/5 \div 12/3$. $9/10$
19. Solve for x: $4x - 9/3 = -19/3$. $-5/6$
20. $3/5 \cdot (6/7 + 3/9) = (3/5 \cdot 6/7) + (3/5 \cdot 3/9)$.

488

21. Insert the correct symbol between the pair of rational numbers 1/7 and 4/21. 1/7 _____ 4/21.
(<, >)

22. Express the division $15 \div 7$ (a) in terms of quotient and remainder, $15 =$ _____ + _____, and (b) as a mixed number, _____.

23. What multiplicative property of the rational numbers is not a multiplicative property of the integers? _____

24. Why does 0 not have a multiplicative inverse? _____

---

1. equivalence class

2. $\left\{ \cdots \dfrac{4}{-18}, \dfrac{2}{-9}, \dfrac{-2}{9}, \dfrac{-4}{18}, \dfrac{-6}{27}, \cdots \right\}$.

3. 5/4.

4. $\left\{ \cdots \dfrac{6}{-2}, \dfrac{3}{-1}, \dfrac{-3}{1}, \dfrac{-6}{2}, \cdots \right\}$.

5. $(-a)/b \ [\text{or } a/(-b)]$

6. -6.

7. 23/6.

8. 0.

9. $(-a)/b$.

10. 29/52.

11. 38/9.

12. $3\frac{3}{11}$.

13. $8\frac{7}{12}$.

14. 6/23.

15. 1.

16. b/a.

17. 4/5.

18. 9/10.

19. $x = -5/6$.

20. $(3/5 \cdot 3/9)$

21. $<$

22. (a) 2, 7, 1.   (b) $2\frac{1}{7}$

23. Existence of multiplicative inverse.

24. If a/b is the multiplicative inverse of 0, then $0(a/b) = 1$. But this cannot be true.

24

Rational Numbers as Decimals

Before beginning this chapter you should review decimal notation (Chapter 13) and should be familiar with the standard algorithms for the operations of arithmetic (Chapters 14, 15, 16, and 17). Moreover you should have completed Chapter 23, Rational Numbers. To test your preparation for this chapter, answer the questions in the following Readiness Test.

READINESS TEST

1. In expanded decimal notation $625 =$ _____.

$$(6 \times 10^2) + (2 \times 10) + 5$$

2. The compact form of $(7 \times 10^3) + (3 \times 10) + 7$ is _____.

7037

3. $10^2 \times [(a_2 \times 10^2) + (a_1 \times 10) + a_0] =$ _____.

$$(a_2 \times 10^4) + (a_1 \times 10^3) + (a_0 \times 10^2)$$

4. The algorithm for division with remainder states that if a and d are whole numbers with $d \neq 0$, then there exist whole numbers q and r with r _____ d such that _____.

$<$ $a = qd + r$

5. The fraction a/b is in lowest terms if a and b are _____.

relatively prime

6. The prime factors of 10 are _____. Hence $10^p =$ _____ (in terms of 2 and 5).

2 and 5 $2^p \cdot 5^p$

If you are ready, proceed with Section 24.1.

24.1 Elementary Ideas

In our ordinary decimal (base ten) system of numeration, we have observed that every whole number a can be written in the "expanded form"

$$a = (a_n \times 10^n) + \cdots + (a_1 \times 10) + a_0$$

where $a_0, \ldots, a_n$ are digits between 0 and 9 inclusive. This expansion can be extended to the right to represent certain nonnegative rational numbers. Let r be defined to be the sum

$$r = (a_n \times 10^n) + \cdots + (a_1 \times 10) + a_0 + \frac{b_1}{10} + \cdots + \frac{b_m}{10^m}$$

where $a_0, \ldots, a_n$ and $b_1, \ldots, b_m$ are digits between 0 and 9 inclusive. Then it follows at once that r is the sum of rational numbers and hence is itself a rational number. The usual notation for such a rational number is

$$r = a_n a_{n-1} \cdots a_1 a_0 . b_1 \cdots b_m$$

where the "decimal point" separates the digits $a_n, \ldots, a_0$ from the digits $b_1, \ldots, b_m$.

EXAMPLES. In this notation

$$25.74 = (2 \times 10) + 5 + \frac{7}{10} + \frac{4}{10^2}$$

$$1.362 = 1 + \frac{3}{10} + \frac{6}{10^2} + \frac{2}{10^3}$$

$$0.48 = \frac{4}{10} + \frac{8}{10^2}$$

$$35.0063 = (3 \times 10) + 5 + \frac{0}{10} + \frac{0}{10^2} + \frac{6}{10^3} + \frac{3}{10^4}$$

DECIMAL FRACTION   DEFINITION.   Numbers expressed in the form

$$r = (a_n \times 10^n) + \cdots + (a_1 \times 10) + a_0 + \frac{b_1}{10} + \cdots + \frac{b_m}{10^m}$$

are called *decimal fractions.*

REMARKS

1. A decimal fraction is a name for a rational number.

2. Decimal fractions have only a finite number of digits to the right of the decimal point. Thus they are to be distinguished from expressions such as $3.3333\ldots$, which we shall later call "infinite decimal expansions". When we wish to distinguish decimal fractions from "infinite decimal expansions, we shall call them "finite decimal fractions".

3. In this chapter we shall treat only positive decimal fractions. Of course, negative decimal fractions such as -23.564 also exist as names for negative

rational numbers. But their arithmetic is obtained from the arithmetic of positive decimal fractions by the usual rules for $+$ and $-$ signs. Hence we shall not treat them here.

4. It is good practice to write 0.48 instead of .48, for otherwise the decimal point may go unnoticed.

5. If desired, additional zeros may be added to the right of a decimal fraction without changing it. Thus $15.37 = 15.370 = 15.3700 = \cdots$.

Our tasks now are to answer the following questions:

(1) What rational numbers can be expressed as decimal fractions?

(2) When this representation is possible for a rational number how can we find the appropriate decimal fraction? Conversely, when we have a decimal fraction, what is the corresponding rational number?

(3) What are the rules for the arithmetic of decimal fractions?

24.2 Representation of Rational Numbers as Decimal Fractions

This section depends upon the following theorem:

RATIONAL NUMBERS AS DECIMAL FRACTIONS

THEOREM 1. The positive rational number r can be written as the decimal fraction

$$r = (a_n \times 10^n) + \cdots + (a_1 \times 10) + a_0 + \frac{b_1}{10} + \cdots + \frac{b_m}{10^m}$$

if and only if there is a whole number p such that $10^p \times r$ is a whole number.

Proof

1. First suppose that r has the expansion stated in the theorem. Then taking $p = m$,

$$10^m \times r = (a_n \times 10^n \times 10^m) + \cdots + (a_1 \times 10 \times 10^m)$$

$$+ (a_0 \times 10^m) + \left(b_1 \times \frac{10^m}{10}\right) + \cdots + \left(b_m \times \frac{10^m}{10^m}\right)$$

$$= (a_n \times 10^{n+m}) + \cdots + (a_1 \times 10^{m+1}) + (a_0 \times 10^m)$$

$$+ (b_1 \times 10^{m-1}) + \cdots + b_m$$

which is the decimal expansion of a whole number.

2. Next suppose that $10^p \times r$ is a whole number, say a, where

$$a = (a_n \times 10^n) + \cdots + (a_1 \times 10) + a_0$$

Then

$$r = \frac{a}{10^p} = \left(a_n \times \frac{10^n}{10^p}\right) + \cdots + \left(a_1 \times \frac{10}{10^p}\right) + \frac{a_0}{10^p}$$

which is a decimal fraction.

493

Let us begin with some examples:

EXAMPLE. Express $\frac{1}{2}$ as a decimal fraction.

Solution. We observe that $10(\frac{1}{2}) = 5$, a whole number. Hence

$$\frac{1}{2} = \frac{5}{10} = 0.5$$

a decimal fraction.

EXAMPLE. Express $\frac{3}{4}$ as a decimal fraction.

Solution. We observe that $10^2(\frac{3}{4}) = \frac{300}{4} = 75$, a whole number. Hence

$$\frac{3}{4} = \frac{75}{10^2} = \frac{(7 \times 10) + 5}{10^2}$$

$$= \frac{7}{10} + \frac{5}{10^2}$$

$$= 0.75$$

a decimal fraction.

In general, Theorem 1 states that the rational number a/b can be expressed as a decimal fraction whenever there is a power of 10, say 10^p, such that $10^p(a/b)$ is a whole number. For what a/b is this possible? If we write a/b in lowest terms, then $10^p(a/b)$ is a whole number if and only if b is a divisor of 10^p. This means that b must have a factorization into primes of the form

$$b = 2^u 5^v$$

where u and v are whole numbers. This argument proves Theorem 2.

THEOREM 2. The rational number a/b (in lowest terms) can be expressed as a decimal fraction if and only if the prime factorization of b is of the form

$$b = 2^u 5^v$$

where u and v are whole numbers.

---

1. Which of the following rational numbers in lowest terms can be expressed as a decimal fraction? (a) 5/8. (b) 11/20. (c) 7/12. (d) 2/3. (e) 37/50.

(a), (b), and (e).

2. Write the decimal fractions that correspond to those rational numbers of frame 1 that can be so expressed. (a) _____ . (b) _____ .
(e) _____ .

> (a) 0.625.   (b) 0.55.   (c) 0.74.

3. In Theorem 2 why must b have the form $b = 2^u 5^v$? _____

> Since $10 = 2 \cdot 5$, $10^p = 2^p \cdot 5^p$. If b is to divide 10^p, the prime factors of b must be included among the prime factors of 10^p. That is, we must have $b = 2^u 5^v$ where $u \le p$, and $v \le p$.

4. Why can 1/3 not be represented as a decimal fraction? _____

> The prime factors of 3 are not powers of 2 and 5.

5. But everyone knows that $\frac{1}{3} = 0.333 \ldots$. Why does this fact not contradict frame 4? _____

> $\frac{1}{3} = 0.333 \ldots$ indicates an infinite decimal expansion. A decimal fraction can have at most a finite number of entries to the right of the decimal point.

6. What is the value of $\frac{1}{3} - 0.3$? We have $\frac{1}{3} - 0.3 = \frac{1}{3} - \frac{3}{10} =$ _____

> 1/30

7. What are the values of $\frac{1}{3} - 0.33$ _____ and $\frac{1}{3} - 0.333$ _____?

> 1/300   1/3000

8. From frames 6 and 7 we observe that 0.3, 0.33, and 0.333 are successively closer _____ to $\frac{1}{3}$ but that none of them are precisely _____ to $\frac{1}{3}$.

> approximations   equal

9. Write the following rational numbers in lowest terms and state which of them can be expressed as decimal fractions.
(a) $36/15 =$ _____ ; _____ .
               (lowest terms)   (yes, no)
(b) $25/15 =$ _____ ; _____ .
(c) $48/36 =$ _____ ; _____ .
(d) $21/70 =$ _____ ; _____ .

(a) 36/15 = 12/5; yes   (b) 25/15 = 5/3; no   (c) 48/36 = 4/3; no   (d) 21/70 = 3/10; yes

10. Any decimal fraction can be interpreted as the name of some rational number. For example, $0.654 = 6/10 + \underline{\hspace{1cm}}/10^2 + \underline{\hspace{1cm}}/10^3 = 600/10^3 + \underline{\hspace{1cm}}/10^3 + \underline{\hspace{1cm}}/10^3 = \underline{\hspace{2cm}}/10^3$. Thus 0.654 is a name for the rational number another of whose names is $\underline{\hspace{1cm}}$.

5   4   50   4   654   654/1000

11. What is another name for the rational number which is represented by the decimal fraction 32.079? $\underline{\hspace{3cm}}$

$$32\frac{79}{1000} = \frac{32,079}{1000}.$$

12. Write each of the following decimal fractions as a rational number in lowest terms. (a) 2.36. $\underline{\hspace{1cm}}$ (b) 0.45. $\underline{\hspace{1cm}}$ (c) 1.85. $\underline{\hspace{1cm}}$

(a) 59/25.   (b) 9/20.   (c) 37/20.

24.3 Arithmetic of Decimal Fractions

In view of the expanded form of a rational number as a decimal fraction, addition and subtraction of rational numbers written in this form obey the rules that we developed for whole numbers in Chapters 14 and 15. The essential key to these rules is again the extended distributive law.

EXAMPLE. Find the sum of 16.23, 9.375, and 0.085.

Solution. Write this in columnar form with the decimal points in a vertical column:

ADDITION
$$\begin{array}{r} 16.23 \\ 9.375 \\ +0.085 \\ \hline \end{array}$$

For convenience add a zero on the right of 16.23 so that all summands are three-place decimals.

$$\begin{array}{r} 16.230 \\ 9.375 \\ +0.085 \\ \hline \end{array}$$

Then add as in the case of whole numbers. The result is

$$
\begin{array}{r}
16.230 \\
9.375 \\
+0.085 \\
\hline
25.690
\end{array}
$$

This answer may also be written 25.69, but 25.690 is equally correct.

EXAMPLE. Perform the subtraction

SUBTRACTION

$$
\begin{array}{r}
419.0762 \\
-85.36 \\
\hline
\end{array}
$$

Solution. Again add zeros on the right of 85.36 and rewrite the problem as

$$
\begin{array}{r}
419.0762 \\
-85.3600 \\
\hline
\end{array}
$$

Now subtract as in the case of whole numbers. The result is

$$
\begin{array}{r}
419.0762 \\
-85.3600 \\
\hline
333.7162
\end{array}
$$

As preparation for the algorithm for multiplying two decimal fractions, consider the following example:

EXAMPLE. Find the product

MULTIPLICATION

$$41.2 \times 3.76$$

Solution. First we use Theorem 1 to write

$$10 \times 41.2 = 412$$
$$10^2 \times 3.76 = 376$$

Hence

$$(10 \times 41.2) \times (10^2 \times 3.76) = 412 \times 376$$
$$= 154{,}912$$

Therefore,

$$10^3 \times 41.2 \times 3.76 = 154{,}912$$

or

$$41.2 \times 3.76 = 154{,}912/10^3$$
$$= 154\frac{912}{1000}$$
$$= 154.912$$

From this example we observe two facts about the product of decimal fractions:

(1) If we ignore all decimal points, the product is found exactly as in the multiplication of whole numbers.

(2) The decimal point in the product is located so that the number of digits to the right of this decimal point is equal to the sum of the number of digits to the right of the decimal point in each of the two factors.

DIVISION In the case of division the procedure is quite similar: We divide as if the decimal fractions were whole numbers and then must find a means of locating the decimal point in the quotient and in the remainder.

First, let us consider the case where the divisor is a whole number.

EXAMPLE

$$37 \overline{)25.13}$$

Solution. If we ignore the decimal point in the dividend, we obtain

$$
\begin{array}{r}
67 \\
37 \overline{)2513} \\
222 \\
\hline
293 \\
259 \\
\hline
34
\end{array}
$$

That is,

$$2513 = 67 \times 37 + 34$$

To convert 2513 to the given dividend, 25.13, we must divide by 100. Thus we obtain

$$25.13 = 0.67 \times 37 + 0.34$$

In dividing the term 67×37 by 100, we have left the divisor, 37, unchanged and divided the quotient 67 by 100. Hence the answer to the original problem is $q = 0.67, r = 0.34$.

A convenient algorithm for this process is

$$
\begin{array}{r}
.67 \\
37 \overline{)25.13} \\
22\ 2 \\
\hline
2\ 93 \\
2\ 59 \\
\hline
.34
\end{array}
$$

where you will notice that all the decimal points are in a vertical line.

When we divide by a decimal fraction, the idea is to convert the problem into an equivalent problem with an integral divisor and then to proceed as above.

EXAMPLE.

$$5.7\overline{)47.66}$$

Solution. The quotient is unchanged if we multiply both dividend and divisor by 10, so we have the problem

$$57\overline{)476.6}$$

whose solution is

```
          8.3
57 ) 476.6
     456
     ___
      20 6
      17 1
      ____
       3 5
```

so the quotient is 8.3, but the position of the decimal point in the remainder is still undetermined. If all the numbers involved were integers, we would have

$$4766 = 83 \times 57 + 35$$

Dividing by 100, we obtain

$$47.66 = 8.3 \times 5.7 + 0.35$$

So the remainder is 0.35.

A convenient algorithm for this calculation is

```
            8.3
5.7 ) 4 7 . 6ˇ6
      4 5  6
      _____
      2  0 6
      1  7 1
      _____
          . 3 5
```

The caret indicates the proper position of the decimal point in the quotient, and the decimal point in the remainder is directly under the decimal point in the dividend.

Sometimes it is possible to obtain an exact quotient even when it appears at first sight that the division involves a remainder. Consider the following example.

EXAMPLE

```
            6.7
3.2 ) 2 1 . 6ˇ5
      1 9  2
      _____
      2  4 5
      2  2 4
      _____
         . 2 1
```

Solution. The apparent answer is that the quotient is 6.7 and the remainder is 0.21. But suppose that we continue the division by adding zeros to the dividend as follows:

$$
\begin{array}{r}
6.765625 \\
3.2\,\overline{)21.6\,{}^{\smile}500000} \\
19\,2 \\
\hline
2\,45 \\
2\,24 \\
\hline
210 \\
192 \\
\hline
180 \\
160 \\
\hline
200 \\
192 \\
\hline
80 \\
64 \\
\hline
160 \\
160 \\
\hline
\end{array}
$$

The exact quotient is 6.765625 and there is no remainder. How could we have expected such a result in advance?

Consider the related problem: Can we express $\dfrac{2165}{32}$ as a decimal fraction? In view of Theorem 2, the answer is "yes" since $32 = 2^5$. Therefore, the quotient $21.65 \div 3.2$ is also expressible as a decimal fraction which we can find by the process above. Thus we arrive at the following conclusion:

If d (considered as a whole number) is of the form $2^u 5^v$, the quotient a/d can be expressed as a decimal fraction without remainder.

The converse of the above statement is false, but the following approximate converse is true:

The quotient a/d can be expressed as a decimal fraction without remainder only if, when a/d is expressed in lowest terms as r/s, s is of the form $2^u 5^v$

---

1. Find the sum of 156.2, 24.76, and 85.217. _____

266.177.

2. Find the difference

$$
\begin{array}{r}
392.134 \\
-\ 25.672 \\
\hline
\end{array}
$$

500

366.462

3. Find the product 75.62 × 13.7. _____ 1034.994 _____ *(handwritten)*

1035.994.

4. In frame 3 the number of digits to the right of the decimal point in 75.62 is __2__ ; the corresponding number in 13.7 is __1__ . Hence there must be __1+2=3__ digits to the right of the decimal point in the product.

2   1   1 + 2 = 3

5. Compute 6.9⟌499.56. Quotient = __72.4__ , remainder = __0__ .

72.4   0

6. Compute 5.3⟌357.86. Quotient = __67.5__ , remainder = __0.11__ .

67.5   0.11

7. In frame 6 is there any hope of obtaining a quotient without remainder if the division process is carried further?
__No__ Why? __35,786 is in lowest terms.__ *(handwritten: 35,786 / 53)*
(yes, no)

No.   Since 53 and 35,786 are relatively prime, $\dfrac{35{,}786}{53}$ is in lowest terms. But 53 is not of the form $2^u 5^v$.

8. Find the value of 2.5⟌49.41. Quotient = __19.7__ , remainder = __.16__ .

19.7   0.16

9. In frame 8 is there any hope of obtaining a quotient without remainder if the division process is carried further?
__Yes__ . Why? _____
(yes, no)

Yes. $25 = 5^2$

501

10. Since the answer to frame 9 is "yes", continue the division and find the corresponding quotient without remainder.

$$
\begin{array}{r}
19.7\,64 \\
2.5\,\overline{)\,49.4\,^{\vee}100} \\
25 \\
\overline{24}\ 4 \\
22\ 5 \\
\overline{1}\ 91 \\
1\ 75 \\
\overline{160} \\
\overline{150} \\
100 \\
100 \\
\overline{0}
\end{array}
$$

$$
\begin{array}{r}
19.764 \\
2.5\,\overline{)\,49.4\,^{\vee}100} \\
25 \\
\overline{24}\ 4 \\
22\ 5 \\
\overline{1}\ 91 \\
1\ 75 \\
\overline{160} \\
150 \\
\overline{100} \\
100
\end{array}
$$

11. In the division of $44\,\overline{)\,99}$ we find that the quotient is 2.25. But 44 is not of the form $2^u 5^v$. How could we have told in advance that this quotient can be expressed as a decimal fraction? _____

_____

Reduce 99/44 to its lowest terms 9/4. Now 4 is of the form $2^u 5^v$.

12. $27.13 = (2 \times 10) + 7 + \dfrac{1}{\rule{1cm}{0.4pt}} + \dfrac{3}{\rule{1cm}{0.4pt}}.$

10   10^2

13. From frame 12,

$$10 \times 27.13 = (2 \times 10^2) + (7 \times \rule{1.5cm}{0.4pt}) + \rule{1cm}{0.4pt} + \rule{1cm}{0.4pt}$$

$$= \rule{2cm}{0.4pt} \text{ as a decimal fraction}$$

10   1   3/10   271.3

14. From frames 12 and 13 it follows that to multiply a decimal fraction by 10, move the decimal point _____ place to the _____.

> one   right

15. To multiply a decimal fraction by 10^2, move the decimal point _____ places to the _____.

> two   right

16. To multiply a decimal fraction by 10^n, move the decimal point _____ places to the _____.

> n right

17. $10^3 \times 4.2 =$ _____.

> 4200

18. To multiply a decimal fraction by $1/10^n$, move the decimal point _____ places to the _____.

> n left

19. $1/10 \times 39.13 =$ _____.

> 3.913

20. $1/10^4 \times 75.317 =$ _____.

> 0.0075317

24.4 Per cent

Decimal fractions may be written in another notation in terms of per cent.

EXAMPLE

$$2\% = 0.02$$
$$12\% = 0.12$$
$$75\% = 0.75$$
$$136\% = 1.36$$
$$4.7\% = 0.047$$

Rational Numbers as Decimals

As suggested by this example, we have the definition:

PER CENT   **DEFINITION.** If r is a decimal fraction, $r\%$ is defined to be the decimal fraction $\dfrac{r}{10^2}$.

---

1. Write as decimal fractions: (a) $3\% =$ _.03_ . (b) $4.2\% =$ _.042_ . (c) $21.5\% =$ _.215_ . (d) $236\% =$ _2.36_ . (e) $0.8\% =$ _.008_ .

| (a) 0.03 | (b) 0.042 | (c) 0.215 | (d) 2.36 | (e) 0.008 |

2. To convert $r\%$ to a decimal fraction, move the decimal point in r _two_ places to the _left_ .

| two | left |

3. Sometimes you will encounter expressions such as $1\frac{1}{2}\%$ and $3\frac{1}{4}\%$. To write these as decimal fractions first convert $1\frac{1}{2}$ and $3\frac{1}{4}$ to decimal fractions and then proceed as in frame 2. (a) $1\frac{1}{2}\% = 1.5\% =$ _.015_ . (b) $3\frac{1}{4}\% =$ _3.25_ $=$ _.0325_ .

| (a) 0.015 | (b) 3.25%; 0.0325 |

4. Write the following decimal fractions in terms of per cent. (a) $0.02 =$ _2_ %. (b) $0.125 =$ _12.5_ %. (c) $2.14 =$ _214_ %.

| (a) 2 | (b) 12.5 | (c) 214 |

5. To write a decimal fraction r in terms of per cent, move the decimal point of r _two_ places to the _right_ .

| two | right |

6. In baseball statistics a batter who has made 20 hits in 100 times at bat is said to have a batting average of 0.200. Sometimes this is written 200%. Is this a correct use of the notation of per cent? _No_ . What is the correct expression for 0.200 as a percentage? _20%_

yes, no

| No. | 20%. |

Rational numbers are frequently expressed in terms of per cent by means of equations such as those in the following example:

EXAMPLE. $\frac{3}{4} = \frac{x}{100}$, where x is the desired percentage. Thus $x = 75$, and we say that $3/4 = 75\%$.

Similarly, $\frac{5}{8} = \frac{x}{100}$ gives us $5/8 = 62.5\%$.

---

7. Express the following rational numbers in terms of per cent:
(a) $3/8 = x/100$; $x = $ _____375_____ ; $3/8 = $ __37.5__ %.
(b) $1/10 = x/100$; $x = $ _____10_____ ; $1/10 = $ __10__ %.
(c) $5/2 = x/100$; $x = $ _____250_____ ; $5/2 = $ __250__ %.
(d) $7/4 = x/100$; $x = $ _____175_____ ; $7/4 = $ __175__ %.
(e) $2/5 = x/100$; $x = $ _____40_____ ; $2/5 = $ __40__ %.

(a) 37.5; 37.5   (b) 10; 10   (c) 250; 250   (d) 175; 175
(e) 40; 40

24.5 Scientific Notation

SCIENTIFIC NOTATION

In many branches of science decimal fractions are expressed in a standard form such as 3.127×10^2; 4.18×10^{-3} called *scientific notation*. In this notation there is a single digit (nonzero) to the left of the decimal point and an adjustment to obtain the true position of the decimal point is made by multiplying by the proper power of ten.

EXAMPLE

$$3.127 \times 10^2 = 312.7$$

$$4.18 \times 10^{-3} = 0.00418$$

Recall that 10^{-n} means $1/10^n$.

EXAMPLE. Write the following decimal fractions in scientific notation:

$$49.27 = 4.927 \times 10$$

$$3527 = 3.527 \times 10^3$$

$$0.068 = 6.8 \times 10^{-2}$$

$$0.0073 = 7.3 \times 10^{-3}$$

1. The following decimal fractions are expressed in scientific notation. Find their usual expressions as decimal fractions.
   (a) $7.86 \times 10^2 = \underline{786}$.   (b) $2.107 \times 10 = \underline{21.07}$.
   (c) $6.35 \times 10^3 = \underline{6350}$.   (d) $4.3 \times 10^{-2} = \underline{.043}$.
   (e) $5.9 \times 10^{-4} = \underline{.00059}$.

   (a) 786   (b) 21.07   (c) 6350   (d) 0.043   (e) 0.00059

2. Write the following decimal fractions in scientific notation.
   (a) $279.1 = \underline{2.791 \times 10^2}$ (b) $16.34 = \underline{1.634 \times 10}$.
   (c) $0.352 = \underline{3.52 \times 10^{-1}}$ (d) $7.12 = \underline{7.12}$.
   (e) $0.0049 = \underline{4.9 \times 10^{-3}}$.

   (a) 2.791×10^2 (b) 1.634×10 (c) 3.52×10^{-1} (d) 7.12
   (e) 4.9×10^{-3}

24.6 Infinite Decimal Expansions

As we discussed in Section 24.2, only certain rational numbers can be expressed exactly as decimal fractions; for example, $\frac{1}{3}$, $\frac{4}{7}$, $\frac{2}{9}$, and $\frac{5}{11}$ have no such expressions. We also observed, however, that

$$0.3,\ 0.33,\ 0.333,\ 0.3333, \ldots$$

were successively better approximations to $\frac{1}{3}$, and indeed there are similar approximations to the other examples mentioned above. This suggests that it might be desirable to write $\frac{1}{3}$ as the infinite decimal expansion

$$\tfrac{1}{3} = 0.3333\ldots$$

where the dots indicate that 3's are to be entered to the right forever and ever.

At first sight such an infinite decimal expansion does not make sense, for it requires us to add an infinite number of rational numbers $3/10$, $3/10^2$, $3/10^3, \ldots$. We could never finish the job! As a matter of fact, however, it is possible to give a definition for such an expansion that does make sense, but we cannot do so in this book. The definition involves the concept of a *limit*, which is one of the standard topics in calculus. Knowing that this difficulty can be resolved by such advanced methods, and relying on your intuition, we shall feel justified in discussing such infinite decimal expansions in this section.

REPEATING DECIMALS   To find such an infinite decimal expansion for a rational number, we carry out the usual process of long division (supplying zeros on the right of the dividend) as long as our patience holds out.

EXAMPLE.   Express $\frac{1}{3}$ as an infinite decimal.

Solution

$$
\begin{array}{r}
.333 \\
3\overline{)1.000} \\
9 \\
\overline{10} \\
9 \\
\overline{10} \\
9 \\
\overline{1}
\end{array}
$$

There is no point in continuing, for the process is repetitive. Every remainder is 1, and so every partial quotient is 3.

EXAMPLE. Express $\frac{1}{7}$ as an infinite decimal.

Solution

$$
\begin{array}{r}
.142857 \\
7\overline{)1.000000} \\
7 \\
\overline{30} \\
28 \\
\overline{20} \\
14 \\
\overline{60} \\
56 \\
\overline{40} \\
35 \\
\overline{50} \\
49 \\
\overline{1}
\end{array}
$$

We stop at this point, for the remainder is 1 and now the process repeats. Thus we can write

$$\tfrac{1}{7} = 0.142857142857142857\ldots$$

1. Express $\frac{2}{9}$ as an infinite decimal. $\frac{2}{9} = 0.$ _2222 . . . ._

0.2222 . . . .

2. Express $\frac{5}{11}$ as an infinite decimal. $\frac{5}{11} = 0.$ _454545 . . ._

0.454545 . . . .

3. The process begins to repeat when we have reached the stage where zeros are being brought down from the dividend and when we reach a _remainder_ which had occurred earlier in this stage of the computation.

remainder

4. What possible remainders exist? $0, 1, \ldots, 9 - 1,$

The integers $0, 1, \ldots, d - 1$, where d is the divisor.

5. Is the number of possible remainders always finite? yes

Yes.

6. Why must this division process repeat after a finite number of steps?

There are only a finite number of possible remainders, and when the number of divisions exceeds this number of remainders, repetitions must occur.

It is inconvenient to continue to write expressions such as

$$\tfrac{1}{3} = 0.333\ldots$$

$$\tfrac{1}{7} = 0.142857142857142857\ldots$$

$$\tfrac{2}{9} = 0.222\ldots$$

$$\tfrac{5}{11} = 0.4545\ldots$$

and so we need a simpler notation. In each case there is a group of one or more digits that is repeated over and over. Let us write this just once and place a bar over it to indicate repetition:

$$\tfrac{1}{3} = 0.\overline{3}$$

$$\tfrac{1}{7} = 0.\overline{142857}$$

$$\tfrac{2}{9} = 0.\overline{2}$$

$$\tfrac{5}{11} = 0.\overline{45}$$

NOTATION FOR REPEATING DECIMALS

DEFINITION. A decimal expansion of the form $0.\overline{a_1 a_2 \ldots a_p}$ is called an *infinite repeating decimal fraction.*

REMARK

Repeating decimal fractions may also have an "integral part" such as $36.4\overline{13}$, or be of the form $15.25\overline{13}$.

The discussion above contains a proof of the following theorem:

THEOREM 3. Every rational number can be expressed either as a decimal fraction (in the strict sense) or as an infinite repeating decimal fraction.

One final question remains: Does every infinite repeating decimal fraction represent a rational number? Consider the following examples:

EXAMPLE. Show that $0.\bar{3}$ represents $\frac{1}{3}$.

Solution. Let $a = 0.\bar{3}$. Then $10a = 10 \times 0.333\ldots = 3.\bar{3}$. So $10a - a = 3.\bar{3} - 0.\bar{3} = 3.0$ or $9a = 3$ and $a = \frac{1}{3}$.

EXAMPLE. What rational number is represented by $0.\bar{7}$?

Solution. Let $a = 0.\bar{7}$. Then $10a = 7.\bar{7}$. $10a - a = 7.0$. $9a = 7$ and $a = \frac{7}{9}$.

$7.7 - .7 = 7.0$

EXAMPLE. What rational number is represented by $0.\overline{35}$?

Solution. Let $a = 0.\overline{35}$. Then $100a = 35.\overline{35}$. $100a - a = 35.0$ $99a = 35$ and $a = \frac{35}{99}$.

EXAMPLE. What rational number is represented by $0.4\bar{9}$? This notation means $0.4\bar{9} = 0.4999\ldots$.

Solution. Let $a = 0.4\bar{9}$. Then $10a = 4.\bar{9}$. $100a = 49.\bar{9}$. $100a - 10a = 49.\bar{9} - 4.\bar{9} = 45$. So $90a = 45$ and $a = \frac{1}{2}$.

This is a surprising result, for we know that $\frac{1}{2} = 0.5$. The conclusion is that $\frac{1}{2}$ has two decimal expansions: (1) an ordinary finite decimal fraction 0.5, and (2) an infinite repeating decimal expansion $0.4\bar{9}$. Thus $\frac{1}{2}$, 0.5, and $0.4\bar{9}$ are all names for the rational number "one half", and so

$$\tfrac{1}{2} = 0.5 = 0.4\bar{9}$$

A generalization of this method provides a proof of the following theorem:

THEOREM 4. Every infinite repeating decimal fraction represents a rational number.

---

7. What rational numbers are represented by the following infinite repeating decimal fractions? (a) $0.\bar{1} = $ ___1/9___ . (b) $0.\bar{5} = $ ___5/9___ .
(c) $0.\overline{23} = $ ___23/99___ . (d) $0.\overline{417} = $ ___139/333___ . (e) $0.\bar{9} = $ ___1___ .

| (a) 1/9 | (b) 5/9 | (c) 23/99 | (d) 417/999 = 139/333 | (e) 1 |

In this chapter we have defined *finite decimal fractions* and have shown that every finite decimal fraction is a rational number. Since some rational numbers cannot be expressed as finite decimal fractions, we introduced *infinite decimal expansions.* We then defined *infinite repeating decimal fractions* as special cases of infinite decimal expansions. Finally we proved that

(1) Every infinite repeating decimal fraction represents a rational number.
(2) Every rational number can be expressed as either
    (a) a finite decimal fraction, or
    (b) an infinite repeating decimal fraction.

So far we have not considered infinite decimal expansions that are not repeating. These clearly do not represent rational numbers and so must have some other interpretation. We shall discuss them in Chapter 25.

As technical matters we have discussed the algorithms for the arithmetic of decimal fractions with emphasis on the placement of the decimal points. Percent was introduced as another notation for decimal fractions, and scientific notation was introduced.

Now review these ideas and techniques and check your understanding of them by working the following Post Test.

POST TEST

1. When possible, express the following rational numbers as decimal fractions: (a) $\frac{3}{8}$. _37.5_ (b) $\frac{17}{21}$. _80.4761_ (c) $\frac{11}{320}$. _.034375_

2. Express the following decimal fractions as rational numbers in standard notation: (a) 0.645. _645/1000_ (b) 0.625. _625/1000_ (c) 0.1262. _1262/10,000_

3. Find the sum:

$$3.43216$$
$$+0.9002134$$
_4.3323734_

4. Find the difference:

$$0.3671931$$
$$-0.0628122$$
_0.3043809_

5. Find the product:

$$2.132462$$
$$\times .00005$$
_.000106623110_

6. Find the quotients, obtaining a remainder of 0, if possible. Otherwise, state the remainder.

(a) $8.2\,\overline{)283.8348}$. Quotient _34.614_, remainder _0_

(b) $2.9\,\overline{)421.638}$. Quotient _145.39_, remainder _.007_

7. Simplify $10^3 \times 64.50$. _64,500_

510

8. Write as decimal fractions: (a) 1.635%. _00635_ (b) $3\frac{1}{2}$%. _.035_

9. Write as percents: (a) 15.98. _1598%_ (b) 0.1225. _12.25%_
(c) $\frac{5}{8}$. _62.5%_ (d) $\frac{8}{5}$. _160%_

10. Write in scientific notation: (a) 0.0067. _6.7×10⁻³_ (b) 0.000001.
_1.0 × 10⁻⁶_

11. Write as decimal fractions: (a) 2.371×10^2. _237.1_ (b)
2.6×10^{-4}. _.00026_

12. Express as a repeating decimal (a) $\frac{2}{3}$. _.6_ (b) $\frac{1}{27}$. _.037_

13. Express as a rational number: (a) $1.\overline{9}$. _2_ (b) $2.\overline{7}$. _25/9_

14. True or false:

(a) The only possible remainders occurring in the process of dividing $\frac{11}{37}$ are 0, 1, 2, 3, 4, 5, 6, 7, 8, 9. _F_

(b) The number of possible distinct remainders occurring in the process of dividing a/b is never infinite. _T_

(c) Some rational numbers can be expressed as infinite *nonrepeating* decimal expansions such as 0.10110111011110.... _F_

(d) Every infinite decimal expansion, repeating or nonrepeating, represents a rational number. _F_

---

1. (a) 0.375. (b) no decimal fraction. (c) 0.034375.
2. (a) 645/1000 (or 129/200). (b) 625/1000 (or 5/8). (c) 1262/10,000 (or 631/5000).
3. 4.3323734
4. 0.3043809
5. 0.00010662310
6. (a) 34.614 ; 0. (b) 145.39 ; 0.007. (Other answers are possible.)
7. 64,500.
8. (a) 0.01635. (b) 0.035.
9. (a) 1598%. (b) 12.250%. (c) 62.5%. (d) 160%.
10. (a) 6.7×10^{-3}. (b) 1.0×10^{-6}.
11. (a) 237.1. (b) 0.00026.
12. (a) $0.\overline{6}$. (b) $0.\overline{037}$.
13. (a) 2. (b) $\frac{25}{9}$.
14. (a) F. (b) T. (c) F. (d) F.

Now proceed to Chapter 25, The Real Number System.

25

The Real Number System

Before beginning this chapter you should have completed the Post Test for Chapter 24. You should also review the Theorem of Pythagoras in a geometry book or in Section 29.6. To be sure that you are prepared for this chapter, work the following Readiness Test.

READINESS TEST

1. True or false:
(a) Every rational number represents a point on the number line. _____
(b) It has been proved in Chapter 24 that we can find a rational number to represent every point on the number line. _____
(c) Every rational number has a decimal expansion that is finite or repeating. _____
(d) Every infinite decimal represents a rational number. _____

> (a) T.   (b) F.   (c) T.   (d) F.

2. In the right triangle in the figure the theorem of Pythagoras states that $a^2 + b^2 =$ _____ .

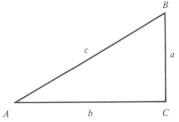

> c^2

3. If the legs of a right triangle are of length 3 and 4, respectively, the length of the hypoteneuse is _____ .

> 5

4. Suppose that we assume that proposition p is true, and that we know that proposition r is true. Then from our assumption that p is true we prove that r must be false. What conclusion can we draw from these facts?

_____

> We were wrong in our assumption that p is true.

You should now be ready to proceed with Chapter 25.

25.1 Need for an Additional Type Number

Since the rational numbers appear to be adequate for the usual purposes of arithmetic, it may seem reasonable to conclude our study of numbers at this point. There are, however, several kinds of problems that need investigation before we drop the subject entirely.

In the first place, we have Theorem 3 of Chapter 24, which tells us that the rational numbers can be expressed either as finite decimal fractions or as infinite repeating decimal fractions. Can there be such a thing as an infinite nonrepeating decimal fraction? If we are to describe such a number, we must have a rule for finding its expression to any number of decimal places; just a few decimal places will not do. How can we do this?

One possibility is to consider the infinite expansion

NONREPEATING DECIMAL EXPANSION

$$a = 0.010110111011110\ldots$$

Clearly the rule is to follow the first 0 with one 1, the second zero with two 1's, the third 0 with three 1's, and so on. In this way we can write out the expansion as far as we please. Two points are worthy of attention: (1) a should be some kind of a number (intuition), and (2) a is not a repeating decimal and hence does not represent a rational number. What on earth can a be?

To take a second approach, we have observed that there is a one-to-one correspondence between the rational numbers and a set of points on the number line. Can every point on the number line be represented in this way? At first sight the answer seems to be "yes" for the following reason. If we choose any two rationals a and b, then there is another rational $\dfrac{a+b}{2}$ between them. This is true even if a and b are very close to each other such as $\dfrac{1}{100}$ and $\dfrac{1}{101}$. For

$$\frac{\dfrac{1}{100} + \dfrac{1}{101}}{2} = \frac{201}{20{,}200}$$

is between $\dfrac{1}{100}$ and $\dfrac{1}{101}$. By a continuation of this process we can show that we can find infinitely many rational numbers between any pair of rationals a and b. The formal statement of this property is given by saying that the

DENSE SET

points on the line corresponding to the rational numbers form a *dense* set. There seems to be no room for any other points, and so the existence of other types of numbers becomes questionable.

Thus we seem to have a dilemma. The infinite nonrepeating decimals should represent some type of irrational (not rational) numbers, but since the rationals are dense on the number line, there appears to be no room for irrational numbers. How can we resolve this difficulty?

---

1. An infinite decimal expansion is constructed by writing the natural numbers in order from left to right to the right of the decimal point. The first 13 decimal places are

$$a = 0.1234567891011\ldots$$

Write the next six decimal places _____ .

> 121314

2. The expansion in frame 1 is an infinite _____
(repeating, nonrepeating)
decimal expansion.

> nonrepeating

3. An infinite decimal expansion is constructed in which the first digit to the right of the decimal point is 1, there are 2 zeros, then a 1, then three zeros, then a 1, and so on, so that the number of zeros between successive 1's increases by one in each block of zeros from left to right. Write the first 19 decimal places of this expansion:
0. _____

> 0.1001000100001000001 . . . .

4. The expansion in frame 3 is an infinite _____
(repeating, nonrepeating)
decimal expansion.

> nonrepeating

5. Why is $a = 3.14159\ldots$ an inadequate description of an infinite decimal expansion unless more information is given? _____
_____

> We do not know how to continue the expansion.

6. Find a rational number between $\frac{1}{3}$ and $\frac{1}{2}$. _____

> Many answers, such as 5/12 or 11/24.

7. Find a rational number between $\frac{1}{3}$ and $\frac{5}{12}$. _____

> Many answers, such as 9/24, 17/48, or 19/48.

8. How many rational numbers are there between $\frac{1}{3}$ and $\frac{1}{2}$? _____
_____

> Infinitely many.

515

9. How many rational numbers are there between $\dfrac{1}{1,000,000}$ and $\dfrac{1}{1,000,001}$? _____

> Infinitely many.

10. What do we mean by saying that the rationals are *dense* on the number line? _____

_____

> We can find infinitely many rational numbers between any pair of rationals a and b.

11. Are the integers dense on the number line? _____

> No.

12. Are the rationals of the form $a/2$, where a is an integer, dense on the number line? _____

> No.

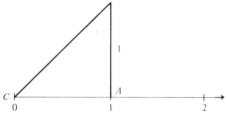

FIGURE 25.1. *Isosceles right triangle with sides of length 1.*

CONSTRUCTION OF $\sqrt{2}$

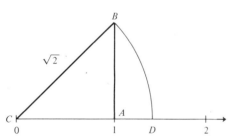

FIGURE 25.2. *The point D represents* $\sqrt{2}$.

PROOF THAT $\sqrt{2}$ **IS IRRATIONAL**

25.2 The Problem of $\sqrt{2}$

A solution to the dilemma raised in Section 25.1 can be obtained by considering the nature of $\sqrt{2}$. This is defined to have the property that $(\sqrt{2})^2 = 2$.

First, let us construct a right isosceles triangle whose equal legs are each one unit long (Figure 25.1). From the theorem of Pythagoras,

$$\overline{BC}^2 = \overline{AC}^2 + \overline{AB}^2$$
$$= 1^2 + 1^2$$
$$= 2$$

Hence

$$\overline{BC} = \sqrt{2}$$

Now with C as center and CB as radius construct an arc of a circle intersecting the number line at D (Figure 25.2). The construction assures us that $CD = CB = \sqrt{2}$. So D marks a point on the number line which is represented by $\sqrt{2}$.

The question now is the following: Is $\sqrt{2}$ a rational number? Let us suppose that it is. Then there is a rational number a/b (which we take in lowest terms) such that

$$\frac{a}{b} = \sqrt{2} \quad \text{or} \quad \frac{a^2}{b^2} = 2$$

Therefore, $a^2 = 2b^2$. That is, a^2 is an even whole number.

If a is odd, we can write $a = 2n + 1$, where n is a whole number. Then $a^2 = (2n + 1)^2 = 4n^2 + 4n + 1$. But $4n^2 + 4n + 1$ is an odd number. Since we know that our a^2 is even, it follows that a cannot be odd. Therefore, a is even and can be written $a = 2p$, where p is a whole number.

Let us substitute $a = 2p$ for a in the equation $a^2 = 2b^2$. The result is

$$4p^2 = 2b^2 \quad \text{or} \quad 2p^2 = b^2$$

The previous argument shows that b is even and hence can be written $b = 2q$. Therefore,

$$a/b = 2p/2q$$

and so a/b is not in lowest terms. We assumed, however, that a/b was in lowest terms; and now we find that this is false. Hence we have arrived at a contradiction.

The conclusion is that we began with a false assumption, namely that $\sqrt{2}$ is a rational number. *Therefore, $\sqrt{2}$ is not a rational number; it is irrational.*

The chief result of this section is that there are points on the number line (such as D in Figure 25.2) which cannot be represented by rational numbers. Even though the rationals are dense on the number line, there are still more points than those which correspond to rationals. Hence it is necessary for us to develop a further extension of our number system.

---

1. Show that $3 + \sqrt{2}$ is irrational. If $3 + \sqrt{2}$ is rational then there is a rational number a/b such that $3 + \sqrt{2} = a/b$. Then $\sqrt{2} = a/b -$ _____ or $\sqrt{2} =$ _____ $/b$. Hence $\sqrt{2}$ is _____ , which is a _____ _____ .

3	$a - 3b$	rational	contradiction

2. Show that $5 - \sqrt{2}$ is irrational. _____

If $5 - \sqrt{2} = a/b$, then $\sqrt{2} = 5 - a/b = \dfrac{5b - a}{b}$, so $\sqrt{2}$ is rational.

3. Show that $3\sqrt{2}$ is irrational. _____

If $3\sqrt{2} = a/b$, then $\sqrt{2} = a/3b$, so $\sqrt{2}$ is rational.

4. Prove that if a is rational and b is irrational, then $a + b$ is irrational.

Suppose that $a + b$ is rational. Then $-a + (a + b)$ is rational. But $-a + (a + b) = b$. So b is rational. Contradiction.

5. Draw a figure similar to Figure 25.2 showing how to locate the point on the number line corresponding to $\sqrt{3}$.

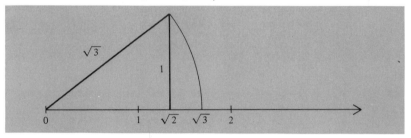

The next sequence of frames proves that $\sqrt{3}$ is irrational

6. Any whole number a has one of the following forms, where n is an integer:

$$a = \begin{cases} 3n \\ 3n + 1 \\ 3n + 2 \end{cases}$$

Then

$$a^2 = \begin{cases} 9n^2 \\ \underline{\hspace{3cm}} \\ \underline{\hspace{3cm}} \end{cases}$$

$9n^2 + 6n + 1 \qquad 9n^2 + 12n + 4$

7. In the expression for a^2 in frame 6, which is (are) divisible (exactly) by 3? _____

Only $9n^2$

8. Hence if a^2 is divisible by 3, a is divisible _____.

by 3

9. Now suppose $\sqrt{3} = a/b$, where a/b is in lowest terms. Then $3 =$ _____ and $3b^2 =$ _____. Hence a^2 is divisible by 3, and so (frame 8) _____. Therefore, $a = 3p$, where p is some natural number.

| a^2/b^2 | a^2 | a is divisible by 3 |

10. Since in frame 9, $3b^2 = a^2$ and $a = 3p$, by substitution for a we get $3b^2 = \underline{\hspace{1cm}}$, or $b^2 = \underline{\hspace{1cm}}$. Hence by frame 8, $\underline{\hspace{3cm}}$ and $b = 3q$.

| $9p^2$ | $3p^2$ | b is divisible by 3 |

11. Therefore, from frames 9 and 10, $a/b = 3p/3q$. This is a contradiction. Why? $\underline{\hspace{4cm}}$

a/b was assumed to be in lowest terms.

12. Because of frames 9, 10, and 11, it follows that $\sqrt{3}$ is $\underline{\hspace{2cm}}$.

irrational

25.3 Real Numbers

The number system to which the system of rational numbers is extended is called the real number system. This curious name derives from the fact that in later developments the real numbers are to be distinguished from other types of numbers called "imaginary numbers", an example of which is $\sqrt{-1}$. Although the name *real numbers* is not especially meaningful, it is the standard name in all of mathematics, and so we shall stick with it

Intuitively, the real number system includes the integers, the rational numbers, and the new types of numbers which we have called irrational. A description of the real numbers which is adequate for our purposes is the following:

REAL NUMBER   DEFINITION. A *real number* is a finite decimal fraction or an infinite decimal expansion, repeating or nonrepeating.

REMARKS

1. A real number is rational if its decimal expansion is finite or repeating; irrational if the expansion is nonrepeating.
2. The real numbers are in one-to-one correspondence with the set of all points of the number line.

25.4 The Number $\sqrt{2}$ Again

We have proved that $\sqrt{2}$ is irrational and have said that every irrational number has an infinite nonrepeating decimal expansion. How can we find this expansion for $\sqrt{2}$? The method is to approximate $\sqrt{2}$ with decimal fractions.

First, $1^2 < 2 < 2^2$. Continuing this procedure we find that

DECIMAL APPROXIMATION TO $\sqrt{2}$

$$(1.4)^2 = 1.96 < 2 < (1.5)^2 = 2.25$$

$$(1.41)^2 = 1.9881 < 2 < (1.42)^2 = 2.0264$$

$$(1.414)^2 = 1.999396 < 2 < (1.415)^2 = 2.002225$$

$$(1.4142)^2 = 1.99996164 < 2 < (1.4143)^3 = 2.0002449$$

Therefore,

$$1 < \sqrt{2} < 2$$
$$1.4 < \sqrt{2} < 1.5$$
$$1.41 < \sqrt{2} < 1.42$$
$$1.414 < \sqrt{2} < 1.415$$
$$1.4142 < \sqrt{2} < 1.4143$$

This process can be continued as far as is needed and shows that the decimal expansion of $\sqrt{2}$ is

$$\sqrt{2} = 1.4142\ldots$$

---

1. Find the decimal expansion of $\sqrt{3}$ to three decimal places. _____

$$1 < \sqrt{3} < 2 \qquad 1.73 < \sqrt{3} < 1.74$$
$$1.7 < \sqrt{3} < 1.8 \qquad 1.732 < \sqrt{3} < 1.733$$

The answer is $1.732\ldots$.

25.5 Other Irrational Numbers

Irrational numbers arise in a great variety of situations in mathematics. We shall describe only four of these.

(1) Let a be a whole number that is not a perfect square. That is, a cannot be expressed as $a = p^2$, where p is a whole number. Then by methods similar to those we have used above we can prove that $\sqrt{a}$ is irrational.

(2) As a generalization of (1), let a be a whole number that is not a perfect nth power. That is, a cannot be expressed as $a = p^n$, where p is a whole number and n is a whole number greater than 1. Then $\sqrt[n]{a}$ is irrational.

(3) You have undoubtedly heard of the number π which has the property that 2π is the length of the circumference of a circle of radius 1. It is possible to prove that π is irrational, but such a proof requires methods too advanced for this book.

There is frequently confusion about the definition of π, so let us define it once and for all.

DEFINITION OF π

DEFINITION. The real number π is defined as the number such that 2π is the length of the circumference of a circle of radius 1.

REMARK

It is incorrect to define π to be 22/7 or 3.1416, for these are merely rational approximations to the *irrational* number π.

APPROXIMATION TO π

It is possible to approximate π by inscribing regular polygons in a circle of radius 1, circumscribing polygons about this circle and computing the lengths of their perimeters. Figure 25.3 shows a polygon with eight sides inscribed in a circle and another eight-sided polygon circumscribed about the circle.

By algebraic methods we can compute the entries in Table 1. In the headings of this table p_n stands for a regular polygon of n sides inscribed in a circle of radius 1 and P_n for the corresponding circumscribed polygon.

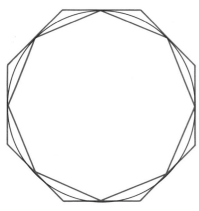

FIGURE 25.3. *Eight-sided regular polygons inscribed in a circle and circumscribed about it.*

TABLE 1. **An approximation for π**

Number of Sides of the Regular Polygon, n	Perimeter of the Inscribed Regular Polygon in Circle of Radius 1, p_n	Length of Circumference of Circle of Radius 1, C	Perimeter of the Circumscribed Regular Polygon about Circle of Radius 1, P_n
6	(2)(3.000000)	< C <	(2)(3.411017−)
12	(2)(3.105828+)	< C <	(2)(3.215391−)
24	(2)(3.132628+)	< C <	(2)(3.159660−)
48	(2)(3.139350+)	< C <	(2)(3.146087−)
96	(2)(3.141031+)	< C <	(2)(3.142715−)
192	(2)(3.141452+)	< C <	(2)(3.141874−)
384	(2)(3.141557+)	< C <	(2)(3.141664−)
768	(2)(3.141583+)	< C <	(2)(3.141611−)
1,536	(2)(3.141590+)	< C <	(2)(3.141598−)
3,072	(2)(3.141592+)	< C <	(2)(3.141594−)
6,144	(2)(3.141592+)	< C <	(2)(3.141593−)

Thus $\pi = 3.141592\ldots$.

Research into the nature of π and computation of its decimal expansion have been topics of interest since the very earliest times. A crude, but elementary, approximation to π may be obtained by measuring the circumference of a circle (say by putting a wire around a circular cylinder) and dividing this observed length by the diameter of the circle. In I Kings 7:23 and in II Chronicles 4:2 the value of π is given as 3. Later by geometrical methods Archimedes (287–212 B.C.) proved that $3\frac{1}{7} < \pi < 3\frac{10}{71}$. The approximation 3.1416 was known to Ptolemy in 150 A.D. By 1596 the value of π to

521

35 decimal places has been computed by Ludolph von Ceulen. And in 1873, Shanks used algebraic methods to compute (incorrectly) π to 707 decimal places. With the advent of modern electronic computers, it was possible to go much further, and π is now known to more than 100,000 decimal places. The irrationality of π was first established by Lambert in 1761.

(4) If P dollars are invested at simple interest at the rate of 100% per annum, the amount A to which this will grow in one year is

COMPOUND INTEREST

$$A = P(1 + 1)$$

If the interest is compounded semiannually the amount after six months is $P(1 + \frac{1}{2})$. This is then reinvested for the next six months so that the amount A at the end of the first year is

$$A = P(1 + \tfrac{1}{2})^2$$

If the interest is compounded quarterly, the amount A at the end of one year is

$$A = P(1 + \tfrac{1}{4})^4$$

If it is compounded weekly,

$$A = P(1 + \tfrac{1}{52})^{52}$$

and if it is compounded daily,

$$A = P(1 + \tfrac{1}{365})^{365}$$

Of course this process can be continued so that interest is compounded every hour, every minute, every second, and so on, but nobody bothers to do this. (Some banks, however, do compound daily.)

As the number of compoundings increases indefinitely, we get the expression

$$A = P\left[\lim_{n \to \infty} \left(1 + \frac{1}{n}\right)^n \right]$$

where $\lim\limits_{n \to \infty}$ is read "the limit as n tends to infinity".

DEFINITION OF e

The limit $\lim\limits_{n \to \infty} \left(1 + \dfrac{1}{n}\right)^n$ is called e and has the approximate value: $e = 2.71828\ldots$. By advanced methods it can be proved that e is an irrational number.

25.6 Arithmetic of Real Numbers

The processes of arithmetic $(+, -, \times, \div)$ can be extended to the real numbers, but this extension is a rather delicate matter. Somehow we must be able to add and multiply infinite decimals! The idea is to use rational approximations to the real numbers involved, add and multiply these, and finally to arrive at results for the sums and products of real numbers.

The important fact is that the properties of the arithmetic of real numbers are identical with those of the rational numbers, as given in the summary at the end of Chapter 23.

25.7 Equivalence of Infinite Sets

At this point the following kinds of questions may occur to you.

(1) Are there more positive rational numbers than natural numbers?

(2) Are there more positive real numbers than positive rational numbers?

To answer such questions it is necessary to know what "more" means. When you think about this, you will realize that questions (1) and (2) really concern the cardinal numbers of the sets of natural numbers, positive rational numbers, and positive real numbers. Are these the same or different? From Chapter 5 you know that the cardinal numbers of equivalent sets are equal, and that the cardinal numbers of nonequivalent sets are not equal. So let us consider the equivalence or nonequivalence of the sets of natural numbers, positive rational numbers and positive real numbers.

Our questions are answered by the following two theorems:

THEOREM 1. The set of positive rational numbers is equivalent to the set of natural numbers.

Proof. Arrange the positive fractions in the following array, which clearly contains all positive fractions. Now traverse the path shown in color

$$
\begin{array}{ccccc}
\dfrac{1}{1} \rightarrow & \dfrac{1}{2} & \dfrac{1}{3} \rightarrow & \dfrac{1}{4} & \dfrac{1}{5} \quad \cdots \\[2mm]
\dfrac{2}{1} & \dfrac{2}{2} & \dfrac{2}{3} & \dfrac{2}{4} & \dfrac{2}{5} \quad \cdots \\[2mm]
\dfrac{3}{1} & \dfrac{3}{2} & \dfrac{3}{3} & \dfrac{3}{4} & \dfrac{3}{5} \quad \cdots \\[2mm]
\vdots & \vdots & \vdots & \vdots & \vdots \quad \cdots
\end{array}
$$

in the given direction, and write the fractions in the resulting sequence. A fraction such as 2/2 is omitted if it is equivalent to a fraction that occurs earlier in the sequence.

Thus a sequence is obtained which contains each positive rational number precisely once and which is equivalent to the set of natural numbers, as is shown by the correspondence

$$
\begin{array}{cccccc}
1 & 2 & 3 & 4 & 5 & 6 \quad \cdots \\
\updownarrow & \updownarrow & \updownarrow & \updownarrow & \updownarrow & \updownarrow \\
1 & \tfrac{1}{2} & 2 & 3 & \tfrac{1}{3} & \tfrac{1}{4} \quad \cdots
\end{array}
$$

This theorem can be interpreted to state that there are just as many positive rational numbers as there are natural numbers.

THEOREM 2. The set of real numbers between 0 and 1 is *not* equivalent to the set of natural numbers.

Proof. The proof is indirect. Suppose that the two sets are equivalent. Then we can write a sequence of *all* real numbers between 0 and 1 beginning as follows:

$$a = 0.a_1 \quad a_2 \quad a_3 \quad a_4 \ldots$$
$$b = 0.b_1 \quad b_2 \quad b_3 \quad b_4 \ldots$$
$$c = 0.c_1 \quad c_2 \quad c_3 \quad c_4 \ldots$$
$$d = 0.d_1 \quad d_2 \quad d_3 \quad d_4 \ldots$$
$$\vdots \qquad \vdots \quad \vdots \quad \vdots \quad \vdots \ldots$$

Form the real number x between 0 and 1 as follows:

$$x = 0.x_1 x_2 x_3 x_4 \ldots$$

where $x_1 \neq a_1$, $x_2 \neq b_2$, $x_3 \neq c_3$, $x_4 \neq d_4, \ldots$. Then x is not equal to any of the real numbers in the given sequence, and so it is not in the sequence. But this is a contradiction, for the sequence was supposed to contain *all* real numbers between 0 and 1. Hence the two sets are not equivalent.

This theorem can be interpreted to state that there are more real numbers between 0 and 1 than there are natural numbers. Hence there are more positive real numbers than natural numbers and more positive real numbers than positive rational numbers.

---

1. Set up a one-to-one correspondence to show that the set of integers is equivalent to the set of natural numbers.

1	2	3	4	5	6	7	$\cdots$
$\updownarrow$	$\updownarrow$	$\updownarrow$	$\updownarrow$	$\updownarrow$	$\updownarrow$	$\updownarrow$	

1	2	3	4	5	6	7	$\cdots$
$\updownarrow$	$\updownarrow$	$\updownarrow$	$\updownarrow$	$\updownarrow$	$\updownarrow$	$\updownarrow$	
0	1	-1	2	-2	3	-3	$\cdots$

2. Set up a one-to-one correspondence to show that the set of rational numbers is equivalent to the set of integers.

$$
\begin{array}{ccccccccc}
0 & 1 & -1 & 2 & -2 & 3 & -3 & 4 & -4 & \cdots \\
\updownarrow & \updownarrow & \updownarrow & \updownarrow & \updownarrow & \updownarrow & \updownarrow & \updownarrow & \updownarrow & \\
0 & 1 & -1 & \frac{1}{2} & -\frac{1}{2} & 2 & -2 & 3 & -3 & \cdots
\end{array}
$$

for example.

REFERENCES

Beaumont, R. A., and R. S. Pierce, *The Algebraic Foundations of Mathematics*, Addison-Wesley, Reading, Mass., 1963, Chap. 7.

Henkin, Leon, W. N. Smith, V. J. Varineau, and M. J. Walsh, *Retracing Elementary Mathematics*, Macmillan, New York, 1962, Chaps. 13 and 14.

Niven, Ivan, *Irrational Numbers*, Carus Monograph 11, Wiley, New York, 1956.

Shanks, Daniel, and J. W. Wrench, Jr., "Calculation of π to 100,000 Decimals", *Mathematics of Computation*, Vol. 16, pp. 76–99 (1962).

This chapter completes our account of the development of the real number system. Beginning with the whole numbers we worked our way through the successive generalizations of them to the integers, rational numbers, and now finally to the real numbers. The following Post Test will tell you how well you have kept up with us in this journey.

POST TEST

1. If a and b are whole numbers, the equation $b + x = a$ has a whole number solution if and only if _____.

2. If a and b are integers, the equation $b + x = a$ has an integer solution for _____ a and b.

3. If a and b are rational or real numbers, the equation $b + x = a$ has a rational or real solution for _____ a and b.

4. If a and b are whole numbers, the equation $bx = a$ with $b \neq 0$ has a whole number as a solution if and only if b _____ a.

5. If a and b are integers, the equation $bx = a$, with $b \neq 0$, has an integer as a solution if and only if b _____ a.

6. If a and b are rational or real numbers, the equation $bx = a$ with $b \neq 0$ has a rational or real solution for _____ a and b.

7. If b is a positive whole number, integer, or rational number, the equation $x^2 = b$ has a rational solution if and only if b is a perfect _____.

8. If b is a positive real number, the equation $x^2 = b$ has a real solution for _____ b.

9. Does the equation $x^2 = b$ have a real solution for every real number b? _____

10. A real number is defined in the following fashion. The first digit to the right of the decimal point is 0, the next 1, then 0, then 2, etc., so that the numbers between successive pairs of zeros are the natural numbers in their usual order.

(a) Write the first 24 places of this number. 0. _____

(b) Is this number rational? _____

11. Find a rational number that lies between $\frac{1}{7}$ and $\frac{1}{6}$. _____

12. Are the natural numbers dense on the number line? _____

13. Show that $4 - \sqrt{2}$ is irrational, given that $\sqrt{2}$ is irrational. _____

14. Draw a figure to locate $\sqrt{5}$ on the number line.

15. Find the first three decimal places of the decimal expansion of $\sqrt{5}$. _____

16. To how many decimal places is $\frac{22}{7}$ a correct approximation to π? _____

17. The real number π is defined by what geometric property? _____

18. A real number is defined to be (in terms of decimal expansions).

1. $a \geq b$
2. all
3. all
4. divides
5. divides
6. all
7. square
8. all
9. No. $x^2 = -1$ does not have a real solution.
10. (a) 0.010203040506070809010011 .... (b) No.
11. $\frac{13}{84}$, for instance.
12. No.
13. If $4 - \sqrt{2} = a/b$, then $\sqrt{2} = 4 - (a/b) = (4b - a)/b$, so $\sqrt{2}$ would be rational.

14.

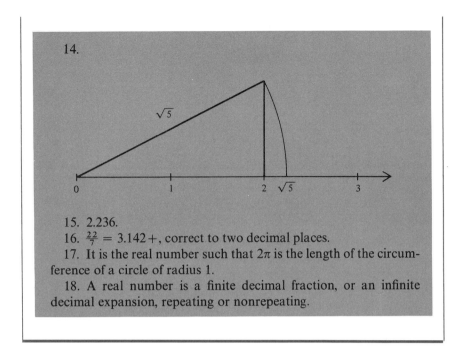

15. 2.236.

16. $\frac{22}{7} = 3.142+$, correct to two decimal places.

17. It is the real number such that 2π is the length of the circumference of a circle of radius 1.

18. A real number is a finite decimal fraction, or an infinite decimal expansion, repeating or nonrepeating.

This concludes our study of number systems. Now proceed to Chapter 26, where we shall discuss an important application of them.

26

Ratio and Proportion

Since the concepts of ratio and proportion are closely related to that of a rational number, you should review Chapter 24, Rational Numbers, before beginning this chapter.

Now proceed with Chapter 26 and work the exercises included in it.

26.1 Introduction

RATIO

The term *ratio* is used to describe the relative sizes of two sets. For example, if a room contains 36 men and 24 women, the ratio of the number of men to the number of women is said to be "36 to 24". Similarly, if a bookstore has on hand 180 books for 240 students, the ratio of the number of books to the number of students is "180 to 240".

Various notations are used for ratios. In particular, the ratio "a to b" is often written "$a:b$". Some people use the notation a/b for such a ratio, but this confuses ratios with rational numbers and should be avoided. Since a ratio merely represents a pair of numbers in a particular order, we can also write it as an ordered pair (a, b). The trouble with this usage is that ordered pairs are used in a great variety of contexts, and so we must continually write "the ratio (a, b)" to indicate that (a, b) represents a ratio. So that we can have a notation for a ratio which is simple and unambiguous we shall

NOTATION $a:b$ hereafter use the notation $a:b$ to represent the ratio of a to b. In this notation we shall assume that a and b are natural numbers.

529

26.2 Equality of Ratios

There is a concept of equality for ratios which is analogous to that of equality for rational numbers.

$a:b = c:d$ **DEFINITION.** The ratios $a:b$ and $c:d$ are equal (that is, $a:b = c:d$) if and only if $ad = bc$.

EXAMPLE. $36:24 = 3:2$ and $180:240 = 3:4$.

There is another way of expressing the equality of ratios that is frequently useful. Suppose that $a = kc$ and $b = kd$, where k is a rational number. Then $ad = kcd$ and $bc = kcd$. Hence $ad = bc$ and $a:b = c:d$. This proves Theorem 1:

THEOREM 1. If $a = kc$ and $b = kd$, where a, b, c, and d are natural numbers and k is a rational number, then $a:b = c:d$.

EXAMPLE. Since $6 = (3/5)10$ and $9 = (3/5)15$, the ratios $6:9$ and $10:15$ are equal. Each of these ratios is also equal to $2:3$.

The converse to Theorem 1 is also true:

THEOREM 2. If $a:b = c:d$, where a, b, c, and d are natural numbers, there is a rational number k such that $a = kc$ and $b = kd$.

Proof. $k = a/c$ has the required property. For
1. $a = (a/c)c$.
2. Since $ad = bc$ by hypothesis, we can substitute the formula for a given in 1 and obtain
$$(a/c)cd = bc$$
Hence
$$b = (a/c)d$$

PROBLEM. As a problem concerning ratios let us consider the room which contains 36 men and 24 women. If 12 additional men enter the room, how many additional women are required to restore the original ratio of men to women?

Solution. The original ratio of men to women is $36:24 = 3:2$. The new ratio will be $(36 + 12):(24 + x) = 48:(24 + x)$, where x is the number of additional women. The problem requires us to find x such that
$$48:(24 + x) = 3:2$$
Hence
$$3(24 + x) = 48 \cdot 2 = 96$$
$$24 + x = 32$$
$$x = 8$$

A generalization of this problem concerning ratios can be stated as follows: Let us be given sets A and B such that the ratio of $n(A)$ to $n(B)$ is $a:b$. We also have another set C with cardinal number $n(C) = c$. The problem is to find the cardinal number of a further set D, $n(D) = d$, such that the ratio of $n(A)$ to $n(B)$ is equal to the ratio of $n(C)$ to $n(D)$.

Then we have the equation $a:b = c:d$ or $ad = bc$, where a, b, and c are known and d is unknown. This may be solved to get $d = (bc)/a$.

In the most general problem concerning ratios we are given three of the numbers a, b, c, and d and the equality $a:b = c:d$ or $ad = bc$. We are then asked to solve for the unknown number.

---

1. The registrar at Siwash College released the following table showing fall enrollments:

Year	Men	Women
1967	2400	3600
1968	2700	3300
1969	3200	3200

The ratios of the number of men to the number of women were as follows. (a) In 1967 _____ : _____ = 2 : _____. (b) In 1968 _____ : _____ = 9 : _____. (c) In 1969 _____ : _____ = 1 : _____.

(a) $2400:3600$; 3   (b) $2700:3300$; 11   (c) $3200:3200$; 1

2. The popular course, Psychology 6, "Dr. Kinsey tell all" in campus slang, was limited to 240 students because the lecture hall had only 240 seats. In 1968, of the 240 students who registered for the course, 1/8 were left-handed. Only 20 seats had left-handed writing arms.
   (a) The number of left-handed students was _____.
   (b) The number of right-handed students was _____.
   (c) The ratio of the number of left-handed students to the number of right-handed students was _____.
   (d) The ratio of the number of left-handed seats to the number of right-handed seats was 20 : _____ or 1 : _____.
   (e) The ratio of the number of left-handed students to the number of left-handed seats was _____.
   (f) True or false? Some left-handed students had to sit in right-handed seats. _____

(a) 30   (b) 210   (c) $30:210 = 1:7$ (d) 220, 11   (e) $3:2$
(f) T.

3. The college bookstore had a policy of ordering in advance 3 textbooks for every 4 students expected to enroll in a course.

(a) The ratio of the number of students to the number of books was _____.

(b) How many books would be ordered for an expected enrollment of 68 students? Solve $4:3 = 68:x$; $x =$ _____.

(c) How many books would be ordered for an expected enrollment of 240 students? _____.

(d) How many books would be ordered for an expected enrollment of $4n$ students? _____.

(a) 4:3   (b) 51   (c) 180   (d) 3n

4. In the first week of the baseball season the Moguls won 2 of 5 games.

(a) What was the ratio of the number of wins to the number of games played? _____

(b) How many games must the Moguls win out of their first 40 games in order to maintain this same ratio? _____

(c) In x games the Moguls had 24 wins. If the ratio of the number of wins to the number of games played is still 2 to 5, how many games were played? _____.

(a) 2:5.   (b) $x:40 = 2:5$, $x = 16$.   (c) $24:x = 2:5$, $x = 60$.

5. Let k be the GCD of c and d. Prove that

$$c:d = (c \div k):(d \div k)$$

$c(d \div k) = (cd) \div k$ and $d(c \div k) = (dc) \div k$. Hence $c(d \div k) = d(c \div k)$.

6. Use the result of frame 5 to reduce $72:96$ to a simpler form. $72:96 =$ _____.

3:4

7. Since $4:6 = 10:15$, there is a rational number k such that $4 = 10k$ and $6 = 15k$. Find it. $k =$ _____.

$\frac{2}{5}$

8. Since $80:60 = 64:48$ there is a rational number k such that $80 = 64k$ and $60 = 48k$. Find it. $k =$ _____.

$\frac{5}{4}$

9. Is there a rational number k such that $7 = 3k$ and $12 = 4k$? _____

(yes, no)

What conclusion can you draw about the equality of $7:12$ and $3:4$?

_____

> No.   Not equal.

10. Prove that if $a:b = c:d$, then $a:c = b:d$. (In old books this is called the "Theorem of Alternation".) _____

> In each case $ad = bc$.

26.3 Proportion

The statement that two ratios are equal is often called a *proportion*.

PROPORTION   **DEFINITION.** If $a:b$ and $c:d$ represent ratios, the statement that $a:b = c:d$ is called a *proportion*. When this equality is true, the ordered pairs (a, b) and (c, d) are said to be *proportional*.

Thus we may restate Theorems 1 and 2 as follows:

THEOREM 3. The ordered pairs (a, b) and (c, d) are proportional if and only if there is a rational number k such that $a = kc$ and $b = kd$.

NOTATION $k(c, d)$ **NOTATION.** For convenience the pair of equations in Theorem 3 can be written as the single equation $(a, b) = k(c, d)$, where $k(c, d)$ is defined to be equal to (kc, kd).

So far we have used ratio and proportion to compare the sizes of two sets with the sizes of two other sets. The concept of proportion can be extended to compare the sizes of three (or more) sets with the sizes of three (or more) sets.

For example, if we are given two similar triangles ABC and $A'B'C'$ as in Figure 26.1, the lengths of the sides ABC are proportional to the lengths of the sides of $A'B'C'$, for $A'B' = 2AB$, $B'C' = 2BC$, and $A'C' = 2AC$.

FIGURE 26.1.
Similar triangles.

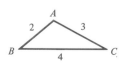 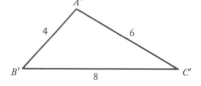

This concept of proportionality can be extended to ordered sets of real numbers in the following fashion.

533

NONZERO ORDERED SET   DEFINITION. A *nonzero ordered set* of real numbers is an ordered set of real numbers at least one of whose members is not zero.

EXAMPLES
1. $(4, 6, 9, -3)$ is a nonzero ordered set.
2. $(0, 0, 0, 1)$ is a nonzero ordered set.
3. $(0, 0, 0, 0)$ is a zero ordered set.

Proportionality of nonzero ordered sets is defined as follows:

PROPORTIONAL   DEFINITION. The nonzero ordered set of real numbers $(a, b, c, \ldots)$ is *proportional* to the nonzero ordered set of real numbers $(r, s, t, \ldots)$ if and only if there is a nonzero real number k such that

$$a = kr;\ b = ks;\ c = kt, \ldots$$

We can write these equations more compactly as the single equation $(a, b, c, \ldots) = k(r, s, t, \ldots)$, where $k(r, s, t, \ldots) = (kr, ks, kt, \ldots)$.

EXAMPLE. If the sides of a triangle are of lengths: $AB = 6$, $BC = 3$, $AC = 5$, and if ABC is similar to $A'B'C'$, where $A'B' = 8$, find $B'C'$ and $A'C'$.

Solution.   We are given that $A'B' = (4/3)AB$. Hence $B'C' = (4/3)BC = 4$ and $A'C' = (4/3)AC = 20/3$.

REMARK

Sometimes the statement that (a, b, c) is proportional to (r, s, t) is written in the notations

$$a:b:c = r:s:t \quad \text{or} \quad a:b:c::r:s:t \quad \text{or} \quad a:r = b:s = c:t$$

Thus

$$2:3:4 = 4:6:8 \quad \text{or} \quad 2:3:4::4:6:8 \quad \text{or} \quad 2:4 = 3:6 = 4:8$$

---

1. Find s and t such that $(3, 2, 5)$ and $(9, s, t)$ are proportional. $s = $ _____, $t = $ _____.

6   15

2. Which of the following pairs of ordered sets are proportional?
   (a) $(1, -2, 6)$ and $(-4, 8, -24)$.
   (b) $(3, 8, -4)$ and $(3/4, 2, -1)$.
   (c) $(4, 15, 9)$ and $(3, 14, 18)$.
   (d) $(4, -12, 16, 20)$ and $(3, -9, 12, 15)$.
   (e) $(1/2, 1/3, 1/4)$ and $(-1/3, -1/4, -1/5)$. _____

(a), (b), and (d).

3. Complete the second set of numbers so that the two sets are proportional

$$(6, -5, 8, 7); (4, \underline{\quad}, \underline{\quad}, \underline{\quad})$$

$$-10/3 \qquad 16/3 \qquad 14/3$$

4. A recipe calls for 2 eggs, 3 cups of flour, and 1 cup of milk. Only 2 cups of flour are available. What quantities of the other ingredients should be used to maintain the same proportions? \underline{\quad} eggs; \underline{\quad} cups of milk

$$\frac{4}{3} \qquad \frac{2}{3}$$

5. A college of 1000 students requires 70 faculty members, a library of 100,000 volumes, 5 deans, and 500 parking spaces. How should these requirements be modified if the college grows to 1200 students and the same proportions are maintained? \underline{\quad} faculty, \underline{\quad} volumes, \underline{\quad} deans, \underline{\quad} parking spaces.

$$84 \qquad 120{,}000 \qquad 6 \qquad 600$$

6. *Prove:* The nonzero ordered set (a, b, c) is proportional to itself.

$$(a, b, c) = 1 \cdot (a, b, c).$$

7. *Prove:* If (a, b, c) is proportional to (r, s, t) then (r, s, t) is proportional to (a, b, c).

Proof

1. $(a, b, c) = k(r, s, t)$, where $k \neq 0$ \qquad \underline{\qquad\qquad}
(reason)

2. $(1/k)(a, b, c) = (r, s, t)$ since $k \neq 0$
3. (r, s, t) is proportional to (a, b, c) \qquad \underline{\qquad\qquad}
(reason)

Definition of proportional. \qquad Definition of proportional.

8. *Prove:* If (a, b, c) and (r, s, t) are proportional, and if (a, b, c) and (x, y, z) are proportional, then (r, s, t) and (x, y, z) are proportional.

Proof

1. $(a, b, c) = k_1(r, s, t)$ \qquad \underline{\qquad\qquad}
(reason)

2. $(a, b, c) = k_2(\underline{\qquad})$ \qquad \underline{\qquad\qquad}
(reason)

3. $k_1(r, s, t) = k_2(x, y, z)$ _____
(reason)

4. Hence _____.

> 1. Definition of proportional.
> 2. x, y, z; Definition.
> 3. Substitution.
> 4. $(r, s, t) = k_2/k_1(x, y, z)$ and the two triples are proportional

9. Prove that the proportionality of two nonzero ordered sets is an equivalence relation. _____

> Proportionality is reflexive (frame 6), symmetric (frame 7), and transitive (frame 8).

10. Prove that if (a, b, c) and (r, s, t) are proportional and if $(a, b, c) \neq -(r, s, t)$, then each of these is proportional to $(a + r, b + s, c + t)$.

Proof
1. $k(a, b, c) = ($_____, _____, _____$)$ with $k \neq -1$. Definition.
2. $a + r = a + ka = (1 + k)a$, where $1 + k \neq 0$.
Similarly, $b + s = $_____
$c + t = $_____.
3. Hence $(a + r, b + s, c + t) = $_____ (a, b, c).
4. Further, $(a + r, b + s, c + t)$ is proportional to (r, s, t) _____
(reason)

> (r, s, t) $(1 + k)b$ $(1 + k)c$ $1 + k$ Frame 8.

11. Since $(3, 5, 9)$ and $(6, 10, 18)$ are proportional, frame 10 shows that each of these is proportional to $($_____, _____, _____$)$.

> $(9, 15, 27)$

12. *Prove:* If (a, b, c) and (r, s, t) are proportional and if $(a, b, c) \neq (r, s, t)$, then each of these is proportional to $(a - r, b - s, c - t)$.
1. _____
2. _____
3. _____
4. _____

> Same proof as in frame 10, with $-$ substituted for $+$.

13. Since $(4, 2, 7)$ and $(12, 6, 21)$ are proportional, what can be said about $(12 - 4, 6 - 2, 21 - 7) = (8, 4, 14)$? _____

All three are proportional.

14. Frame 10 proves that if $a:b = c:d$, then $a:b = c:d = (a + c):(b + d)$. This may suggest that we can add fractions by adding their numerators and denominators! Why is such a statement an incorrect conclusion?

_____

We are *not* adding fractions. We are stating instead that if the ratio of a to b is equal to the ratio of c to d, then each of these ratios is equal to the ratio of $a + c$ to $b + d$.

15. *Prove:* If $a:b = c:d$, and if none of $a + b$, $a - b$, $c + d$, $c - d$ are zero, then $(a + b):(a - b) = (c + d):(c - d)$.
(In old books this result is called the "theorem of composition and division". Although this language is not in current use, you may possibly run across it in your reading.)

Proof
1. If $a:b = c:d$, then $a:c = b:d$ Section 26.2, frame 10.
2. $a:c = b:d =$ _____   Frame 10 above.
3. $a:c = b:d =$ _____   Frame 12 above.
4. $(a + b):(c + d) = (a - b):(c - d)$ Steps 2 and 3.
5. Finally $(a + b):(a - b) = (c + d):(c - d)$ Section 26.2, frame 10.

$(a + b):(c + d)$ $(a - b):(c - d)$

REMARK

Some authors call an ordered set such as (a, b) or (a, b, c) a *vector*. Then two vectors are proportional if, for example, $(a, b, c) = k(r, s, t)$. This usage agrees with that in physics and other parts of science but is uncommon in the elementary school. This analogy with vectors has tempted some authors to carry over other properties of vectors to proportions, and occasionally you will find the statement that

$$(a, b, c) + (r, s, t) = (a + r, b + s, c + t)$$

This equation, unfortunately, has no meaning for proportions, and hence it should be strictly avoided.

We have defined a ratio as a comparison of the sizes of two sets and used the notation $a:b$ for the ratio of a to b. Two ratios, $a:b$ and $c:d$, are equal if and only if $ad = bc$.

Two nonzero ordered sets $(a, b, c, \ldots)$ and $(r, s, t, \ldots)$ are proportional if $(a, b, c, \ldots) = k(r, s, t, \ldots)$, where $k \neq 0$. Proportionality is an equivalence relation. Finally, if (a, b, c) and (r, s, t) are proportional, each is proportional to $(a \pm r, b \pm s, c \pm t)$.

Now you should be ready for the following Post Test.

POST TEST

1. On a 4-day hike into the mountains each of three equally strong hikers starts with a 30-pound pack.

(a) What is the ratio of the number of pounds to the number of hikers? _____

(b) If the first dinner weighed a total of 4 pounds, what is the ratio of the number of pounds to the number of hikers after dinner? _____

(c) After several meals the total weight is now 78 pounds. Would it be fair if one hiker carried 28 pounds? _____ 26 pounds? _____
                                                                  (yes, no)   (yes, no)

20 pounds? _____
             (yes, no)

(d) On the last day of the hike the total weight is down to 75 pounds, but the hikers had to carry water since there would be none where they were going. If they carried a total of 4 pounds of water, what would be the ratio of the number of pounds to the number of hikers? _____

(e) On the last day three more hikers joined the party. If their pound to hiker ratio was $9:1$ and the pound to hiker ratio of the original party (before adding the water) was $25:1$, what would be the ratio after the weight (without the water) had been distributed evenly among all six hikers? _____

2. The admissions office of a small college counted on 2 out of every 5 students who were admitted to actually enroll for the fall term.

(a) If the college wanted 350 new students, how many should it accept? _____

(b) If the college accepted 830 new students, how many are expected to actually enroll? _____

(c) If the college could provide living for only 300 new students, how many should it accept? _____

3. Correct the following false statement: The ratio $c:d$ is equal to the ratio $r:s$ if and only if there is a rational number n/m such that $c = (n/m)s$ and $d = (n/m)r$. _____

4. Find k such that (a) $(3, 7) = k(6, 14)$. _____ (b) $(1/4, 5) = k(5/4, 25)$. _____

5. Complete the second ordered set of numbers so that the two ordered sets are proportional. (a) $(3, 5, 1)$; $(27, \underline{\quad}, \underline{\quad})$. (b) $(6, -5, 8, 7)$; $(-4, \underline{\quad}, \underline{\quad}, \underline{\quad})$.

6. If we were told that (a, b, c) and $(4, 7, 9)$ are proportional and that $(r, 14, 18)$ and (a, b, c) are proportional, then what do we know about $(r, 14, 18)$ and $(4, 7, 9)$? _____ What is the value of r? _____

1. (a) 30:1. (b) 86:3. (c) No. Yes. No. (d) 79:3. (e) $102:6 = 17:1$.
2. (a) 875. (b) 332. (c) 750.
3. $c = (n/m)r$ and $d = (n/m)s$.
4. (a) $\frac{1}{2}$. (b) $\frac{1}{5}$.
5. (a) (27, 45, 9). (b) $(-4, 10/3, -16/3, -14/3)$.
6. They are proportional. 8.

You should now be ready to study Chapter 27.

27

Word Problems

Before beginning this chapter you should review Section 24.4, Percent, and you also should be certain that you can solve simple algebraic equations. To be sure of these matters, test your skill with the following Readiness Test.

READINESS TEST

1. Write as decimal fractions: (a) 5.6%. ——————— (b) 125%. ——————— (c) 0.03%. ———————

> (a) 0.056.   (b) 1.25.   (c) 0.0003.

2. Write as percentages: (a) 0.465. ——————— (b) 0.0071. ——————— (c) 25.36. ———————

> (a) 46.5%.   (b) 0.71%.   (c) 2536%.

3. Write as percentages: (a) 5/8. ——————— (b) 7/2. ——————— (c) 1/20. ———————

> (a) 62.5%.   (b) 350%.   (c) 5%.

4. If $\frac{7}{8} = x/100$, then x is the expression for $\frac{7}{8}$ in ———————.

> per cent

5. Solve for x: $4x + 7 = 21$. ———————

> 3.5.

6. Solve for x: $12 = (3/8)x$. ———————

> 32.

7. If the width of a rectangle is 3 and its length is 8, its perimeter is ——————— and its area is ———————.

> 22   24

Now you should be prepared to begin this chapter by reading Sections 27.1 through 27.3 and working the exercises at the end of Section 27.3.

541

27.1 Introduction

In Chapters 14 through 26 you have learned how to carry out the arithmetic operations in a variety of number systems. Here we wish to apply this knowledge to the solution of various kinds of problems that are more or less practical. The difficulties in such problems are those of determining just what numbers should be added, subtracted, multiplied, or divided in order to find the answer to the problem. It is to no avail for you to know how to do the arithmetic if you do not know when to use a particular arithmetic operation.

The "practical" problems we shall consider will be stated in ordinary English sentences and consequently are called "word problems" or "story problems". Easy problems of this type can often be solved by simple reasoning (even without any written calculations), but to solve more complicated problems it is necessary to translate them into one or more equations which then can be solved by the methods of our earlier chapters. Here is a very easy problem that we shall solve in three ways.

EXAMPLE. $250 is to be divided between James and John so that James will receive $50 more than John. How much does each receive?

First solution. Give James $50 and split the $200 that is left evenly between James and John. So James gets $150 and John gets $100.

This solution required a small amount of insight. If you did not have this insight you might have solved it this way:

Second solution. Let x be the amount that James receives. Then $x - 50$ is the amount that John receives. Therefore

$$x + (x - 50) = 250$$
$$2x = 300$$
$$x = \$150, \text{ James' share}$$
$$x - 50 = \$100, \text{ John's share}$$

Our final solution may seem more complicated, but it illustrates a method that is often easier when the problem before you is more difficult.

Third solution. Let x be the amount that James receives and y be the amount that John receives. Then the problem states that

$$x + y = 250 \quad \text{and} \quad x = 50 + y$$

Therefore,

$$50 + 2y = 250 \text{ or } 2y = 200$$
$$y = 100$$

and hence

$$x = 150$$

Answer :

$$x = \$150, \text{ what James receives}$$

$$y = \$100, \text{ what John receives}$$

Problems of this type are frequently difficult for students, not because they cannot solve the equations involved but because they cannot write down the appropriate equations. The difficulty is that of translating the problem from the language of ordinary speech to that of mathematics. This process is similar to that of translating from English to a foreign language, such as French.

When we learn how to translate from English to French, we first learn a vocabulary and translate individual words. Then we proceed to phrases and short sentences and finally to paragraphs. In word problems, we often expect students to translate paragraphs at the outset. It is, therefore, no wonder that they have difficulties. In this chapter we shall begin with the translation of words and short sentences, and finally paragraphs. By following this procedure we hope to help you avoid the usual difficulties with word problems.

27.2 Words—Construction of a Miniature Dictionary

In a story problem the key nouns are numbers. These are of two types: (1) given numbers, and (2) unknown numbers that we wish to find.

Frequently the given numbers represent amounts of money (dollars, cents), intervals of time (years, days, hours, etc.), measurements of distance (miles, yards, feet, inches, etc.), measurements of velocity (miles per hour, feet per second, etc.) or measurements of area (square feet, square inches, square miles, etc.). In some problems numbers of the same type are given in different units, as in the example below:

EXAMPLE. A coin collection consisting of dimes and quarters is worth $2.25. There are twice as many dimes as quarters. Find the number of coins of each denomination.

In this problem we have two units of money, dollars and cents. Before proceeding with the solution, we must express these in terms of a single unit. Either of the following is satisfactory:

	Total	*Dime*	*Quarter*
Dollars	2.25	0.10	0.25
Cents	225	10	25

If you are nervous about decimals, you will probably choose the second of these alternatives. In general, we shall wish to adopt the procedure: *When the given numbers representing the same kind of quantity are expressed in different units, change them so that they are all in the same units.*

The unknown numbers will be represented in our mathematical language by letters, generally x and y. But in elementary arithmetic other symbols are often used, such as $\square$ and $\triangle$.

EXAMPLE. Find the number that must be added to 3 to obtain the sum of 9.

This may be written

$$3 + x = 9$$

or

$$3 + \square = 9$$

MINIATURE DICTIONARY Before proceeding we must construct a miniature dictionary which tells us how to translate from the unknown numbers, expressed in words, to the unknown numbers, expressed in letters. This is usually accomplished by statements such as the following:

Let x = the amount that James receives (dollars)
y = the amount that John receives (dollars)

Let x = the number of dimes
y = the number of quarters

Let $\square$ = the number to be added

27.3 Short Sentences

Using the miniature dictionary so constructed, we are ready to translate short sentences from English to mathematics. Here are some common examples:

(1) *English* $250 is to be divided between James and John.
Mathematics $250 = x + y$

Note that the English suggests the operation of division, but that it is the sum that is really intended.

(2) *English*   James and John together have $250.
Mathematics $250 = x + y$.

(3) *English*   James receives $50 more than John.
Mathematics $x - 50 = y$ or $x = 50 + y$.

(4) *English*   The difference between James's share and John's share is $50.
Mathematics $x - y = \$50$.

Note that in a difference you must watch the order of the terms.

(5) *English*   A dress that cost $15 is sold at a sales price such that the profit is $5.
Mathematics   Let x be the sales price (dollars). Then $x - 15 = 5$.

(6) *English*   The average price of two dresses is $25.
   Mathematics Let x = the price of one dress (dollars) and y = price of the second dress (dollars). Then $\dfrac{x + y}{2} = 25$.

(7) *English*   The length of one road is three times the length of another road.
   Mathematics Let x be the length of the first road (miles) and y be the length of the second road (miles). Then $x = 3y$.

(8) *English*   In a sale, the sale price is $\frac{1}{3}$ off the regular price.
   Mathematics Let x = regular price (dollars) and y = sale price (dollars). Then $y = x - (\frac{1}{3})x = (\frac{2}{3})x$.

(9) *English*   Because of higher costs, the selling price of a steak is increased by $\frac{1}{4}$.
   Mathematics Let x = former price (cents) and y = new price (cents). Then $y = x + (\frac{1}{4})x = (\frac{5}{4})x$.

(10) *English*   Bob has four more than twice as many marbles as Bill.
   Mathematics Let x = number of Bob's marbles and y = number of Bill's marbles. Then $x = 4 + 2y$.

Translate the following English sentences into "mathematics". Be sure to state your miniature dictionary in each case.

1. Three times a certain number is 10 more than twice that number.
Dictionary. _____
Translation. _____

   Let x be the "certain number". Then $3x = 10 + 2x$.

2. One number is three times another number and their sum is 28.
Dictionary. _____
Translation. _____

   Let x be the first number and y the second number. Then $x = 3y$ and $x + y = 28$.

3. Mary is 3 years older than Sue and the sum of their ages is 45.
Dictionary. _____
Translation. _____

   Let x be Mary's age (years) and y be Sue's age (years). Then $x = 3 + y$, and $x + y = 45$.

4. A piece of string, 20 inches long, is cut into pieces such that one piece is three times as long as the other.

Dictionary. _____
Translation. _____

> Let x = length of one piece (inches) and y = length of the other piece (inches). Then $x = 3y$ and $x + y = 20$.

5. A purse containing nickels, dimes, and quarters has twice as many dimes as nickels and twice as many quarters as dimes. The total is $5.00.
Dictionary. _____
_____
Translation. _____
_____

> Let x = number of nickels, y = number of dimes, and z = number of quarters. Then $y = 2x$, $z = 2y$, and $5x + 10y + 25z = 500$ (cents).

6. When 2 feet are added to each side of a square, its area increased by 100 square feet.
Dictionary. _____
Translation. _____

> Let x = length of side of original square (feet). Then $(x + 2)^2 = x^2 + 100$.

7. For two consecutive integers, the difference of their squares is 3.
Dictionary. _____
Translation. _____

> Let x = larger integer and y = other integer. Then $x = y + 1$ and $x^2 - y^2 = 3$.

8. One side of a rectangular field is 5 yards less than the other side, and the area of the field is 150 square yards.
Dictionary. _____
Translation. _____

> Let x be the length of the first side (yards) and y be the length of the other side (yards). Then $x = y - 5$ and $xy = 150$.

9. A rectangle has perimeter 24 feet and area 35 square feet.
Dictionary. _____
Translation. _____

> Let x = length of one side and y = length of other side. Then $2x + 2y = 24$ and $xy = 35$.

10. One side of the right triangle is 7 inches less than the other side. The hypoteneuse is 13 inches long.

Dictionary. _____

Translation. _____

Let x = length of one side (inches) and y = length of other side (inches). Then $x = y - 7$, $x^2 + y^2 = 13^2$.

27.4 The Word "of"

A common source of trouble is the common use of the word "of" to mean "times".

EXAMPLES

1. 8 is $\frac{2}{3}$ of 12 means $8 = (\frac{2}{3})12$.
2. $\frac{3}{4}$ of 16 is 12 means $(\frac{3}{4})16 = 12$.
3. What number is $\frac{6}{5}$ of 18? means $x = (\frac{6}{5})18$.
4. 10 is $\frac{2}{5}$ of what number? means $10 = (\frac{2}{5})x$.
5. 15 is what fraction of 25? means $15 = x(25)$.

PERCENT   This language is especially common in problems involving per cent.

EXAMPLES

6. What is 3% of 10 means $x = (0.03)(10)$

$$\text{or } x = \frac{3}{100}(10)$$

7. 5 is 30% of what? means $5 = (0.30)x$

$$\text{or } 5 = \frac{30}{100}x$$

8. 20 is what per cent of 80? means $20 = x(80)$
where x is a decimal fraction which
must be converted into percent

$$\text{or } 20 = \frac{y}{100}(80)$$

where y is the required per cent.

You should notice that Examples 1 through 8 all involve an equation of the form

$$a = bc \quad \text{or} \quad a = \frac{b}{100}c$$

where two of a, b, and c are given and the third is the unknown.

547

Word Problems

In frames 1 through 6 translate the given sentences into equations of the form $a = bc$ or $a = \dfrac{b}{100}c$. Solve for the unknown.

1. What number is $\frac{3}{5}$ of 20? Equation. _____ Unknown. _____ _____

$x = (\frac{3}{5})20.$ $x = 12.$

2. 24 is $\frac{3}{8}$ of what number? Equation. _____ Unknown. _____ _____

$24 = (\frac{3}{8})x.$ $x = 64.$

3. 12 is what fraction of 36? Equation. _____ Unknown. _____ _____

$12 = x(36).$ $x = \frac{1}{3}.$

4. What is 4% of 50? Equation. _____ Unknown. _____

$x = (0.04)(50) \left[\text{or } x = \left(\dfrac{4}{100}\right)50 \right].$ $x = 2.$

5. 15 is 25% of what number? Equation. _____ Unknown. _____

$15 = (0.25)x \left[\text{or } 15 = \dfrac{25}{100}x \right].$ $x = 60.$

6. 36 is what per cent of 720? Equation. _____ Unknown. _____

$36 = x(720).$ $x = 0.05 \ (5\%).$ $\left(\text{Or } 36 = \dfrac{y}{100}720; y = 5\%. \right)$

7. A man has a savings account with a balance of $800. The bank pays 5% interest per annum. Find the interest payable at the end of one year. Equation. _____ Interest. _____

$x = (0.05)\$800$ $\$40. \left[\text{Or } x = \left(\dfrac{5}{100}\right)(\$800) = \$40. \right]$

8. The outstanding balance on a credit card is $250. The monthly interest charge is $1\frac{1}{2}\%$. How much interest is due at the end of 1 month? Equation. _____ Interest. _____

$$x = (0.015)(\$250). \quad \$3.75. \quad \left[\text{Or } x = \left(\frac{1.5}{100}\right)(\$250) = \$3.75. \right]$$

9. A store charged interest of $8.00 per month on an outstanding balance of $400. What was the rate of interest in per cent per month? Equation. _____ Rate. _____

$$\$8.00 = x(400). \quad x = 0.02 \ (2\%).$$
$$\left[\text{Or } \$8.00 = \left(\frac{x}{100}\right)(\$400), \ x = 2\%. \right]$$

10. The annual interest on a bond paying 7% was $350. What was the face value of the bond? Equation. _____ Value. _____

$$\$350 = (0.07)x. \quad x = \$5000. \quad \left[\text{Or } \$350 = \frac{7}{100}x, \ x = \$5000. \right]$$

27.5 Other Translation Problems

Although we cannot anticipate every word problem that you may encounter later, here are some additional types that are relatively common.

(1) PROBLEMS INVOLVING RATES

RATES   Problems of this type are based upon the formula

$$d = rt$$

where d = distance traveled (in feet, miles, etc.)
        r = rate (or speed) of travel (in feet per second, miles per hour, etc.); r is assumed to be constant
        t = elapsed time (in seconds, minutes, hours, etc.)

To apply this formula it is required that the units of measurement be consistent. That is, if distance is measured in feet and time in seconds, the rate is measured in feet per second and *not* in feet per minute or miles per second or anything else like these.

In such problems two of the three quantities d, r, and t are given, and you are asked to find the third.

549

EXAMPLE. If a train traveled a distance of 480 miles in $7\frac{1}{2}$ hours, what was its speed?

Solution. Let x be the speed in miles per hour. Then

$$480 = x(7\tfrac{1}{2})$$

or

$$480 = \frac{15x}{2}$$

$$x = 64 \text{ miles per hour}$$

(2) INTEREST PROBLEMS

INTEREST

If a principal amount P (in dollars) is invested at $r\%$ per annum simple interest, the interest I (in dollars) paid at the end of 1 year is given by the formula

$$I = \frac{r}{100}P$$

Again two of the quantities I, r, and P are given, and you are asked to find the third.

(3) DISCOUNT PROBLEMS

DISCOUNT

EXAMPLE. A favored customer is granted a discount of $r\%$ from the published sales price of a commodity. If the published price is p (in dollars), find the amount of the discount, d, and the net price, q, which the customer pays.

Solution. The basic equation is

$$d = \frac{r}{100}p$$

Hence

$$q = p - d$$

$$= p - \frac{r}{100}p$$

$$= p\left(1 - \frac{r}{100}\right)$$

$$q = p\left(\frac{100 - r}{100}\right)$$

550

(4) OTHER PER CENT PROBLEMS

These are best illustrated by examples.

EXAMPLE. A team played 54 games in a season and won 37 of them. What per cent of games played was lost?

Solution. The number of games lost is $54 - 37 = 17$. Let $x =$ per cent lost. Then

$$17 = \left(\frac{x}{100}\right)54$$

SUCCESSIVE PER CENTS

EXAMPLE. A merchant marks up his prices by 25%. Shortly after that he reduces his prices by 20%. Is the final sales price more or less than the original price (before the markup)?

Solution. Let $x =$ original price. Then $x + 0.25x = 1.25x$ is the price after the markup. Next

$$1.25x - 0.20(1.25x) = (1.25 - 0.25)x = x$$

is the price after the reduction. The two prices are the same.

The difficulty in this problem is that of keeping straight the prices to which the markup and reduction apply. The markup is applied to the original price x, but the reduction is applied to the marked-up price $1.25x$

EXAMPLE. After one year a teacher received a salary increase of 6% and after the second year an increase of 7%. Her total increase in two years was what per cent of her original salary?

Solution. Let s be her original salary. Then $s + 0.06s = 1.06s$ is her salary after the first increase. Next $1.06s + (0.07)(1.06s) = 1.1342s$ is her salary after the second increase. Her total increase is thus $0.1342s$ or 13.42% of s.

EXAMPLE. Because of inflation the price of a house has increased from $20,000 to $24,000. What was the per cent increase?

Solution. The increase is clearly $24,000 - $20,000 = $4,000$. There are then two conceivable interpretations of the problem:
(1) $4000 is what per cent of $20,000?
(2) $4000 is what per cent of $24,000?
Thus there is ambiguity, although (1) is the usual interpretation. Problems like this should be more clearly stated. In this case the problem would be unambiguous if the final sentence were "The increase is what per cent of the price before inflation?". Percentages are always taken "of something", and it is most important that this "something" be clearly stated.

With this modification, the translation of the problem into mathematics is

$$4000 = \left(\frac{x}{100}\right)20,000$$

27.6 Methods of Solving Equations

(1) ELEMENTARY

Many of the mathematical statements of problems like those in previous sections are of the form

$$a = bc \qquad \text{or} \qquad a = \left(\frac{b}{100}\right)c$$

where two quantities are known and one is unknown. We have already discussed solutions of such equations in earlier chapters.

(2) SIMULTANEOUS LINEAR EQUATIONS

LINEAR EQUATIONS   Frequently the problem translates into a pair of two equations in two unknowns such as

$$x + y = 250$$
$$x = 50 + y$$

To handle these we eliminate one of the unknowns by substituting its expression in one equation into the other equation. In the above example we substitute the expression for x given in the second equation into the first equation and obtain

$$(50 + y) + y = 250$$

or

$$50 + 2y = 250$$
$$2y = 200$$
$$y = 100$$

Then from the second equation of the problem

$$x = 50 + 100 = 150$$

QUADRATIC EQUATIONS   ### (3) QUADRATIC EQUATIONS (OPTIONAL)

In frame 10 of Section 27.3 we considered the following problem:

One side of a right triangle is 7 inches less than the other side. The hypoteneuse is 13 inches long. Find the lengths of the two sides.

The mathematical translation consisted of the pair of equations

$$x = y - 7$$
$$x^2 + y^2 = 13^2$$

When we substitute the expression for x in the first of these into the second, we obtain

$$(y - 7)^2 + y^2 = 13^2$$

or

$$y^2 - 14y + 49 + y^2 = 169$$

552

or

$$2y^2 - 14y - 120 = 0$$

or

$$y^2 - 7y - 60 = 0$$

To solve such an equation, we must factor the expression on the left-hand side. In general,

$$(y + a)(y + b) = y^2 + (a + b)y + ab$$

so we are looking for two numbers, a and b, whose sum is -7 and whose product is -60.

To find these we examine the pairs of numbers whose product is -60. These are

$$1 \text{ and } -60, \ -1 \text{ and } 60, \ 2 \text{ and } -30, \ -2 \text{ and } 30$$

$$3 \text{ and } -20, \ -3 \text{ and } 20, \ 4 \text{ and } -15, \ -4 \text{ and } 15$$

$$5 \text{ and } -12, \ -5 \text{ and } 12, \ 6 \text{ and } -10, \ -6 \text{ and } 10$$

In only one of these pairs, 5 and -12, is the sum equal to -7. Therefore,

$$y^2 - 7y - 60 = (y + 5)(y - 12)$$

and the equation to be solved becomes

$$(y + 5)(y - 12) = 0.$$

According to Theorem 7, Section 11.4, the product of two numbers is zero only if at least one of them is zero. So either

$$y + 5 = 0 \quad \text{and} \quad y = -5$$

or

$$y - 12 = 0 \quad \text{and} \quad y = 12.$$

The solution $y = -5$ does not satisfy the conditions of the problem—that y is the length of a side of the triangle. So y must be 12 and x must be 5.

In this problem, as in all others, the answers should be referred back to the problem as stated in words to make sure that they are correct. In this problem, $12 - 5 = 7$, so one side *is* 7 inches less than the other side, as is required. Also $12^2 + 5^2 = 144 + 25 = 169 = 13^2$, as is required. Hence our solution is correct.

---

1. Three times a certain number is 10 more than twice that number. Find the number. (See frame 1, Section 27.3.) ‾‾‾‾‾‾

10.

2. One number is three times another number and their sum is 28. Find the numbers. (See frame 2, Section 27.3.) _____

7, 21.

3. Mary is 3 years older than Sue and the sum of their ages is 45. How old are Mary and Sue? (See frame 3, Section 27.3.) Mary _____, Sue _____.

24   21

4. A piece of string, 20 inches long, is cut into pieces such that one piece is three times as long as the other. Find the lengths of the pieces. (See Frame 4, Section 27.3.) _____

15 inches, 5 inches.

5. A purse containing nickels, dimes, and quarters has twice as many dimes as nickels and twice as many quarters as dimes. The total is $5.00. Find the numbers of nickels, dimes, and quarters. (See frame 5, Section 27.3.) Nickels _____, dimes _____, quarters _____.

4   8   16

6. When 2 feet are added to each side of a square, its area is increased by 100 square feet. Find the length of the side of the original square. (See frame 6, Section 27.3.) _____

24 feet.

7. For two consecutive positive integers, the difference of their squares is 3. Find the integers. (See frame 7, Section 27.3.) _____

1, 2.

Frames 8, 9, and 10 lead to quadratic equations and should be omitted if you have skipped the optional section on quadratic equations.

8. One side of a rectangular field is 5 yards less than the other side and the area of the field is 150 square yards. Find the dimensions of the field. (See frame 8, Section 27.3.) _____

10 yards by 15 yards.

9. A rectangle has perimeter 24 feet and area 35 square feet. Find its dimensions. (See frame 9, Section 27.3.) _____

5 feet by 7 feet.

10. Of two positive numbers, the first is three more than the second and their product is 54. Find the numbers. _____

6 and 9

11. Of a certain class, 40% are men. If the number of men is 80, how many students are in the class? _____

200.

12. A stock increases in value by 10% of its original value, and then declines by 10% of its increased value. Its final value is what per cent of its original value? _____

99%

13. A stock increases in value by 100% of its original value, and then declines by 100% of its increased value. What is its final value? _____

Zero.

14. Two men each earned a salary of $1000 per month. A's salary was first raised 15% and then lowered 15%. B's salary was lowered 15% and then raised 15%. What is the difference in their present salaries? _____

None. Both earn $977.50 per month.

15. After one year a teacher received a salary increase of 5% and after the second year an increase of 7%. Another teacher received no increase after the first year and a 12% increase after the second year. Which teacher received the largest per cent increase (of her original salary) by the end of the second year? _____

The first teacher's total increase was 12.35%. The second teacher's was 12%.

16. A salesman receives a commission of 9% of sales. His taxes are 20% of his income from commissions. What is his net income after taxes as a percentage of sales? _____

Let s = sales. Then income = $\frac{9}{100}s = 0.09s$. Taxes = $(\frac{20}{100})(\frac{9}{100})s = 0.018s$. Hence net income = $0.072s$, or 7.2% of sales.

17. If bank interest is compounded continuously (or daily as many banks advertise) at a rate of 5% the value of a deposit of $1 will have increased to $1.0513 at the end of one year. What has been the per cent increase? _____ (For your information, the value of a deposit of $1 compounded quarterly at 5% will increase to $1.0509 at the end of one year.)

5.13%.

18. If bank interest is compounded continuously at a rate of 5%, the value of a deposit of $1 will have increased to $1.2840 at the end of five years. This is equivalent to what rate of simple interest per annum? _____

5.68%.

19. How many gallons of water must be added to 20 gallons of a 30% solution of acid to obtain a 20% solution? _____

Let x = amount of acid present (gallons) and y = number of gallons of water to be added. Then $x = (\frac{30}{100})20$ and $x = \frac{20}{100}(20 + y)$. So $y = 10$.

20. How many gallons of cream which is 10% butterfat must be mixed with 15 gallons of cream which is 20% butterfat to obtain a cream which is 16% butterfat? _____

Let x = amount of butterfat in the 10% cream (gallons) and y = amount of 10% cream to be added (gallons). Then $x = (\frac{10}{100})y$. And $x + (\frac{20}{100})15 = (\frac{16}{100})(y + 15)$. So $y = 10$.

Now see if you can work the following problems before referring to the answers.

POST TEST

1. Find two consecutive whole numbers whose sum is 43. _____
2. The perimeter of a rectangle is six times its width. The length of the rectangle is 8 feet. Find the width. _____
3. A man invests $1000 at one bank at a certain rate of interest per annum and $2000 in another bank at a rate twice that of the first bank. His total annual income from these investments is $200. Find the rate of interest paid by each bank. _____

4. The sum of a number and three times that number is 20. Find the number. _____

5. A boy runs at the rate of 200 yards in 20 seconds. Find his speed. _____

6. A bank pays 5% interest per annum. If the annual interest is $120, how much is on deposit? _____

7. 18 students of a class of 30 students were present one day. Ten were absent because of illness. What percent of students in the class were absent? _____

8. An automobile traveled 400 miles at a speed of 50 miles per hour. How long did the trip take? _____

9. A supermarket made a profit of 2% of the amount of its sales. If the annual profit, was $30,000, what was the total amount of sales for the year? _____

10. A salesman receives a salary of $500 per month and a commission of 3% of his sales. He sells $25,723 worth of goods in a year. What is his total income for the year? _____

11. A wholesaler marked up the manufacturer's price of an item by 20% of the manufacturer's price. A retailer marked up the wholesaler's price by 25% of the wholesaler's price. What percent of the manufacturer's price is the total markup? _____

1. 21, 22.
2. 4 feet.
3. 4%, 8%.
4. 5.
5. 10 yards per second.
6. $2400.
7. 40%. This problem contains misleading information.
8. 8 hours.
9. $1,500,000.
10. $6771.69.
11. 50%.

This concludes Part IV of this book. Before proceeding to Part V, use the following Summary Test to help you to review Part IV. Your instructor will tell you how to handle this test.

Summary Test for Part IV

A

Circle the number of every true statement in this section.

1. Let a, b, and m be whole numbers. Then $a \equiv b \bmod m$ if and only if $a + b$ is divisible by m.
2. $24 \equiv 3 \bmod 7$.
3. Since $17 \equiv 5 \bmod 3$ and $26 \equiv 2 \bmod 3$, $17 + 26 \equiv 5 + 2 \bmod 3$, or $43 \equiv 7 \bmod 3$.
4. Let $\langle \ \rangle$ represent congruence classes mod 5. Then $\langle 2 \rangle + \langle 3 \rangle = \langle 1 \rangle$.
5. In the notation of question 4, $\langle 2 \rangle \times \langle 3 \rangle = \langle 1 \rangle$.
6. $(\text{opp } a) \cdot b = \text{opp}(ab)$.
7. $(\text{opp } a) \cdot (\text{opp } b) = (\text{opp } a) \cdot [\text{opp}(\text{opp } b)]$.
8. $\text{opp } {}^{+}|a| = {}^{-}|a|$.
9. Subtraction is a binary operation on the set of integers.
10. If a and b are any integers and $a \neq 0$, the equation $ax = b$ has a unique integer x as a solution.
11. A fraction is an equivalence class of rational numbers.
12. The rational numbers a/b and c/d are equal if and only if $ad = bc$.
13. An infinite repeating decimal expansion represents a rational number.
14. No rational number is a real number.
15. The product of two irrational numbers must be irrational.
16. The rational number 65/52 has a finite decimal expansion.
17. $\pi = 3.1416$.
18. 25 is 25% of 1000.
19. 15% of 25% of a is 40% of a.
20. $a : b = c : d$ if and only if $ab = cd$.

B

21. It is now 8 o'clock. What time will it be 75 hours from now? _____

22. Check the following multiplication by casting out nines.

$$
\begin{array}{r}
4678 \\
\times\ 25 \\
\hline
22280 \\
8356\ \ \\
\hline
105840 \\
\end{array}
$$

23. $\text{opp } {}^{+}5 = $ _____, $|\text{opp } {}^{+}5| = $ _____, $|{}^{+}5| = $ _____.
24. If a and b are integers, $(\text{opp } a) + (\text{opp } b)$ is equal to opp (_____).
25. If n and m are natural numbers and $n < m$, then ${}^{+}n + {}^{-}m$ is defined to be _____.
26. If a and b are integers, $a - b$ is defined to be _____.
27. Subtraction _____ an associative binary operation on the set
        (is, is not)
of integers.

28. Solve for x: $^-3 + x = {}^+7$. $x =$ _____.
29. If n and m are natural numbers, then $^+n \cdot {}^-m$ is defined to be
_____.
30. If a and b are integers, (opp a) $\cdot$ (opp b) is equal to what simpler
expression. _____
31. Multiplication _____ a commutative binary operation on the
   (is, is not)
set of integers.
32. $[^-6 \cdot ({}^+3 - {}^-2)] + [({}^+5 + {}^+3) \div {}^-2] =$ _____.
33. Insert the correct inequality symbol $^-46$ _____ $^-32$.
34. The additive inverse of the integer a is _____.
35. The fractions a/b and c/d are equivalent if and only if _____
_____.

36. An equivalence relation must have what three properties:
(1) _____, (2) _____, and (3) _____.
37. A rational number is defined to be _____.
38. Write five members of the equivalence class of fractions for which
$3/4$ is a suitable name. {_____}.
39. Division _____ a binary operation on the set of all nonzero
   (is, is not)
rational numbers.
40. A simpler expression for $a/b \div c/d$ is _____, where $b, c,$ and
d are nonzero integers.
41. Solve for x: $(\frac{3}{4})x = (-7)/5$. $x =$ _____.
42. The expression $0.\overline{7}$ is equal to what rational number in the usual
notation? _____
43. Every rational number can be expressed as either (1) a _____
_____ decimal or (2) an infinite _____ decimal expansion.
44. The real numbers that are not rational have infinite _____
decimal expansions.
45. There is a _____ between the set of real numbers and
the set of points on the number line.
46. The nonzero ordered sets of real numbers (a, b, c) and (r, s, t) are
proportional if and only if there is a nonzero real number k such that
_____.

47. Express 2.14 as a percent. _____
48. A discount of 8% was applied to a price of $236. What was the price
after the discount? _____
49. In 1968 the cost of living was 3% higher than it was in 1967. In
1969 the cost of living was 4% higher than it was in 1968. Hence in 1969
the cost of living was _____% higher than it was in 1967.
50. One side of a rectangle is 5 feet long. The number of feet in its
perimeter is 6 more than the number of square feet in its area. Find the
length of the other side. _____

*When you have finished this Summary Test you may proceed to Part V,
Geometry.*

PART V

Geometry

Chapters 28 through 32

28

**Geometric
Concepts**

In this chapter we begin Part V of this book, Geometry. Before beginning this chapter, you may need to review some elementary facts which are covered in the following Readiness Test.

R E A D I N E S S   T E S T

1. In a dictionary look up the definition of geometry. Write it down.

_____

_____

_____

Webster's Third New International Dictionary: A branch of mathematics that deals with the measurement, and properties, and relationships of points, lines, angles, surfaces, and solids.

2. What does the prefix *geo* mean? See your dictionary. _____

Earth.

3. What does *-metry* mean? See your dictionary. _____

The process of measuring.

4. So literally *geometry* means _____.

the process of measuring the earth

5. Who was the author of the first comprehensive book on geometry? _____ When did he live? _____ Where did he live? _____

Euclid   About 300 B.C.   Greece.

Now proceed to Sections 28.1 and 28.2.

28.1 Introduction

Geometry is often identified in the minds of students with their own experience in formal, deductive geometry in about grade 10. The usual courses at this level state a number of axioms (or postulates) about geometric figures in the plane and then proceed to prove theorems about them by deductive methods. This formal treatment of geometry in high school can be extremely frustrating

INFORMAL GEOMETRY

to a pupil unless he has first developed sound intuition about geometric figures through a previous study of informal geometry. The purpose of this and the succeeding chapters is to discuss geometry informally (with few deductive proofs) so that those who study this book will be prepared to teach informal geometry in the elementary school.

There is a good chance that you have already studied some plane geometry in high school, but few of you are likely to know much about solid geometry. This is a great pity, for spatial intuition is of great importance in modern life. Thus we must make certain that your knowledge of solid geometry is adequate. In addition, the methods of coordinate (or analytic) geometry are being used earlier and earlier in the schools, and so we must treat these as well.

Our objectives can be summarized as follows:

(1) For grades K through 6, the study of informal geometry through a discussion of the shape, size, and measurement of geometric figures in the plane and in space.

(2) For grades 7 and 8, advanced informal geometry plus elementary topics from the coordinate geometry of the plane.

28.2 Blocks

The simplest way to begin geometric instruction in the very early grades is to use readily available materials like blocks. These come in a great variety of shapes, such as cubes, pyramids, cylinders, and cones. These can be used to introduce many geometric concepts and to develop a proper geometric vocabulary.

POINTS

Let us first consider a cube. We observe that it has eight corners called *vertices* (singular *vertex*). These are examples of *points*. How big is a point? It has neither length, width, nor thickness and so has no size at all. It is not a physical object but a mathematical abstraction. A point may be represented by a dot on a piece of paper or by a dust particle in the air, but these do have size (no matter how small they are) and so they are only approximations to a point.

SEGMENTS

The cube also has 12 edges. These are examples of *line segments*. A line segment is that portion of a line which is contained between two points, and so lines and line segments must not be confused. A line (like the number line) extends indefinitely in both directions, whereas a line segment has finite length. A line is an abstraction that no one has ever seen. It has no breadth or thickness, and it extends beyond the limits of our imagination. Hence it is a pure abstraction. Line segments are also abstractions, but they can be represented by sketches on paper or by light beams in space.

The six faces of the cube are subsets of planes. Again a plane is an abstraction which no one has ever seen. But approximations to subsets of a plane such as a floor, a tabletop, and a piece of paper are familiar to everyone.

POLYGONAL REGIONS

The faces of a cube are examples of polygonal regions in a plane; we shall discuss these in more detail in the next section.

Cubes are by no means the only kind of blocks whose faces are polygonal regions of a plane. The following examples of regular solids are worthy of attention.

28.2 Blocks

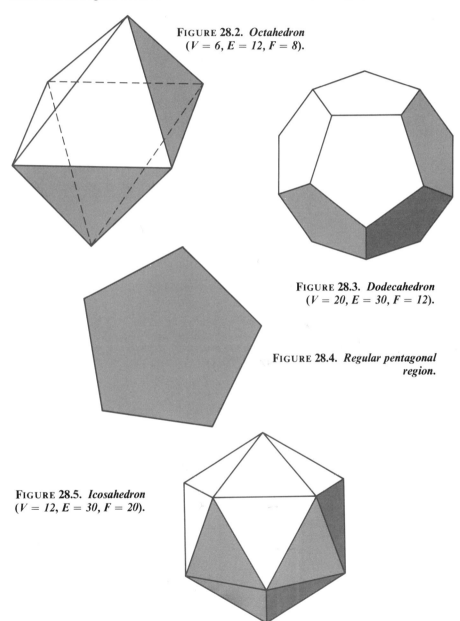

(1) TETRAHEDRON (FOUR-FACED BLOCK)

This is formed by joining four identical equilateral triangular regions, as indicated in Figure 28.1. A tetrahedron has 4 vertices, 6 edges, and 4 faces.

(2) OCTAHEDRON (EIGHT-FACED BLOCK)

This is formed by joining eight identical equilateral triangular regions, as indicated in Figure 28.2. An octahedron has 6 vertices, 12 edges, and 8 faces.

FIGURE 28.2. *Octahedron* ($V = 6, E = 12, F = 8$).

FIGURE 28.1. *Tetrahedron* ($V = 4, E = 6, F = 4$).

FIGURE 28.3. *Dodecahedron* ($V = 20, E = 30, F = 12$).

FIGURE 28.4. *Regular pentagonal region.*

FIGURE 28.5. *Icosahedron* ($V = 12, E = 30, F = 20$).

(3) DODECAHEDRON (TWELVE-FACED BLOCK)

This is formed by joining 12 identical regular pentagonal regions, as indicated in Figure 28.3. Each face is of the form shown in Figure 28.4. A dodecahedron has 20 vertices, 30 edges, and 12 faces.

(4) ICOSAHEDRON (TWENTY-FACED BLOCK)

This is formed by joining together 20 identical equilateral triangular regions, as indicated in Figure 28.5. An icosahedron has 12 vertices, 30 edges, and 20 faces.

The best way to visualize these various blocks is to make them out of stiff paper or plastic. Patterns for doing so are given in Figures 28.6 through 28.10. The adjacent faces may be joined by using tape. Another way to make these is to begin with a number of soda straws (of large diameter) equal to the number of edges. These straws can be joined by pipe cleaners to make the faces and eventually to complete the blocks.

PATTERNS ### PATTERNS FOR MAKING THE REGULAR SOLIDS

(Unless you have very nimble fingers, the lengths of the edges in your construction should be several times as long as those shown in the pattern!)

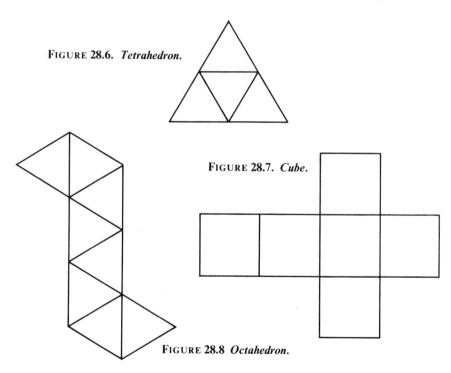

FIGURE 28.6. *Tetrahedron.*

FIGURE 28.7. *Cube.*

FIGURE 28.8 *Octahedron.*

These solids are called *regular solids* because
(1) Each face has the same number of edges.
(2) The edges have the same length.
(3) The angles of the polygonal faces are all equal.
(4) Each vertex is the junction of the same number of edges.

566

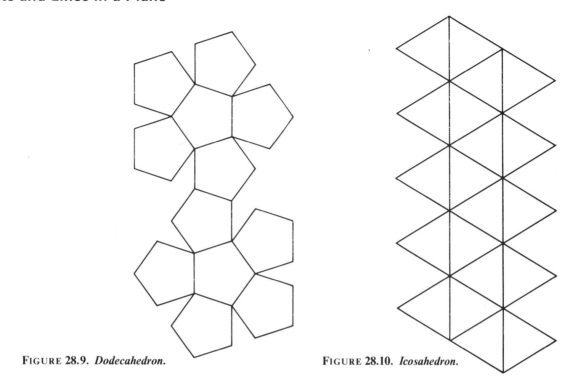

FIGURE 28.9. *Dodecahedron.*   FIGURE 28.10. *Icosahedron.*

REGULAR SOLIDS   The remarkable fact is that these are the *only* possible regular solids. This fact was known to Plato, and so these solids are often called *Platonic solids*.

1. As directed by your instructor make one or more of the regular solids.
2. (Discovery Exercise) Fill out the table from the data given in this section. *V* represents the number of vertices, *E* the number of edges, and *F* the number of faces. By examining this table find an algebraic relation among *V*, *E*, and *F* which is true for all five regular solids.

Solid	V	E	F
Tetrahedron			
Cube			
Octahedron			
Dodecahedron			
Icosahedron			

28.3 Points and Lines in a Plane

The most important concepts in the geometry of the plane are those of point and line. It is not possible to define either of these, so your intuition about them will have to serve. The most important facts concerning them are these:

567

Geometric Concepts

INCIDENCE PROPERTIES

(1) There is one and only one line that can be drawn through two distinct points. If the points are *A* and *B*, we shall speak of the line *AB* (Figure 28.11).

The line segment $\overline{AB}$ consists of those points of line *AB* which lie between *A* and *B*, together with the points *A* and *B* themselves.

FIGURE 28.11. *The unique line AB through A and B.*

(2) Two distinct lines in a plane have at most one point in common. If the lines have no point in common they are called parallel (Figure 28.12).

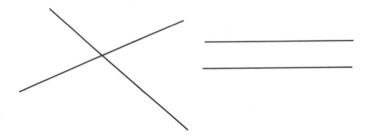

FIGURE 28.12. *Intersecting lines: parallel lines.*

(3) If point *C* is not on line *AB*, there is a unique line in the plane through *C* which is parallel to *AB* (Figure 28.13).

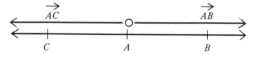

FIGURE 28.13. *Line through C parallel to line AB.*

HALF-LINE

DEFINITION. If *A* is a point on a line, the two (infinite) portions of the line not containing *A* are called *half-lines*. The portion that contains a point, say *B*, is called the half-line $\overrightarrow{AB}$ (Figure 28.14).

FIGURE 28.14. *The half-line $\overrightarrow{AB}$. This does not contain point A.*

Then any point *A* separates a line into three disjoint subsets (Figure 28.15): (1) the point *A*, (2) the half-line $\overrightarrow{AB}$, and (3) the half-line $\overrightarrow{AC}$. The line is the union of these subsets.

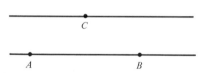

FIGURE 28.15. *Separation of a line by a point A.*

RAY

DEFINITION. If we take the union of point *A* and the half-line $\overrightarrow{AB}$, we obtain the *ray $\overrightarrow{AB}$*.

SEPARATION PROPERTIES

DEFINITION. If *l* is a line in a plane, the two (infinite) portions of the plane not containing *l* are called *half-planes*. That portion that contains a point *A* (not on *l*) is called the *A-side* of *l* (Figure 28.16).

568

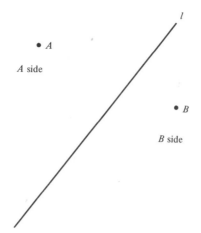

FIGURE 28.16. *Separation of the plane into half-planes.*

Then any line *l* separates a plane into three disjoint subsets: (1) the line *l*, (2) the half-plane called the *A*-side of *l*, and (3) the half-plane called the *B*-side of *l*. The plane is the union of these three subsets.

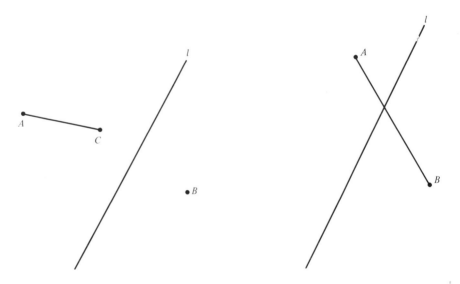

FIGURE 28.17. *Segment $\overline{AC}$ lies on the A-side of l.*

FIGURE 28.18. *The segment $\overline{AB}$ has a unique point in common with l.*

Moreover, if *A* and *C* both lie on the *A*-side of *l*, then the line segment $\overline{AC}$ lies in the *A* side of *l* (Figure 28.17). On the other hand, if *A* and *B* lie on opposite sides of *l*, the segment $\overline{AB}$ has a unique point in common with *l* (Figure 28.18).

All questions below refer to points and lines in a plane.

1. Suppose that three distinct points are chosen in a plane. How many distinct lines can be drawn each of which passes through two or more of the chosen points? _____

Most people will answer "three"; see frame 2.

2. Is the answer "three" to frame 1 correct if all three points lie on the same line? _____

No.

3. In view of frame 2 what is the precise answer to frame 1? _____
_____.

At most three distinct lines

4. Three distinct lines are drawn in the plane. How many points are determined as intersections of these lines? _____

None if all lines are parallel; one if all lines pass through a single point; two if two lines are parallel and are intersected by the third line; three in other cases.

5. Let us extend the definition of parallelism of lines so that we say that any line is parallel to itself. Is parallelism reflexive? _____ Is parallelism symmetric? _____ Is parallelism transitive? _____ Hence what kind of a relation is parallelism? _____

Yes.   Yes.   Yes.   Equivalence.

6. On a separate piece of paper draw an example of an equivalence class of parallel lines.

You should have drawn quite a few lines, all mutually parallel.

7. The subset of the number line $\{x|x > 0\}$ is a _____.

half-line

8. The subset of the number line $\{x|x \leq 0\}$ is a _____.

ray

9. The subset of the number line $\{x|x \geq 2 \text{ and } x \leq 3\}$ is a _____.

segment

10. The subset of the number line $\{x|4 \leq |x|\}$ is the union of _____ _____.

two rays, $\{x|x \geq 4\}$ and $\{x|x \leq -4\}$

11. The intersection of the rays $\{x|x \geq -1\}$ and $\{x|x \leq 5\}$ is a _____ _____.

segment

12. If points B and C lie on the A side of line l, what segments do they define which lie in this A side? _____

$\overline{AB}$, $\overline{AC}$, and $\overline{BC}$

13. If point B lies on the A-side of line l, and point C lies on the opposite side of l, what segments are defined that intersect line l?_____

$\overline{AC}$ and $\overline{BC}$

14. (*Discovery Exercise*) We have seen how a point separates a line and how a line separates a plane. What can be said about the way in which a plane separates space?

28.4 Curves in a Plane

Although we are not in a position to give a precise definition of a plane curve, here is an intuitive description of the concept.

DESCRIPTION (INTUITIVE). Consider a line, a line segment, a ray, or a circle in the plane. Then deform this continuously (without breaking it) into any other position in the plane. The result is a plane curve.

The examples in Figure 28.19 should help you to understand this description. These are all curves: (a) curve with end points A and B; (b) curve with endpoint A; infinite in other direction; (c) curve infinite in both directions; (d) closed curve; and (e) closed curve.

As illustrated in Figure 28.19, curves may or may not have end points. As in curves (d) and (e), they may be closed, or, as in (a), (b), and (c), they may not be closed. A curve need not appear to be "curved". A line is a curve, so is a line segment, and so is the union of line segments in (e).

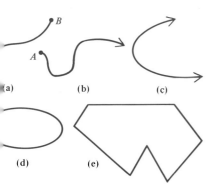

FIGURE 28.19. *Examples of curves.*

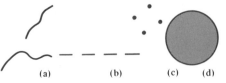

FIGURE 28.20. *Geometric figures that are not curves.*

FIGURE 28.21. *Curves which are not simple.*

For any curve it is possible to put a pencil at some point and then to draw the whole curve without lifting the pencil from the paper. The figures in Figure 28.20 are not curves.

DEFINITION. A curve is *simple* if and only if it does not intersect itself.

The curves in Figure 28.19 are all simple, but those in Figure 28.21 are not simple.

There is a very remarkable and intuitively obvious theorem about simple, closed curves which is extremely hard to prove. It is called the *Jordan curve theorem* and is stated below.

THEOREM 1. (Jordan Curve Theorem.) If we are given any *simple closed* curve, C, then C divides the plane into two regions called the interior and exterior for each of which C is the boundary.

This theorem is evidently true for the ellipse in Figure 28.22(a) but is less obvious for the curve in Figure 28.22(b). In Figure 28.22(b) is P in the interior or the exterior?

FIGURE 28.22. *Simple closed curves.*

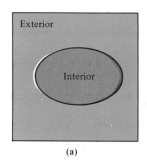

(a)

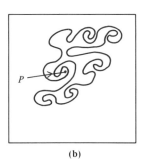

(b)

Circle.   Circular disk.
FIGURE 28.23.

Certain simple closed curves play a prominent role in elementary geometry, and so we turn our discussion to them.

(1) CIRCLE

DEFINITION. A *circle* is the set of points in a plane that are at a given distance from a fixed point called the center.

Note that a circle is a curve (Figure 28.23) and that the concept of circle must be distinguished from that of the circular disk which is its interior.

(2) POLYGONS

POLYGONS   **DEFINITION.** A *polygon* is a simple closed curve which is the union of a finite number of line segments.

Examples of polygons include triangles, rectangles, squares, and pentagons.

REGULAR POLYGONS   **DEFINITION.** A polygon is *regular* if all its sides have the same length and if all its angles have equal measures.

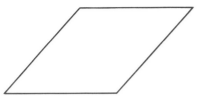

FIGURE 28.24. Rhombus.

Examples of regular polygons are equilateral triangles and squares. Note that both conditions are required to insure regularity. For all the sides of a rhombus are equal (Figure 28.24), but it is not regular. And a general rectangle has all its angles equal but it is not regular.

Because of the Jordan curve theorem, every polygon has an interior. The interior of a triangle, for example, is a *triangular region* whose boundary is a *triangle*. The interior of any polygon is called a *polygonal region*. In ordinary speech, however, the distinction between a polygon and a polygonal region is frequently not made. Thus *square* can refer to either the boundary or to the interior of the square region. It is probably impossible to be completely consistent in your usage, but you should be as careful as you can to make this distinction.

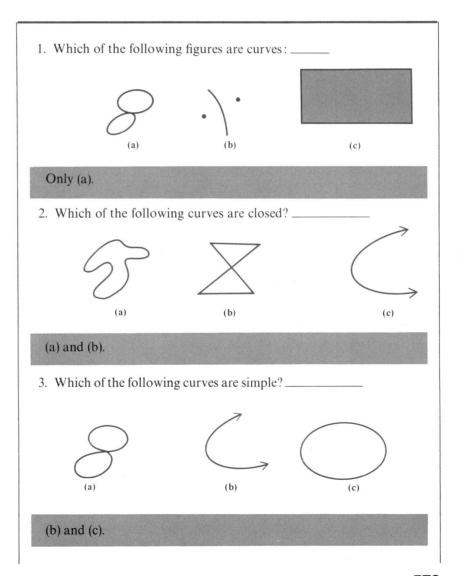

1. Which of the following figures are curves: _____

   (a) (b) (c)

   Only (a).

2. Which of the following curves are closed? _____

   (a) (b) (c)

   (a) and (b).

3. Which of the following curves are simple? _____

   (a) (b) (c)

   (b) and (c).

4. Which curves in frames 1, 2, and 3 are simple closed curves? _____
_____

2(a) and 3(c).

5. Which of the following curves are polygons? _____
Which are regular polygons? _____

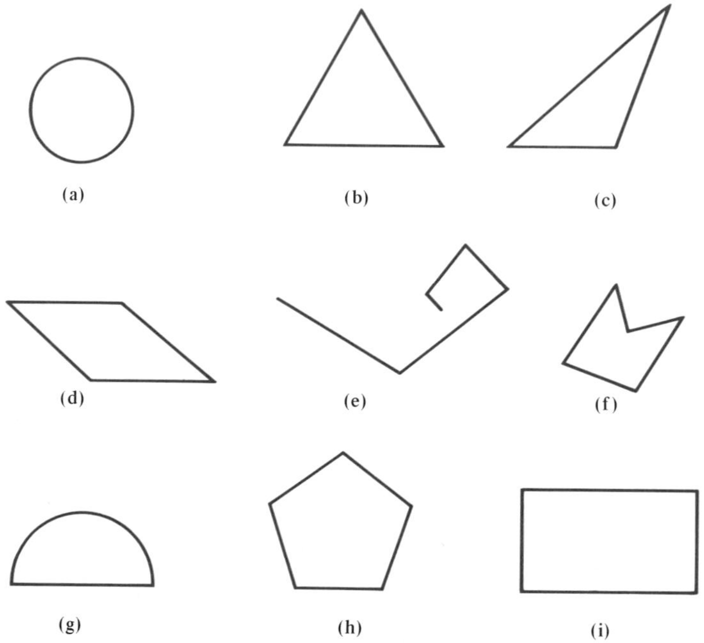

(a)   (b)   (c)

(d)   (e)   (f)

(g)   (h)   (i)

(b), (c), (d), (f), (h), and (i).   (b) and (h).

6. The names of the polygons with *n* sides are as follows:

(a) $n = 3$. _____   (b) $n = 4$. _____
(c) $n = 5$. _____   (d) $n = 6$. _____

(a) Triangle.   (b) Quadrilateral.   (c) Pentagon.   (d) Hexagon.

7. A parallelogram is a quadrilateral whose pairs of opposite sides are
_____ .

parallel (or equal)

ELLIPSE

8. An ellipse is a curve defined as follows. Let F and F' be two points in the plane. Fasten the ends of a string (longer than the segment $\overline{FF'}$) at F and F'. Now put a pencil so that the string is taut and let it move. In this

574

way draw the figure shown. If the length of the string is L, then the length of $\overline{FP}$ + the length of $\overline{F'P}$ = _____.

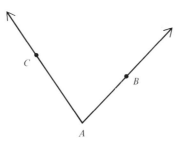

Ellipse

L

28.5 Angles in the Plane

In plane geometry an angle is defined as follows:

ANGLE   **DEFINITION.** An *angle* is the union of two rays which have the same initial point and which do not lie on the same line. Their common point is called the vertex of the angle (Figure 28.25).

FIGURE 28.25. *Angle with vertex at A.*

If B lies on one of the rays and C lies on the other ray, we speak of the angle BAC.

As a special case not covered in the above definition we define a straight angle as follows:

FIGURE 28.26. *Straight angle BAC.*

STRAIGHT ANGLE   **DEFINITION.** A *straight angle* is the union of two rays with the same initial point which lie on the same line and point in opposite directions (Figure 28.26).

All angles except straight angles have an interior, as is shown in Figure 28.27.

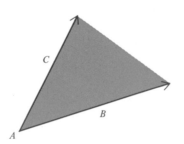

FIGURE 28.27. *Interior of angle BAC.*

INTERIOR OF AN ANGLE   DEFINITION.   The *interior* of angle *BAC* is the intersection of the *B*-side of line *AC* with the *C*-side of line *AB*.

1. The interior of angle *BAC* has been defined to be the intersection of the *B*-side of line *AC* with the *C*-side of line *AB*.

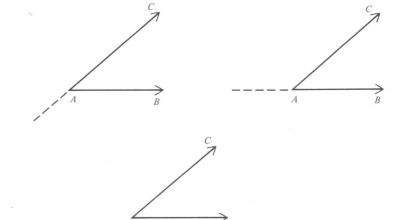

Shade the *B*-side of line *AC*   Shade the *C*-side of line *AB*

Shade the intersection of the two half-planes just drawn

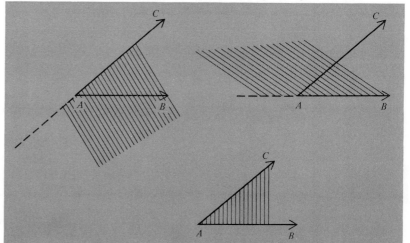

2. Why can we not use the above definition of interior to find the interior of a straight angle? _____

_____

_____

> Since *A*, *B*, and *C* are on the same line, the *B* side of *AC* and the *C* side of *AB* are not defined. We say that a straight angle has no interior.

28.6 Lines in Space

Lines in space have the following properties:

INCIDENCE PROPERTIES

(1) There is one and only one line which can be drawn through two distinct points in space. (The same as for lines in the plane.)

(2) Two distinct lines have at most one point in common. (The same as for lines in the plane.)

(3) Two distinct lines are *parallel* if they lie in the same plane (which itself lies in space) and if they have no point in common.

(4) Two distinct lines are *skew* if they do not lie in the same plane (Figure 28.28).

Thus there are three possibilities for two distinct lines in space: intersecting, parallel, skew.

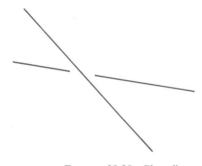

FIGURE 28.28. *Skew lines.*

28.7 Planes in Space

As in the cases of points and lines we cannot define a plane, but we can imagine a piece of a plane by thinking of a stiff piece of cardboard, a floor, or a table-top. By experiment or intuition answer the following questions with reference to lines and planes in space.

1. How many planes can be drawn through two distinct points? _____

_____

> Infinitely many.

2. How many planes can be drawn through a given line? _____

_____

> Infinitely many.

3. How many planes can be drawn through three points which do not lie on the same line? _____

One.

4. How many planes can be drawn through a given line and a given point not on that line? _____

One.

5. How many planes can be drawn through four distinct points? State your assumptions about the locations of the points. _____
_____
_____
_____

If all points lie on a line, infinitely many. If all points lie in a plane, one. If three points lie on a line and the fourth point does not lie on that line, one. If three points lie on a plane but not on a line and the fourth point does not lie on this plane, none.

6. Why does a three-legged stool always rest firmly on a flat floor, whereas a four-legged chair may wobble? _____

See frames 3 and 5.

7. A plane separates a space into two half-spaces. If A and B lie in the same half-space, where does the segment $\overline{AB}$ lie? _____
_____

In the given half-space.

8. If A and B lie in opposite half-spaces, what can be said about the segment $\overline{AB}$? _____

It intersects the separating plane.

9. Two distinct planes are parallel if _____ .

they have no point in common

10. If points A and B lie on a plane, the line AB lies _____ .

on that plane

11. If two distinct planes are not parallel, they intersect in a _____ .

line

12. Can two distinct planes have only one point in common? _____

No.

28.8 Surfaces in Space

A surface is a two-dimensional subset of space like those described below.

(1) *Plane*. A plane is a surface.

SPHERE

(2) *Sphere*. A sphere is the set of points in space that are at a given distance from a fixed point called the center. Note that a sphere is a surface; its interior is called a *ball*.

(3) *Polyhedron*. A polyhedron is a simple closed surface in space which is the union of a finite number of polygonal regions (or faces) and a finite number of line segments (or edges). The five regular solids discussed earlier are examples of polyhedra. Every polyhedron has an interior that is three-dimensional.

In this chapter we have discussed the following concepts:

Plane geometry: point, line, half-line, ray, curve, polygon, interior of a simple closed curve, and angle

Solid geometry: point, line, plane, surface, and polyhedron

REFERENCE

Geometry (*K to 13*), Ontario Institute for Studies in Education, 102 Bloor Street West, Toronto 5, Ontario. This booklet is full of excellent ideas for the classroom presentation of the materials in Chapters 28 through 32 of this book.

Now test your understanding of these concepts by taking the following Post Test.

POST TEST

1. Complete the following table, where V stands for the number of vertices, E the number of edges, and F the number of faces.

Surface	V	E	F	V − E + F
Tetrahedron				
Cube				
Octahedron				
Dodecahedron				
Icosahedron				

2. If three distinct points are chosen in a plane, how many distinct lines can be drawn each of which passes through two (or more) of the chosen points? _____

3. If four distinct points are chosen in space such that no three lie on the same line, how many distinct planes can be drawn each of which passes through three (or more) of the chosen points? _____

4. Consider the relation between lines l and m: "l intersects m". Is this an equivalence relation? _____ Why? _____
_____

5. The subset of the number line: $\{x \mid x \geq 6\}$ is a _____.

6. By definition a simple curve does not _____.

7. Which of the following figures is a circle? _____

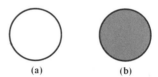

(a)   (b)

8. Why is a rhombus not a regular polygon? _____

9. An angle in the plane is the _____ of two rays which have the same _____ and which do not lie on the same _____.

10. In space, there are three possible relations between two distinct lines: (1) _____, (2) _____, and (3) _____.

11. In space a unique plane is determined by _____ distinct points which do not _____.

12. If line l lies in a plane in space and point A does not lie on l, must A lie on the plane? _____

13. State the Jordan curve theorem. _____
_____

14. (*Discovery Exercise*) Given a simple closed curve in the plane and a point P not on the curve. Find a means for determining whether P lies in the interior or exterior.

15. (*Discovery Exercise*) Consider the "torus", which is a rectangular doughnut as shown. As in frame 1, find V, E, F, and $V − E + F$. Can you guess the value of $V − E + F$ for a doughnut with two holes? With n holes?

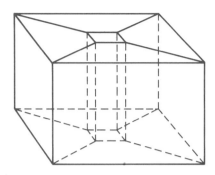

1.

Surface	V	E	F	$V - E + F$
Tetrahedron	4	6	4	2
Cube	8	12	6	2
Octahedron	6	12	8	2
Dodecahedron	20	30	12	2
Icosahedron	12	30	20	2

2. At most three.
3. At most four.
4. No. It is neither reflexive nor transitive.
5. ray
6. intersect itself
7. (a).
8. Angles are not equal.
9. union, initial point, line
10. intersect, parallel, skew
11. three, lie in the same line
12. No.
13. (See Theorem 1.)

Now proceed to Chapter 29, Measurement.

29

Measurement

Before beginning this chapter you should have completed Chapter 28 and should be acquainted with the terminology used there. You will also need to remind yourselves of the definitions of a few other terms, which are covered in the following Readiness Test.

R E A D I N E S S   T E S T

1. A line segment $\overline{AB}$ consists of those points of line AB which lie _____, together with the points _____ themselves.

> between A and B A and B

2. When are two segments equal (i.e., identical)? _____
_____

> When they have the same end points.

3. An angle is the _____ of two _____ with a common _____ point.

> union   rays   initial (or end)

4. When are two angles equal (i.e., identical)? _____

> When they have the same vertex and rays.

5. A triangle is called *equilateral* if its _____ have equal _____.

> sides   lengths

6. A triangle is called isosceles if at least two of its sides have _____
_____.

> equal lengths

7. The base angles of an isosceles triangle have _____.

> equal measures

8. In an equilateral triangle all the angles have _____ measures

> equal (to 60°)

583

9. An acute angle is an angle whose measure is less than _____.

90°

10. Into how many *degrees* is a circle divided? _____

360.

11. What is the length of the circumference of a circle whose radius is 1?
_____

2π.

Now proceed with Section 29.1.

29.1 Length of a Line Segment

The first concept to be developed is that of comparative length—longer, the same, or shorter. Intuition is not necessarily reliable when the two segments are far apart so that comparison is difficult, or in situations like that in Figure 29.1. Some intermediate device is necessary. For example, one can mark the edge of a piece of stiff paper so that the marks represent the ends of one segment and then by moving the paper match these marks to the other segment. Thus the lengths can be compared. An extension of this method can be used to compare the lengths of the closed curves in Figure 29.2.

FIGURE 29.1. *Which segment is longer?*

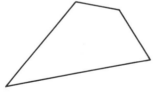

FIGURE 29.2. *Which polygon has the longer perimeter?*

This concept becomes more sophisticated when we measure the length of a segment with a ruler and conclude, for example, that the length of the segment is $1\frac{1}{2}$ inches. What is really meant by such a statement? This depends upon the number of subdivisions into which the ruler is marked. Suppose that we choose a normal ruler which is marked into eighths of an inch. Then

PRECISION OF MEASUREMENT

our statement that the length of the segment is $1\frac{1}{2}$ inches means that the length is greater than $1\frac{7}{16}$ inches and less than $1\frac{9}{16}$ inches. For, our statement that the length is $1\frac{1}{2}$ inches means that the true length is closer to $1\frac{1}{2}$ inches than it is to $1\frac{3}{8}$ inches or to $1\frac{5}{8}$ inches. As shown in Figure 29.3, this requires

GPE OF LENGTH

the true length to be between $1\frac{7}{16}$ inches and $1\frac{9}{16}$ inches. Thus the greatest possible error (GPE) is $\frac{1}{16}$ inch.

584

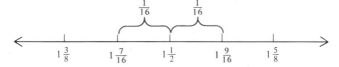

FIGURE 29.3. *For a ruler marked in 8th's, GPE = 1/16 inch.*

Although a segment does have some definite length, no measurement will tell us this length precisely without some possible error. That is, all measurements are to some degree approximations. So in precise measurements, the accuracy of the approximation needs to be stated.

Most measurements of length in the United States use the British system, which is based on inches, feet, yards, and miles. In a great part of the rest of the world and in scientific work in the United States the metric system of measurement is used. The basic unit in this system is the *meter*, which is approximately equal to one ten-millionth of the distance along a meridian on the earth from the equator to a pole. The official meter used to be the length of a platinum–iridium bar which was carefully preserved at constant temperature in a vault in Sèvres, France. Since 1960, however, the meter has been defined to be 1,650,763.53 wavelengths of a certain line in the spectrum of the gas krypton. For very precise measurements this new definition is very helpful, for the spectrum of krypton can be produced in the laboratory and so there is no need to refer to the bar in Sèvres.

METRIC SYSTEM

Associated with the meter are other units which are subdivisions or multiples of it. Some of these, together with their British equivalents, are given in Tables 1 and 2.

TABLE 1. Metric Units and British Equivalents

Name	Definition	Approximate British Equivalent
Millimeter	One thousandth of a meter	0.03937 inches
Centimeter	One hundreth of a meter	0.3937 inch
Meter	—	39.37 inches
Kilometer	One thousand meters	3,280.8 feet or 0.621 statute mile

TABLE 2. British Units in terms of Metric Units

British	Metric (exact equivalent)
1 inch	2.54 centimeters
1 foot	30.48 centimeters
1 statute mile†	1609.344 meters
1 nautical mile† (6,076.11549 feet)	1852 meters

† Statute miles are used for measurements on land, nautical miles at sea and in the air.

Since metric units are so common throughout the world, it is important that children be introduced to them at an early age.

Measurement

1. Use a ruler divided into eighths of an inch to measure the length of the segment ————————————. Normally we would say

A   B

that this length is ——— inches. This means that its length is greater than ———— inches and less than ———— inches. What is its approximate length in centimeters? ————.

2	$1\frac{15}{16}$	$2\frac{1}{16}$	5.08

2. Using a ruler divided into sixteenths of an inch, we measure the length of a segment to be $2\frac{1}{4}$ inches. This means that the true length is between ———— inches and ———— inches. The GPE = ————.

$2\frac{7}{32}$	$2\frac{9}{32}$	$\frac{1}{32}$ inch

3. Using a ruler marked in millimeters we find the length of a segment to be 4.7 centimeters. What does this mean? The length is between ———— centimeters and ———— centimeters. The GPE = ————.

4.65	4.75	0.5 millimeter = 0.05 centimeter

4. 400 meters is how many yards? ————

437.4.

5. 25 meters is how many feet? ————

82.02.

6. 12 feet is how many meters? ————

3.6576.

7. 35 statute miles is how many kilometers? ————

56.38

8. A car is traveling at a speed of 60 kilometers per hour. What is its speed in miles per hour? ————

37.26.

9. The speed limit on an American highway is 60 miles per hour. What is this speed limit in kilometers per hour? ————

586

96.56.

10. An airplane is traveling at a speed of 600 nautical miles per hour. What is its speed in kilometers per hour? _____

1111.2.

11. A speed of 60 miles per hour is equal to what speed in feet per second? _____

88.

12. A speed of 60 miles per hour is equal to what speed in centimeters per second? _____

2682.24.

29.2 Length of Curves

It is relatively easy to find the length of a curve that is a union of line segments, such as a polygon. Just add up the lengths of the segments. For polygons the length is called the *perimeter*.

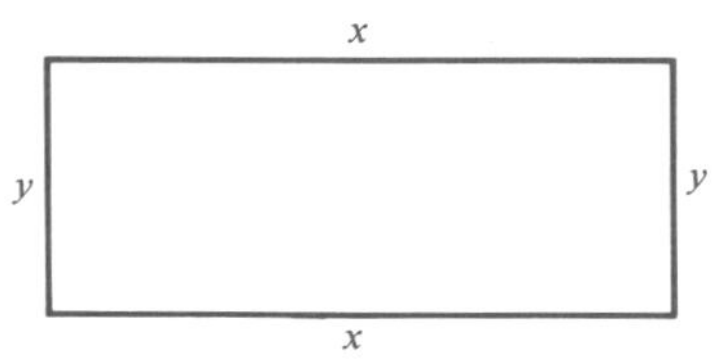

PERIMETER

FIGURE 29.4. *The perimeter is P = 2(x + y).*

EXAMPLE. The perimeter of a rectangle whose sides have lengths x and y is $2(x + y)$ (Figure 29.4).

The lengths of other curves are somewhat more sophisticated. The length of a circle (its circumference) can be approximated by placing a string around a cylinder with a circular base and then measuring the length of the string. The exact formulation, however, of the length of a curve is based upon the idea of finding the length of a polygonal approximation, as was discussed in Section 25.5 for a circle.

Choose a finite number of points on the curve and join consecutive points with line segments. The sum of the lengths of these segments is an approximation to the length of the curve. To get a better approximation, choose more points. The length of the curve is then defined to be the limit of the lengths of these approximations as the number of points increases indefinitely.

1. Find an approximation to the length (in inches) of the curve below by dividing it into four parts, joining their end points with segments, and

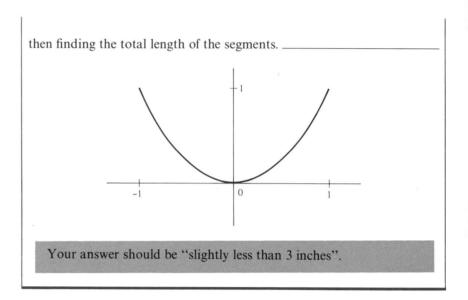

then finding the total length of the segments. _____

Your answer should be "slightly less than 3 inches".

29.3 Areas of Polygons

Although in Section 28.4 we distinguished between a *polygon* (a curve) and a *polygonal region* (the interior of a polygon), we shall now simplify our language by speaking of the *area of a polygon* when we really mean the area of the corresponding polygonal region.

Our first problem here is to compare the areas of two rectangles. Is the area of one larger, equal to, or smaller than the area of the second? Intuition here can be misleading. Which of the rectangles in Figure 29.5 has the greater

FIGURE 29.5. *Which rectangle has the greater area?*

area? Many children will say (a), for it is longer and clearly has a greater perimeter. What do you say? (Actually the areas are equal.)

Since intuition is a bad guide for comparing areas, what is a better way for doing it? We might divide Figure 29.5(a) into a number of small squares and then put them on Figure 29.5(b) and see whether they approximately cover this square or whether their union is too small or too large. Children tend to confuse perimeter with area, and this misconception can be removed by considering a number of rectangles with the same area but with different perimeters.

Of course, this method has its limitations, and so we need a firm method of measuring area. The fundamental definition is based upon the intuition that has been developed in the preceding discussion.

AREA OF A RECTANGLE

DEFINITION. The *area of a rectangle* (in square units) is the product of the number of units in its base times the number of units in its height. Thus $A = b \times h$ square units.

If the sides are given in inches, we compute the area in square inches, and so on.

This definition can be motivated by situations like that drawn in Figure 29.6.

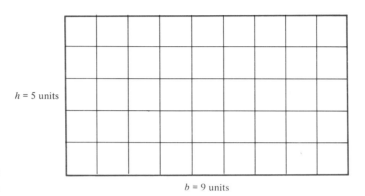

$h = 5$ units

$b = 9$ units

FIGURE 29.6. *$A = 9 \times 5$ square units.*

REMARKS

1. This definition (and Figure 29.6) suggests that the area of a rectangle is defined only when its two sides can be subdivided into integral multiples of the same unit. This is the case if b and h are both rational numbers, for the LCM of their denominators is a suitable unit. This type of subdivision, however, does not work in general if b and h are irrational. Nevertheless, we say that in all cases $A = b \times h$.

2. When b and h are measured, there are inevitable inaccuracies which will produce an inaccuracy in the area. Suppose that we find

$$b = 2 \quad \text{and} \quad h = 3$$

using a ruler divided into eighths of an inch. Then we know that

$$1\tfrac{15}{16} < b < 2\tfrac{1}{16} \quad \text{and} \quad 2\tfrac{15}{16} < h < 3\tfrac{1}{16}$$

So the area must satisfy the inequalities

$$1\tfrac{15}{16} \times 2\tfrac{15}{16} < A < 2\tfrac{1}{16} \times 3\tfrac{1}{16}$$

or

$$\frac{31}{16} \times \frac{47}{16} < A < \frac{33}{16} \times \frac{49}{16}$$

or

$$\frac{1457}{256} < A < \frac{1617}{256}$$

or

$$5.7 < A < 6.3$$

Hence we can write the answer: $A = 6 \pm 0.3$ square inches. The error ± 0.3 can be obtained more simply from the formula

$$\text{GPE of area} = (b + h) \times (\text{GPE of length})$$

where we remind you that GPE is an abbreviation for *greatest possible error*. In the above case, we have GPE of length $= \frac{1}{16}$, so

$$\text{GPE of area} = (2 + 3) \times \tfrac{1}{16} = \tfrac{5}{16} = 0.3 \text{ square inch}$$

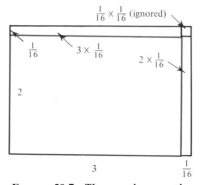

$\frac{1}{16} \times \frac{1}{16}$ (ignored)

$\frac{1}{16}$ $3 \times \frac{1}{16}$ $2 \times \frac{1}{16}$

2

3    $\frac{1}{16}$

To see why this formula is approximately correct consider Figure 29.7. The error in computing the area is at most

$$(2 \times \tfrac{1}{16}) + (3 \times \tfrac{1}{16}) = \tfrac{5}{16} \approx 0.3$$

In order to define the areas of other regions we rely on the following principles:

(1) Let A and B be two regions in the plane which have no points in common except possibly points on their boundaries. Then

$$\text{area } A \cup B = \text{area } A + \text{area } B$$

FIGURE 29.7. *The error in computing the area is at most $(2 \times 1/16) + (3 \times 1/16) = 5/16 \approx 0.3$.*

(2) If A and B are two regions which have the same shape and size, then

$$\text{area } A = \text{area } B$$

Using these principles we can now derive formulas for the areas of polygonal regions.

From the area of a rectangle, we can find a formula for the area of a right triangle (Figure 29.8). If we are given the right triangle ABC with sides b and

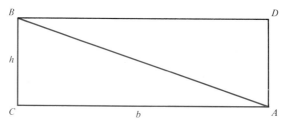

FIGURE 29.8. *Area of triangle $ABC = \frac{1}{2}\mathbf{b} \times \mathbf{h}$.*

h, we can construct a corresponding rectangle $ABCD$ with sides b and h. The two triangles ABC and ADB surely have the same area, so area $ABC = \frac{1}{2}$ area $ABCD = \frac{1}{2}b \times h$. This is Theorem 1.

THEOREM 1. The area of a right triangle is $\frac{1}{2}b \times h$ square units.

Let us now find the area of the parallelogram $ABCD$ in Figure 29.9.

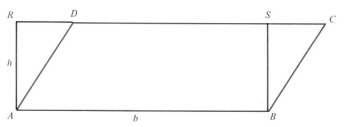

FIGURE 29.9. *Area $ABCD = b \times h$.*

First we draw the corresponding rectangle $ABSR$. It is evident that the right triangles ARD and BSC have the same area, so area $ABCD$ = area $ABSR$ = $b \times h$. This gives us the following result:

AREA OF A PARALLELOGRAM

THEOREM 2. The area of a parallelogram with base b and height h is

$$\text{area} = b \times h$$

Finally, consider a general triangle ABC (Figure 29.10). We can construct the corresponding parallelogram $ABCD$. Then triangles ABC and BDC have equal areas, and so area $ABC = \frac{1}{2}$ area $ABDC = \frac{1}{2}b \times h$. This gives us Theorem 3.

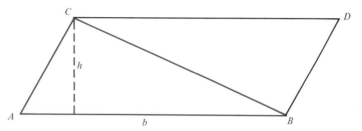

FIGURE 29.10. *Area* $ABC = \frac{1}{2} b \times h$.

AREA OF A TRIANGLE

THEOREM 3. The area of a triangle with base b and height h is

$$\text{area} = \frac{1}{2}b \times h$$

To find the area of a polygon, we can divide it into triangles and apply the formula for the area of a triangle (Figure 29.11).

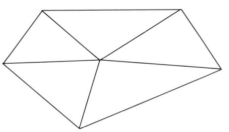

FIGURE 29.11. *The area of the polygon is the sum of the areas of the indicated triangles.*

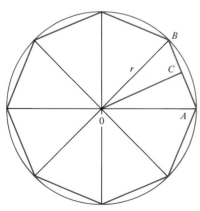

FIGURE 29.12. *Regular polygon inscribed in a circle of radius r.*

The area of a region whose boundary is not the union of line segments is a more subtle concept. Here we discuss only the circle. In a circle of radius r we inscribe a regular polygon such as that in Figure 29.12. The triangles of the subdivision have equal areas, so let us consider only one of them, say triangle AOB (Figure 29.12).

$$\text{area of triangle } AOB = \frac{1}{2} \text{ (length of } \overline{AB}) \times \text{(length of } \overline{OC})$$

So an approximation to the area of the circle is

$$\frac{1}{2} \text{ (perimeter of the polygon)} \times \text{(length of } OC)$$

If we now do the same for a sequence of polygons with ever-increasing numbers of sides, the areas of the polygons will be better and better approximations to the area of the circle. When the number of sides of one of the polygons is very large,

591

(1) Its perimeter is very nearly $2\pi r$.

(2) The length of $\overline{OC}$ is very nearly r.

So the area of the polygon is very nearly $\frac{1}{2}(2\pi r) \times r = \pi r^2$. By this process we conclude the truth of Theorem 4:

AREA OF A CIRCLE　　**THEOREM 4.**　The area of a circle of radius r is πr^2.

REMARK

We have used various amounts of intuition in the proofs of Theorems 1, 2, 3, and 4 which make them believable. The full, rigorous, proofs require the full axiomatic treatment of geometry, which is inappropriate for the elementary school.

---

1. Measure the areas of the rectangles in Figure 29.5. The area of rectangle (a) is $A = $ _____ $\pm$ _____. The area of rectangle (b) is $A = $ _____ $\pm$ _____. Hence to within the accuracy of our measurements these areas are _____.

> If the ruler is divided into sixteenths, (*a*) $A = \frac{9}{16} \pm 0.1$, (*b*) $A = \frac{9}{16} \pm 0.05$, equal to within the accuracy of measurement.

2. Assuming the lengths of the sides of the following rectangles to be exact as stated, find their perimeters and areas. (a) $A = $ _____, $P = $ _____. (b) $A = $ ____, $P = $ _____. (c) $A = $ _____, $P = $ _____.

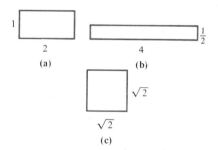

> (a) 2, 6　　(b) 2, 9　　(c) 2, $4\sqrt{2}$

3. In a rectangle the base is measured to be 4 ± 0.1 inches and the height to be 7 ± 0.1 inches. Find the area and the corresponding GPE. _____
_____

> 28, 1.1 square inches.

4. Assuming exact dimensions as stated find the areas of the triangles: (a) _____. (b) _____. (c) _____.

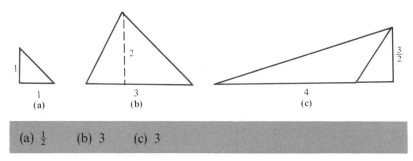

1	2	$\frac{3}{2}$
1	3	4
(a)	(b)	(c)

(a) $\frac{1}{2}$ (b) 3   (c) 3

5. The GPE for the area of a triangle is given by the formula GPE of area $= \frac{1}{2}(b + h) \times$ (GPE of length). Find the area and the GPE for a triangle where $b = 10 \pm 0.2$ and $h = 15 \pm 0.2$. $A =$ _____, GPE = _____.

75   2.5

6. The GPE for the area of a circle is given by the formula GPE of area $= 2\pi r \times$ (GPE of length). The radius of a circle is found to be 5.4 centimeters when a ruler divided into millimeters is used. Find the area of the circle and its GPE. _____

$A = 29.16\pi$ square centimeters, GPE $= 0.54\pi$.

7. In a rectangle the dimensions are measured to be $b = 20 \pm 0.1$, $h = 5 \pm 0.1$. What per cent of the measured lengths are the GPE's? For b, per cent error = _____; for h, per cent error = _____.

0.5%   2%.

8. In frame 7 the area is $A =$ _____ $\pm$ _____. The GPE of A is what per cent of A? _____

100   2.5   2.5%

9. (*Discovery Exercise*) Find the per cent error in the area of a rectangle in terms of the per cent error in b and the per cent error in h.

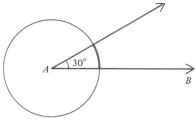

FIGURE 29.13. *Angle whose measure is 30°.*

29.4 Measurement of Angles

As you know, it is customary to divide a circle into 360 equal parts, called degrees. If we draw an angle with its vertex at the center of the circle, its two rays cut the circle in two points which divide the circle into two arcs. The number of degrees in the shorter of these two arcs is the measure of the angle in degrees (Figure 29.13).

593

NOTATION. For the measure of angle ABC we shall write $m(\angle ABC)$.

MEASURE OF AN ANGLE

Although two angles are equal only if they have the same vertex and rays, two distinct angles can have equal measures (Figure 29.14).

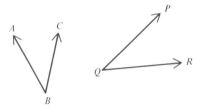

FIGURE 29.14. *Although* $\angle ABC \neq \angle PQR$, $m(\angle ABC) = m(\angle PQR)$.

Let ray $\overrightarrow{AD}$ divide the straight angle CAB into two angles BAD and CAD with equal measures (Figure 29.15). Since $m(\angle BAC) = \frac{1}{2}360° = 180°$, $m(\angle BAD) = m(\angle CAD) = 90°$. The angles are called right angles, and the lines BC and AD are perpendicular (that is, $BC \perp AD$).

EXAMPLE 1. If we are given $\angle BAC$ (Figure 29.16) and rays $\overrightarrow{AP} \perp \overrightarrow{AC}$ and $\overrightarrow{AQ} \perp \overrightarrow{AB}$ as in the figure, what is the relation between $m(\angle PAQ)$ and $m(\angle BAC)$?

FIGURE 29.15. $m(\angle BAD) = m(\angle CAD) = 90°$.

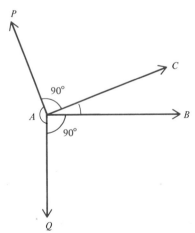

FIGURE 29.16. $m(\angle PAQ) + m(\angle BAC) = 180°$.

Solution. Since the sum of the measures of all the angles with vertex at A is 360°, it follows that

$$m(\angle BAC) + 90° + m(\angle PAQ) + 90° = 360°$$

Hence

$$m(\angle PAQ) + m(\angle BAC) = 180°$$

SUPPLEMENTARY ANGLES

DEFINITION. Two angles are called *supplementary* if the sum of their measures is 180°.

Thus $\angle PAQ$ and $\angle BAC$ in Figure 29.16 are supplementary.

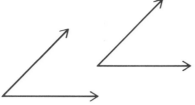

FIGURE 29.17. *Angles with edges which are parallel and which point in the same direction.*

EXAMPLE 2. Suppose two angles have their rays, respectively, parallel and pointing in the same directions (Figure 29.17). How are their measures related?

Answer. From the figure it is evident that their measures are equal.

Now we are in a position to demonstrate a celebrated theorem:

ANGLE SUM OF A TRIANGLE

THEOREM 5. The sum of the measures of the interior angles of a triangle is 180°.

Proof. Let *ABC* be the given triangle (Figure 29.18). At each vertex draw the outward rays shown in color perpendicular to the corresponding sides. The angles 1, 2, and 3 are called *outer angles*. Through an interior point *D* draw the colored rays as shown perpendicular to the sides of the triangle.

OUTER ANGLES

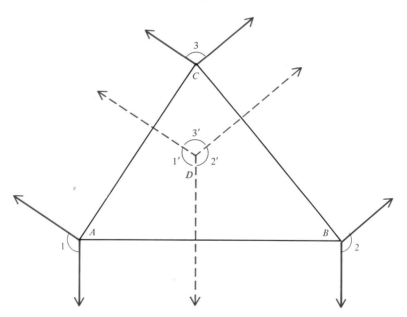

FIGURE 29.18. *Angle sum of a triangle.*

From Example 2 the outer angle 1 has the same measure as the angle 1′ at *D*, and similarly for 2 and 2′ and for 3 and 3′.

Since the sum of the measures of angles 1′, 2′, and 3′ is 360°, we see that

$$m(\angle 1) + m(\angle 2) + m(\angle 3) = 360°$$

But from Example 1, $m(\angle 1) = 180° - m(\angle A)$, $m(\angle 2) = 180° = -m(\angle B)$, and $m(\angle 3) = 180° - m(\angle C)$. Therefore, $180° - m(\angle A) + 180° - m(\angle B) + 180° - m(\angle C) = 360°$. This equation can be rewritten

$$m(\angle A) + m(\angle B) + m(\angle C) = 180°$$

and so Theorem 5 is proved.

DIHEDRAL ANGLE In space two half-planes with a line as their common edge form a *dihedral angle* (Figure 29.19). To define the measure of a dihedral angle choose a point A on the edge (Figure 29.20) and draw rays $\overrightarrow{AB}$ and $\overrightarrow{AC}$ in the two

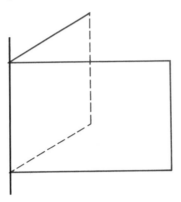

FIGURE 29.19. *Dihedral angle.*   **FIGURE 29.20.** *How to measure a dihedral angle.*

planes perpendicular to the edge. Then the measure of the dihedral angle is the measure of the angle BAC. Thus the measure of the dihedral angle formed by the floor and a wall of a room is 90°, and these two planes are said to be perpendicular.

1. In an isosceles right triangle what is the measure of the acute angles? _____

45°

2. If a right triangle has one acute angle whose measure is 30°, what is the measure of the other acute angle? _____

60°

3. In an equilateral triangle, what is the measure of each of the angles? _____

60°

4. What is the sum of the measures of the interior angles of a parallelogram? _____ Of the outer angles? _____

5. What is the sum of the measures of the interior angles of a pentagon like that in the figure? _____ Of the outer angles? _____

596

To answer the first question you may wish to subdivide the pentagon as shown.

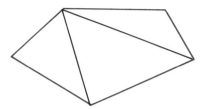

540°   360°

6. If two angles have their corresponding rays parallel, but drawn as shown, what is the relation between $m(\angle ABC)$ and $m(\angle PQR)$? _____
_____

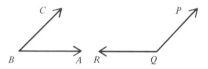

$m(\angle ABC) + m(\angle PQR) = 180°.$

7. Two angles are called supplementary if the sum of their measures is _____. In Figure 29.18, $\angle 1$ and $\angle A$ are _____.

180°   supplementary

8. If line l is parallel to line m as shown, what angles have the same measure as angle 1? _____ What angles are supplementary to angle 1? _____

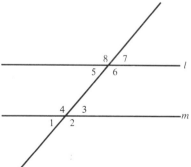

3, 5, and 7.   2, 4, 6, and 8.

9. In the parallelogram *ABCD* what is the relation between the measures of ∠1 and ∠2? _____ Between ∠1 and ∠3? _____

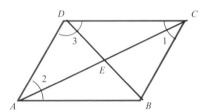

What is the relation between the lengths of segments $\overline{AE}$ and $\overline{EC}$? _____ Between $\overline{DE}$ and $\overline{EB}$? _____

> Equal.   Supplementary.   Equal.   Equal.

10. In right triangle *ABC*, where ∠*C* is a right angle, what is the relation between the measures of ∠1 and ∠3? _____ Of ∠2 and ∠4? _____

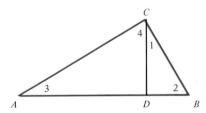

> In each case they are equal.

11. If a room has four walls, a floor, and a ceiling, how many dihedral angles are formed? _____

> Twelve.

12. If two distinct lines in the plane *l* and *m*, are each perpendicular to line *AB*, what is the relation between *l* and *m*? _____ Is your result still true for two lines *l* and *m* in space? _____

> Parallel.   No.

13. Consider the relation between pairs of lines in a plane: *l* ⊥ *m*. Is this relation an equivalence relation? _____ Why? _____

> No.   It is neither reflexive nor transitive. It is symmetric, however.

14. (*Discovery Exercise*) Formulate an exact statement which describes the fact that a line and a plane in space are perpendicular.

15. (*Discovery Exercise*) (*Morley's theorem*, named after its discoverer Professor Frank Morley, the father of the American author Christopher Morley). In any triangle *ABC* draw the trisectors of the three inner angles and let them meet in the vertices of triangle *PQR*, as shown. What is the best statement that can be made about triangle *PQR*? Your statement should be true for any original triangle *ABC*.

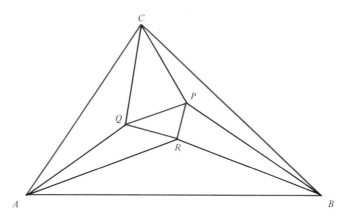

16. (*Discovery Exercise*) Consider any quadrilateral *ABCD* and connect its midpoints as shown. What is true of the quadrilateral *PQRS*?

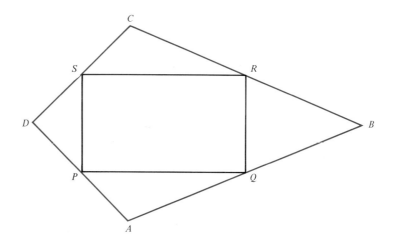

17. (*Discovery Exercise*) Let *ABCD* be any quadrilateral, and erect squares on each side as shown. *P, Q, R,* and *S* are the centers of these squares. What is true of segments $\overline{PR}$ and $\overline{QS}$?

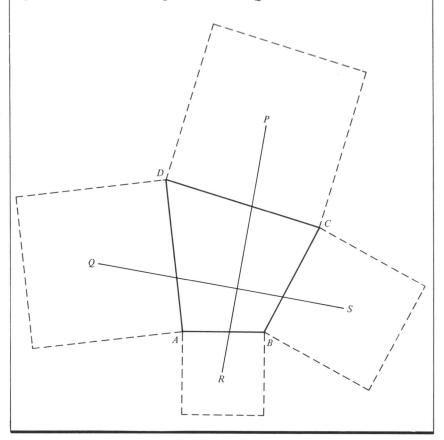

29.5 Congruence and Similarity

Although two segments are equal only if they have the same end points, two segments are called *congruent* if their lengths are equal. For congruent segments we write

$$\overline{AB} \cong \overline{CD}.$$

Similarly, two angles are *congruent* if their measures are equal, and we write

$$\angle ABC \cong \angle PQR$$

CONGRUENCE   In general, two geometric figures are *congruent* if they have the same *shape* and *size*. Thus if two polygons are congruent, their pairs of corresponding sides are congruent, their pairs of corresponding angles are congruent, and their areas are equal. Two circles are congruent if the lengths of their radii are equal. Tests for the congruence of geometric figures form a large part of the study of elementary geometry.

In the case of triangles, there are three famous results of Euclid (Figure 29.21).

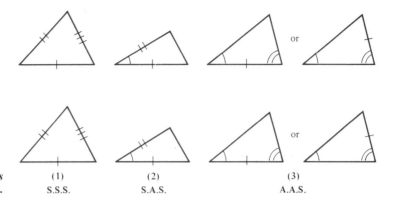

or

or

FIGURE 29.21. *Congruence theorems for triangles.*

(1)
S.S.S.

(2)
S.A.S.

(3)
A.A.S.

(1) SSS. Two triangles are congruent if their pairs of corresponding sides are congruent.

(2) SAS. Two triangles are congruent if two pairs of corresponding sides are congruent, and their included angles are congruent.

(3) AAS. Two triangles are congruent if two pairs of corresponding angles are congruent and one pair of corresponding sides are congruent.

You might guess that congruence theorems like those for the triangle hold for other geometric figures, but consider SSSS for a quadrilateral. The hypothesis of SSSS is true in Figure 29.22, but the two figures are not congruent.

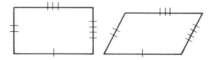

FIGURE 29.22. *SSS does not prove that two quadrilaterals are congruent.*

This observation justifies the common realization that a triangle is rigid but that a rectangle is not rigid. It is for this reason that diagonal bracing is used in the construction of a girder as in Figure 29.23, or why a diagonal brace is often inserted in a door to keep it from sagging (Figure 29.24).

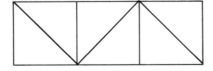

FIGURE 29.23. *Diagonal bracing to make a girder rigid.*

You might think that two triangles are congruent if AAA is true (that is, three pairs of corresponding angles are congruent). But this is false, as can be seen in Figure 29.25. Figure 29.25 illustrates the notion of *similarity*.

601

FIGURE 29.24. *Stiffener in door to prevent sagging.*

FIGURE 29.25. *Two triangles with AAA but which are not congruent.*

SIMILARITY

DEFINITION. Two geometric figures are *similar* if they have the same shape but not necessarily the same size.

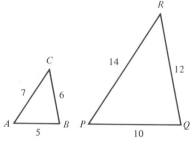

FIGURE 29.26. *Similar triangles.*

When two figures are similar, their pairs of corresponding angles are congruent, but their pairs of corresponding sides are proportional. For example, consider the similar triangles in Figure 29.26. In this figure $m(\angle A) = m(\angle P)$; $m(\angle B) = m(\angle Q)$; and $m(\angle C) = m(\angle R)$; and $(10, 12, 14) = 2(5, 6, 7)$. (See Chapter 26 for notation.)

Similar right triangles are used in a form of indirect measurement called the "Boy Scout" method. Suppose that a scout wishes to find the height of a tree (Figure 29.27). From the foot of the tree the scout steps off 40 feet to

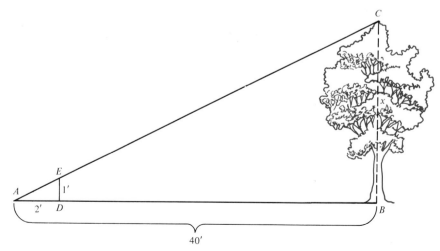

FIGURE 29.27. *Method of finding height of a tree, x. x:1 = 40:2, so x = 20'.*

point A. Then a friend adjusts a vertical foot ruler, ED, so that points A, E, and C are on a line of sight. The distance AD is then measured to be 2 feet. Since triangles ADE and ABC are similar, $x:1 = 40:2$. Hence $x = 20$ feet.

602

There are several variations of this method, and a similar procedure can be used to find the width of a river.

1. Two geometric figures are congruent if they have the same _____ and _____.

> shape   size

2. Two geometric figures are similar if they have the same _____.

> shape

3. If two geometric figures are congruent, what is true of their pairs of corresponding sides? _____ Of their pairs of corresponding angles? _____

> They are congruent.   They are congruent.

4. If two geometric figures are similar, what is true of the lengths of their pairs of corresponding sides? _____ of their pairs of corresponding angles? _____

> Proportional.   Congruent.

5. Which pairs of the following triangles are congruent? _____ Which pairs are similar? _____

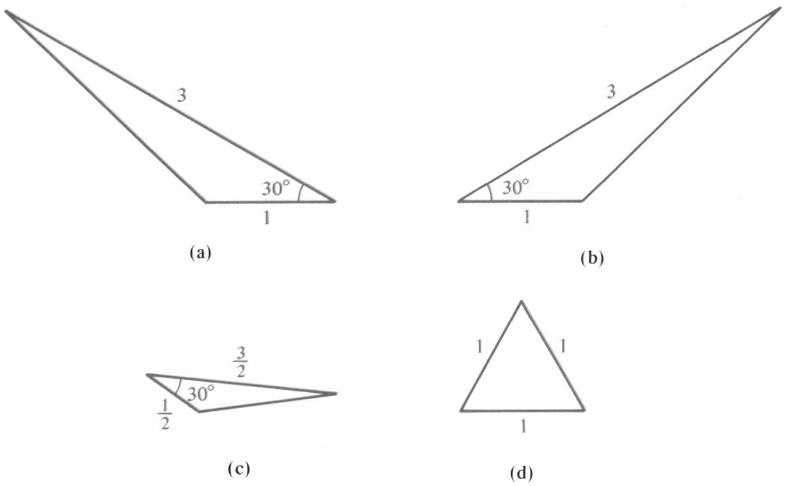

(a)

(b)

(c)

(d)

> (a) and (b).   (a), (b), and (c).

6. Can two triangles be congruent without being similar? _____
Can two triangles be similar without being congruent? _____

> No.　Yes.

7. Triangles *ABC* and *PQR* are both equilateral (all three sides are equal in length). Are they necessarily congruent? _____ Are they necessarily similar? _____

> No.　Yes.

8. For any two rectangles, the pairs of corresponding angles have equal measures (90°). Does this prove that any two rectangles are similar? _____

> No.

9. Let *ABC* be a right triangle (as in the figure) with $m(\angle C) = 90°$, and let *CD* be $\perp$ *AB*. What is true of triangles *ABC* and *ADC*? _____
What is true of triangles *ABC* and *BCD*? _____

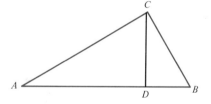

> All three triangles are similar.

10. To find the height of a tree, a Scout steps off 11 convenient units from its base and marks the spot labeled *A* in the figure. Then he steps off 1 more unit, to point *B*. A vertical stick is held at point *A* by a friend.

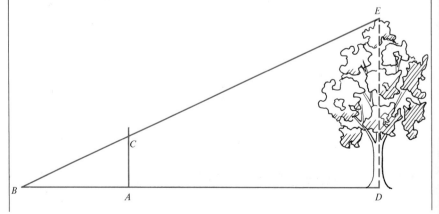

Then the Scout puts his eye on the ground and sights the top of the tree and his friend marks the spot C on the stick where the line of sight BE cuts the stick. The length of AC is then measured with a ruler to be 15 inches. How high is the tree? _____ Why? _____

---

15 feet.   Triangles ABC and DBE are similar. So $AC:DE = 1:12$.

___ 11. In triangle ABC, E is the midpoint of $\overline{AC}$ and F is the midpoint of $\overline{BC}$. What relationships are true of segments $\overline{EF}$ and $\overline{AB}$ _____ _____ What two triangles are similar? _____

$EF = \frac{1}{2}AB,\ \overline{EF} \| \overline{AB}$ ABC and EFC

29.6 Theorem of Pythagoras

The celebrated theorem of Pythagoras is the following:

THEOREM OF PYTHAGORAS

THEOREM 6. THEOREM OF PYTHAGORAS. If ABC is a right triangle (Figure 29.28) with hypotenuse of length c and legs of length a and b, then $c^2 = a^2 + b^2$.

There are literally hundreds of proofs of this theorem, but the following one is suitable for intuitive proof in numerical cases in the early grades and for more complete proofs later.

Proof. Draw the square $ABCD$ whose sides are of length $a + b$ and locate points P, Q, R, and S as indicated in Figure 29.29. Then triangles SAP, PBQ, QCR, and RDS are congruent. They are each right triangles with legs a and b and hypotenuse c, and the area of each of these triangles is $\frac{1}{2} ab$.

Next, the quadrilateral $PQRS$ is a square. We know that its sides are all equal; what about its angles? By our construction $m(\angle APS) + m(\angle QPB) = 90°$, for these angles are congruent to the acute angles of the right triangle

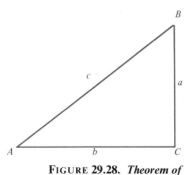

FIGURE 29.28. *Theorem of Pythagoras:* $c^2 = a^2 + b^2$.

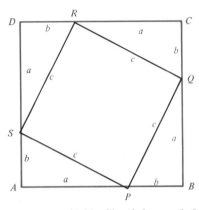

FIGURE 29.29. *Sketch for proof of Theorem of Pythagoras.*

SAP. Also

$$m(\angle APS) + m(\angle SPQ) + m(\angle QPB) = 180°$$

Therefore,

$$m(\angle SPQ) = 90°$$

and so $PQRS$ is a square, and area $PQRS = c^2$. Finally,

$$\text{area } ABCD = (a + b)^2 = a^2 + 2ab + b^2$$

$$\text{area } ABCD = 4 \text{ area } SAP + \text{ area } PQRS$$

Therefore,

$$a^2 + 2ab + b^2 = 4[\tfrac{1}{2}ab] + c^2$$

Thus

$$a^2 + 2ab + b^2 = 2ab + c^2$$

or

$$a^2 + b^2 = c^2$$

---

1. (*Discovery Exercise*) A Pythagorean triangle is a right triangle such that the lengths of all three sides are positive integers (such as 3, 4, 5). Find as many Pythagorean triangles as you can. Can you find a formula that will give you all Pythagorean triangles?

29.7 Distance

In triangle ABC (Figure 29.30) draw the altitude BD. Then according to the Theorem of Pythagoras

$$c^2 = p^2 + h^2$$

So

$$c^2 > p^2 \quad \text{and} \quad c > p$$

Similarly,

$$a^2 > q^2 \quad \text{and} \quad a > q$$

Therefore,

$$a + c > p + q = b$$

This establishes Theorem 7.

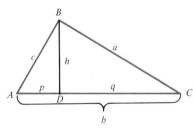

FIGURE 29.30. $a + c > b$.

THEOREM 7. The sum of the lengths of two sides of a triangle is greater than the length of the third side.

By an extension of the method used to prove Theorem 7, it is possible to prove Theorem 8.

THEOREM 8. Given two points A and B, the length of the segment AB is less than the length of any curve joining A and B.

This leads us to the definition of *distance*.

DISTANCE **DEFINITION**   Given two points A and B, the *distance AB* is the length of segment $\overline{AB}$.

REMARKS

1. The distance AB is less than the length of any curve joining A and B other than the segment $\overline{AB}$.

2. If we have three points A, B, and C such that

$$\text{distance } AB + \text{distance } BC = \text{distance } AC$$

it follows that B is located on the segment $\overline{AB}$. For if it were somewhere else, the equality above would not be true.

POST TEST

1. Using a ruler divided into eighths of an inch, the sides of a rectangle are measured to be 3 inches and 4 inches. The area of the rectangle is _____ square inches with a GPE of _____.

2. The speed limit on a road in France is 60 kilometers per hour. What is this in miles per hour? _____

3. The base and altitude of a triangle are measured to be: $b = 5$ inches, $h = 4$ inches with a GPE of 0.1 inch. Find the area of the triangle and its GPE _____.

4. A regular hexagon of side 1 inch is divided into triangles as shown. The length of segment $\overline{CD}$ is _____. (Use the theorem of Pythagoras.) The area of the hexagon is _____ square inches.

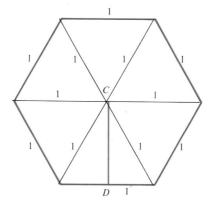

---

5. What is the length of the altitude h of the rhombus? _____
What is the area of the rhombus? _____

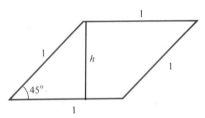

6. The radius of a circle is measured to be 4 ± 0.02 inches. Find the area of the circle and its GPE. _____

_____

7. The side of a square is measured to be 5 inches with a GPE of $\frac{1}{16}$. Find the area A of the square and the GPE of A as a per cent of A. _____

_____

8. The sum of the exterior angles of a parallelogram is _____.
9. Two angles are supplementary if _____.
10. How many dihedral angles are formed by the sides and bottom of a topless box? _____
11. What are the three theorems concerning the congruence of triangles? _____

12. If AAA is true for a pair of triangles, the triangles are _____.
13. Two geometric figures are congruent if they have the same _____ and _____.
14. Two geometric figures are similar if they have the same _____.
15. If two triangles are similar, the lengths of their pairs of corresponding sides are _____.
16. Two congruent segments have equal _____. Two congruent angles have equal _____.
17. Prove the theorem of Pythagoras.
18. If distance AC + distance CB = distance AB, where is C? _____
19. To find the width of a river (without crossing it), a Scout selects a

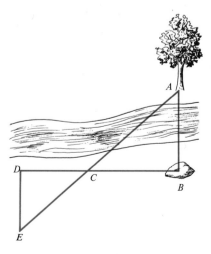

tree at point *A* on the opposite bank. Then he places a stone at point *B* exactly opposite *A*. He then paces a suitable distance along the bank to point *C* and continues an equal distance to point *D*. He puts markers at *C* and *D*. Then he paces inland from *D* until he reaches the point *E* at which *E*, *C*, and *A* are in a straight line. What segment does he now measure to find the width of the river? _____ Justify your response. _____

---

1. $12, \frac{7}{16}$
2. 37.26.
3. $A = 10$ square inches, GPE = 0.45.
4. $\frac{\sqrt{3}}{2}$; $6 \times \frac{1}{2} \times 1 \times \frac{\sqrt{3}}{2} = \frac{3\sqrt{3}}{2}$
5. $\sqrt{\frac{1}{2}} = \frac{\sqrt{2}}{2}$; $\frac{\sqrt{2}}{2}$.
6. $A = 16\pi$ square inches, GPE = 0.16π.
7. $A = 25$ square inches, GPE = 2.5% of *A*.
8. 360°
9. the sum of their measures is 180°
10. Eight.
11. SSS, SAS, AAS
12. similar
13. Shape, size
14. shape
15. proportional
16. length, measures
17. (See Theorem 6.)
18. On segment AB.
19. $\overline{DE}$. Triangles *DEC* and *BAC* are congruent by ASA.

Now you should be ready to study Chapter 30.

30

Geometric Transformations in the Plane

This chapter depends heavily on Chapter 29, which you should have completed by now. As a review of the needed concepts, you should work the following Readiness Test.

READINESS TEST

1. Two segments are congruent if and only if they have the _____ _____.

   same length

2. Two angles are congruent if and only if they have the _____ _____.

   same measure

3. The three congruence theorems for triangles are _____.

   SSS, SAS, AAS

4. The distance between points A and B is the length of _____ _____.

   segment $\overline{AB}$

5. If distance AB + distance BC = distance AC, where is B? _____

   On segment $\overline{AC}$.

6. The perpendicular bisector of segment $\overline{AB}$ is a line _____ _____ to line AB and passing through the _____ of segment $\overline{AB}$.

   perpendicular   midpoint

7. In a parallelogram pairs of opposite sides are _____ and _____.

   parallel   congruent

8. Two lines each of which is perpendicular to a third line are _____ _____.

   parallel

You should now be prepared to proceed with Section 30.1.

30.1 Introduction

One of the most inviting topics in the study of intuitive geometry is that of geometric transformations. A geometric transformation assigns to each point P in the plane a point P', which may or may not be P itself. For example, we can slide the plane 2 inches to the right. Then each point P goes into a point P' 2 inches to the right of P. Or we can rotate the plane about any chosen point. Or we can imagine the plane to be made of rubber and stretch the plane so that the distance of each point P' from some fixed point O becomes three times the distance of P from O. Or we can flip the plane about a fixed (vertical) line so that every point to the right of this line goes into a point on the left, and every point on the left goes into a point on the right. Those transformations which preserve distances are called *rigid motions*, and it is with these that we shall be concerned in this chapter.

RIGID MOTION **DEFINITION.** A transformation is a *rigid motion* if it preserves distances.

An immediate consequence of this definition is stated in Theorem 1.

THEOREM 1. A rigid motion transforms lines into lines.

Proof. Suppose that a rigid motion transforms line AB into the colored figure $A'B'$ (Figure 30.1). Let C be on AB between A and B. Then

$$\text{distance } AC + \text{distance } CB = \text{distance } AB$$

Since the transformation is a rigid motion,

$$\text{distance } AC = \text{distance } A'C'$$
$$\text{distance } CB = \text{distance } C'B'$$
$$\text{distance } AB = \text{distance } A'B'$$

Therefore,

$$\text{distance } A'C' + \text{distance } C'B' = \text{distance } A'B'$$

But this requires C' to be on line $A'B'$ and not as is drawn in color in Figure 30.1.

COROLLARY A. Rigid motions carry segments into congruent segments.

COROLLARY B. A rigid motion transforms a triangle into a congruent triangle. (Use SSS.)

COROLLARY C. A rigid motion transforms an angle into a congruent angle. (Let the angle be an angle of a triangle and use Corollary B.)

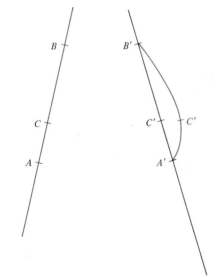

FIGURE 30.1. *C′ must lie on the black line A′B′.*

A very special case of a rigid motion is one in which every point is transformed into itself. We shall call this a *trivial motion*. More interesting rigid motions are the reflections, translations, and rotations, which are discussed in the next three sections.

30.2 Reflections

A reflection of the plane can be intuitively described as a flipping of the plane about a fixed line. More precisely a reflection can be defined as follows.

DEFINITION. Let *l* be a fixed line in the plane. Then under a reflection a point *P* on one side of *l* is transformed into a point *P'* on the other side of *l* such that
(1) The line *PP'* ⊥ *l*.
(2) If *Q* is the intersection of *PP'* and *l*, then the segments $\overline{PQ}$ and $\overline{P'Q}$ are congruent (Figure 30.2). If *P* lies on *l*, it remains unchanged.

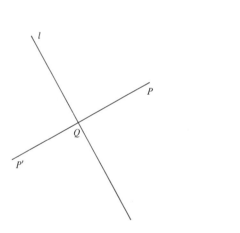

FIGURE 30.2. *Reflection about line l.*

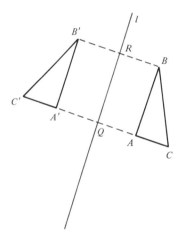

FIGURE 30.3. *Reflection of triangle ABC about l.*

Let us see what happens to a geometric figure as a result of a reflection. First consider triangle *ABC*, which is on one side of *l*, with *AB* ∥ *l* and *AC* ⊥ *l* (Figure 30.3). Then the image of $\underline{ABC}$ after the reflection is *A'B'C'*. By the definition of a reflection $\overline{CQ} \cong \overline{C'Q}$ and $\overline{AQ} \cong \overline{A'Q}$. Hence $\overline{AC} \cong \overline{A'C'}$. Moreover, figure *ABB'A'* is a rectangle, so $\overline{AB} \cong \overline{A'B'}$. Since $m(\angle A) = m(\angle A') = 90°$, it follows from the Pythagorean theorem that $\overline{BC} \cong \overline{B'C'}$. Thus the distance between *B* and *C* is preserved by the reflection.

Although the argument above assumes that *B* and *C* lie on one side of *l*, the same result is true when *B* and *C* have other relative positions. Hence we have the following theorem:

THEOREM 2. A reflection is a rigid motion.

613

A reflection about *l* may transform a figure into itself, as in the case of a circle where *l* is a diameter (Figure 30.4). In such a case we say that the figure is *symmetric about l*, or that *l* is a *line of symmetry* for the figure.

SYMMETRY

FIGURE 30.4. *The circle is symmetric about l.*

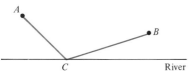

FIGURE 30.5. *To find C such that the path ABC is shortest.*

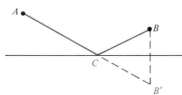

FIGURE 30.6. *Reflect B into B′. Draw AB′ and find C.*

As an example of the use of reflections to solve problems, consider the following:

EXAMPLE. A man wishes to travel from point *A* to point *B* (Figure 30.5), but on his way he must stop at the river for a drink. What will be his shortest path?

Solution. Reflect *B* in the river so that it transforms into *B′* (Figure 30.6). Then $\overline{CB} \cong \overline{CB'}$. So the length of the path *ACB* = the length of the path *ACB′*. Now where is *C* such that the path *ACB′* is shortest? Clearly when *ACB′* is a straight line. So *C* should be chosen at the intersection of the river with line *AB′*.

1. Draw the reflections of the given figures in the line *l*.

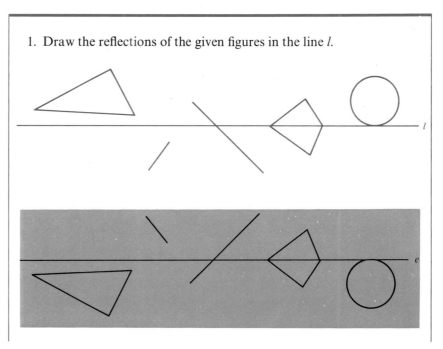

2. Here are some figures which have lines of symmetry. Draw these lines.

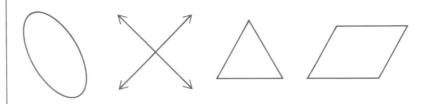

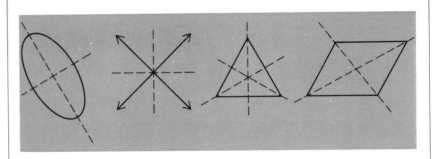

3. If segment $\overline{AB}$ is reflected about a line l into a segment $\overline{A'B'}$, then $\overline{AB}$ and $\overline{A'B'}$ are _____.

congruent

4. If angle A is reflected about line l into angle A', then these two angles are _____.

congruent

5. A triangle ABC is reflected about a line l into triangle $A'B'C'$. Then triangles ABC and $A'B'C'$ have the same shape and _____. Hence they are _____.

size   congruent

6. In Figure 30.3 let us traverse triangle ABC by moving from A to B to C to A. Then we have moved around the triangle in a clockwise direction. In what direction do we move if we traverse triangle $A'B'C'$ in the same way? _____

Counterclockwise.

7. In the figure traverse triangle ABC as in frame 6. In doing so we move in a _____ direction. In traversing triangle $A'B'C'$ we move in a _____ direction.

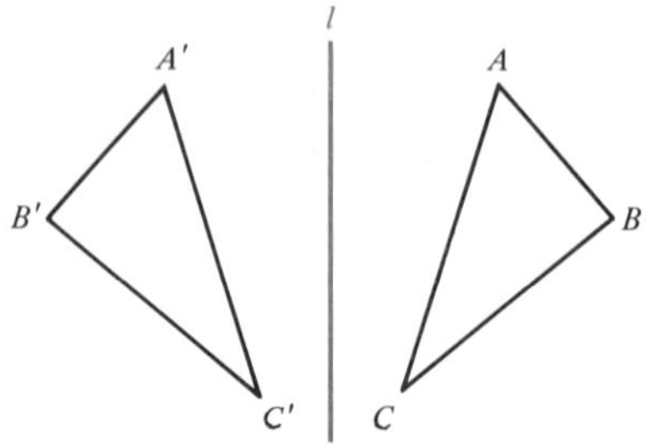

clockwise	counterclockwise

From frames 6 and 7 it is seen that a reflection changes a clockwise motion into a counterclockwise motion and a counterclockwise motion into a

ORIENTATION

clockwise motion. More formally we say that *under a reflection the orientation of the plane is reversed.*

8. Consider the isosceles triangle ABC, where $\overline{AB} \cong \overline{AC}$. Draw the altitude $\overline{AD}$. Why is $BD \cong DC$? Theorem of _____.

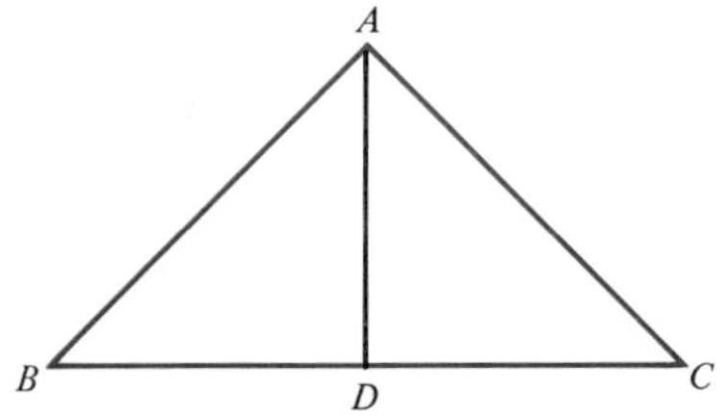

Pythagoras

9. If triangle ABC of frame 8 is reflected about line AD, the image of C is _____ and the image of B is _____. Also the image of $\overline{AC}$ is _____.

B	C	$\overline{AB}$

10. In the reflection of frame 9, the image of angle B is _____. Hence angles B and C are _____.

angle C	congruent

616

11. If we are given two points A and A', how can we find a line l such that a reflection about l transforms A into A'?

l is the perpendicular bisector of $\overline{AA'}$.

12. If C_1 and C_2 are circles with equal radii as shown, draw the line l such that the reflection about l transforms C_1 into C_2.

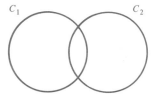

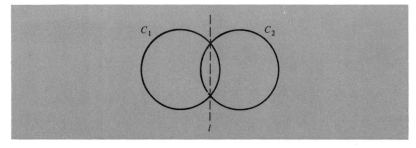

13. How many points does a reflection leave unchanged? _____

Infinitely many, every point on l.

30.3 Translations

The intuitive idea of a translation is a sliding of the plane in a certain direction. In order to give a precise definition, we must introduce some new ideas.

DEFINITIONS

DIRECTED LINE   1. A *directed line* is a line on which we have placed an arrow indicating a positive direction on this line. This direction is called the *sense* of the line.

2. Two directed lines are *parallel* if and only if they are parallel as lines and have the same sense. Two parallel lines with opposite senses are called *antiparallel* (Figure 30.7).

Now we can define a translation.

TRANSLATION   **DEFINITION.** A *translation* of the plane is a transformation of the plane for which each point P is sent into a point P' such that

617

(1) The line PP', directed from P to P', is parallel to a fixed directed line l.

(2) For each P, the length of the segment $\overline{PP'}$ is a fixed number d.

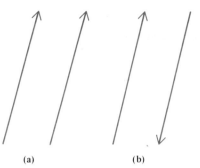

FIGURE 30.7. (a) *Parallel directed lines.* (b) *Antiparallel directed lines.*

(a)   (b)

Thus we have defined a translation with distance d in the direction of l (Figure 30.8).

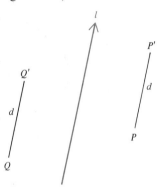
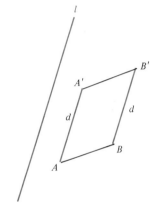

FIGURE 30.8. *Translation with distance d in the direction of l.*

FIGURE 30.9. *Translation of segment* $\overline{AB}$.

We must consider what a translation does to an arbitrary segment $\overline{AB}$. Let $\overline{AB}$ be as in Figure 30.9. Since $\overline{AA'}$ and $\overline{BB'}$ are parallel and congruent, figure $ABB'A'$ is a parallelogram, and so $\overline{AB} \parallel \overline{A'B'}$ and $\overline{AB}$ and $\overline{A'B'}$ are congruent. Hence we have the following theorem:

THEOREM 3. A translation is a rigid motion.

1. A translation sends a segment into a _____ segment.

congruent (or parallel)

2. A translation sends an angle into a _____ angle.

congruent

3. A translation sends a triangle into a _____ triangle.

> congruent

4. Does a translation _____ the orientation of the plane?
(preserve, reverse)
(See frames 6 and 7, Section 30.2.)

> preserve

5. How many points of the plane does a nontrivial translation leave fixed? _____

> None.

6. A translation in the direction of a directed line *l*, transforms the (whole) line *l* into _____.

> itself, but not pointwise

7. In which of the pairs of figures is there a translation that moves figure 1 into figure 2? _____

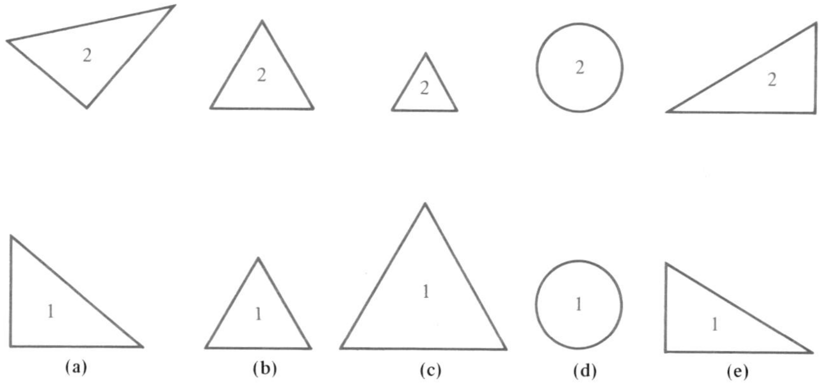

> (b) and (d) only.

8. Suppose that a translation carries *A* into *A'*. Construct the image *B'* of *B*.

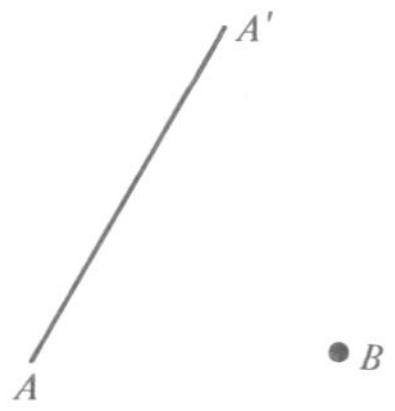

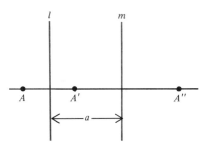

9. Consider two parallel lines *l* and *m* which are *a* units apart. Reflect the plane about *l* and then about *m*. Let *A* be any point, *A'* its image in the reflection about *l*, and *A"* the image of *A'* in the reflection about *m*. How long is segment $\overline{AA''}$? _____

2a.

10. The result of the two reflections in frame 9 is a _____ in the direction ⊥ to *l* and *m* with distance _____ .

translation   2a

11. A translation is equivalent to the result of two reflections about two _____ lines.

parallel

12. Let *l* and *m* be two directed lines intersecting at 0 at an angle of 90°. Then a translation in the direction of *l* with distance *d* followed by a translation in the direction of *m* and with the same distance *d* is a translation in the direction of what line _____ and with what distance? _____ .

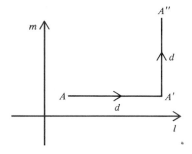

620

| The bisector of the angle between *l* and *m* | $d\sqrt{2}$ |

30.4 Rotations

The idea of rotating a plane about a point *O* should be immediately clear. The precise definition is as follows.

ROTATION

DEFINITION. A counterclockwise *rotation* of the plane about *O* is a transformation that moves every ray $\overrightarrow{OP}$ into a ray $\overrightarrow{OP'}$ such that the counterclockwise angle *POP'* has a fixed measure $\theta°$ and $\overline{OP} \cong \overline{OP'}$ (Figure 30.10).

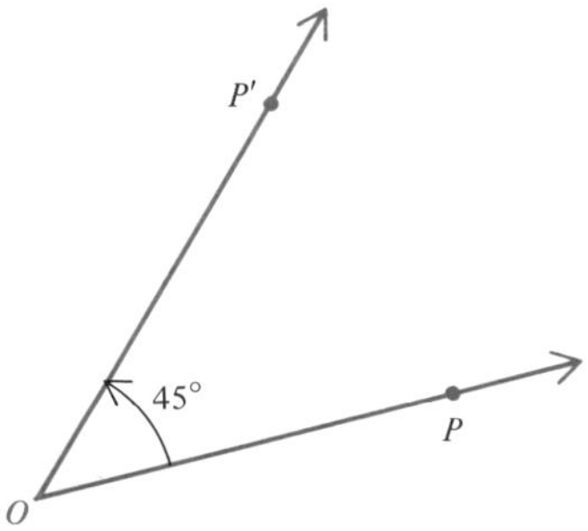

There is a similar definition for a clockwise rotation.

DEFINITION. Rotations with angle $\theta°$ and angle $\theta° + n \cdot 360°$ (where *n* is an integer) are considered to be identical. A rotation with angle $0°$ or $n \cdot 360°$ is a trivial motion.

We wish to show that a rotation is a rigid motion. First, let *A* and *B* be on the same ray through *O* (Figure 30.11). Then $\overline{OA} \cong \overline{OA'}$, and $\overline{OB} \cong \overline{OB'}$. Therefore, $\overline{AB} \cong \overline{A'B'}$.

FIGURE 30.10. *Counterclockwise rotation of 45° about O.*

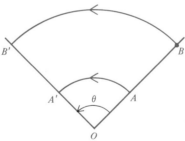

FIGURE 30.11. *Rotation of $\overline{AB}$ where A and B are on the same ray through O.*

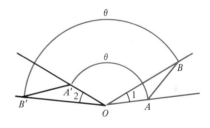

FIGURE 30.12. *Rotation of $\overline{AB}$ when A and B are on different rays through O.*

Then let *A* and *B* be on different rays through *O* (Figure 30.12). From the definition of a rotation it follows that $\overline{OA} \cong \overline{OA'}$, $\overline{OB} \cong \overline{OB'}$, and $\angle 1 \cong \angle 2$. Therefore, by SAS, triangles *AOB* and *A'OB'* are congruent. Because of this, $\overline{AB} \cong \overline{A'B'}$. This establishes Theorem 4.

THEOREM 4. A rotation is a rigid motion.

Suppose that we have a rotation that sends *A* into *A'*, what can we say about its center? Consider Figure 30.13. Let *OD* be the altitude of triangle

CENTER OF A ROTATION AOA'. Since $\overline{OA}$ and $\overline{OA'}$ are congruent, triangles OAD and $OA'D$ are congruent, and so D is the midpoint of $\overline{AA'}$. This establishes the following partial answer to our question.

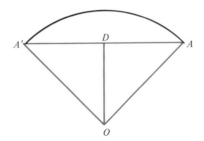

FIGURE 30.13. *The center of a rotation that sends A into A' lies on OD, the perpendicular bisector of $\overline{AA'}$.*

THEOREM 5. If a rotation sends A into A', its center O lies on the perpendicular bisector of $\overline{AA'}$.

1. A rotation sends segments into _____ segments, and angles into _____ angles.

> congruent   congruent

2. A rotation sends a triangle into a _____ triangie.

> congruent

3. A rotation _____ the orientation of the plane.
   (preserves, reverses)

> preserves

4. A nontrivial rotation leaves how many points fixed? _____

> One.

5. If a rotation has two fixed points, how may we describe it? _____
   _____

> Trivial rotation.

6. If a rotation sends A into A' and B into B' as shown, construct its center (use Theorem 5).

7. If $\overline{AA'}$ and $\overline{BB'}$ are parallel, as shown, is there a rotation that sends A into A' and B into B'? _____

No.

8. A rotation about O sends a circle with center at O into _____
_____.

itself, but not pointwise.

SUCCESSIVE REFLECTIONS ABOUT INTERSECTING LINES

9. Let l and m be two lines meeting at O and forming an angle whose measure is 60°. Let A be as shown so that the angle between OA and l has measure 20°. After a reflection about l, OA' is defined and the angle between OA' and l has measure _____.

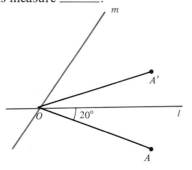

20°

10. After the reflection of frame 9, reflect again about line m, so that A' is sent into A''. Then the angle between OA'' and m has measure _____.

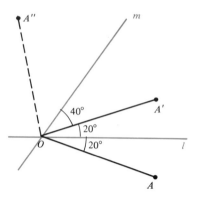

40°

11. From frames 9 and 10, what is the measure of angle AOA''? _____

120°

12. Let us generalize frames 9, 10, and 11. If l and m are two lines meeting at O and forming an angle whose measure is $\theta°$, a reflection about l followed by a reflection about m is a _____ with center _____ and angle of measure _____.

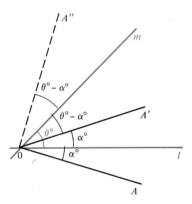

rotation O $2\theta°$

13. A rotation is equivalent to two successive reflections in _____ _____ lines.

intersecting

14. Lines l and m form an angle of 90° at O. Choose a point P not on either line, reflect it about l into P', then about m into P'', about l into P''', and finally about m into $P^{(iv)}$. Where is $P^{(iv)}$? _____

At P. (The first two reflections are equivalent to a rotation of 180° about O. So are the second two reflections.)

15. If the lines l and m of frame 14 form an angle of 60°, how many reflections in l, m, l, m, ... are needed to bring P back to its original position? _____

Six. (Each pair of reflections about l and m is equivalent to a rotation about O of 120°.)

30.5 Rigid Motions

In this section we shall discuss some general properties of rigid motions. First, suppose that we have three noncollinear points A, B, and C in the plane and three other points, A', B', and C'. Is there a rigid motion that takes A into A', B into B' and C into C'? If so, is it unique? Since a rigid motion preserves distances, we clearly must assume that triangles ABC and $A'B'C'$ are congruent. Making this assumption we shall answer these questions in Theorems 6 and 7.

THEOREM 6. Let triangles ABC and $A'B'C'$ be congruent. Then there is a rigid motion that takes A into A', B into B', and C into C'.

Proof. We shall prove this theorem by showing that there is a sequence of at most three reflections which takes A, B, C into A', B', C'.
1. If $A = A'$, proceed to step 3.
2. If $A \neq A'$, reflect about the perpendicular bisector of $\overline{AA'}$. Then A goes into A', B into some point, say B_1, and C into some point, say C_1.
3. If $B_1 = B'$, proceed to step 5.
4. If $B_1 \neq B'$, reflect about the perpendicular bisector of $\overline{B_1B'}$.
(a) A' remains unchanged, for A' is on the perpendicular bisector of $\overline{B_1B'}$. This follows from the fact that $\overline{A'B_1} \cong \overline{AB} \cong \overline{A'B'}$.
(b) B_1 goes into B'.
(c) C_1 goes into some point C_2.
Thus the sequence of reflections in steps 2 and 4 takes ABC into $A'B'C'_2$.
5. If $C_2 = C'$; we are finished.
6. If $C_2 \neq C'$, reflect about the perpendicular bisector of $\overline{C'C_2}$.
(a) A' remains unchanged, for $\overline{A'C_2} \cong \overline{AC} \cong \overline{A'C'}$, and so A' is on the perpendicular bisector of $\overline{C'C_2}$.
(b) B' remains unchanged, for $\overline{B'C_2} \cong \overline{BC} \cong \overline{B'C'}$, and so B' is on the perpendicular bisector of $\overline{C'C_2}$.
(c) C_2 goes into C'.
The sequence of reflections in steps 2, 4, and 6 takes ABC into $A'B'C'$.

625

Of course, this sequence of reflections could have been chosen in other ways. But no matter how we do them, the result is unique. This is Theorem 7.

THEOREM 7. The rigid motion of Theorem 6 is unique.

Proof. We must show that the image P' of any point P is uniquely determined. Suppose that we have two rigid motions that take the non-collinear points A, B, and C into A', B', and C' and that one of these takes P into P' and the other takes P into P'', where $P' \neq P''$. Then

$$\overline{AP} \cong \overline{A'P'} \cong \overline{A'P''}$$

$$\overline{BP} \cong \overline{B'P'} \cong \overline{B'P''}$$

$$\overline{CP} \cong \overline{C'P'} \cong \overline{C'P''}$$

Hence A', B', and C' lie on the perpendicular bisector of $\overline{P'P''}$; but this is impossible, since they are noncollinear.

From Theorems 6 and 7 we conclude the truth of Theorem 8.

THEOREM 8. Any rigid motion is equivalent to a sequence of at most three reflections.

We know that a sequence of two reflections about parallel lines is a translation, and a sequence of two reflections about intersecting lines is a rotation. Hence every rigid motion is one of the following types:

TYPES OF RIGID MOTIONS
(1) reflection
(2) translation
(3) rotation
(4) translation followed by reflection, or reflection followed by translation.
(5) rotation followed by reflection, or reflection followed by rotation.

Moreover, we know that translations and rotations preserve orientations but that reflections reverse orientations. Thus from (1) through (5) it follows that an orientation-preserving rigid motion must be a translation or a rotation.

In this chapter we have discussed rigid motions and proved that the following special cases are rigid motions:
reflections
translations
rotations
These have the properties given in the table:

Properties of Special Rigid Motions

Motions	Number of Fixed Points	Effect on Orientation	Equivalent Reflections
Reflection	Infinite	Reverses	—
Translation	None	Preserves	About two parallel lines
Rotation	One	Preserves	About two intersecting lines

In addition, we proved that any rigid motion is equivalent to a sequence of at most three reflections.

Now test your comprehension of this material by working the following Post Test.

POST TEST

1. A geometric transformation is a rigid motion if it preserves _____ _____.

2. A rigid motion sends segments into _____ segments, angles into _____ angles, and triangles into _____ triangles.

3. Let a reflection in *l* send circle *C* into circle *C'*. If a point *P* traverses *C* in the counterclockwise direction, its image *P'* traverses *C'* in the _____ direction.

4. Let a translation send circle *C* into circle *C'*. If a point *P* traverses *C* in the counterclockwise direction, its image *P'* traverses *C'* in the _____ direction.

5. Let a rotation send circle *C* into circle *C'*. (The center of rotation is not necessarily the center of *C*.) If a point traverses *C* in the counterclockwise direction, its image *P'* traverses *C'* in the _____ direction.

6. Assuming that the following rigid motions are nontrivial, state what they must be:
   (a) Has exactly one fixed point. _____
   (b) Has two distinct fixed points. _____
   (c) Has no fixed points and preserves orientation. _____

627

(d) Preserves orientation. _____

(e) Reverses orientation. _____

(f) Preserves orientation and has a fixed point. _____

7. A sequence of two translations is equivalent to a _____.

8. A sequence of two reflections is equivalent to a _____.

9. A sequence of two rotations with the same center is equivalent to a _____.

10. Any rigid motion is equivalent to a sequence of _____ reflections.

11. Any orientation-preserving rigid motion is equivalent to a sequence of _____ reflections.

12. A translation followed by a rotation is a _____.

13. A rotation followed by a translation is a _____.

---

1. distance
2. congruent, congruent, congruent
3. clockwise
4. counterclockwise
5. counterclockwise
6. (a) Rotation, possibly followed by or preceded by a reflection about a line through the fixed point. (b) Reflection. (c) Translation. (d) Translation or rotation. (e) Reflection, possibly followed by or preceded by a translation or a rotation. (f) Rotation.
7. translation
8. translation or rotation
9. rotation with the same center
10. at most three
11. two
12. rotation
13. rotation

Now proceed to Chapter 31.

31

Geometric Constructions

In studying this chapter you will need a ruler and a simple compass, and you should know how to use these. You will also need several ideas from Chapters 28, 29, and 30, which are reviewed in the following Readiness Test.

READINESS TEST

1. Given two distinct points A and B, how many distinct lines can be drawn through A and B? _____

One.

2. Given the segment $\overline{AB}$ and any point C. Using your compass draw a circle with center C whose radius is equal to the length of $\overline{AB}$.

A B

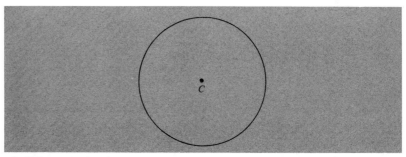

3. What are the three congruence theorems for triangles? _____ _____

SSS, SAS, AAS.

4. Is SSA a congruence theorem for triangles? _____

No.

5. If triangle ABC is reflected in line AB into triangle ABC' is triangle $ABC \cong$ triangle ABC'? _____

Yes.

6. If the measures of $\angle A$ and $\angle B$ of triangle ABC are known, how can we compute $m(\angle C)$? _____

$m(\angle C) = 180° - [m(\angle A) + m(\angle B)]$.

7. In triangle *ABC*, the length of $\overline{AB}$ plus the length of $\overline{BC}$ is _____ _____ the length of $\overline{AC}$.

greater than

8. In a circle with center *O*, a tangent to the circle at point *P* is perpendicular to _____.

OP

9. Any angle inscribed in a semicircle is a _____ angle.

right

With these facts in mind, proceed to Sections 31.1 and 31.2.

31.1 Introduction

The introduction of simple geometric constructions is also a very desirable topic in the study of intuitive geometry. It helps students to learn the facts of geometry, it introduces them to the use of drawing instruments, and it can inspire their imagination when they are asked to invent constructions.

TOOLS ALLOWED BY THE GREEKS This subject goes back to Euclid, whose pioneering textbook on geometry is full of geometric constructions. Euclid followed the philosophy of the Greek mathematics of his time and permitted the use of just two tools for constructions: (1) a straightedge (an unmarked ruler), and (2) a compass adjustable to any radius. Although there is no special reason today to restrict ourselves to such tools, the Greek philosophy still has an important influence, and there is a common belief that the use of other tools is incorrect. Certainly in the elementary school we should free ourselves of these Greek restrictions and allow the use of any available drawing instruments. So we shall begin with ruler and compass and introduce other tools when the need arises.

31.2 Ruler-and-Compass Constructions

RULER (1) *Ruler*. There is just one operation that can be performed with an unmarked ruler. This is the construction of a line segment passing through two distinct points.

630

COMPASS

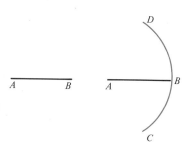

FIGURE 31.1. *Use of compass.*

(2) *Compass.* A compass can be used to draw a circle or a circular arc with a given center and radius. Sometimes the radius can be chosen at will, but in other cases the radius will be given as the length of a certain segment, as in Figure 31.1. In this case we are given a center A and a radius AB; we set the point of our compass on A, adjust the pencil so that it passes through B, and draw the arc CD.

A point is determined as the intersection of two lines, or as one of the intersections of two circles, or as one of the intersections of a line and a circle.

31.3 Standard Construction Problems

SEGMENT **PROBLEM 1.** Given a segment $\overline{AB}$, a line l, and a point C on l. Construct a segment $\overline{CD}$ on l congruent to $\overline{AB}$ (Figure 31.2).

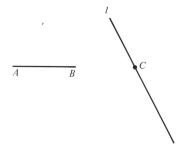

FIGURE 31.2. *Given data for problem (1).*

Solution. Set the compass so that its radius is the length of $\overline{AB}$. With C as center and this radius draw a circle intersecting l at D and D'. Each of the segments $\overline{CD}$ and $\overline{CD'}$ is congruent to $\overline{AB}$ (Figure 31.3).

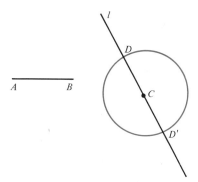

FIGURE 31.3. *Solution to problem (1):* $\overline{AB} \cong \overline{CD} \cong \overline{CD'}.$

ANGLE **PROBLEM 2.** Given an angle BAC, a line l, and a point P on l. Construct an angle QPR one of whose sides is on l, whose vertex is P, and such that angle $BAC \cong$ angle QPR (Figure 31.4).

Solution. With A as center draw any arc intersecting ray $\overrightarrow{AB}$ at D and ray $\overrightarrow{AC}$ at E (Figure 31.5). With P as center draw an arc ST with this same radius intersecting l at Q. Then $\overline{AD} \cong \overline{PQ}$.

631

Set the compass so that its radius is the length of segment $\overline{DE}$. With Q as center and this radius draw an arc intersecting arc ST at R. Draw ray $\overrightarrow{PR}$. We observe that $\overline{PR} \cong \overline{AE}$ and $\overline{QR} \cong \overline{DE}$.

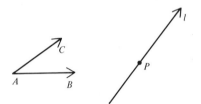

FIGURE 31.4. *Given data for problem* (2).

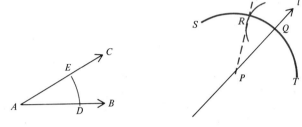

FIGURE 31.5. *Solution to problem* (2). *Angle QPR $\cong$ angle BAC.*

FIGURE 31.6. *Four solutions to problem* (2).

Then the triangles BAC and QPR are congruent from SSS, and so the angles BAC and QPR are congruent.

It will be observed that variations in this construction will give any of three other angles QPR which satisfy the required conditions (Figure 31.6).

PROBLEM 3. Given three segments $\overline{AB}$, $\overline{CD}$, and $\overline{EF}$. To construct a triangle whose sides are congruent to these three segments (Figure 31.7).

FIGURE 31.7. *Given data for problem* (3).

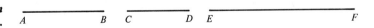

Solution. With A as center draw an arc with radius equal to the length of $\overline{CD}$. With B as center draw an arc of radius equal to the length of $\overline{EF}$ (Figure 31.8).

These arcs may not intersect, as in Figure 31.8(a). Then length $\overline{CD}$ + length $\overline{EF}$ < length $\overline{AB}$. There is no solution. But if

TRIANGLE

$$\text{length } \overline{CD} + \text{length } \overline{EF} > \text{length } \overline{AB}$$

there are two points of intersection H and H'. Draw AH and BH, or AH' and BH'. Either of the two congruent triangles ABH or ABH' has the required properties.

We observe that this construction gives an intuitive proof of SSS. For given three segments, the solution of Problem 3 is unique to within a reflection.

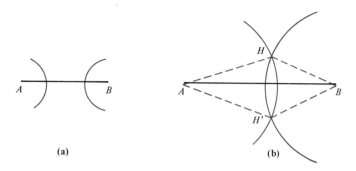

FIGURE 31.8. *Solution to problem (3).*   (a)   (b)

PERPENDICULAR BISECTOR

PROBLEM 4. Given a segment $\overline{AB}$, to construct its perpendicular bisector.

Solution. With A as center draw an arc with radius greater than one-half the length of $\overline{AB}$. Draw another arc with center B and this same radius. These arcs intersect at C and C'. Then CC' is the perpendicular bisector of $\overline{AB}$ (Figure 31.9). This result is correct, for by our construction Figure 31.9

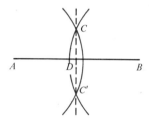

FIGURE 31.9. *Construction of perpendicular bisector of $\overline{AB}$.*

is symmetric about CC', and so a reflection about CC' takes A into B and B into A. Therefore, $\overline{AD} = \overline{BD}$ and $AB \perp CC'$.

SUBDIVISION OF A SEGMENT

PROBLEM 5. Given a segment $\overline{AB}$, to subdivide it into three congruent segments.

Solution. Through A draw line l not containing B. On l lay off (with a compass) the three congruent segments $\overline{AP}$, $\overline{PQ}$, and $\overline{QR}$ (Figure 31.10). Draw line RB. Through Q draw $\overline{QD}$ parallel to RB by making angle AQD congruent to angle ARB. Similarly, draw PC parallel to RB.

Then triangles APC, AQD, and ARB are similar. From this fact we conclude that the triple (length $\overline{AC}$, length $\overline{CD}$, length $\overline{DB}$) is proportional to the triple (length $\overline{AP}$, length $\overline{PQ}$, length $\overline{QR}$). By our construction $\overline{AP} \cong \overline{PQ} \cong \overline{QR}$. Therefore, $\overline{AC} \cong \overline{CD} \cong \overline{DB}$.

By similar constructions we can divide $\overline{AB}$ into any number of congruent segments.

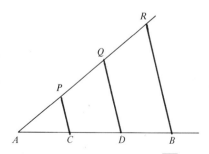

FIGURE 31.10. *Subdivision of $\overline{AB}$ into three congruent segments.*

REMARK

By applying constructions like this to the segment from 0 to 1 on the number line, we can locate any rational number between 0 and 1, and by a similar procedure we can locate any rational number whatsoever.

1. Use the method of Problem 5 to locate $\frac{2}{5}$ on the number line.

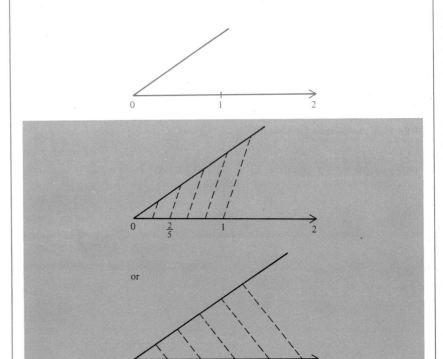

2. Using the result of frame 1 and a compass locate $-\frac{2}{5}$ on the number line.

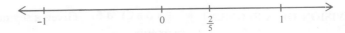

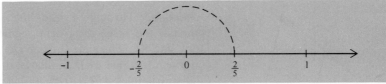

3. On the number line locate $\sqrt{2}$ by ruler and compass.

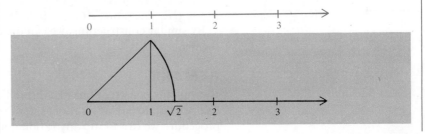

4. By methods like frame 3, you can locate $\sqrt{n}$, where n is a natural number. Can you devise a method for $\sqrt[3]{2}$? _____

No. This is not possible by ruler and compass.

5. Given segments $\overline{PQ}$ and $\overline{RS}$ and angle A, construct triangle ABC with $\overline{AB} \cong \overline{PQ}$ and $\overline{AC} \cong \overline{RS}$. What congruence theorem about triangles does this construction suggest? _____

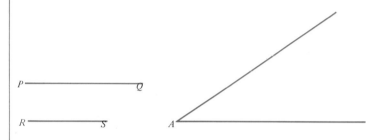

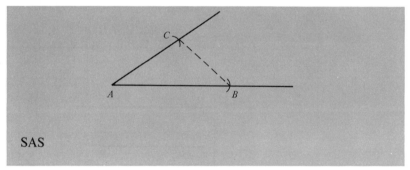

SAS

6. Given $\angle P$, $\angle Q$, and segment $\overline{TS}$. Construct triangle ABC with $\angle A \cong \angle P$, $\angle B \cong \angle Q$, and $\overline{AC} \cong \overline{TS}$. What congruence theorem about triangles does this suggest? _____ When is this construction possible?

_____

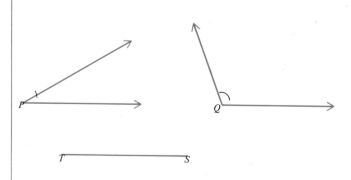

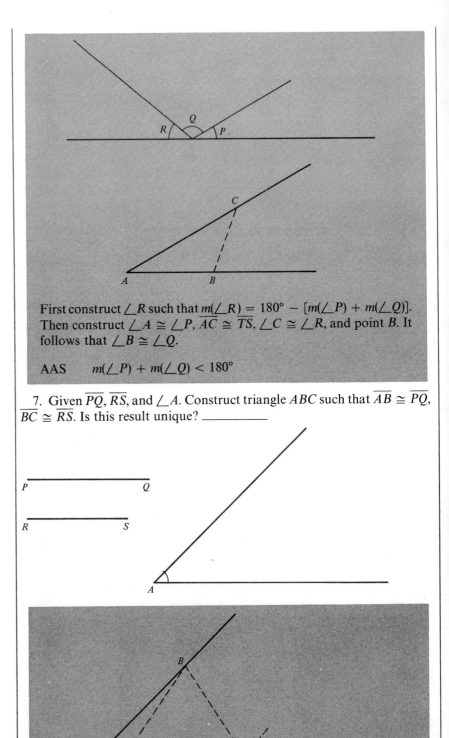

First construct $\angle R$ such that $m(\angle R) = 180° - [m(\angle P) + m(\angle Q)]$. Then construct $\angle A \cong \angle P$, $\overline{AC} \cong \overline{TS}$, $\angle C \cong \angle R$, and point B. It follows that $\angle B \cong \angle Q$.

AAS $m(\angle P) + m(\angle Q) < 180°$

___7. Given $\overline{PQ}$, $\overline{RS}$, and $\angle A$. Construct triangle ABC such that $\overline{AB} \cong \overline{PQ}$, $\overline{BC} \cong \overline{RS}$. Is this result unique? _____

No.

8. Carry out the construction of frame 7 using the segments and angle below. Is this construction possible? _____

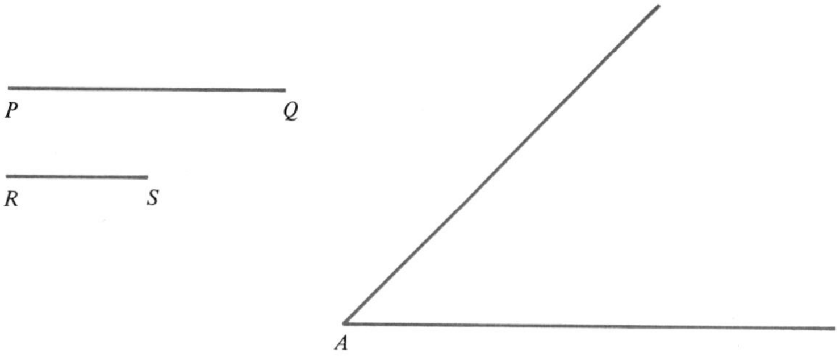

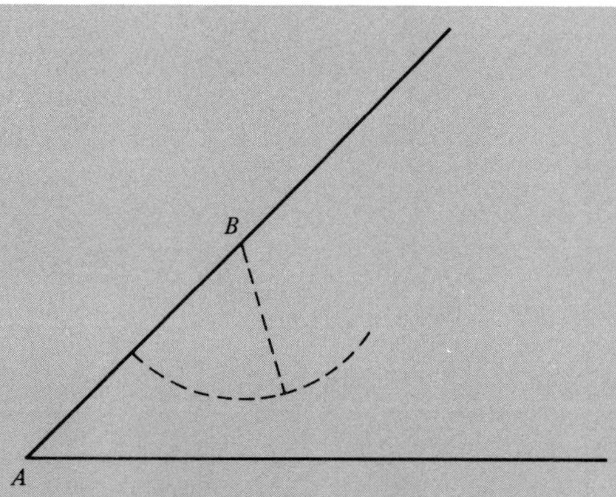

P ———————— Q

R ———— S

No.

9. Carry out the construction of frame 7 using the segments and angle below. Is this construction unique? _____

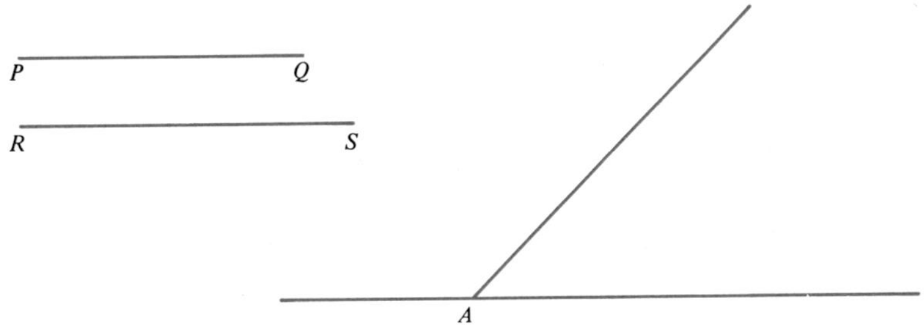

P ———————— Q

R ———————— S

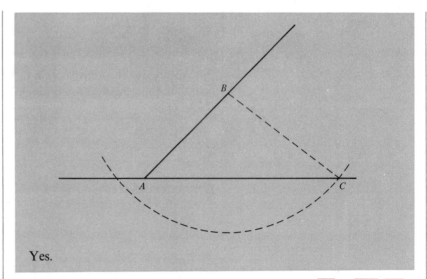

Yes.

___ 10. In triangles ABC and $A'B'C'$, we are given that $\overline{AB} \cong \overline{A'B'}$, $\overline{BC} \cong \overline{B'C'}$, and $\angle A \cong \angle A'$. Are the triangles necessarily congruent? _____ Review frames 7 and 9 before giving your answer. This situation is called the *ambiguous case*.

No.

11. Given line l and point P not on l. Construct a line through P parallel to l.

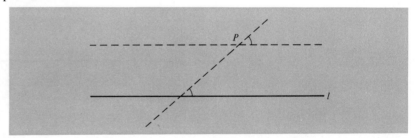

12. Given a circle C with center O and a point P on C. Construct the tangent to C at P.

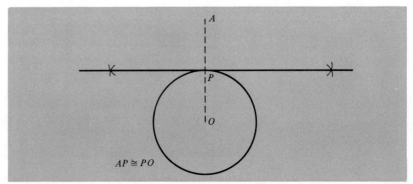

$AP \cong PO$

13. Given a circle *C* with center *O* and a point *P* outside *C*. Construct the two tangents to *C* passing through *P*. (*Hint:* If a triangle is inscribed in a circle so that one side is a diameter, the angle opposite this diameter is a right angle.)

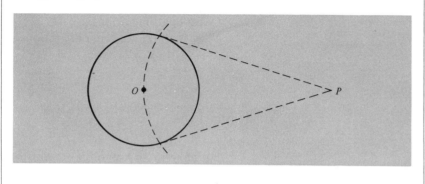

31.4 Three Classical Problems of Antiquity

The Athenian Greeks in roughly 400 B.C. were unable to solve three classical construction problems. Although none of these is of any mathematical importance today, attempts to solve them during the following 2300 years resulted in the development of an amazing amount of modern mathematics. Even though these problems are now completely disposed of, a surprisingly large number of misguided citizens are still working on them and frequently demand that mathematics teachers explain why their "solutions" are incorrect. For this reason, every teacher of mathematics needs to know the true facts of the case.

The problems are to use ruler (unmarked) and compass (as we have been doing in this chapter) to

FAMOUS PROBLEMS

(1) trisect an arc or an angle.

(2) double the cube, that is, find a cube whose volume is twice that of a given cube.

(Eratosthenes ascribes the second problem to an unfortunate situation that occurred in Delos. The Delians were suffering from a pestilence and were ordered by the oracle to double a certain cubical altar. The workmen simply constructed a cube with edges twice as long, but stupid work like that did not satisfy the gods. Once the error was discovered, the problem was turned over to the mathematicians of the day.)

(3) "square the circle", that is, find a square whose area is equal to that of a given circle.

The answer is that there is *no solution* with unmarked ruler and compass to any of these problems. *Approximate* solutions entirely satisfactory for every day life do exist, but there is no *exact* solution. On the other hand, it is possible to obtain *exact* solutions if methods other than those specified by the Greeks are used.

Although the proofs of the impossibility of the ruler and compass solutions of (1) and (2) are fairly elementary, they are too difficult to present in this book. But perhaps the following discussion will give you some idea of what is involved. There are two essential steps:

(a) If a segment of length 1 is given, ruler and compass constructions permit us to locate points on the number line which are obtained from 1 by rational operations ($+$, $-$, $\times$, $\div$) and the extraction of square roots. Thus, if a, b, c, d, e, and f are rational, we can locate

$$\sqrt{a + b\sqrt{c + d\sqrt{e + f\sqrt{\cdots}}}}$$

But cube roots cannot be so constructed, as was proved by P. L. Wantzel in 1837.

(b) Problem (1) for the trisection of a $60°$ angle can be shown to be equivalent to the solution of the equation

$$x^3 - 3x - 1 = 0$$

But the roots of this equation are not of the form described in (a), and so the construction is not possible.

In problem (2) consider a cube whose edge is of length 1 and whose volume is 1. We wish to find a cube whose edge is x and whose volume is 2. Hence $x^3 = 2$, and $x = \sqrt[3]{2}$. But from (a) this cannot be constructed by ruler and compass, so problem (2) does not have a solution.

The proof that the "squaring of the circle" is impossible rests upon the fact that π is not a solution of any polynomial equation with integer coefficients. This matter was not settled until 1889, when C. L. F. Lindemann completed the necessary research.

In spite of what a citizen can be told in school, there are thousands of people who still wish to trisect angles. Well, here is a way to do it! (But it is certainly not in keeping with the ancient rules.)

TRISECTION OF A ANGLE

Let us put two marks on a ruler any distance apart, say d (this violates the rules). Also let us be given angle AOB (Figure 31.11). With O as center draw a circle of radius d. (This much is all right.) Now align the ruler so that the

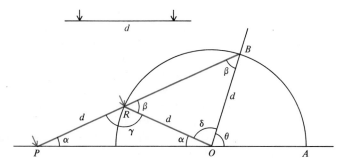

FIGURE 31.11. *Trisection of the angle AOB.*

first mark is on OA (at point P), the second mark is on this circle (at point R), and the ruler passes through B. (This is an "illegal" step.) Then the measure of angle APB is $\frac{1}{3}$ that of angle AOB.

Proof
1. Triangle POR is isosceles, so the angles marked α are congruent.
2. Triangle BOR is isosceles, so the angles marked β are congruent.
3. $m(\angle\beta) = 2m(\angle\alpha)$, since

$$m(\angle\beta) + m(\angle\gamma) = 180° = 2m(\angle\alpha) + m(\angle\gamma)$$

4. $m(\angle\theta) = m(\angle\beta) + m(\angle\alpha) = 3m(\angle\alpha)$. For

$$m(\angle\theta) + m(\angle\delta) + m(\angle\alpha) = 180°$$
$$= m(\angle\alpha) + m(\angle\beta) + m(\angle\alpha) + m(\angle\delta)$$

(See triangle POB)

POST TEST

1. The Greek rules for constructions permit the use of an _____ _____ ruler and a _____.

2. The ruler can be used to draw a _____ through two distinct _____.

3. The compass can be used to draw an arc with a given point as _____ and a given _____.

4. Points are determined as intersections of _____ or _____ or as intersections of a line and a _____.

5. The trisection construction in Section 31.4 violates these rules because _____.

6. Given a line l and a point P on l, construct a line through P perpendicular to l.

7. Given a line l and a point P not on l, construct a line through P perpendicular to l.

• P

_____ l

8. Given the segment from 0 to 1 on the number line construct the point that corresponds to $\frac{2}{3}$.

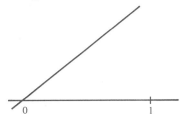

9. Construct a right triangle given its hypotenuse $\overline{AB}$ and leg $\overline{BC}$. (See the hint in frame 13, Section 31.3.) Is this construction always possible?

_____

| A | B | B | C |

10. Given the base and altitude of an isosceles triangle, construct the triangle.

| A | | B | | h |
| | Base | | | Altitude |

1. unmarked, compass
2. line segment, points
3. center, radius
4. lines, circles, circle
5. the ruler is marked
6.

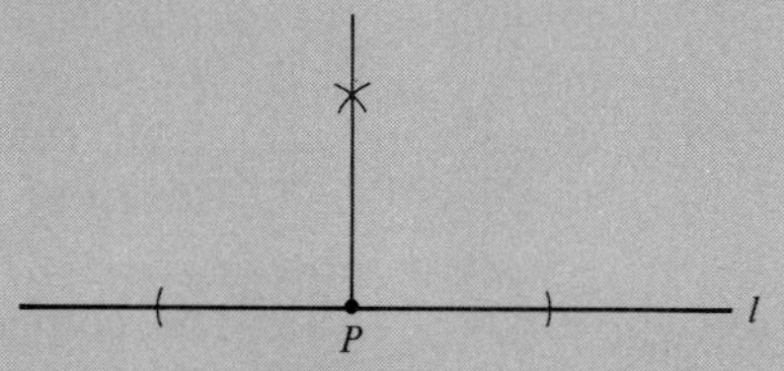

7.

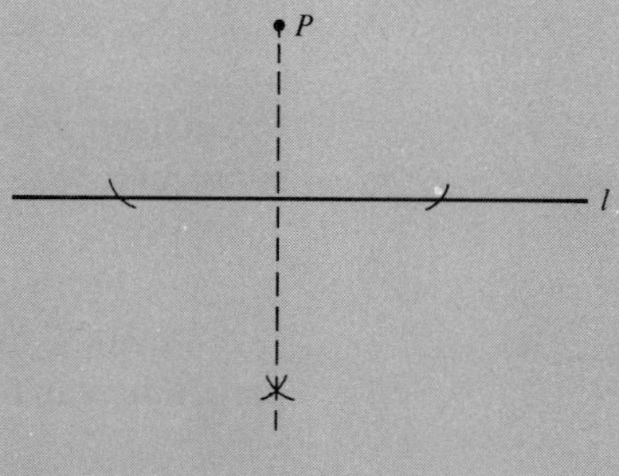

8.

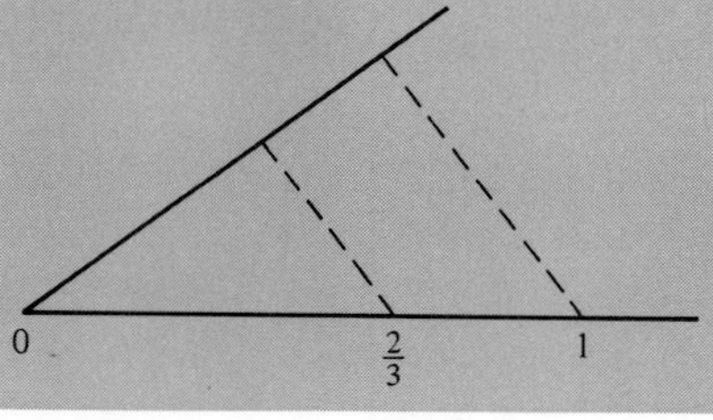

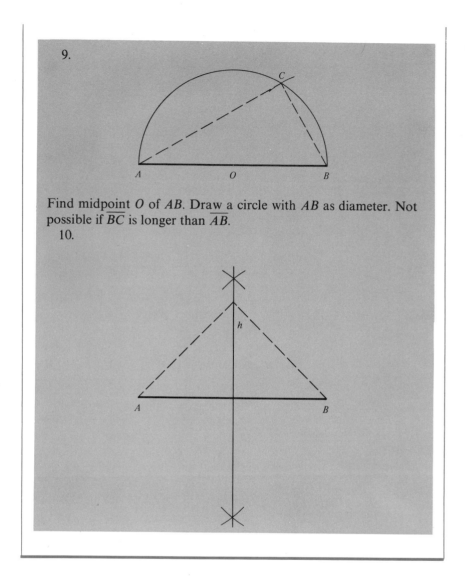

9.

Find midpoint *O* of *AB*. Draw a circle with *AB* as diameter. Not possible if $\overline{BC}$ is longer than $\overline{AB}$.

10.

You should now be ready to begin the last chapter on geometry, Chapter 32, Analytic Geometry.

32
Analytic Geometry

In this final chapter we shall combine arithmetic and geometry into a single subject. A review of the necessary topics is included in the following Readiness Test.

READINESS TEST

1. The Cartesian product of two sets A and B is the set of _____ _____ (a, b), where a is an element of _____ and b is an element of _____.

> ordered pairs A B

2. There is a one-to-one correspondence between the set of real numbers and the set of points on the _____.

> two-way number line

3. The distance AB is the length of the _____ joining A and B.

> segment

4. According to the theorem of Pythagoras the square of the length of the hypotenuse of a right triangle is equal to _____.

> the sum of the squares of the lengths of its legs

5. If $a:b = c:d$, where a, b, c, d are nonzero real numbers, there is a real number k such that $a = kc$ and _____.

> $b = kd$

6. $|-5| =$ _____, $|-5|^2 =$ _____.

> 5   25

7. If the pairs of opposite sides of a quadrilateral are congruent, the figure is a _____.

> parallelogram

8. If $2x + y = 5$ and $y = 1$, find x. _____

> 2

Now proceed to Section 32.1.

32.1 Coordinate System in the Plane

Analytic geometry, which was invented by René Descartes (1596–1650), is a means for treating geometrical problems by the methods of arithmetic and algebra. This chapter, which gives a brief introduction to analytic geometry, will thus serve to unify the materials presented in all the previous chapters.

COORDINATE SYSTEM

The fundamental concept in analytic geometry is the use of a coordinate system in the plane. To obtain this system we draw the number line in its usual position (Figure 32.1) and call it the X axis. Through the point of this line labeled O we draw another, vertical, number line directed upward, called the Y axis. The scales on these axes are the same. The intersection of these two lines is called the origin and is labeled O.

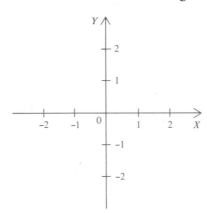

FIGURE 32.1. *Coordinate system in the plane.*

COORDINATE OF A POINT

To any point, P, in the plane we associate the ordered pair (x, y) of real numbers by the following procedure (Figure 32.2). Through P draw a vertical line meeting the X axis at Q. The number x is the real number associated with Q. Similarly, through P draw a horizontal line meeting the Y axis at R. The number y is the real number associated with R. The numbers x and y are called the *coordinates* of P. Points on the X axis such as Q have coordinates $(x, 0)$ and points on the Y axis have coordinates $(0, y)$. The origin 0 has coordinates $(0, 0)$.

Conversely, if we are given an ordered pair (x, y) of real numbers, we can find the corresponding point P in the plane by reversing the procedure just

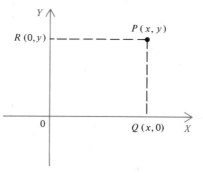

FIGURE 32.2. *Coordinates of point P.*

described. There is thus a one-to-one correspondence between the points P of the plane and ordered pairs (x, y) of real numbers. So the plane is the Cartesian product of the set of real numbers with itself.

The two axes divide the plane into four regions called quadrants, which **QUADRANTS** are labeled I, II, III, and IV as in Figure 32.3. In

quadrant I, x is positive and y is positive
quadrant II, x is negative and y is positive
quadrant III, x is negative and y is negative
quadrant IV, x is positive and y is negative

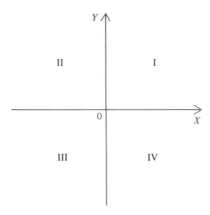

FIGURE 32.3. *Quadrants.*

1. Plot the points whose coordinates are $P_1(2, 4)$, $P_2(-1, 3)$, $P_3(-2, -3)$, $P_4(4, -3)$, $P_5(0, -2)$, and $P_6(-4, 0)$.

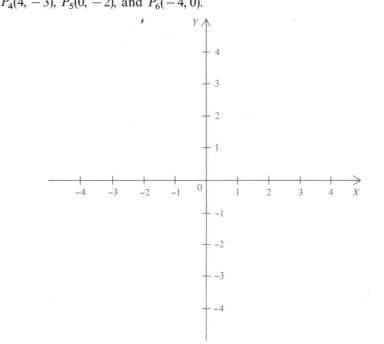

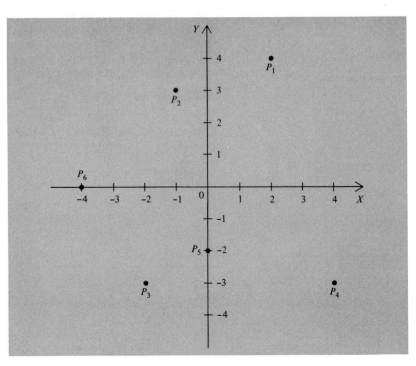

2. What are the coordinates of P_1, P_2, P_3, and P_4 as shown? P_1 _____, P_2 _____, P_3 _____, P_4 _____.

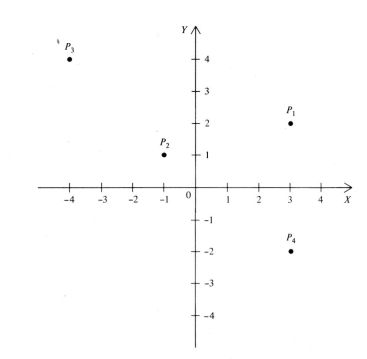

$(3, 2)$ $(-1, 1)$ $(-4, 4)$ $(3, -2)$

3. In quadrant II, x is _____, y is _____.
   $(+, -)$ $(+, -)$

   $-$ $+$

4. In quadrant IV, x is _____, y is _____.
   $(+, -)$ $(+, -)$

   $+$ $-$

5. In which quadrants do the following points lie? $P_1(-2, 6)$ _____,
   $P_2(4, 3)$ _____, $P_3(4, -1)$ _____, $P_4(-3, -4)$ _____.

   II   I   IV   III

6. The segment $\overline{P_1 P_2}$ where P_1 is $(2, 6)$ and P_2 is $(-4, 6)$ is parallel to
   the _____ axis.

   X

7. The points with coordinates $(0, y)$ lie on what line? _____

   The Y axis,

8. The plane is considered to be the _____ of the
   set of real numbers with _____.

   Cartesian product   itself

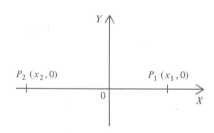

FIGURE 32.4. *Distance between P_1 and P_2 is $d = |x_2 - x_1|$.*

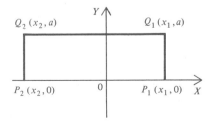

FIGURE 32.5. *Distance between Q_1 and Q_2 is $d = |x_2 - x_1|$.*

32.2 Distance between Two Points

Consider two points, P_1 and P_2, on the X axis with coordinates $(x_1, 0)$
and $x_2, 0)$ as in Figure 32.4. The distance, d, between P_1 and P_2 is the length
of the segment $\overline{P_1 P_2}$. This is clearly given by the formula

$$d = |x_1 - x_2|$$

where the vertical bars indicate absolute value.

If now $Q_1(x_1, a)$ and $Q_2(x_2, a)$ are on a horizontal line a units from the
X axis, the figure $P_1 Q_1 Q_2 P_2$ is a rectangle (Figure 32.5). So $\overline{Q_1 Q_2} \cong \overline{P_1 P_2}$,
and the distance between Q_1 and Q_2 is also given by

$$d = |x_2 - x_1|$$

649

Analytic Geometry

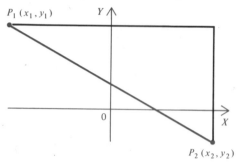

$P_1\,(x_1, y_1)$

$P_2\,(x_2, y_2)$

FIGURE 32.6. $d^2 = (x_2 - x_1)^2 + (y_2 - y_1)^2$.

In the same way, if $R_1(b, y_1)$ and $R_2(b, y_2)$ are on a vertical line, the distance between R_1 and R_2 is given by

$$d = |y_2 - y_1|$$

Finally, suppose that $P_1(x_1, y_1)$ and $P_2(x_2, y_2)$ are any two points in the plane (Figure 32.6). Draw the right triangle P_1QP_2, where Q has coordinates (x_2, y_1). Then distance $P_1Q = |x_2 - x_1|$, and distance $QP_2 = |y_2 - y_1|$. So by the theorem of Pythagoras the distance d between P_1 and P_2 is given by

$$d^2 = |x_2 - x_1|^2 + |y_2 - y_1|^2$$

This may be written in either of the alternative forms

$$d^2 = (x_2 - x_1)^2 + (y_2 - y_1)^2$$

or

$$d^2 = (x_1 - x_2)^2 + (y_1 - y_2)^2$$

This gives us Theorem 1:

DISTANCE FORMULA

THEOREM 1. The distance d between the points $P_1(x_1, y_1)$ and $P_2(x_2, y_2)$ is given by

$$d^2 = (x_2 - x_1)^2 + (y_2 - y_1)^2$$

1. Find the distance between $(3, 5)$ and $(-4, 5)$. _____

7.

2. Find the distance between $(-4, -2)$ and $(-4, 7)$. _____

9.

3. Find the distance between $(1, 3)$ and $(2, -1)$. _____

$\sqrt{17}$.

4. Find the distance between $(-4, 5)$ and $(-2, -6)$. _____

$\sqrt{125} = 5\sqrt{5}$.

5. Show that the triangle $A(0, 0)$, $B(2, 0)$, $C(1, \sqrt{3})$ is equilateral. Length $\overline{AB} =$ _____, length $\overline{AC} =$ _____, length $\overline{BC} =$ _____. Therefore, _____.

$2, 2, 2:$ the sides have equal length.

650

6. Show that the triangle $A(0, 3)$, $B(4, 11)$, $C(4, 1)$ is a right triangle. Length $\overline{AB}$ = _____, length $\overline{AC}$ = _____, length $\overline{BC}$ = _____. Therefore, _____.

$\sqrt{80}$ $\sqrt{20}$ 10 $80 + 20 = 100$ and BC is the hypotenuse.

7. Show that the points $A(1, 2)$, $B(-2, -1)$, $C(2, 1)$, and $D(5, 4)$ are the vertices of a parallelogram. _____

Length $\overline{AB} = \sqrt{18}$, length $\overline{BC} = \sqrt{20}$, length $\overline{CD} = \sqrt{18}$, length $\overline{DA} = \sqrt{20}$. So the opposite sides are congruent.

8. Show that $P(4, 4)$ is on the perpendicular bisector of the segment $\overline{AB}$, where $A = (3, -1)$ and $B = (-1, 5)$. Length $\overline{AP}$ = _____, length $\overline{BP}$ = _____.

$\sqrt{26}$ $\sqrt{26}$

9. Show that $P(3, 4)$ lies on the circle with center O and radius 5. _____

Length $\overline{OP} = \sqrt{3^2 + 4^2} = 5$.

MIDPOINT FORMULA

10. Show that $P\left(\dfrac{x_1 + x_2}{2}, \dfrac{y_1 + y_2}{2}\right)$ is the midpoint of the segment joining $P_1(x_1, y_1)$ and $P_2(x_2, y_2)$. _____

Length $\overline{P_1 P} = \sqrt{\left|\dfrac{x_2 - x_1}{2}\right|^2 + \left|\dfrac{y_2 - y_1}{2}\right|^2} = $ length $\overline{PP_2}$.

11. Find the midpoint of the segment joining $(4, -3)$ and $(6, 7)$. (x, y) = _____.

$x = \dfrac{4 + 6}{2} = 5, y = \dfrac{-3 + 7}{2} = 2$. So $(x, y) = (5, 2)$.

12. Suppose that the plane is reflected about the Y axis. What are the coordinates of the image of $P(x, y)$? _____

$(-x, y)$

13. Suppose that the plane is reflected about the X axis. What are the coordinates of the image of $P(x, y)$? _____

$(x, -y)$

32.3 Equations and Graphs

The central problem of analytic geometry is to develop a relationship between algebraic equations and geometric graphs. For example, suppose we have the equation

$$x + 2y = 3$$

An ordered pair, such as $(1, 1)$, which satisfies this equation is called a solution. There are, of course, many solutions of this equation, such as $(1, 1)$, $(3, 0)$, or $(5, -1)$. The set of all solutions is the *solution set* of the equation.

Every solution is an ordered pair (x, y), which corresponds to a point in the plane. The set of all points corresponding to all members of the solution set is called the *graph* of the equation. If we plot the three solutions of

$$x + 2y = 3$$

given above we obtain Figure 32.7. These seem to lie on a straight line, and, in fact, every solution of our equation does lie on this line. So the graph of the equation is the line shown in Figure 32.8.

GRAPH OF AN EQUATION

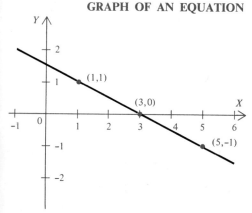

FIGURE 32.7. *Points on the graph of* $x + 2y = 3$.

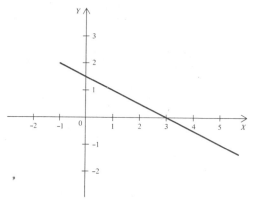

FIGURE 32.8. *Graph of* $x + 2y = 3$.

EQUATION OF A CIRCLE

On the other hand, suppose that we start with a geometric figure and wish to find its equation. As an example, suppose that we have a circle whose center is the origin and whose radius is 1. What is the corresponding equation? In Figure 32.9 it is clear that the distance from any point $P(x, y)$ on the

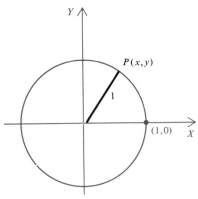

circle to the origin is 1. Hence

$$(x - 0)^2 + (y - 0)^2 = 1$$

or

$$x^2 + y^2 = 1$$

This is the equation of the given circle.

Thus our problem is to describe the graphs of various equations and to find the equations of various graphs.

FIGURE 32.9. *The equation of the circle is $x^2 + y^2 = 1$.*

32.4 Lines through the Origin

In this chapter we shall concentrate for the most part on lines and leave the more complicated situations to more advanced books. We begin by considering lines through the origin.

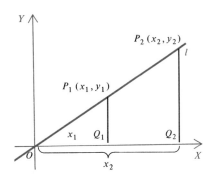

FIGURE 32.10. $y_1 : y_2 = x_1 : x_2$.

Let line l pass through the origin and not be vertical (Figure 32.10). Choose arbitrary points $P_1(x_1, y_1)$ and $P_2(x_2, y_2)$ on l and draw vertical lines P_1Q_1 and P_2Q_2. The triangles P_1Q_1O and P_2Q_2O are similar and so $y_1 : y_2 = x_1 : x_2$. From Chapter 26, Theorem 1, there is a real number m such that

$$y_1 = mx_1 \qquad \text{and} \qquad y_2 = mx_2$$

SLOPE   This number m is called the *slope* of l. Since P_1 and P_2 are any two points on l, it follows that for any point on l,

$$y = mx$$

This is then an equation of l.

EXAMPLE.   Find an equation of the line through O and $P(3, -2)$.

Solution.   The slope m must satisfy $y = mx$ for $x = 3$ and $y = -2$, so $-2 = m \cdot 3$. Thus $m = -\frac{2}{3}$. An equation of the line is

$$y = -\frac{2x}{3}$$

653

Other equations of this line are $3y + 2x = 0$, $y = -\dfrac{4x}{6}$, $6y + 4x = 0$, and so on.

If, on the contrary, you are given the equation $y = mx$, and wish to draw the corresponding line, find a point $P(x, y)$ whose coordinates satisfy the equation and draw the line joining this to the origin.

In Chapter 23 a rational number was defined as an equivalence class of fractions, and rational numbers were represented by lines through the origin in Figure 23.1, which is reproduced here as Figure 32.11. You will observe that the points corresponding to fractions in the equivalence class

$$\left\{ \cdots, \frac{-4}{-6}, \frac{-2}{-3}, \frac{2}{3}, \frac{4}{6}, \cdots \right\}$$

all lie on a line through O with slope $\frac{2}{3}$. Moreover, any point on this line

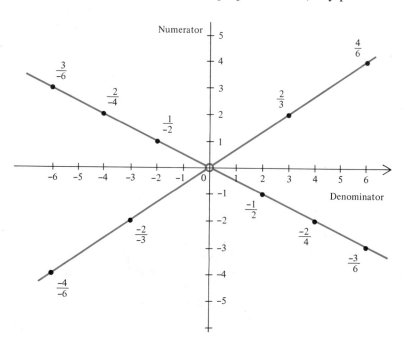

FIGURE 32.11. *Rational numbers represented by lines through O.*

whose coordinates are integers corresponds to a member of this equivalence class. Thus rational numbers can be represented by lines through the origin whose slopes are rational numbers.

1. Find an equation of the line through O and $(-3, 5)$. _____

$y = -\dfrac{5x}{3}$ (or $5x + 3y = 0$).

2. Find an equation of the line through O and $(4, 7)$. _____

$$y = \frac{7x}{4} \text{ (or } 7x - 4y = 0\text{)}.$$

3. If we are given an equation of a line in the form $ax + by = 0$, where $b \neq 0$, we can find its slope by solving for $y : y = -\dfrac{ax}{b}$. Then $m = -\dfrac{a}{b}$. Find the slope of the line whose equation is $5x - 9y = 0$. _____

$\frac{5}{9}$.

4. On a sheet of graph paper draw the line of frame 3.

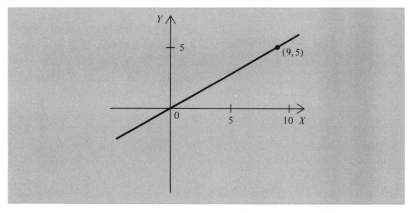

5. An equation of a line is $4x + 3y = 0$. Find its slope and draw the line on a sheet of graph paper. $m =$ _____

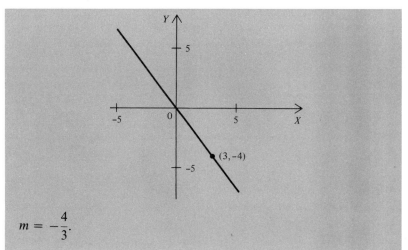

$m = -\dfrac{4}{3}.$

6. Describe a line through O whose slope is zero. _____

The X axis.

7. The Y axis has the equation $x = 0$ or $x + 0 \cdot y = 0$. Why does it not have a slope? _____

_____

The equation cannot be solved for y, for we must not divide by zero.

8. The multiplication table for "3 times" can be written as the equation $y = 3x$, where $x = 1, 2, 3, \ldots$ and the corresponding values of y are 3, 6, 9, ... Plot the corresponding ordered pairs $(1, 3)$, $(2, 6)$, and $(3, 9)$ on a sheet of graph paper. They lie on a line through O with slope _____.

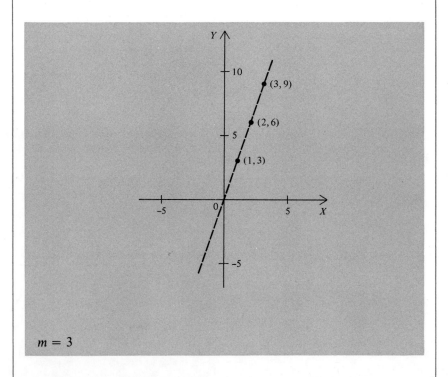

$m = 3$

9. Repeat frame 8 for the "2 times" multiplication table.

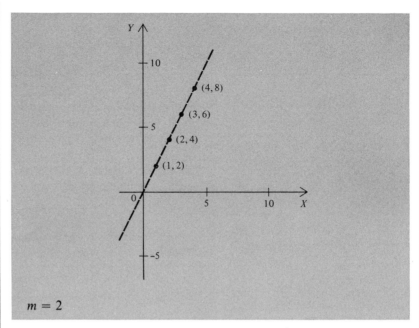

$m = 2$

10. Find the ordered pairs that satisfy $y = \frac{3}{4}x$, where $x = 1, 2, 3,$ $-1, -2, -3$. $(1, \underline{\hspace{1cm}}), (2, \underline{\hspace{1cm}}), (3, \underline{\hspace{1cm}}), (-1, \underline{\hspace{1cm}}), (-2, \underline{\hspace{1cm}}),$ $(-3, \underline{\hspace{1cm}})$.

| 3/4 | 3/2 | 9/4 | −3/4 | −3/2 | −9/4 |

11. On a sheet of graph paper plot the points corresponding to the ordered pairs in frame 10.

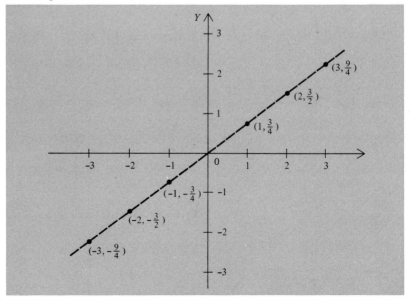

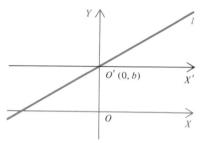

32.5 General Lines

Let us consider a line which is not vertical and which does not pass through the origin (Figure 32.12). This line will intersect the Y axis in a point O' with coordinates $(0, b)$. Through O' draw a horizontal line which we shall call the X' axis.

FIGURE 32.12. *Line l not through the origin.*

As a result of this construction we have two sets of axes: the XY axes and the $X'Y$ axes. Each point P has two sets of coordinates: (x, y) and (x, y'). It is clear that $x = x'$. From Figure 32.13 we see that $y = y' + b$ or $y' = y - b$.

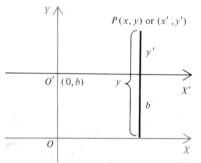

With respect to the $X'Y$ axes we have the situation discussed in Section 32.4 and l has an equation of the form

$$(1) \qquad y' = mx$$

where m is its slope. To find the equation of l with respect to the XY axes, substitute $y - b$ for y' in (1). The result is

$$y - b = mx$$

or

$$(2) \qquad y = mx + b$$

FIGURE 32.13. $x = x'$; $y' = y - b$.

DEFINITION. If a line l intersects the Y axis in a point whose coordinates are $(0, b)$, the real number b is called the Y intercept of l.

REMARK

When $b = 0$, l passes through the origin O.

All of this leads to the following general result:

SLOPE-INTERCEPT FORM OF
EQUATION OF A LINE

THEOREM 2. Any nonvertical line in the plane has an equation of the form

$$y = mx + b$$

where m is its slope and b is its Y intercept.

We also have the following result:

EQUATION OF A VERTICAL
LINE

THEOREM 3. Any vertical line in the plane has an equation of the form $x = c$.

From Theorems 2 and 3, we can conclude Theorem 4.

GENERAL EQUATION OF A
LINE

THEOREM 4. Any line in the plane has an equation of the form

$$Ax + By + C = 0$$

where A and B are not both zero.

The following related result is also true:

THEOREM 5. Every equation of the form

$$Ax + By + C = 0$$

(where A and B are not both zero) is an equation of a line in the plane.

Proof
1. If $B \neq 0$, we can solve for y and obtain

$$y = -\frac{Ax}{B} - \frac{C}{B}$$

This is a nonvertical line with slope $-A/B$ and Y intercept $-C/B$.
2. If $B = 0$, then A cannot be zero, so we can solve for x (putting $B = 0$):

$$x = -\frac{C}{A}$$

a vertical line.

Several types of problems can now be solved.

PROBLEM 1. Suppose that l passes through $P_1(x_1, y_1)$ and $P_2(x_2, y_2)$. Find its slope.

Solution. By hypothesis,

$$y_1 = mx_1 + b$$
$$y_2 = mx_2 + b$$

Hence by subtraction of the first of these from the second,

$$y_2 - y_1 = m(x_2 - x_1)$$

SLOPE, GIVEN TWO POINTS   or

$$m = (y_2 - y_1)/(x_2 - x_1)$$

EXAMPLE. Find the slope of the line passing through $(2, 4)$ and $(1, 6)$.

Solution. $m = \dfrac{6 - 4}{1 - 2} = \dfrac{2}{-1} = -2.$

PROBLEM 2. Suppose that l passes through $P_1(x_1, y_1)$ and $P_2(x_2, y_2)$. Find an equation of l.

Solution. First find m as in (1). If (x, y) is any point on l, the argument in (1) shows that

$$\frac{y - y_1}{x - x_1}$$

659

is also equal to *m*. So an equation of *l* is

$$\frac{y - y_1}{x - x_1} = \frac{y_2 - y_1}{x_2 - x_1}$$

EXAMPLE. Find an equation of the line passing through $(2, 4)$ and $(1, 6)$.

Solution. An equation is

TWO-POINT FORM OF EQUATION OF A LINE

$$\frac{y - 4}{x - 2} = \frac{6 - 4}{1 - 2}$$

or

$$y - 4 = (x - 2)(-2)$$

or

$$y = -2x + 8$$

or

$$2x + y - 8 = 0$$

SLOPE AND *Y* INTERCEPT

PROBLEM 3. Given the equation $Ax + By + C = 0$ (where *A* and *B* are not both zero) to find the slope and *Y* intercept of the corresponding line.

This problem was solved in the proof of Theorem 4.

EXAMPLE. Find the slope and *Y* intercept of the line whose equation is

$$2x - 3y + 6 = 0$$

Solution. Solve for *y*:

$$3y = 2x + 6$$

$$y = \frac{2x}{3} + 2$$

$$m = \tfrac{2}{3} \qquad b = 2$$

1. Every line in the plane has an equation of the form _____ _____ where _____ are not both zero.

$Ax + By + C = 0$ *A* and *B*

660

2. Every equation of the form $Ax + By + C = 0$, where A and B are not both zero is the equation of a _____ in the plane.

line

3. Find the slope of the line passing through (4, 3) and (2, 7). _____

-2

4. Find an equation of the line passing through (4, 3) and (2, 7). _____

_____

$2x + y - 11 = 0.$

5. Find the slope of the line passing through (2, 5) and (4, 11). _____

3

6. Find an equation of the line passing through (2, 5) and (4, 11). _____

_____

$3x - y - 1 = 0$

7. Find the slope of the line passing through $(-4, 7)$ and (6, 7). _____

zero

8. Find an equation of the line passing through $(-4, 7)$ and (6, 7).

_____

$y = 7.$

9. Find the slope of the line passing through (2, 6) and $(2, -3)$. _____

This is a vertical line; it has no slope.

10. Find an equation of the line passing through (2, 6) and $(2, -3)$.

_____

$x = 2.$

11. Find two ordered pairs (x, y) that satisfy $x - 2y + 4 = 0$, plot the corresponding points, and draw the line on a sheet of graph paper.

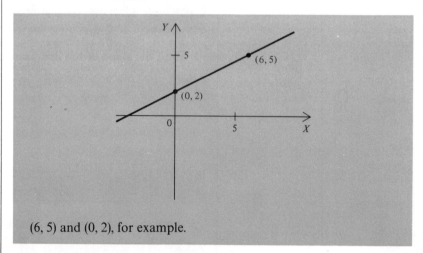

(6, 5) and (0, 2), for example.

12. Find the slope and Y intercept of the line whose equation is $x - 2y + 4 = 0$. $m =$ _____, $b =$ _____.

$\frac{1}{2}$ 2

13. Find two ordered pairs (x, y) that satisfy $3x + 7y - 21 = 0$, plot the corresponding points and draw the line on a sheet of graph paper. _____

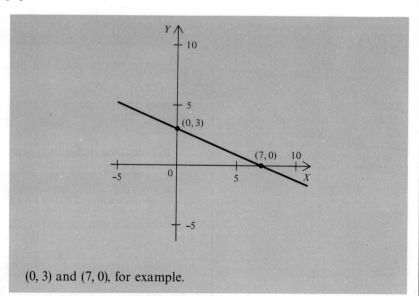

(0, 3) and (7, 0), for example.

14. Find the slope and Y intercept of the line whose equation is $3x + 7y - 21 = 0$. $m =$ _____, $b =$ _____.

-3/7   3

15. Draw the line whose equation is $y = -5$.

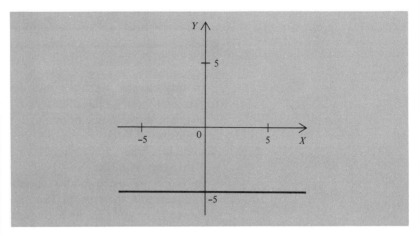

16. Draw the line whose equation is $x = -4$.

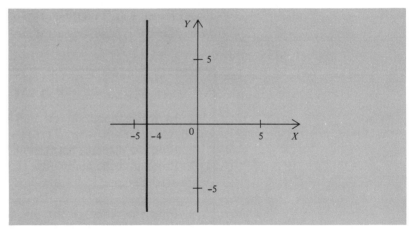

17. In Figure 21.1, Section 21.3, we represented equivalence classes of ordered pairs (n, m) as certain lines in the plane. The equivalence relation was $(n_1, m_1) \sim (n_2, m_2)$ if and only if $n_1 + m_2 = n_2 + m_1$. Let $(n_1, m_1) = (4, 2)$ and $(n_2, m_2) = (x, y)$. Then we have the equation $4 + y = 2 + x$ or $x - y = 2$. Plot this line and compare with Figure 21.1. We conclude that the points in the plane corresponding to members of the equivalence class $\{(3, 1), (4, 2), (5, 3), \ldots\}$ all lie on the line _____. This equivalence class represents the integer _____.

$$x - y = 2 \qquad 2$$

18. Generalize the result of frame 17 as follows. The points in the plane, corresponding to the equivalence class which represents the integer *a*, all lie on the line whose equation is ——————.

$$x - y = a$$

In this chapter we have introduced coordinate systems in the plane. In terms of these we have discussed
distance between two points
equations of lines
slope of a line
Y intercept of a line

In more advanced books equations of other geometrical figures are introduced and their properties are discussed. But we have stopped here since we have gone as far as is needed for applications in the elementary school.

Before closing this chapter, test your understanding of these concepts by working the following Post Test.

POST TEST

1. In which quadrant do the following points lie? $(2, -1)$ ——, $(4, 2)$ ——, $(-3, -5)$ ——, $(-5, 7)$ ——.
2. Find the distance between $(4, -6)$ and $(-2, 5)$. ——————
3. Prove that the points $A(1, 1)$, $B(4, 2)$, and $C(3, 3)$ are the vertices of a right triangle. ——————————————————————————————

4. Find the slope of the line passing through $(5, -2)$ and $(-6, 3)$. ——————

5. Find an equation of the line passing through $(4, -1)$ and $(6, 7)$. ——————

6. Find an equation of the line passing through $(2, 5)$ and $(2, -6)$. ——————

7. Find the slope and *Y* intercept of the line whose equation is $7x + 9y - 12 = 0$. $m =$ ——, $b =$ ——.
8. What are the coordinates of the midpoint of the segment whose end points are $(-5, 10)$ and $(11, 4)$? ——————

9. Find the coordinates of point D such that $ABCD$ is a rectangle, given $A(2, 6)$, $B(2, 10)$, and $C(5, 6)$. _____

10. Find an equation of the circle with center at O and radius 6. _____

_____

1. IV, I, III, II
2. $\sqrt{157}$.
3. Length $\overline{AB} = \sqrt{10}$, length $\overline{AC} = \sqrt{8}$, length $\overline{BC} = \sqrt{2}$.
4. $-5/11$
5. $4x - y - 17 = 0$
6. $x = 2$
7. $-7/9, 4/3$
8. $(3, 7)$.
9. $(5, 10)$.
10. $x^2 + y^2 = 36$.

This concludes Part V, Geometry. As your last bit of work in this book, review Geometry by answering the questions in the following Summary Test.

Summary Test for Part V

A

Circle the number of every true statement in this section.

1. A tetrahedron has exactly four edges.
2. There are exactly five regular solids.
3. There is one and only one line parallel to line AB and passing through a point C not on AB.
4. If two lines in space do not intersect, they must be parallel.
5. A plane can be drawn through any four noncollinear points.
6. A simple closed curve cannot have an exterior.
7. Given any simple closed curve C, then any point P not on C is in the interior of C or in the exterior of C.
8. If a length is measured with a ruler marked in sixteenths of an inch, the GPE of measurement of length is $\frac{1}{8}$ inch.
9. The area of a circle is $2\pi r$.
10. If two triangles are congruent, then they must be similar.
11. No rigid motion has any fixed points.
12. Under a reflection lines are taken into lines.
13. Under a translation a line is taken into a parallel line.
14. A nontrivial rotation cannot have two fixed points.
15. Any rational number can be constructed on the number line by ruler and compass.
16. No irrational number can be constructed on the number line by ruler and compass.
17. The concept of slope is defined for every line in the plane.
18. The equation $x^2 + y^2 = 1$ is an equation of a line.
19. Every line has an equation of the form $Ax + By + C = 0$, where A and B are not both zero.
20. The Y intercept of the line $3x + 2y + 6 = 0$ is 6.

B

21. A cube has _____ vertices, _____ edges, and _____ faces.
22. If two lines in the plane do not intersect, they must be _____
_____ .
23. A line divides a plane into what mutually disjoint subsets? _____
_____
24. An angle is the _____
_____
25. State the Jordan curve theorem. _____
_____
26. 325 meters is equal to how many yards? _____ (1 meter = 39.37 inches.)
27. The side of a square is measured to be 3 inches with a GPE of $\frac{1}{16}$ inch. Find the area of the square and its GPE. _____
_____

28. Find the area of a regular hexagon that is inscribed in a circle of radius 2. _____

29. The measure of a straight angle is _____.

30. The SSS congruence theorem for triangles states that _____
_____

31. If the lengths of the legs of a right triangle are 2 inches and 5 inches, how long is its hypotenuse? _____

32. The distance between two points is defined to be _____
_____.

33. What tools for geometric constructions were permitted by the Greeks? _____

34. When is it impossible to construct a triangle whose sides are congruent to three given segments? _____
_____

35. Given $\angle A$ and segments $\overline{PQ}$ and $\overline{RS}$. Construct a triangle ABC such that $\overline{AB} \cong \overline{PQ}$ and $\overline{AC} \cong \overline{RS}$.

P _____ Q

R _____ S   A

36. Given a circle, describe a construction that will locate its center.
_____
_____
_____

37. What are the three classical construction problems of antiquity?
_____
_____

38. Any angle can be trisected if we are permitted to use what tools?
_____

39. To double a cube whose edge has length 1 inch we need to construct a segment whose length is _____ inches.

40. What does it mean to "square a circle"? _____
_____
_____

41. Find the distance between (1, 6) and (2, −3). _____

42. Find an equation of the line passing through (2, −1) and (−3, 5).
_____

43. The slope of the line through (7, 9) and (−4, −6) is _____.

44. Find the slope and Y-intercept of the line whose equation is $3x - y + 7 = 0$. $m =$ _____, $b =$ _____.

45. An equation of the Y axis is _____

46. An equation of the X axis is _____

47. $x^2 + y^2 = 4$ is an equation of a _____.

48. Find an equation of the line with slope $\frac{2}{3}$ which passes through $(4, 6)$. _____

49. Find an equation of a vertical line which passes through $(1, 9)$. _____

50. The statement that $P(x, y)$ is equidistant from $(3, 6)$ and $(2, 7)$ can be expressed by what equation? _____

You have now finished this book. We wish you every success in your career as an elementary teacher.

Index

Index